Readings in *POPULATION* *and* *COMMUNITY ECOLOGY*

WILLIAM E. HAZEN, Ph.D.

ASSISTANT PROFESSOR OF ZOOLOGY,
SAN DIEGO STATE COLLEGE

W. B. SAUNDERS COMPANY

Philadelphia and London, 1964

Library of Congress catalog card number 64-11774.

Preface

This volume of readings had its inception at the College of the University of Chicago where I taught a course in field biology which relied heavily on original source material. I have revised and extended this list while teaching general ecology at San Diego State College. The purpose of a collection such as this is to introduce students to the literature of ecology as soon as they begin their study of the subject. The study of ecology, which is one of the great theoretical subject matters of biology, thereby gains interest, currency, and intellectual vigor. These readings are intended for use by third and fourth year students, in conjunction with a text and lectures. I attempt to use laboratory and field work to supplement the rest of the course.

I am indebted to my former colleagues at the University of Chicago, especially to Gerson Rosenthal, who first suggested several of the readings. Rodger Mitchell of the University of Florida has offered advice, criticism, and encouragement. The ecologists at the University of Michigan first introduced me to the nature and scope of ecology. Among them, Nelson Hairston, Lawrence Slobodkin, and Frederick Smith have been more than usually stimulating and helpful.

I have found it difficult to reduce my first list to the 25 papers reprinted here. The errors of omission are entirely my own.

San Diego, California William E. Hazen

Contents

Part IV COMMUNITY METABOLISM: ENERGETICS AND PRODUCTIVITY

Part V COMMUNITY STRUCTURE

Editor's Introduction

The current focus of interest in ecology, which emphasizes populations and communities as the proper objects of study in the science, is largely due to the stimulus of two books published in the 1920's, Lotka's *Elements of Physical Biology* and Elton's *Animal Ecology*. Both these volumes stressed the role of populations, with population dynamics or kinematics having central positions. Volterra's classic study should also be mentioned; its influence was more marked after 1931, when a translation of it appeared as an appendix to Chapman's *Animal Ecology*. In the next decade such works as Gause's *The Struggle for Existence* and Bodenheimer's *Problems of Animal Ecology* redirected the attention of investigators to theoretical problems and to their experimental solution. In plant ecology, the discussions of Tansley, who proposed the term ecosystem for the fundamental ecological unit, had a similar function. More recently, it is difficult to point to particular authors, but Lindeman should be mentioned as one who directed the activity of working ecologists to the problems of productivity and efficiency. In an intellectual sense, I am particularly indebted to Slobodkin's *Growth and Regulation of Animal Population*, which has been the immediate stimulus for my current interests in ecology.

The collection of papers in this volume attempts to explore some of the avenues that research and speculation in population and community ecology have taken. The articles are grouped under four substantive headings, with one of Hutchinson's papers acting as a general introduction. The rubrics under which the papers fall are: "Single Species Populations," "Relationships Between Species," "Community Metabolism," and "Community Structure." Because of the arbitrary nature of the divisions, some of the articles do not fall neatly into place. For example, the Smith paper treats models for predation, as well as those for growth of a single species. Engelmann's work might equally well be treated as a study in community energetics; it is placed where it is because it could not be understood without a prior knowledge of

MacArthur's theoretical analysis of the niche. In general, I have placed the papers to permit their being read sequentially.

By using different criteria, the papers could be grouped differently than they appear here. One of these possible groupings would correspond to the different kinds of activities which the authors undertake. Thus there are theoretical papers, which use the rational processes of logic and mathematics to investigate the possible ways of ordering ecological subject matters, and empirical ones, which investigate the world of art and nature; that is, ecology is studied by experiment or simple observation. I have made no attempt to "cover" ecology. My lack of familiarity with plant ecology has made it impossible to include any of the more detailed portions of that part of the science. The papers are uneven in their level of difficulty and some will be too difficult for undergraduates. For this I offer the defense that it is better for students to be shown the scope of the science in all its difficulty and particularity than to be fed predigested pap.

The introductory paper by G. E. Hutchinson, after discussing the general significance of structure, analyzes in more detail two kinds of patterns, stochastic and coactive, the former dependent on random enviromental forces, the latter on interaction between species. Competition, an example of coaction, is discussed and is related to the niche. The final portion discusses the patterns found in the enumeration of individuals belonging to different species found in samples. As it stands, this article introduces all the topics found in the rest of the book other than energetics and productivity. For these areas, either Lindeman or the *Scientific Monthly* article by Pearson is an adequate introduction.

In the first group of papers, "Single Species Populations," the unit of study is the population; both the individual, with its private environment, and the community, with its complex of populations, are excluded. The patterns studied here are (1) distributions in space and (2) changes in time. Cole's study of the animals found under boards placed in a woodland analyzes the spatial patterns of the different species found there by use of the Poisson series. Clark and Evans give a method for making the same judgment without, however, the use of quadrats. Inasmuch as the effectiveness of the method using the Poisson series depends in part on quadrat size, non-quadrat methods have a marked advantage. For a more complete discussion, see Grieg-Smith's text, *Quantitative Plant Ecology*.

I have chosen to begin the study of changes of populations in time with concrete examples of life histories as found in life tables. Such tables have the advantage of being easy to understand, and information from them is necessary for the calculation of the intrinsic rate of increase. The life tables of salamanders of the genus *Desmognathus* provide an example of how life tables may be used in comparing the biology of different organisms. From such tables, with the additional knowledge of the distribution of fecundity with age, the intrinsic rate of natural increase can be estimated. The calculation and theoretical importance of this statistic are adequately discussed by Birch. Finally, Smith discusses various mathematical formulations related to population dynamics and the experimental methods appropriate to testing these models. Among the cases he considers are growth of a single species and interactions of species in predation, thereby serving as a bridge to the next major section.

In his book Lotka considered the types of relationships that can occur between species and attempted to formulate equations which would express these relationships. I have included papers which treat competition and predation; symbiosis and commensalism are discussed briefly by Gause and Witt only. I believe that, in this portion, the importance and general relevance of each of the selected papers is self-evident. Theories of competition lead most directly to a consideration of niches as is evident in both field and laboratory studies. Theories of predation lead to a consideration of energy flow in ecosystems. I regret that I have been unable to find a paper on predation in nature which is succinct enough for inclusion. For class use I have assigned the account on predation found in Lack's *The Natural Regulation of Animal Numbers.*

The section on "Community Metabolism and Productivity" is also largely self-explanatory. It begins with Lindeman's pioneering study of energy flow and efficiency in lakes. Although the details of his formulation and of his estimates may be open to criticism—the decomposers are not treated separately, and net productivity rates seem high—this is too important a piece of work to omit. Pearson deals with simple systems both theoretically and practically, and Slobodkin derives a set of equations applicable to three different kinds of efficiency: ecological, population, and growth. These relationships are applied to experimental *Daphnia* populations. The two last papers discuss how to estimate productivity in two different kinds of ecosystems: streams and the oceans.

The last and most difficult portion is entitled "Community Structure." Two kinds of attempts to analyze communities are included. The first, more closely connected logically to the earlier sections, proceeds from considerations of competition and energy flow through an attempt to analyze the ecological meaning of "niche" to an understanding of community structure. The second uses statistical associations of species for the analysis of communities.

If one can speak of a community as being "structured," this means that the populations of organisms present are not mere haphazard assemblages, but are functionally related to one another. The question arises, "What are the parts that constitute the whole?" In an abstract community either the populations can be so conceived, or the activities of the encompassed populations can play the role of structural elements. I believe that in ecology the sets of activities—that is, the niches corresponding to the populations present—are fundamental in a functional concept of community. The first set of papers here, that is, through Engelmann, deals with the structure and function of communities and attempts to relate the niches to the populations found in nature. The model of the community proposed by MacArthur, a model deduced from simple biological premises, has been useful in that it led to a great deal of research by ecologists. Hairston criticizes this model in detail, and reviews other attempts to make sense out of populations in nature, most of which are based on empirical, not logical, grounds. The last two papers, in addition to analyzing statistical association between species found in the areas sampled, are excellent examples of synthesizing masses of data concerning factors which influence the animal populations present.

In conclusion, my bias in favor of the concept of biological control of the numbers of species in nature and of the necessity of treating communities as wholes is evident. Although it seems clear that there is now no ready solution to the problem of constructing a general theory covering the kinds and numbers of organisms present at a place, progress is being made toward a solution. The construction of such a theory is a problem of sufficient difficulty and interest to occupy the best scientific minds of any age. I believe the articles presented in this book show that ecology has attracted a fair share of such minds in the middle of the twentieth century.

San Diego, California WILLIAM E. HAZEN

PART I
INTRODUCTION

THE CONCEPT OF PATTERN IN ECOLOGY *

BY G. EVELYN HUTCHINSON
Director of Graduate Studies in Zoology, Yale University

In any general discussion of structure, relating to an isolated part of the universe, we are faced with an initial difficulty in having no a priori criteria as to the amount of structure it is reasonable to expect. We do not, therefore, always know, until we have had a great deal of empirical experience, whether a given example of structure is very extraordinary, or a mere trivial expression of something which we may learn to expect all the time.

If, with the surrealists, we imagine ourselves encountering in the middle of a desert a rock crystal carving of a sewing machine associated with a dead fish to which postage stamps are stuck, we may suspect that we have entered a region of the imagination in which ordinary concepts have become completely disordered. Macroscopically, we are in the realm of what Elizabeth Sewell (1951), in her remarkable book *The Structure of Poetry*, defines as nightmare. On a smaller scale, since we can recognize the individual objects and give them names, we are still in the familiar world. The fish may be expected to have the various skull bones which have been enumerated by vertebrate morphologists; if it departed too radically from the accepted structure, we should see at once that it was not a fish. The rock crystal would have the ordinary physical properties of quartz; if it did not, we should not recognise and name it as such.

---

* An address given upon presentation of the Leidy Medal to the author on December 4, 1952, at the Academy of Natural Sciences of Philadelphia. (See notice of the award in *Proceedings* of the Academy, vol. 104, p. 249, 1952.)

When we push our analysis as far as we can, we end up with a series of statements of relations between entities, which at the present state of development of science are apparently unanalysable. What we call knowledge appears to consist of a series of known relationships between unknown elements. The latter may become known as new techniques permit their study, but it is reasonable to suppose that they too will become in the process of investigation relationships between new unknown entities of a higher degree of abstraction. Actually, the degree of abstraction which has been reached in modern theoretical physics is already so great that it is practically impossible to say anything intelligible in words about what the universe is made of. Our preliminary exploration thus suggests that the completely disordered is unimaginable and that the known consists of a collection of relationships between temporarily unknown entities. If we are going to say anything at all, some structure is certain to be involved, but, as has already been indicated, the amount of structure per unit volume cannot be guessed in advance.

Very roughly, in an empirical and qualitative way, we may distinguish a number of kinds of structure. The ordinary small-scale structure of the inorganic world, as exemplified in crystals, we may call, as is usually done, *order*. *Disorder* in physical science usually means random as opposed to placed in a particular order, such as that of a crystal lattice.

There is another important kind of structure in purely physical systems, which is in a sense a sort of converse of order, and which may be called *arrangement*. By this is meant the kind of structure exhibited by having the sun in one place, radiating energy, the earth in another receiving some of it. *Arrangement* in this limited sense decreases as entropy increases. Measured as negative entropy it is essentially what organisms eat. It is obviously a very different concept from order, thought the two are often confused by biologists.

The order of a system increases as we lower its temperature and is maximal at absolute zero. Order is an equilibrium phenomenon. Arrangement in the energetic sense in which it has been used, decreases as the *whole* system exhibiting it approaches absolute zero. It is essentially a non-equilibrium phenomenon, and most of modern cosmology is devoted ultimately to trying to find out how it came or comes into existence.

The characteristic structure of the living world will be called *organization*. Much order is also present, and, as organisms lay up an energy supply, arrangement is there also. The really characteristic structure of organisms, however, only exists near transition points. The art of living consists fundamentally of just crystallizing or just going into solution at the right time and place. Living matter is poised precariously between the solid and liquid states. Organization is never an equilibrium phenomenon in the physical sense.

The structure which results from the distributions of organisms in, or from, their interactions with, their environments, will be called *pattern.* As is organization, pattern is essentially a steady state rather than an equilibrium phenomenon, though it will be convenient to speak of equilibrium and non-equilibrium communities in a later paragraph when the phenomena are completely abstracted from physico-chemical categories. Pattern is obviously closely related to the arrangement of the inanimate world in which it developed.

The structure which organisms may impose on material systems to convey information, or in the construction of tools, may be called *design.* Human artifacts of all sorts, including works of art, come into this category. Design may be an equilibrium phenomenon and may be unchanged by cooling. A sentence written with appropriate materials is still the same sentence in the neighborhood of absolute zero, though the organization of the man who wrote it and the pattern of the community in which he lived, could not survive such extensive cooling. There are, however, remarkable formal mathematical analogies between arrangement and design.

These categories are to be considered as qualitative and suggestive; they are set up mainly to indicate how complex the problem of structure becomes even when an effort is made to keep the matter as simple as possible. The justification for the use of such categories is that confusion may often be avoided by asking which are appropriate to any structure under discussion.

Pattern, in the sense used above, appears to be of five kinds. The distribution of organisms and of their effects on their environment may be determined by external forces, such as light, temperature, humidity or density gradients, changes of state in certain directions, currents, winds, etc. Patterns produced in this way will be termed *vectorial.* The distribution may be determined by genetic continuity, offspring remaining near the parent, giving a *reproductive* pattern. The distribution may be determined by signalling of various kinds, leading either to spacing or aggregation, producing *social pattern.* The distribution may be determined by interaction between species in competition leading to *coactive* pattern. The distribution may depend on random forces producing a *stochastic* pattern.

The main theme of the present address is the coactive and stochastic types of pattern and their interaction.

Stochastic patterns.—The distribution of a plankton organism by night is commonly conceived as becoming increasingly random. Moreover, when horizontal distribution across a vertical light gradient is considered, many investigators have unconsciously assumed the same random distribution to hold. It is a mistake to consider such a random distribution to be structureless or lacking in pattern. The probabilities involved may be regarded as quite definite. Only if such probabilities were completely indeterminate, could we get an irrational series of surprises and enter the world of nightmare above a certain size level.

If a number of samples of a habitat is considered, and the probability of the occurrence of any particular species is low, the incidence of that species will appear at first very irregular. Examination of the number of samples containing no specimen, one specimen, two ... n specimens, etc., however, will indicate the existence of stochastic patterns. The simplest of such patterns is that in which the number of samples of each rank from 0 to n approximates to a Poisson series. It is the property of such a distribution that the variance in the statistical sense is equal to the mean. Where the variance is much greater than the mean (*superdispersion*) the organisms are grouped together more than would be expected on the simple random hypothesis; where the variance is much less than the mean (*infradispersion*) they are much more evenly spaced than in a randomly distributed population (fig. 1).

In the plankton of lakes, the distribution of different species of animals has been studied from this point of view by Ricker (1937), by Langford (1938) and perhaps most beautifully by Tonolli (1949). The last-named investigator made series of horizontal tows with the Clarke-Bumpas plankton sampler in Lago Maggiore in November, three series of tows being made at each depth. The results of some of his investigations are shown in figures 1 and 2. Out of a large number of series of comparisons, ninety-three in all, infradispersion appeared to be significantly demonstrated in only two. Since the significance limit was set as the degree of infradispersion which would occur by chance only in 1% of the cases studied, we are probably at liberty to regard infradispersion as a chance phenomenon. Superdispersion was observed far more often and is certainly significant. In three common species, *Eudiaptomus vulgaris, Daphnia longispina* and *Asplanchna priodonta* there is a very obvious tendency for the superdispersion to be most marked in the 5-10 m. layer. Presumably in these species, the tendency of the individuals to disperse at random in a horizontal plane, to move like the molecules of a gas, is modified by some hydrographic factor, probably turbulent movement, itself a random phenomenon. The organisms may be supposed to react to such random turbulent movements, so that they collect in certain regions and not in others. In *Cyclops strenuus* the superdispersion is differently distributed and must be due to different factors. Bliss (1953) in a very important recent paper

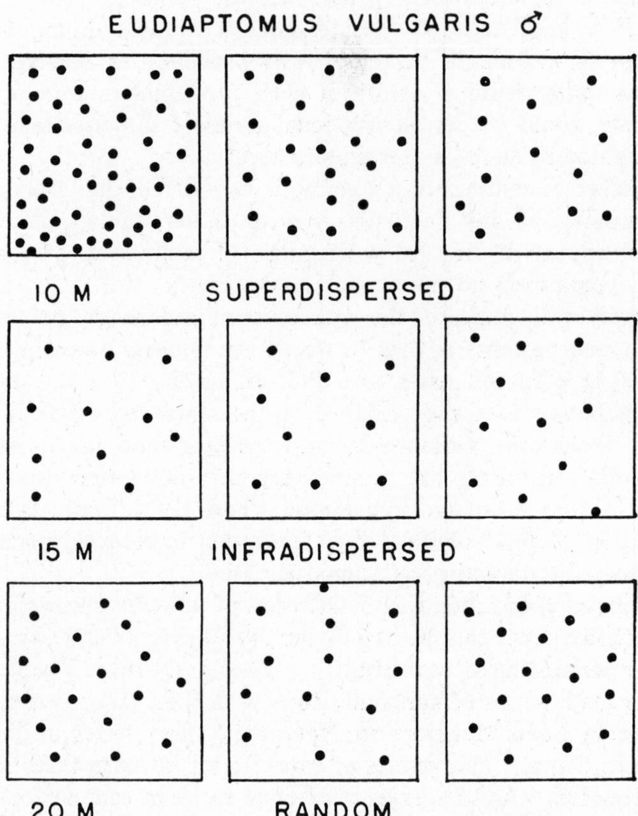

Fig. 1.—Approximate distribution of males of *Eudiaptomus vulgaris* in three successive plankton samples at three different depths in Lago Maggiore, showing *superdispersion*, *infradispersion* and *random distribution*. (From the data of Tonolli 1949.)

has shown that in one marine copepod the superdispersed distribution approximates to the so-called negative binomial, which is to be expected when one stochastic process is superimposed on another. Tonolli's data are not appropriate for testing this particular distribution, but it is very likely that stochastic patterns dependent on the superimposed operation of random events involving different size dimensions, of the microorganisms themselves and of much larger convention cells for instance, may ultimately be found to produce a number of different kinds of stochastic pattern.

Coactive Pattern. The fundamental regularity underlying the distribution of all organisms in a community is Gause's principle, or, as it is more properly termed, the Volterra-Gause principle, that in an equilibrium

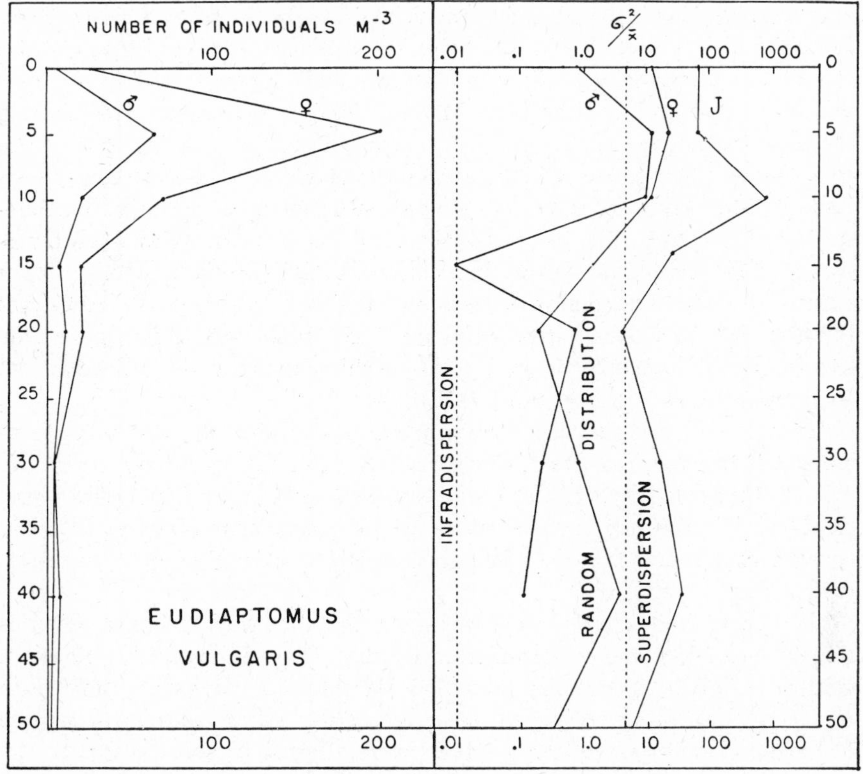

Fig. 2.—Vertical distribution of males and females, and of the ratio of the variance to the mean for males, females and immature individuals of *Eudiaptomus vulgaris* in Lago Maggiore. The absolute numbers of immature specimens are much greater than of mature individuals but are similarly distributed. The dotted lines indicate superdispersion and infradispersion significant to the 1% level. (From the data of Tonolli 1949.)

community no two species occupy the same ecological niches. A formal statement of the principle emerged early in Volterra's mathematical studies of biological associations (Volterra 1926), and Gause (1934, 1935) showed by an elegant series of experiments that in cultures of protozoa under conditions in which two species were forced to occupy a space of such simple structure that no niche diversification was possible, only one species could survive indefinitely.

In natural communities of a kind in which equilibrium may be expected, all subsequent studies have indicated that the generalization is true. Recently a number of studies largely by ornithologists have indicated that allied species which apparently live together under equilibrium conditions, may actually be occupying niches which are largely distinct. A particularly beautiful case is provided by three species of African weaver birds, *Ploceus intermedius cabanisi*, *P. collaris nigriceps* and *P. melanocephalus duboisii*, which all live together near Lake Mweru, the last two species even sharing the same communal nests. All feed on different foods; in the case of the two species which share a communal nest, one is a seed-eater and one is insectivorous (White 1951). A similar situation has recently been described among the owls, the Saw-whet, *Aegolius a. acadicus* and the Long-eared, *Asio otus wilsonianus*, in coniferous plantations in Ohio. Both occupy the same sleeping territory by day, but by night the Saw-whet hunts mainly in wooded areas catching large numbers of *Peromyscus*; the Long-eared owl mainly in open land catching many more *Microtus* and *Cryptotis* (Randle and Austing 1952).

Instances of this sort can be multiplied indefinitely and, where apparent exceptions to the Volterra-Gause principle of niche-specificity occur, we may legitimately suspect that a true equilibrium between the species is not established. We can in fact speak of *equilibrium* and *non-equilibrium* communities which may be distinguished by observing whether the principle holds.

Whenever two species are competing, the direction of competition is largely dependent on environmental factors. This is critically shown in
* Gause's (1935) experiments in which *Paramecium candatum* tended to replace *P. aurelia* in frequently renewed media, and *P. aurelia* to replace
* *P. candatum* when metabolic products were allowed to accumulate.

Precisely similar results have been long recognised in plant ecology. Many species which appear to be calciphil or calciphobe in nature can actually grow quite well when isolated in cultivation in soils of a wide range of calcium contents. The apparent restriction shows up only when the plants have to enter into competion with the rest of the flora to which they belong.

Ecological zonation is largely dependent on the competitive relations of species as controlled by the environment, and so is as much a coactive as a vectorial type of pattern. The production of a discontinuous discrete type of biological zonation in a continuous gradient of salinity, soil moisture or other physical variable is easily understood in terms of competition theory, since the direction of competition will change at a definite point on the gradient, below which one species, above which another species, will be successful (Gause and Witt 1935). It is probable that this process plays a considerable part in regulating the invasion of fresh waters from the sea. It is often apparent that species exhibit far greater salinity tolerances in the laboratory than in nature. In Joseph Leidy's day, the Schuylkill near Philadelphia contained a serpulid worm *Manayunkia*

*Author's note: Candatum should have been caudatum.

speciosa Leidy, one of the very few species of fresh-water polychaets. Allied species occur in the Great Lakes drainage, in Lake Baikal and in salt water in the Arctic. The nearest local marine ally of *M. speciosa* is *Fabricia sabella,* a marine species found on the Atlantic seaboard. J. P. Moore (in Johnson 1903) long ago showed that at least the adults of these worms could be acclimated to water of the normal salinity of each other's environments. Similar situations are found among the amphipoda of western Europe (Sexton 1939, Reid 1939, Beadle and Cragg 1940). It is probable that, when two species of slightly different tolerances compete in a salinity gradient, selection will cause the optima of values of the salinity of the two species to diverge. The operation of selection on a zonal pattern has doubtless played an immense part in evolution (cf. also Brooks 1950).

The very definite types of pattern which we have just considered are characteristic of equilibrium communities in biotops which contain physico-chemical gradients. Much of the diversity of the living world is due to this sort of pattern, but much is also probably due to the existence of non-equilibrium communities. The first type of non-equilibrium community characterizes those regions in which certain more or less catastrophic events are continually creating new empty biotops. If such biotops are colonized by more than one species, and if the species occupy the same niche, competition will begin and one species will tend to exterminate its weaker competitors. If before this happens, a new adjacent habitat is opened, a new mixed population may be set up. If the original habitat is now destroyed by a catastrophic event, and the process is repeated indefinitely, the mixed population will appear to persist. It is probable that, in order for this to happen, the tendency for the weaker species to disappear by competition must be balanced by a tendency for it to spread a little more easily than the stronger; it must in fact be a *fugitive species* (Hutchinson 1951). Wynne-Edwards (1952) has concluded that the co-existence of very closely allied species of birds in the Arctic, where local populations are easily exterminated by adverse climatic conditions, actually provides a case of this sort.[1]

A more widespread type of non-equilibrium population is dependent on the relation of the life-span or generation time to the seasonal cycle. If we consider two competing species with an annual or longer life cycle, such as is found in mammals, birds, many insects, the larger marine invertebrates, and some quite small aquatic animals such as many copepods, it is obvious that the species must be adapted throughout their life histories to a great variety of conditions. In these circumstances, we can properly

---

[1] I am indebted to James Bond for calling my attention to this case.

consider the two species to compete under some long term mean condition; transitory fluctuations may alter temporarily the direction of competition, but the final result will be the elimination of one of the competitors.

If we now consider two species with exceedingly short life histories, such as those of bacteria dividing rapidly in a favorable medium, it is quite possible that competition leading to extermination might occur so rapidly that no environmental change sufficient to reverse the direction of competition, would have time to occur before one species had been exterminated by the other.

The Volterra-Gause principle of one species per niche should, therefore, hold for very rapidly reproducing and very slowly reproducing organisms. In the intermediate region, in which a number of generations may occur in a year, but the generation time of several days or weeks is sufficient to permit considerable variation in environment in the course of a few generations, there is no reason to suppose that the law would hold. If one species displaced the other at low temperatures and the reverse at high, it is easy to see that, if both appeared from some resting stage in Spring, competition would first favor the first, then the second, and then again the first species.

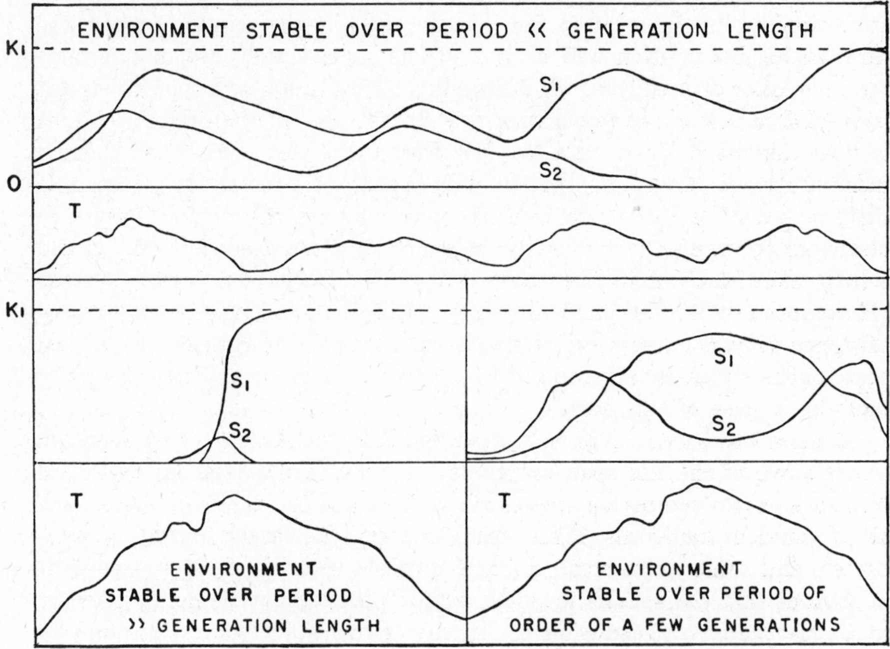

Fig. 3.—Ideal course of competition between two species as regulated by the relation between generation length and the period over which the environment may be taken as stable.

There can be little doubt that the great diversification of the phytoplankton of lakes, the turbulent epilimnia of which can hardly provide to autotrophic euplanktonic organisms greater niche diversity than existed in Gause's culture tubes, is due to the fact that phytoplanktonic organisms in nature probably divide at a mean rate of once every few days or every few weeks (see particularly Grim 1950) and so fall in the intermediate or potentially non-equilibrium category of the three which we have been considering.

It is also probable that some species of limnetic zooplankton form a non-equilibrium community, but here the situation is complicated in some cases by a tendency for the reproductive rate to vary, but with a lag-period, with the feeding rate. Very marked non-equilibrium populations of single species must often be set up during the Spring; the oscillations which follow and which are slowly damped out, may be extensive enough to prevent the species, in the time available for active feeding and reproduction, from ever achieving equilibrium, even with a constant food supply. This phenomenon, which has been most ingeniously studied by Slobodkin (1951) emphasizes the non-equilibrium nature of the plankton, though in its details it differs somewhat from the coactive non-equilibrium of the phytoplankton.

*The Dividing of the Biotophy Coactive Processes

If we consider, not a single species but a whole series of species of a certain taxonomic group, and examine a large collection made at random in some specified habitat, we can enumerate the species which occur once, twice, three times and so on. Recently a good deal of attention has been paid to the regularities exhibited by such an enumeration. Designating the number of specimens per species as r, the rank of the species and the number of species which have that rank as n, Fisher, Corbet and Williams (1943) have concluded that for many kinds of organisms

$$n = \frac{R}{r} x^r$$

where x is a number slightly less than unity, and R a number which characterizes the diversity of the population under examination. The existence of the relationship, which is related to the negative binomial already mentioned, is attributed to a combination of random processes determining the incidence of a species and of individuals of that species in the collection.

Preston (1948), however, has shown that, when the rank coordinate is graduated logarithmically (he used $\log_2 r$) the resulting curves do not take the form implied by the expression given by Fisher, Corbet and Williams. What Preston finds is that there is a definite mode in the number of species

*Author's note: Heading corrected to THE DIVIDING OF THE BIOTOPE BY COACTIVE PROCESS

for one of the logarithmic rank categories, the precise rank depending on the size of the collection. He believes that

$$n = n_0 e^{-(aR)^2}$$

when R is the logarithmic rank measured from the mode. This is, of course, the well-known log normal distribution. It is not entirely clear intuitively what such a distribution means biologically. In discussing the matter with Dr. E. S. Deevey, he suggested that in such cases what we are dealing with is not primarily a distribution of specimens, but rather a distribution of fractions of environments. Actually, nearly thirty years ago Dr. C. F. A. Pantin expressed the same idea (he has now probably forgotten it) when we were discussing the same general type of problem, which was beginning to interest biologists owing to the work of J. C. Willis. Every specimen, whether of diatom, moth, bird or elephant, will have required a certain amount of space for its development. The number of specimens, provided we stick to a single taxonomic group, gives in a certain sense, a measure of the space needed by the successful members of that species. It is probably reasonable that, in dividing up a space by coactive processes, a log normal type of distribution should result. What is really extraordinary is that the constant a, which is actually the reciprocal of $\sqrt{2}$,* should have practically the same numerical value wherever it is encountered. In collections of moths from North America and Europe, Preston found values from 0.152 to 0.227; in a local bird census he obtained 0.194. Dr. Ruth Patrick, who is making very important studies along these lines, using the statistics of diatoms settling on slides submerged in streams, tells me that the constants found by her group of investigators are always close to 0.2. The value, therefore, appears to be independent of the size and reproductive rate of the organisms under investigation and probably applies to both equilibrium and non-equilibrium communities. It is likely that something very important is involved here, but for the present what it may be is a mystery, a very good thing with which to end a discourse.

*Author's note: $\sqrt{2}$ should have been $\sqrt{2\sigma^2}$

References

BEADLE, L. C. and J. B. CRAGG. 1940. The intertidal zone of two streams and the occurrence of Gammarus spp. on South Rona and Raasay (Inner Hebrides). *Jr. Animal Ecol. 9:* 289-295.

BLISS, C. I. 1953. Fitting the negative binomial distribution to biological data. To appear in *Biometrics.*

BROOKS, J. L. 1950. Speciation in ancient lakes. *Quart. Rev. Biol. 25:* 30-60, 131-176.

FISHER, R. A., A. S. CORBET, and C. B. WILLIAMS. 1943. The relation between the number of species and the number of individuals in a random sample of an animal population. *Jr. Animal Ecol. 12:* 42-58.

GAUSE, G. F. 1934. *The Struggle for Existence.* Baltimore. ix + 163 pp.

———. 1935. Verification expérimentales de la théorie mathématique de la lutte pour la vie. *Actualités scientifiques et industrielles,* no. 277. Paris. 63 pp.

GAUSE, G. F. and A. A. WITT. 1935. Behavior of mixed populations and the problem of natural selection. *Amer. Nat. 69:* 596-609.

GRIM, J. 1950. Versuche zur Ermittlung der Produktionskoeffizienten einige Planktophyten in einem flachen See. *Biol. Zentralbl. 69:* 147-174.

HUTCHINSON, G. E. 1951. Copepodology for the ornithologist. *Ecology 32:* 571-577.

JOHNSON, H. P. 1903. Fresh-water nereids from the Pacific coast and Hawaii, with remarks on fresh-water Polychaeta in general. *Mark Anniversary Volume.* New York. pp. 205-224.

LANGFORD, R. R. 1938. Diurnal and seasonal changes in the distribution of the limnetic crustacea of Lake Nipissing, Ontario. *Univ. Toronto Studies, Biol. Ser. 45:* 1-142.

PRESTON, F. W. 1948. The commonness, and rarity, of species. *Ecology 29:* 254-283.

RANDLE, W. and R. AUSTING. 1952. Ecological notes on the long-eared and saw-whet owls in southwestern Ohio. *Ecology 33:* 422-426.

REID, D. M. 1939. On the occurrence of *Gammarus duebeni* Lillj. (Crustacea, Amphipoda) in Ireland. *Proc. R. Irish Acad. 45 B:* 207-214.

RICKER, W. E. 1937. Statistical treatment of sampling processes useful in the enumeration of plankton. *Arch. f. Hydrobiol. 31:* 68-84.

SEXTON, E. W. 1939. On a new species of *Gammarus* (*G. tigrinus*) from Droitwich District. *Jr. Mar. Biol. Ass. 23:* 543-551.

SEWELL, ELIZABETH. 1951. *The Structure of Poetry.* London. Routledge and Kegan Paul Ltd. x + 196 pp.

SLOBODKIN, L. B. 1953. Population dynamics in *Daphnia obtusa* Kurz. (Yale thesis 1951.) To appear in 1953.

TONOLLI, V. 1949. Stuttura spaziale del popolamento mesoplanctico, eterogeneità delle densità dei popolamenti orizzontale e sua variazione in funzione della quota. *Mem. Ist. ital. Idrobiol.* "Dott. Marco de March" *5:* 189-208.

VOLTERRA, V. 1926. Variazioni e fluttuazioni del numero d' individui in specie animali conviventi. *Mem. Accad. Lincei* (6) 2: 31-113.

WHITE, C. M. N. 1951. Weaver birds at Lake Mweru. *Ibis 93:* 626-627.

WYNNE-EDWARDS, V. C. 1952. Zoology of the Baird Expedition (1950). I: The birds observed in central and south-east Baffin Island. *Auk 69:* 352-391.

PART II

SINGLE SPECIES POPULATION: PATTERNS IN SPACE AND TIME

A STUDY OF THE CRYPTOZOA OF AN ILLINOIS WOODLAND

LAMONT C. COLE
Hull Zoological Laboratory, University of Chicago

THE DISTRIBUTION OF THE CRYPTOZOIC ANIMALS WITHIN AREAS

It has been shown that different experimental areas representing slightly different habitats might contain faunas distinct from each other in species composition, seasonal aspects, and in relative abundance of various forms. Faunal variations within specific areas where conditions may be presumed to have been relatively constant may also be examined with respect to individual species to see to what extent individual animals were distributed at random in the available cryptozoic habitat.

A discontinuous integral variate such as the frequency of occurrence of a species of animal in field plots should be expected to correspond to a Poisson distribution (Poisson 1837, Student 1907, Svedberg 1922) if the individual animals are distributed at random. The application of the Poisson frequency distribution to cases where the number of samples is not very great or in cases such as would arise in field plot sampling of a fairly abundant species has sometimes been questioned (Whitaker 1914), but such applications have been vigorously defended by Arne Fisher (1922) and now seem to be generally accepted (Snedecor 1938, R. A. Fisher 1941). It is only profitable to investigate the distribution of the more abundant species because comparisons of observed and theoretical distributions are unsatisfactory for forms so rare that there is little probability of ever finding more than one individual under a particular board.

The distribution of spiders under the boards regularly corresponded to a Poisson distribution indicating a random distribution of individuals. Table 8 shows the distribution of 108 spiders encountered in 240 inspections of boards in Area H for the month of August, 1942.

TABLE 8. The distribution of spiders in Area H—August, 1942. P = 0.527.

	Number of spiders per board				
	0	1	2	3	More
Observed frequencies...	159	64	13	4	0
Expected (Poisson).....	157.0	66.5	14.2	2.0	0.3

The test of the observed distribution by the Chi-square test indicates that as great a deviation from the Poisson distribution could be expected about 53 percent of the time due to chance alone so there is certainly no reason for assuming a non-random distribution of the spiders under the experimental boards. In all experimental areas and at all seasons the spiders were distributed at random.

Editor's Note: Of the nearly 40 pages of this study, only the section dealing with the distribution of members of the Cryptozoic fauna under boards is reprinted. The terms of the Poisson series, formally written

$$P_{(x)} = \frac{m^x}{x!} e^{-m}$$, are for 0, 1, 2, 3 .... occurrences $\frac{1}{e^m}, \frac{m}{e^m}, \frac{m^2}{2e^m}, \frac{m^3}{3.2^m}$ ....

For a further discussion of this series in ecology, see Andrewartha's Introduction to the Study of Animal Populations (University of Chicago Press) and Greig-Smith's Quantitative Plant Ecology (New York, Academic Press).

Reproduced and excerpted with permission from Ecological Monographs, 16: 70-75 (only), 1946. Published by The Duke University Press, Durham, North Carolina.

No other prominent species exhibited a random distribution of individuals. The chilopod Lithobius, which is generally considered to be a solitary animal, was never common enough under the boards to permit a rigid test of the randomness of distribution but, as already observed, they form winter aggregations which certainly indicates a non-random distribution for at least a part of the year.

All of the other important animals exhibited non-random distributions of the type termed "contagious" by Polya (1931). The distribution of 254 diplopods (Scytonotus) in Area H for a series of * 360 inspections made between September 12 and September 22, 1942 will serve as an example of a contagious distribution. This distribution is shown in Table 9 and in Figure 3.

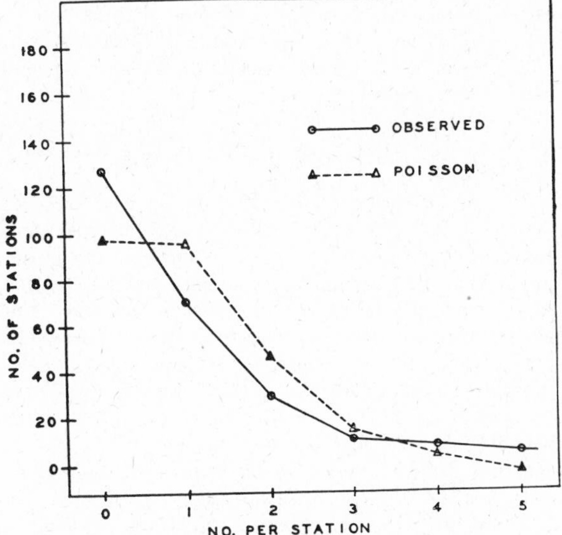

FIG. 3. The contagious distribution of *Scytonotus*.

Contagious distributions are characterized by a tendency for the animals to form aggregations so that the larger numbers of animals under single boards occurred more often than would be the case if the distribution were random.

TABLE 9. The distribution of *Scytonotus granulatus* in Area H. P = 0.0000.

	Number of *Scytonotus* per board						
	0	1	2	3	4	5	More
Observed frequencies	128	71	34	11	8	5	3
** Expected (Poisson)	100.5	94.5	45.4	14.4	3.4	0.7	0.1

In testing randomness of distribution there is danger of confounding the results by lumping together data collected on different days or in different areas. For example, if data from the grazed part of the woods were included in the Scytonotus table, the form of the distribution would be radically altered because nearly all of these boards would show a zero-frequency for diplopods. For this reason, interpretations based on such frequency distributions must be limited to the more common species and to as homogeneous samples as possible.

In the case of Scytonotus distributions were always contagious and showed a tendency to cross the theoretical Poisson distribution at about the level of the frequency class "3 diplopods per board." More detailed investigation might reveal that when about 3 Scytonotus are present under a board of this size they serve to attract other diplopods to the board or influence wandering individuals to remain once they find that particular board. Thus any "social instinct" on the part of the animals would lead to contagious distributions of the type observed.

In the case of the isopod Trachelipus the number of aggregations found usually did not exceed expectation until groups of 7 or 8 individuals were attained. Table 10 illustrates this for Area TP on June 12, 1942.

TABLE 10. Distribution of *Trachelipus rathkei* in Area TP—June 12, 1942.

	Number per board								
	0	1	2	3	4	5	6	7	8
Observed	28	28	14	11	8	11	2	3	3
Expected	5.7	17.5	26.8	27.3	20.9	12.8	6.5	2.8	1.1

	Number per board								
	9	10	11	12	13	14	15	16	17
Observed	3	3	2	0	1	2	1	0	2
Expected	Total expected over 8=0.5								

The isopods obviously tended to form larger aggregations than did the diplopods. The largest aggregation ever encountered under one board contained 56 isopods.

It is obvious that social insects such as the ants are not distributed at random but, aside from a social instinct, there are several other conditions which could cause animals to exhibit contagious frequency distributions. If an animal deposits its eggs in clumps, the newly hatched young will occur in groups and will be contagiously distributed. Neyman (1939), reasoning from this type of situation, has developed a class of theoretical frequency distributions which have been shown by Beall (1940) to give good fits when applied to certain contagiously distributed animals. Neyman's "type A" curve may be thought of as a generalized expression of the Poisson law with another parameter added. This type of distribution, however, seldom gave good fits in the present study where the basic assumptions were not realized. In highly contagious distributions such as those shown by the ants and isopods the fit was little better than that given by the Poisson distribution.

*Author's note: 360 inspections should have been 260 inspections.

**Author's note: Corrected figures are: 97.8 95.4 46.5 15.1 3.6 0.7 0.9

Another condition leading to contagious distributions is heterogeneity in the experimental areas. Unequal suitability of the boards for a particular species may cause the individuals to become aggregated under the boards with the more favorable habitat. This condition may be very difficult to detect because seemingly trivial factors might exert a great effect. It was found that boards over soil with a moisture content of less than 10 percent were definitely deficient in isopods so, at least at certain times, this factor would tend to produce a contagious distribution of isopods. The data on soil moisture are not sufficient for a detailed quantitative analysis of the effects of moisture on isopod distribution but part of the contagiousness of the observed distributions probably results from this factor.

Although soil moisture, and perhaps additional undetected factors, may lead to contagious distributions under the conditions of this study, it seems probable that a considerable part of the aggregating tendency observed is attributable to a mutual attraction between members of the same species. When mating is in progress paired animals are certain to occur more often than would be expected on an assumption of randomness. This is illustrated in Table 11 which shows the distribution of 60 small carabids in 500 inspections made during September, 1942.

Three of the seven observed pairs of small carabids were copulating when found and it is obvious that the frequency of pairs causes this distribution to depart from randomness.

In addition to mating, there are other advantages of associations between members of a species which could be operated upon by natural selection (Allee 1931, 1938) to accentuate aggregating tendencies. In the winter aggregations of centipedes, for example, no survival value is obvious but these aggregations are probably formed as a result of tendencies inherent within the individuals.

TABLE 11. The distribution of small carabid beetles—September, 1942.

	Number per board			
	0	1	2	More
Observed	447	46	7	0
Expected	443.4	53.2	3.2	0.2

Whatever the cause of contagious distributions their occurrence considerably complicates statistical analysis of the data. Mean numbers of animals in different areas or time intervals cannot be compared by the usual methods employing standard errors because these methods assume random distribution of the populations. Also, the correlation coefficient cannot be used to measure association between species when the populations are not normally distributed. Consequently, it has been necessary to use presence or absence in samples as a criterion in making such comparisons.

The fact that nearly all of these species are contagiously distributed also makes it extremely hazardous to use sample collections in estimating any larger population. Even in a mildly contagious distribution this factor may be of considerable importance. For example, in an area of 20 boards such as Area H, 5 boards might be selected at random and the total population estimated by mutiplying the observed number of animals by four. The results which could be obtained in this way can be calculated. As an example the distribution of 39 isopods in Area H on May 3, 1942 is shown in Table 12.

There are 15,504 different ways of drawing a sample of 5 boards from the 20 in this area and, by

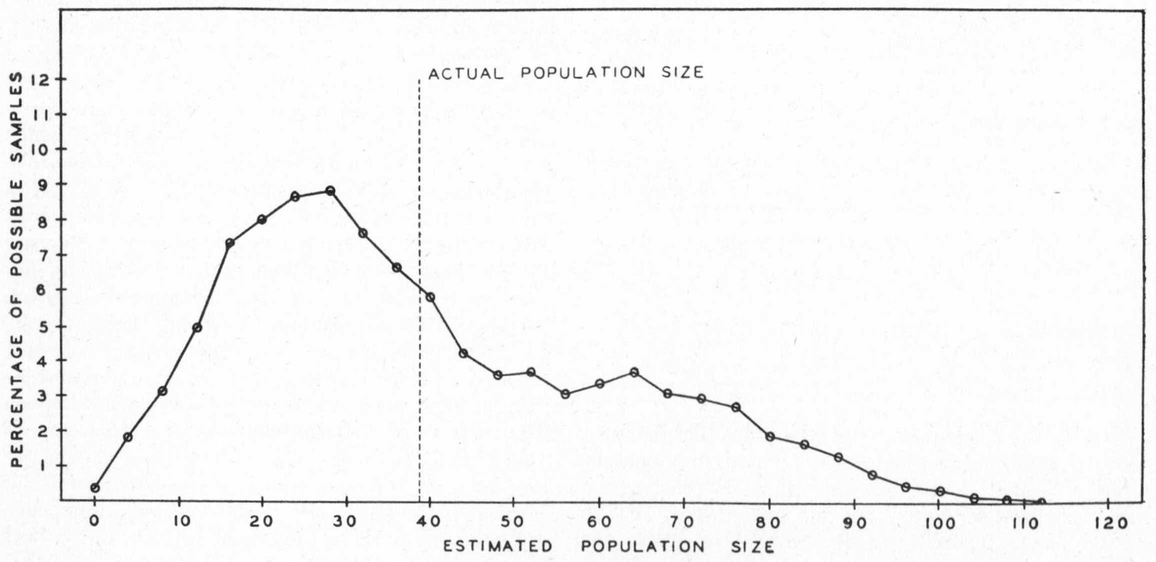

FIG. 4. Distribution of the possible samples for population estimation.

using such a sample to estimate the total isopod population of the 20 boards, 29 different estimates ranging from no isopods to 112 isopods could be obtained. The most frequent estimate of the total population would be 28 isopods and this value would be obtained 8.79 percent of the time. The distribution of the 15,504 possible samples is shown in Figure 4, and it illustrates that such a method of population estimation may lead to very great errors even when the distribution is not highly contagious. It is probably a general characteristic of contagious distributions that the population will tend to be underestimated from the mean of sample collections. This is to be expected because a disproportionately large percentage of the fauna is concentrated into a few units which are unlikely to be included in samples.

Because the observed contagiousness of these distributions seemed to result largely from a social instinct or attraction between individuals, it is very desirable to find some mathematical expression for the tendency to aggregate shown by a species at a particular time. This tendency is not constant but varies from day to day or even from hour to hour and also between experimental areas.

In a Poisson distribution the variance (σ^2) is equal to the mean (m) and the deviation of a frequency distribution from the Poisson distribution may, therefore, be expressed by the ratio: $\frac{m-\sigma^2}{m}$ or $\frac{\sigma^2}{m}$ —1. This expression will have the value O in a true Posson distribution, will be positive when aggregation occurs, and negative when the animals are more evenly distributed (overdispersed) than would occur in the Poisson case. This expression is closely related to a number of others which have been employed such as the Lexis ratio (Arne Fisher 1922, Beall 1935), the second parameter in Neyman's "type A" contagious distribution (Neyman 1939), and the expression used by Svedberg (1922) and discussed by Gause (1936).

Attempts to use the above expression as a measure of aggregating tendency indicated that its value was greatly affected by the number of animals present, an effect also described by Arne Fisher (1922) and by Beall (1935). Since the formula for the variance of a distribution may be written as: $\sigma^2 = \frac{\Sigma x^2 - m\Sigma x}{n}$ where x is the size of any sample and n is the number of samples, the expression: $\frac{\sigma^2}{m}$ —1 will reduce to $\frac{\Sigma x^2}{\Sigma x}$ —m —1 in which form it is obvious that the ratio will tend to increase as the size of the samples increases. The Charlier coefficient of disturbance which may be written: $C = \frac{100\sqrt{\sigma^2 - m}}{m}$ is independent of the number of animals and in the present study, as also found by Beall (1935), proved to be a much more satisfactory index of aggregating tendency. Positive values of C indicate aggregation while C becomes imaginary with overdispersion. Imaginary values would be inconvenient for investigating animals if individuals showed actual antagonism toward each other but in this study all species were typically either underdispersed or randomly distributed so the occasional imaginary values of C were merely taken to indicate zero tendency to aggregate.

TABLE 12. Distribution of isopods in Area H—May 3, 1942.

Number per board	0	1	2	3	4	6	12
Observed frequency	8	4	2	3	1	1	1

A number of attempts were made to correlate values of C with physical or climatic conditions. Because many species tend to form autumn and winter aggregations one might expect to find values of C considerably influenced by low temperatures. Moisture conditions, in the laboratory at least, also influence the formation of aggregations by certain forms such as isopods.

For the period from September 16, 1942 to September 22, 1942 the boards in Area H were inspected every six hours. During this period there was an interval of hard rain and rapid temperature fall. These data then seem well suited for comparing variations in aggregating tendency and weather conditions. In Figure 5 the Charlier coefficient for isopods is plotted along with the air temperature taken some 30 cm. above the soil surface. This temperature was not necessarily the same as the microhabitat temperature to which the animals were responding and the significant parallelism between the two lines is, therefore, all the more striking.

Another way of looking at aggregating tendency is to consider how the quantity Σx^2 varies with the amount of aggregation. If aggregation is complete so that all of the animals are under a single board we will have: $\Sigma x^2 = (\Sigma x)^2$ while if the animals are distributed as evenly as possible so that there is zero aggregation we shall have approximately: $\Sigma x^2 = nm^2 = m\Sigma x$. Therefore, the increment representing amount of aggregation for any observed value of Σx^2 is approximately $\Sigma x^2 - m\Sigma x$ and the maximum possible amount of aggregation is represented approximately by $(\Sigma x)^2 - m\Sigma x$. Expressed as a proportion, the observed degree of aggregation is then the ratio of the observed amount to the possible amount, or: $\frac{\Sigma x^2 - m\Sigma x}{(\Sigma x)^2 - m\Sigma x} = \left(\frac{n}{n-1}\right)\frac{\Sigma x^2}{(\Sigma x)^2} - \frac{1}{(n-1)}$ which is nearly equal to $\frac{\Sigma x^2}{(\Sigma x)^2}$.

At the time these data were being collected the writer made the then purely empirical observation that the quantity $\frac{\Sigma x^2}{(\Sigma x)^2}$ seemed to give a better representation of aggregating tendency as evidenced by significant correlations with air temperature than did the Charlier coefficient. This quantity was not used analytically because of its purely empirical nature

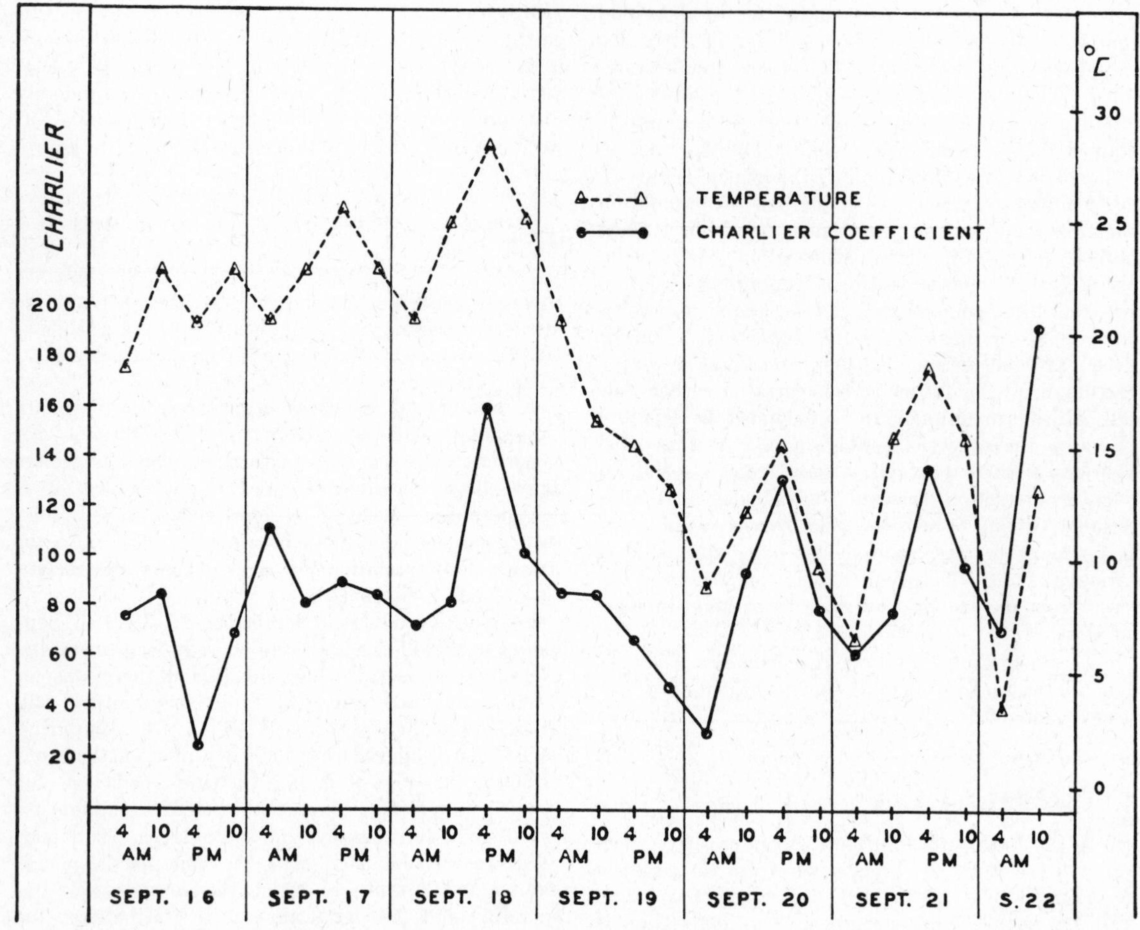

FIG. 5. Relation of isopod aggregating tendency to temperature.

and the lack of a rationale for ignoring the amount of aggregation which would be expected to result from chance. It now appears, however, that some investigation might profitably be devoted to answering the question of whether it is the absolute degree of aggregation or the degree of excess aggregation which tends to vary with environmental factors.

The correlation coefficient between C and temperature was not significant, apparently because the downward trend in temperature was not accompanied by a general downward trend in the tendency of the isopods to aggregate, but the parallelism between the two lines may be tested for statistical significance by comparing the number of times the two lines rise or fall simultaneously. These data give the 4-fold table shown in Table 13.

TABLE 13. Significance test of the parallelism between air temperature and C—the contagiousness of the distribution of isopods. $P = 0.00007$.

	Increase in C	Decrease in C
Temperatures increase	10	1
Temperature decrease	1	13

If C were independent of temperature we should expect to find the two increasing together only about 4.8 times instead of the 10 times observed. The probability value as calculated by Fisher's "exact method" (R. A. Fisher 1941) shows that a parallelism as great as that observed should occur by chance only about 7 times in 100,000 observations. Thus it appears that increases in temperature did increase the tendency of isopods to form aggregations in the cryptozoic niche.

This effect of temperature on aggregation tendency must be independent of any effect on the total number of isopods present because C is independent of this factor. Increases in aggregation then were almost necessarily brought about by isopods leaving slightly occupied boards and moving under boards where more isopods were present. There are evidently two ways in which weather conditions might effect this change. Either some inherent social tendency within the isopods must have been altered, or, as temperature changed, some boards must have become less favorable as habitats so that isopods left them. In this case there was no evidence of heterogeneity in Area H as evidenced by certain boards being consistently more occupied than others. Furthermore, in the entire study, whenever heterogeneity was demonstrable in any experimental area, it tended to disappear when the soil became wet. Figure 5 shows a closer parallel between temperature and isopod aggregation in the period following the rain (the rain stopped at noon September 20) when the area should show less heterogeneity than in the earlier days. Thus the evidence favors the conclusion that some social tendency inherent within the isopods was increased by rising temperature. This is certainly not the only factor affecting the isopod aggregations or a much closer correlation should have been obtained but the temperature effect was highly significant.

This complicated behavior of the isopods, leaving shelter and moving to boards harboring larger numbers of isopods, as well as the vertical migration from unfavorable conditions, suggests that the complexity of aggregation phenomena has been underestimated in attempts to reduce these phenomena ot mechanical responses such as altered rates of turning (Waloff 1941).

Any relationship between weather and aggregating tendency in other species was much less clear than for isopods. In Figure 6 the Charlier coefficient for the diplopod Scytonotus is plotted for the same period shown in Figure 5. A comparison with the isopod graph makes it clear that the factors affecting the aggregating tendency of diplopods differed from those affecting the isopods. It is interesting to note the common tendency of the diplopods under the boards to be unaggregated (imaginary values of C) at the time of the 4 A.M. inspection which parallels the observation that Scytonotus may come out at night to aggregate on top of the boards or to wander in the grass. The early morning frost on September 20 may have been responsible for keeping the diplopods aggregated under the boards and at other times low atmospheric humidity might operate in this way. We do not at present, however, have sufficient data to correlate the aggregating tendency of Scytonotus with external conditions.

No species except Trachelipus and Scytonotus were common enough in this series of data to permit a satisfactory analysis of aggregating tendency. The Charlier coefficient becomes erratic when the mean number of animals per sample is very small and it would also be impossible to detect heterogeneity within the area from such limited data. Larger samples would be necessary to obtain satisfactory results with most of the other species.

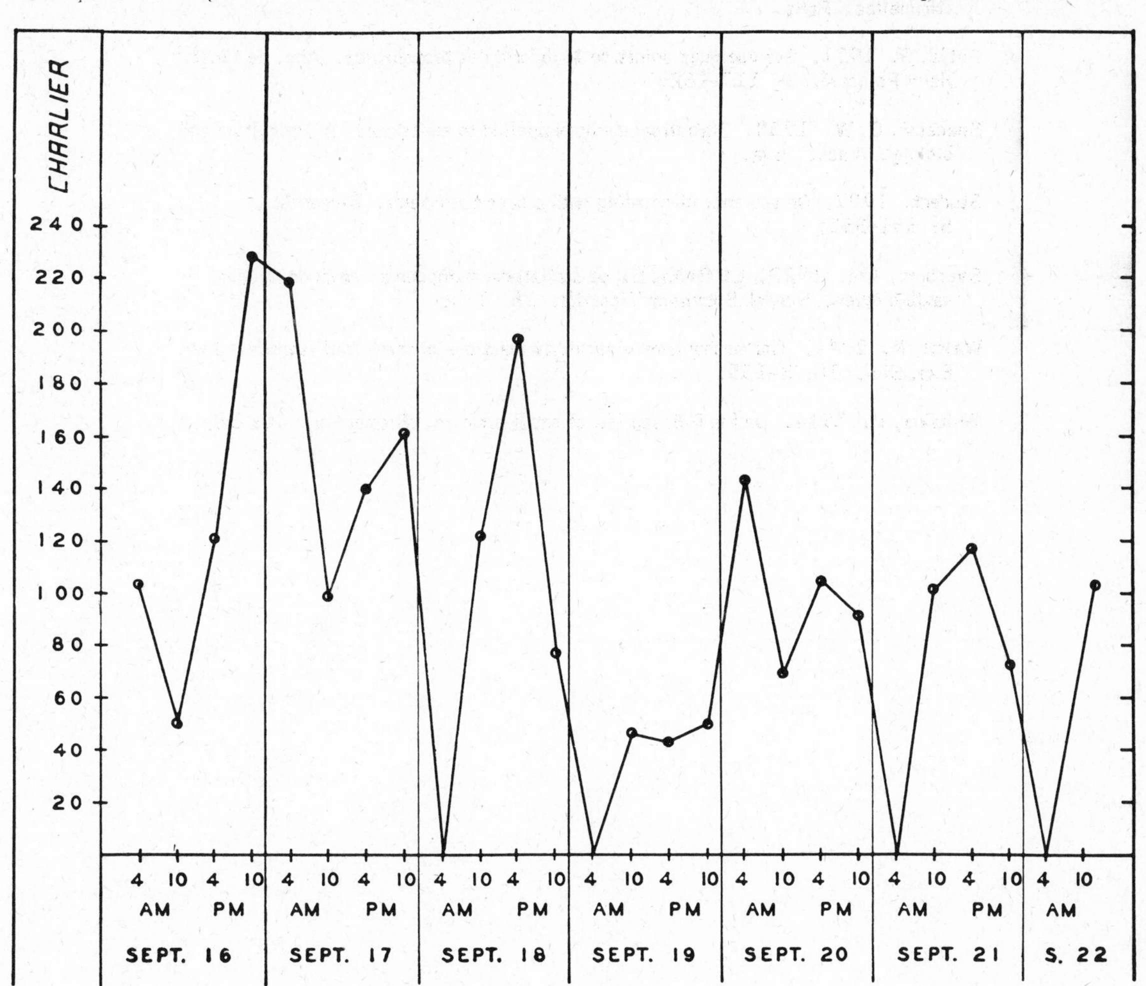

FIG. 6. Tendency of *Scytonotus* to aggregate.

LITERATURE CITED

Allee, W. C. 1926. Studies in animal aggregations. Causes and effects of bunching in land isopods. Jour. Exp. Zool. 45: 255-277.

1931. Animal aggregations. A study in general sociology. Univ. of Chicago Press. Chicago.

1938. The social life of animals. Norton, N. Y.

Beall, G. 1935. Study of arthropod populations by the method of sweeping. Ecol. 16: 216-225.

1940. The fit and significance of contagious distributions when applied to observations on larval insects. Ecol. 21: 460-474.

Fisher, Arne. 1922. The mathematical theory of probabilities. N. Y.

Fisher, R. A. 1941. Statistical methods for research workers. 8th ed. Edinburgh.

Gause, G. F. 1936. Principles of biocenology. Quart. Rev. Biol. 11: 320-338.

Neyman, J. 1939. On a new class of contagious distributions applicable in entomology and bacteriology. Ann. Math. Stat. 10: 35-57.

Poisson, S. D. 1837. Recherches sur la probabilité des jugements en matières criminelles. Paris.

Polya, G. 1931. Sur quelques points de la théorie des probabilités. Ann. de l'Inst. Henri Poincaré. 1: 117-162.

Snedecor, G. W. 1938. Statistical methods applied to experiments in agriculture and biology. Ames. Iowa.

Student. 1907. On the error of counting with a haemocytometer. Biometrika. 5: 351-355.

Svedberg, The. 1922. Ett Bidrag till de statistiska methodernas anvandning inom vaxtbiologien. Svensk Botanisch Tidskrift. 16: 1-8.

Waloff, N. 1941. The mechanisms of humidity reactions of terrestrial isopods. Jour. Exp. Biol. 18: 8-135.

Whitaker, L. 1914. On the Poisson law of small numbers. Biometrika. 10: 36-71.

DISTANCE TO NEAREST NEIGHBOR AS A MEASURE OF SPATIAL RELATIONSHIPS IN POPULATIONS

PHILIP J. CLARK AND FRANCIS C. EVANS
Institute of Human Biology, University of Michigan, Ann Arbor, Michigan

INTRODUCTION

The pattern of distribution of a population of plants or of animals is a fundamental characteristic of that population, but it is a feature that is extremely difficult to describe in precise and meaningful terms. The distributions exhibited by populations of living organisms in their natural environments include an almost infinite variety of patterns. However, the lack of an adequate method of description has prevented the development of any system of pattern classification other than a most general one. The situation is further complicated by the fact that it has generally been considered necessary, for practical reasons, to use samples rather than entire populations as the source of distributional information, and this frequently introduces bias and inaccuracy into the estimates of population parameters. The whole problem of the measurement and description of patterns of distribution has recently been the subject of an excellent review by Goodall (1952) in reference to plant populations. It is evident from this review that many important concepts of phytosociology are based upon the assumption that the individuals of most plant populations are distributed at random. This assumption is no longer a tenable one, and it is probably even less applicable to animal populations. A number of methods of demonstrating the occurrence of non-random distribution are now available, but the degree of departure from random expectation is much more difficult to ascertain, and the significance of differences in the distribution pattern of two or more populations is therefore hard to evaluate. Im-

Reproduced with permission from Ecology, 35: 445-453, 1954. Published by The Ecological Society of America and Duke University Press, Durham, North Carolina.

provement in the quantitative analysis of distribution is greatly to be desired and would surely facilitate the interpretation of dispersion patterns.

Gleason (1920) and Svedberg (1922) seem to have been the first ecologists to test natural distributions of organisms for conformity to random expectation, the former employing the binomial distribution and the latter making use of the Poisson series. Several measures have since been used to test the hypothesis of random dispersion. The data to which these measures have been applied are usually counts of individuals or records of presence or absence in sample plots or quadrats and are generally expressed in terms of frequency. Such data are strongly influenced by the size of quadrat used in their collection (Curtis and McIntosh 1950).

Recognition of the widespread existence of nonrandomly distributed populations has led to the development of mathematical models based on various assumptions about the natural forces active in the formation of particular patterns. Some models (Ashby 1935) attribute primary importance to variations in environmental factors, others (Neyman 1939) to behavioral characteristics of the species concerned. Data from numerous sources have been fitted to these models, with varying degrees of success.

The distance from one individual to another provides a variable for the measurement of spacing that obviates the use of quadrats and therefore eliminates the effect of quadrat size. Viktorov (1947, *fide* Goodall 1952) measured the distance from a given plant to every other individual connected to it by a straight line not crossing another plant and used this information to estimate the variability of the distances. Cottam and Curtis (1949) attempted to ascertain the average distance between trees in a forested area by using "randomly selected" pairs of individuals. Dice (1952) seems to have been the first to use distance between nearest neighbors in measuring departure from randomness. Dice's procedure consists of measuring the distance from a randomly selected individual to its nearest neighbor in each of the six sextants of the circular area which surrounds the chosen "center of origin." The method is somewhat laborious, however, for it requires several measurements from each center of origin and makes use of third moment statistics in testing for the degree of departure from random expectation. One also experiences considerable difficulty in expressing the results of this measure in meaningful terms of spatial relations. Further study of the spacing problem has suggested the following measure, which requires but a single measurement from each center of origin and which we believe to be superior in its simplicity of computation and ease of interpretation. Use of the distance to nearest neighbor in the detection of non-randomness in spatial pattern has also recently been advocated by Skellam (1952), who has given a derivation of the probability distribution of this distance.

Lee R. Dice gave much advice and encouragement in the development of this measure. A letter from David G. Kendall, of Magdalen College, Oxford, offered a valuable suggestion for the derivation of a formula to express the mean expected distance between nearest neighbors in a random distribution of specified density. The measure of spacing described in this paper has been applied to the distributions of three species of grassland forbs charted by the junior author in collaboration with Stanley A. Cain and Fernando Segadas-Vianna, then associated with the Cranbrook Institute of Science, and also to a map of the trees of a woodlot prepared by Morrison Ismond, Bruce Hayward and Theodore Herman. Raymond H. Brand carried out many of the measurements and much of the statistical computation. To all of these sources of information and assistance we are very grateful. Both authors are jointly responsible for the ideas of this paper and have shared in the preparation of the manuscript. The senior author is primarily responsible for the mathematical derivations and statistical treatments.

The Measure

For the purposes of simplification, this measure of spacing is explained here in terms of two-dimensional space, *i.e.*, with reference to populations on plane surfaces. With suitable modification, however, it is equally applicable to populations distributed along a line or dispersed throughout a volume. A generalization of the measure for use with k dimensions has been worked out and will be published later.

The measure of spacing which we propose is a measure of the manner and degree to which the distribution of individuals in a population on a given area departs from that of a random distribution. Some clarification of what is meant by a "random distribution" is therefore desirable. In a random distribution of a set of points on a given area, it is assumed that any point has had the same chance of occurring on any sub-area as any other point, that any sub-area of specified size has had the same chance of receiving a point as any other sub-area of that size, and that the placement of each point has not been influenced by that of any other point. Thus, randomness as here employed is a spatial concept, intimately dependent upon the boundaries of the space chosen by the investigator. A set of points may be random with respect to a specified area but decidedly non-random with respect to a larger space which includes the specified area. For meaningful results, therefore, the areas selected for investigation should be chosen with care.

The distance from an individual to its nearest neighbor, irrespective of direction, provides the basis for this measure of spacing. A series of such distances is measured in a given population, using all of the individuals present or a randomly selected sample, and the value of the mean distance to nearest neighbor is obtained for this set of observations. The mean distance to nearest neighbor that would be expected if the individuals of that population were randomly distributed is also calculated. The ratio of the observed mean distance to the expected mean distance serves as the measure of departure from randomness. The ratios that have been calculated for two or more populations can be directly compared with one another, as a measure of their relative departure from random expectation. Significance tests of the difference between ratios can be made without great difficulty, and the results of comparison can be expressed in terms that are readily visualized. To facilitate presentation, the derivation of some of the formulas used in this paper are included in an Appendix rather than in the body of the text. A list of the symbols and definitions of concepts employed herein is given in Table I.

TABLE I. *A list of the symbols and definitions of concepts employed in a measure of spacing based on the mean distance between nearest neighbors*

Symbol	Definition
N	the number of measurements of distance taken in the observed population or sample. When a single sector is employed, N is also equal to the number of individuals used as centers of measurement.
r	the distance in any specified units from a given individual to its nearest neighbor.
ρ	the density of the observed distribution expressed as the number of individuals per unit of area. (The unit of measurement used in the calculation of rho must be the same as that used in measuring r.)*
Σr	the summation of the measurements of distance to nearest neighbor.
Σr^2	the summation of the squares of the measurements of distance.
$\bar{r}_A = \frac{\Sigma r}{N}$	the mean of the series of distances to nearest neighbor.
$\bar{r}_E = \frac{1}{2\sqrt{\rho}}$	the mean distance to nearest neighbor expected in an infinitely large random distribution of density rho.
$R = \frac{\bar{r}_A}{\bar{r}_E}$	the measure of the degree to which the observed distribution departs from random expectation with respect to the distance to nearest neighbor.
$c = \frac{\bar{r}_A - \bar{r}_E}{\sigma_{\bar{r}_E}}$	the standard variate of the normal curve.
$\sigma_{\bar{r}_E} = \frac{0.26136}{\sqrt{N\rho}}$	the standard error of the mean distance to nearest neighbor in a randomly distributed population of density rho.
F	the ratio of between-group variance to within-group variance in a test of significance of the differences between two or more populations.
p	the number of populations being compared.
k	the number of sectors in a circle of infinite radius surrounding the individual from which measurements of distance are taken.

*Computation of rho on the basis of N - 1 rather than N is theoretically proper, but with large samples the difference in results is negligible.

If, in a population of N individuals having a specified density ρ, the distance r from each individual to its nearest neighbor is measured, the mean observed distance may be represented as $\bar{r}_A = \frac{\Sigma r}{N}$. The mean distance which would be expected if this population were distributed at random, $\bar{r}_E$, can be shown to have a value equal to $\frac{1}{2\sqrt{\rho}}$ (see Appendix). The ratio $R = \frac{\bar{r}_A}{\bar{r}_E}$ can then be used as a measure of the degree to which the observed distribution approaches or departs from random expectation. In a random distribution, $R = 1$. Under conditions of maximum aggregation, $R = 0$, since all of the individuals occupy the same locus and the distance to nearest neighbor is therefore 0. Under conditions of maximum spacing, individuals will be distributed in an even, hexagonal pattern, and every individual (except those at the periphery of the population) will be equidistant from six other individuals. In such a distribution, the mean distance to nearest neighbor will be maximized and will have the value $\frac{1.0746}{\sqrt{\rho}}$ (see Appendix). When this is the case, $R = 2.1491$. Thus, R has a limited range, with values indicative of perfectly uniform, random, and completely aggregated patterns of distribution. In any given distribution, the mean observed distance to nearest neighbor is R times as great as would be expected in a random distribution of the same density. Thus, an R value of 0.5 would indicate that nearest neighbors are, on the average, half as far apart as expected under conditions of randomness. This measure can therefore be readily interpreted in simple terms. Since it is also easily computed, it should be of practical use in describing spatial relations.

TESTS OF SIGNIFICANCE

The usefulness of any measure of spacing will be increased if its reliability can be ascertained. If the value of R indicates that a given population is not randomly distributed, the significance of the departure of $\bar{r}_A$ from $\bar{r}_E$ can be tested by the normal curve. The formula used in this test of significance is

$$c = \frac{\bar{r}_A - \bar{r}_E}{\sigma_{\bar{r}_E}}$$

where c is the standard variate of the normal curve (Mather 1947) and $\sigma_{\bar{r}_E}$ is the standard error of the mean distance to nearest neighbor in a randomly distributed population of the same density as that of the observed population. The value of $\sigma_{\bar{r}_E}$ for a population of density ρ is $\frac{0.26136}{\sqrt{N\rho}}$, where N is the number of measurements of distance made (see Appendix). The c values 1.96 and 2.58 represent respectively the 5 per cent and the 1 per cent levels of significance (for a two-tailed test); for other values one may consult a table of the normal distribution.[1]

When two populations are being compared, it may not be sufficient merely to ascertain whether each of them departs significantly from randomness. One may also want to know whether the populations differ significantly from one another with respect to the direction and magnitude of their departures from random expectation. The significance of the difference in the values of R for two populations can be tested by the Student-Fisher t distribution, or by the F distribution. We have employed the latter method because it can be used with more than two populations (see Appendix for analysis of variance).

The tests of significance proposed above are based on the difference between $\bar{r}_A$ and $\bar{r}_E$. It is theoretically possible, however, for a non-randomly distributed population to exist in which $\bar{r}_A$ and $\bar{r}_E$ are equal. The distribution of such a population cannot be shown to be non-random by these tests. In this case, departure from randomness may be ascertained by comparing the frequency distributions of observed and expected distances to nearest neighbor by means of a χ^2 test (for procedure, see Cochran 1952). The majority of investigations of natural populations, however, will not require so sensitive a test.

Application of the Measure to Actual Data

The measure described above has been tested experimentally by applying it to a synthetically constructed random distribution, to the distributions of three species of grassland plants whose patterns exhibit various degrees of aggregation, and to the distribution of trees participating in the canopy of a woodlot, where competition for light might be expected to bring about a comparatively uniform spacing. The results of these analyses are shown in Table II.

Table II. *Comparison of certain statistics obtained in the application of the measure of spacing to various distributions. Measurements for the synthetic random distribution are in units of millimeters and square millimeters, those for the other distributions in units of feet and square feet*

Statistic	Synthetic random	*Solidago*	*Liatris*	*Lespedeza*	Forest trees
Size of area	25,781	23,936	23,936	23,936	69,696
N	116	89	197	184	174
ρ	.00449944	.00371825	.00823028	.00768717	.00249656
$\sqrt{\rho}$	.0670779	.0609774	.0907209	.0876765	.0499656
Σr	833.12	530.24	601.57	512.60	1979.99
Σr^2	7909.6616	4751.5652	4587.6121	3385.5290	30382.6942
$\bar{r}_A$	7.1821	5.9578	3.0537	2.7859	11.3793
$\bar{r}_E$	7.4540	8.1998	5.5114	5.7028	10.0069
R	0.9635	0.7266	0.5541	0.4885	1.1371
$\sigma_{\bar{r}_E}$	0.3618	0.4543	0.2053	0.2198	0.3965
c	0.75	4.93	11.97	13.27	3.46
Probability of a greater difference between $\bar{r}_E$ and $\bar{r}_A$	.453254	.000002	.000002	.000002	.000540

A synthetic random distribution

An artificial distribution was constructed on cross-section paper of 20 lines per inch by random placement of 116 points on a rectangle of 203 x 116 mm. The distance to the nearest neighbor was measured for each point, and the mean observed distance to nearest neighbor proved to be 7.1821 mm. while the mean expected distance was calculated to be 7.4540 (Table II). For this synthetic distribution, R = 0.96, not far from the 1.00 expected of a perfectly random distribution. A test of the significance of the difference between observed and expected mean distances gave a c value of 0.75, indicating that greater departure from expectation might occur 45 per cent of the time purely by chance. The synthetic model was thus shown to be a satisfactory representation of random dispersion.

Distributions of grassland plants

The locations of all individuals of *Lespedeza capitata* Michx., *Liatris aspera* Michx., and *Solidago rigida* L. occurring on several acres of an abandoned field on the University of Michigan's Edwin S. George Reserve were recently mapped by Cain and Evans (1952). Inspection of the

[1] When N is small, somewhat greater accuracy in this test of significance may be obtained by use of the Pearson type III distribution than by use of the normal curve. It can be shown that the skewness of the distances to nearest neighbor in a randomly dispersed set of points on a plane surface is $\alpha_3 = .631$. The probability of a given difference between $\bar{r}_A$ and $\bar{r}_E$ should therefore be found, with the type III distribution, under $\alpha_3 = \frac{.631}{\sqrt{N}}$. When N is large, say over 100, the difference in results is negligible.

map and quantitative studies of the distributions by Thomson (1952) and Dice (1952) indicated that *Lespedeza* was the most strongly aggregated of the three species, whereas *Solidago* was the least aggregated. The measure of spacing described above has been applied to the distribution patterns of these plans on a portion of the map having field dimensions of 136 x 176 feet. The results of analysis are shown in Table II. For *Lespedeza,* R = 0.49, for *Liatris,* R = 0.55, and for *Solidago,* R = 0.73, thus confirming the relative degrees of aggregation shown by previous studies. None of these R values is close to 1, and in each case the probability of obtaining, in a random distribution of the same density, a c value as large as that observed is less than .000002. All three populations clearly depart from random expectation with a high degree of significance, so far as the distance to nearest neighbor is concerned. An analysis of variance was made for an over-all comparison of the three species and yielded an F value of 4.57, significant at the 5 per cent level, indicating differences in the degree of aggregation. Analysis of individual differences, by the methods of Tukey (1949), then showed that *Solidago* differed from both *Liatris* and *Lespedeza,* but the latter two populations were not shown to differ from each other.

A distribution of forest trees

The measure has also been used to evaluate the spacing between individual trees which formed the canopy of an oak-hickory woodlot on the North Campus of the University of Michigan. The distribution pattern of these trees was not readily discernible, although it was suspected of being more uniform than random. Analysis of the trees which occurred on a square plot of this woodlot measuring 264 feet on a side gave the results indicated in Table II. For this distribution, R = 1.14, indicating a departure from random expectation in the direction of uniformity. This difference was shown to be highly significant by the c test.

Application of the Measure to Large Populations

This measure of spacing requires that the true density of the population under investigation be known. Such knowledge permits the calculation of the exact values of the mean expected distance to nearest neighbor and of its standard error. If an estimate of mean density is substituted for its true value, the rigor of the proposed tests of significance will be lost. We recommend, therefore, that the measure be applied to populations which are small enough to permit ascertainment of the true density. This will involve a complete count or census of the population.

If it is considered impractical to measure the distance to nearest neighbor for all of the individuals in the area selected for study, an estimate of the mean distance can be obtained from a random sample and can be used in the formulas already presented. To obtain a truly random sample of n individuals, it is necessary that every possible combination of n individuals have an equal chance of being drawn. This requires that every individual be identified, *i.e.,* marked in some manner, and that n of these marked individuals be drawn at random. In some situations, this may be impractical and the investigator may wish to obtain his measurements of distance to nearest neighbor from randomly selected quadrats. Some rigor will be lost by this procedure, but the saving in time may be considerable. The method of selecting quadrats at random will differ according to circumstances. Time and labor will be saved if the locations of all quadrats to be examined are established prior to collection of data, for the examination of quadrats can then proceed according to location rather than order of draw. The measurements of distance to nearest neighbor obtained in the series of quadrats should be pooled to provide an estimate of $\bar{r}_A$. This estimate may be used in the estimate of R and in the tests of significance given above but is less satisfactory than an estimate based upon a truly random sample.

The problem of the size of sample needed for a satisfactory estimate is discussed in many statistical textbooks and additional space need hardly be devoted to it here. Briefly, however, the size of sample (*i.e.,* number of individuals) required depends upon the degree of accuracy with which the investigator will be satisfied and upon the variability in the distance to nearest neighbor. The more variable the distance, the larger the size of the sample needed to provide a specified degree of accuracy. In general, it may be said that the less uniform the spacing of the individuals in the population, the greater the variability in distance to nearest neighbor will be and the larger the sample required. In any given case, the number of quadrats needed to secure a sufficient sample will depend upon the size of quadrat used. If many small quadrats are used, the sample will more closely approximate a random sample as defined above, and will therefore be more satisfactory, than if a few large quadrats are employed.

Problems of Procedure

When measurements are being taken, one may find that the nearest neighbor of a given individual lies outside of the specified area. Such distances should be measured and included in the computations. However, no individual lying outside the specified area should be used as a center of measurement.

It may also happen that two individuals selected as centers of measurement are closer to one another than to any other individuals. In this case, the same distance will be measured twice. Such double distances introduce no bias and both measurements should be used in the calculations.

The derivation of the mean expected distance between nearest neighbors in a randomly distributed population of specified density is based on the assumption that the area occupied by the population is infinite. In practice, however, we apply the measure to finite populations occupying definite areas. The presence of a boundary beyond which measurements cannot be made will tend to make the value of $\bar{r}_A$ greater than would be obtained if an infinite area were involved. For this reason it will be desirable, whenever possible, to select an area for investigation that lies well within the total area covered by the entire population.

In the foregoing description of this measure of spacing, the individual components of a population have been treated as dimensionless points, whereas in reality they will occupy definite areas. In many situations, the area occupied by an individual is so small in relation to the total area under examination that the individual can legitimately be treated as a point. However, if the individual occupies an area of some size it can no longer be treated as a point, and its spatial requirements become important in determining its relationship to other individuals. In such cases, this measure of spacing is applicable only to the centers of individuals, and measurements of distance should be taken accordingly. It is possible for individuals to be as closely spaced as their size permits and at the same time to have their centers distributed more uniformly than random. Consequently, R values greater than unity may sometimes result from the spatial requirements of the individuals alone.

Extension of the Method

A description of distribution pattern solely in terms of the distance to nearest neighbor is not entirely complete, for it disregards all of the other spatial relations which exist in a population. The measure as described above may therefore not distinguish between certain types of distribution patterns. For example, a population whose individuals are congregated in one spot will not be distinguished from a population consisting of scattered pairs of individuals, such as conjugating *Paramecium*, for in each case the distance to nearest neighbor will be 0. In such situations, the measure can be extended to make use of additional space relations.

Consider each individual selected as a center of measurement to be surrounded by a circle of infinite radius, which can be divided into equal sectors. The distance from the individual at the center to the nearest individual in each of the sectors can then be measured. These distances become the basis of calculations. In this case, the formulas (1) for the expected mean distance to nearest neighbor in a randomly distributed population of density ρ and (2) for its standard error are respectively $\bar{r}_E = \frac{\sqrt{k}}{2\sqrt{\rho}}$ and $\sigma_{\bar{r}_E} = \frac{0.26136\sqrt{k}}{\sqrt{N\rho}}$ where N is the number of measurements and k is the number of sectors about each individual used as a center of measurement. The ratio of the observed mean distance to nearest neighbor to the mean distance expected if the population were randomly distributed will again indicate deviation from randomness whenever its value is greater or less than 1. For completely aggregated populations, its value is, of course, 0. The value indicative of perfectly even, hexagonal spacing depends upon k and is equal to $\frac{2.1491}{\sqrt{k}}$ when k is not greater than 6.

It should be pointed out that an increase in the number of sectors may not always result in greater knowledge about the population under investigation. For example, the *Liatris* and *Lespedeza* populations previously described were re-examined using 2, 3 and 6 sectors. In no case was a significant F value obtained, and the conclusions as to spacing were identical with those based on a single sector. The number of sectors to be used in any given situation, therefore, will depend upon the nature of the distribution patterns involved. Caution should be observed when increasing the number of sectors, for the assumptions underlying the derivations of $\bar{r}_E$ and $\sigma_{\bar{r}_E}$ preclude the existence of empty sectors. We believe that the use of a single sector, *i.e.*, the entire circular area surrounding an individual chosen as a center of measurement, will be sufficient for the description and comparison of spatial relations in most natural populations.

An alternative to the use of more than one sector might be developed by employing successively the second, third, etc. nearest neighbors. The formulas for such a procedure would, however, be more complex than those used in this paper and we have not attempted to explore this possibility.

Summary

To obtain a measure of the spacing of individuals in a population of known density, the distance, r, from each individual to its nearest neighbor may be measured and the mean value of r, here designated $\bar{r}_A$, computed. The mean value of r which would obtain in an infinitely large random distribution of density ρ is found by the formula $\bar{r}_E = \frac{1}{2\sqrt{\rho}}$. The ratio $R = \frac{\bar{r}_A}{\bar{r}_E}$ of observed to expected mean distance provides a measure of the degree to which the distribution pattern of the observed population deviates from random expectation. This ratio is less than, equal to, or greater than 1 according to whether the distribution pattern of the individuals in the population is more aggregated, the same as, or more uniform than would be expected in an infinitely large random distribution of the same density. R ranges in value from 0 for a distribution with maximum aggregation to 2.1491 for a distribution which is as evenly and widely spaced as possible. The significance of departure from random expectation on the part of a given population may be tested by the normal variate

$$c = \frac{\bar{r}_E - \bar{r}_A}{\sigma_{\bar{r}_E}}$$

where $\sigma_{\bar{r}_E}$, the standard error of $\bar{r}_E$, is $\frac{0.26136}{\sqrt{N\rho}}$. The significance of the differences between values of R from various populations may be tested by a one-way analysis of variance.

To demonstrate the simplicity and ease of interpretation of this measure, it has been applied to a synthetically constructed random distribution, to the distribution of three species of grassland plants whose patterns showed various degrees of aggregation, and to the distribution of trees in an oak-hickory woodlot where the pattern was suspected of being more uniform than random. For the synthetic distribution R = 0.96, a non-significant deviation from unity. The three grassland populations yielded the following R values: 0.73 for *Solidago,* 0.55 for *Liatris,* and 0.49 for *Lespedeza,* all of which are significant departures from randomness in the direction of aggregated spacing. For the trees of the woodlot, R = 1.14, a significant deviation from randomness in the direction of uniform spacing.

This measure requires a knowledge of the true density of the population. If this is known, it can be applied to populations in which it is considered impractical to measure the distance to nearest neighbor for all of the individuals. In such cases an estimate of the mean distance to nearest neighbor may be substituted for its true value. This estimate will give more satisfactory results if it is based upon a truly random sample of individuals but it can be obtained from randomly selected quadrats. The size of sample and the number and size of quadrats required are discussed briefly.

Since this measure involves only the relationship between a given individual and its nearest neighbor, the majority of spatial relations in the population are ignored. An extension of the method may be achieved by constructing a circle of infinite radius about each individual from which distances are to be measured, dividing this circle into equal sectors, and measuring the distance from the individual at the center to the nearest neighbor in each of the sectors. The occurrence of empty sectors should be avoided. It is believed that for most purposes a single sector, *i.e.,* the entire circle surrounding the individual chosen as a center of measurement, will be adequate.

An appendix to the paper gives the derivation of certain formulas employed in the development of the measure.

Appendix

Derivation of formulas for $\bar{r}_E$ *and* $\sigma_{\bar{r}_E}$

The formula for the mean distance to nearest neighbor expected in a randomly dispersed population of specified density seems first to have been derived by Hertz (1909). This paper is virtually unknown to biologists and was brought to our attention by Dr. F. D. Miller, Department of Astronomy, University of Michigan, after the senior author had independently obtained the derivations given below. These are presented here because of the inaccessibility of Hertz's paper and because they are considerably simpler than those given by Hertz.

For a random distribution of points in two dimensions the probability that a randomly chosen area of specified size will contain exactly x points is, by Poisson's exponential function, $\frac{m^x e^{-m}}{x!}$, where m is the mean number of points per area. Let the specified area be a sector of a circle of radius r, formed by dividing the circle into k equal sectors. If ρ is the mean density of the distribution, then $m = \rho k^{-1} r^2$ is the mean number of points per area. In this case

$$\frac{(\rho\pi k^{-1}r^2)^x \, e^{-\rho\pi k^{-1}r^2}}{x!}$$

is the probability of finding exactly x points in an arbitrary area of $\pi k^{-1}r^2$ units. Consequently, $e^{-\rho\pi k^{-1}r^2}$ is the probability that a randomly chosen area of $\pi k^{-1}r^2$ units will contain no points. If our area is a sector of a circle about a randomly chosen point, the probability that the sector will contain no other point within a distance r of the chosen point is also $e^{-\rho\pi k^{-1}r^2}$. Considered as a function of r, this is the proportion of distances to nearest neighbor (within sectors) $\geqq$ r. Consequently $1 - e^{-\rho\pi k^{-1}r^2}$ is the proportion of distances to nearest neighbor $\leqq$ r. Differentiating the last expression with respect to r we obtain $2\rho\pi k^{-1}re^{-\rho\pi k^{-1}r^2}dr$ as the probability distribution of r. The mean of r, called $\bar{r}_E$, can be obtained by multiplying the above expression by r and integrating over the interval from 0 to ∞. Thus $\bar{r}_E = \int_0^\infty 2\rho\pi k^{-1}r^2e^{-\rho\pi k^{-1}r^2}dr$, which can be shown to be $\frac{\sqrt{k}}{2\sqrt{\rho}}$.

The second moment of r, $E(r^2)$, is obtained by multiplying the probability distribution function of r by r^2 and integrating over the interval from 0 to ∞. Thus

$$E(r^2) = \int_0^\infty 2\rho\pi k^{-1}r^3e^{-\rho\pi k^{-1}r^2}dr.$$

This integral has the value $\frac{k}{\rho\pi}$. The variance of r is $E(r^2) - (\bar{r}_E)^2$, which proves to be $\frac{(4-\pi)k}{4\pi\rho}$. The standard error of $\bar{r}_E$, $\sigma_{\bar{r}_E}$, is thus

$$\sqrt{\frac{(4-\pi)k}{4\pi\rho N}} = \frac{0.26136\sqrt{k}}{\sqrt{N\rho}},$$

where N is the number of measurements made.

The upper limit of $\frac{\bar{r}_A}{\bar{r}_E}$

The mean distance between nearest neighbors is maximized in a hexagonal distribution, where each point has 6 equidistant nearest neighbors. Let r_u denote the constant distance between nearest neighbors in this distribution. In such a uniform distribution each point can be shown to occupy an area of $\frac{r_u^2 3^{1/2}}{2}$. The density, ρ, of the population is thus $\rho = \frac{2}{r_u^2 3^{1/2}}$. Solving for r_u we obtain $r_u = \frac{2^{1/2}}{3^{1/4}\rho^{1/2}}$. Since r_u is the greatest possible value of $\bar{r}_A$, the maximum value of the ratio $R = \frac{\bar{r}_A}{\bar{r}_E}$ is $\frac{r_u}{\bar{r}_E}$, or $\frac{2^{3/2}}{3^{1/4}k^{1/2}}$, which is approximately equal to $\frac{2.1491}{\sqrt{k}}$.

The application of the analysis of variance to the ratio R

In applying the analysis of variance, we desire to test for differences in R rather than $\bar{r}_A$. Since

$$R = \frac{\bar{r}_A}{\bar{r}_E} = 2\sqrt{\rho}\ \bar{r}_A$$

it is necessary to multiply each value of r by the square root of the density of the population to which it belongs. Such a transformation is most readily effected by multiplying each Σr by its corresponding $\sqrt{\rho}$ and each Σr^2 by its ρ. If p populations are being compared the following computational scheme may be used:

$$a = \rho_1\Sigma r_1^2 + \rho_2\Sigma r_2^2 + \ldots + \rho_p\Sigma r_p^2$$

$$b = \frac{(\sqrt{\rho_1}\Sigma r_1 + \sqrt{\rho_2}\Sigma r_2 + \ldots + \sqrt{\rho_p}\Sigma r_p)^2}{N_1 + N_2 + \ldots + N_p}$$

$$c = \frac{\rho_1(\Sigma r_1)^2}{N_1} + \frac{\rho_2(\Sigma r_2)^2}{N_2} + \ldots + \frac{\rho_p(\Sigma r_p)^2}{N_p}$$

where the subscripts 1, 2, . . . , p which follow ρ, r, and N represent the populations to which these data pertain. The variance ratio, F, for testing the significance of the difference in the values of R for the p populations is

$$F = \frac{(c-b)(N_1 + N_2 + \ldots + N_p - p)}{(a-c)(p-1)},$$

there being $p - 1$ and $N_1 + N_2 + \ldots + N_p - p$ degrees of freedom for the between-group and within-group variances respectively. If a significant F is obtained from this over-all analysis, we know that not all of the populations are alike in their degrees of clumping. The problem of ascertaining which populations differ from each other, however, is more complicated and will not be discussed here. Tukey (1949) has suggested ways of dealing with this problem.

References

Ashby, E. 1935. The quantitative analysis of vegetation. Ann. Bot. **49**: 779-802.

Cain, S. A., and F. C. Evans. 1952. The distribution patterns of three plant species in an old-field community in southeastern Michigan. Contrib. Lab. Vert. Biol. Univ. Mich. **52**: 1-11.

Cochran, W. D. 1952. The χ^2 test of goodness of fit. Ann. Math. Statist. **23**: 315-345.

Cottam, G., and J. T. Curtis. 1949. A method for making rapid surveys of woodlands by means of pairs of randomly selected trees. Ecology **30**: 101-104.

Curtis, J. T., and R. P. McIntosh. 1950. The interrelations of certain analytic and synthetic phytosociological characters. Ecology **31**: 434-455.

Dice, L. R. 1952. Measure of the spacing between individuals within a population. Contrib. Lab. Vert. Biol. Univ. Mich. **55**: 1-23.

Gleason, H. A. 1920. Some applications of the quadrat method. Bull. Torrey Bot. Club **47**: 21-33.

Goodall, D. W. 1952. Quantitative aspects of plant distribution. Biol. Rev. **27**: 194-245.

Hertz, P. 1909. Über den geigenseitigen durchschnittlichen Abstand von Punkten, die mit bekannter mittlerer Dichte im Raume angeordnet sind. Mathematische Annalen **67** : 387-398.

Mather, K. 1947. Statistical analysis in biology. Interscience Publishers, Inc., New York.

Neyman, J. 1939. On a new class of "contagious" distributions, applicable in entomology and bacteriology. Ann. Math. Statist. **10** : 35-37.

Skellam, J. G. 1952. Studies in statistical ecology. I. Spatial pattern. Biometrika **39** : 346-362.

Svedberg, T. 1922. Ett bidrag till de statistiska metodernas användning inom växtbiologien. Svensk Bot. Tidskr. **16** : 1-8.

Thomson, G. W. 1952. Measures of plant aggregation based on contagious distributions. Contrib. Lab. Vert. Biol. Univ. Mich. **53** : 1-16.

Tukey, J. W. 1949. Comparing individual means in the analysis of variance. Biometrics **5** : 99-114.

Viktorov, S. V. 1947. A study of the distribution and dispersion of plants by aerial photographs. (in Russian) Bull. Soc. Nat. Moscou (sect. biol.), N.S. **52** (4) : 71-78.

LIFE TABLES FOR NATURAL POPULATIONS OF ANIMALS

By EDWARD S. DEEVEY, Jr.

Osborn Zoological Laboratory, Yale University

(Contribution No. 384 from the Woods Hole Oceanographic Institution)

At sperat adulescens diu se victurum, quod sperare idem senex non potest. Insipienter sperat; quid enim stultius quam incerta pro certis habere, falsa pro veris?

—Cicero, *De Senectute*

INTRODUCTION

"THE certainty of death", remarks Sir Thomas Browne, "is attended with uncertainties, in time, manner, places." The same refrain, audible in classical authors from Horace to Hoffenstein, embodies immutable truth. But the rise of life insurance has taught us to ask the fatal question differently. We now substitute "probability" for "certainty," and have exchanged our fates for parameters of populations. The dictum of Galilei, "to measure what can be measured, to make measurable what can not be measured," has been applied to the product of Lachesis' loom, with interesting results.

There is no evidence that man's maximum life span has been lengthened a particle since antiquity. The celebrated cases of fantastic longevity, from Methuselah to Thomas Parr, do not withstand critical scrutiny. The mean length of life, however, differs widely among the races of men, is notably lower for most primitives than for civilized populations, and has been increasing by leaps and bounds in the United States during the last century. In ancient Rome, according to Macdonell's analysis (1913), the expectation of life at age 10 was an additional 22 years, compared to an additional 55 years for a male resident of the United States in 1929–31 (Dublin and Lotka, 1935).

The Romans, in fact, knew more about such matters than might be supposed from their superstition that "ten times twelve solar years were the term fixed for the life of man, beyond which the gods themselves had no power to prolong it; that the fates had narrowed the span to thrice thirty years, and that fortune abridged even this period by a variety of chances, against which the protection of the gods was implored" (Hodge, 1857, cited from Niebuhr's *History of Rome*). A table showing the expection of life at birth, at age 20, and at 5-year intervals thereafter, evidently based on real experience and intended for the computation of annuities, was in use in the third century A.D.; it is attributed to Ulpian (Trenerry, 1926). Even the Babylonians seem to have known about insurance contracts, though this does not necessarily imply any actuarial knowledge, and Horace's reference to "Babylonian numbers"—"Tu ne quaesieris (scire nefas) quem mihi, quem tibi finem di dederint, Leuconoe, nec Babylonios temptaris numeros" (*Odes*, I: 11)—may mean more than he intended.

Having gained some idea of the limits circumscribing his own mortality, man has turned to look at the other animals. In 1935 Pearl and Miner, in their discussion of the comparative mortality of lower organisms, attempted to formulate a general theory of mortality. They quickly gave up the attempt upon realizing that the *environmental* determinants of life duration can not, at least as yet, be disentangled from such *biological* determinants as genetic constitution and rate of living. They ended with a plea for "more observational data, carefully and critically collected for different species of animals and plants, that will follow through the life history from birth to death of each individual in a cohort of statistically respectable magnitude." Thus by implication Pearl and Miner appealed to the ecologists, who for the most part have been busy elsewhere. Accounts of the conceptions and methodology of life tables have not yet found their way into textbooks of ecology, and while field naturalists have devoted increasing attention to the dynamics of natural populations most of them have been content to leave the construction of life tables to the statisticians and laboratory ecologists.

This article, which is designed as an introduction to the subject rather than as a formal review, brings together from the ecological literature a mass of information bearing on the survival of animals in nature. This information has not heretofore been considered relevant by biometricians working with human populations, nor has it ever been considered in its context by ecologists. In collecting the material it was immediately obvious that it is still too early to formulate general theories. Serious deficiencies are only too apparent in the data. But the difficulties differ from case to case, and are therefore not insurmountable. Moreover, the bibliography will show that virtually all of this knowledge has been acquired in the twelve years since the appearance of the review by Pearl and Miner. By taking stock now, and by calling attention to gaps in our information, it is hoped that some guidance can be given to ecologists and others in the gathering of new material.

THE MEANING OF THE LIFE TABLE

A life table is a concise summary of certain vital statistics of a population. Beginning with a cohort, real or imaginary, whose members start life together, the life table states for every interval of age the number of deaths, the survivors remaining, the rate of mortality, and the expectation of further life. These columns are symbolized by d_x, l_x, q_x and e_x, respectively, where x stands for age. Additional columns which may be tabled include the age structure (L_x) or the number of persons living who are between ages x and $x + 1$.

Because all the life table functions can be calculated from each other, it makes little difference where one begins in summarizing the method of construction. It is convenient to begin with deaths at given ages (d_x), since these usually make up the "raw data." A curve obtained by plotting number of deaths against age is obviously a histogram showing the frequency distribution of deaths. It is customary to reduce the data to a relative basis by expressing the observed number of deaths at any age as a fraction of the total number of deaths. Such fractions stated as percentages and carried out to three figures include a decimal place; in this review and elsewhere where small samples are involved, it is the practice to drop the decimal point and put deaths, etc., on a "per thousand" basis. Starting, then, with a cohort of 1000 individuals born together, survivorship (l_x) is obtained by successive subtraction of deaths in the age interval from survivors at the beginning of the age interval. Mortality rate (q_x) is the fraction of those living at the beginning of the age interval who die during the interval, $q_x = d_x/l_x$, and is usually expressed here on a per thousand basis, $1000\ q_x = 1000\ d_x/l_x$.

The calculation of expectation of life is more complicated. For individuals at age 0 (at the beginning of their life span), it is the same as the mean length of life of the cohort. For older individuals, it is the mean life span remaining to those attaining a given age. It could therefore be calculated for any age x by measuring the area under the survivorship curve beyond x and dividing by the number of survivors attaining age x,

$$e_x = \frac{\int_x^\omega l_x \cdot dx}{l_x}$$

However, a life table, among other things, is a device for obtaining such integrals arithmetically, being divided into age intervals so small that changes between age x and $x + 1$ can be regarded as linear functions of x. It is therefore assumed that the *age structure*, L_x, or the number of persons alive who are between ages x and $x + 1$, which is exactly given by

$$L_x = \int_x^{x+1} l_x \cdot dx$$

is in practice given by

$$L_x = \frac{l_x + l_x + 1}{2} \quad *$$

Successive values of L_x obtained in this way are then summed from the bottom of the column up to each age x. This gives T_x, the total number of (persons $\times$ age units), or person-years if age is expressed in years still to be lived by persons of age x. Dividing by l_x, the number of persons, gives the expectation of life in age units,

$$e_x = \frac{T_x}{l_x}$$

Farner (1945) calculates e_x directly for each year of a bird's age by obtaining the mean after lifetime

*Author's note: Corrected equation is $L_x = \frac{l_x + l_{x+1}}{2}$

of birds alive on their first November 1, doing the same for birds alive on their second November 1, and so on. This procedure is cumbersome, and is more accurate than the method given here only if the deaths in any year are so unequally distributed through the year that a serious error results from ignoring the fact (Lack, 1943b).

Nice (1937) gives, as Table XXVIII, the "theory as to age composition of a population of breeding birds; theoretical numbers of each age according to annual survival rate." As this table has been frequently used by students of bird populations, it is as well to understand its construction. Actually, it consists of a group of life table d_x columns, constructed on the assumption of mortality rates which are *constant with respect to age*, but change from column to column between 75 and 25 per cent per year. It may seem surprising that a table of deaths should show the age composition of the living, but this is merely a consequence of starting with a round number of births, 100 in this case. Nice takes a cohort of 100 individuals and obtains their survivorship by successive applications of the assumed mortality rate until the number of survivors is reduced to 1. She then expresses the number living at any age as a percentage of the total number living at all ages, and thus the age composition of the living becomes identical with the number of deaths. For the ratio of the living at any age to the total number living must equal the ratio of the dead at any age to the total number of deaths,

$$\frac{l_x}{\Sigma l_x} = \frac{d_x}{\Sigma d_x}.$$

But $\Sigma d_x = 100$, by convention; therefore

$$100 \frac{l_x}{\Sigma l_x} = d_x.$$

By the same reasoning it can be shown that

$$100 \frac{L_x}{\Sigma L_x} = d_x.$$

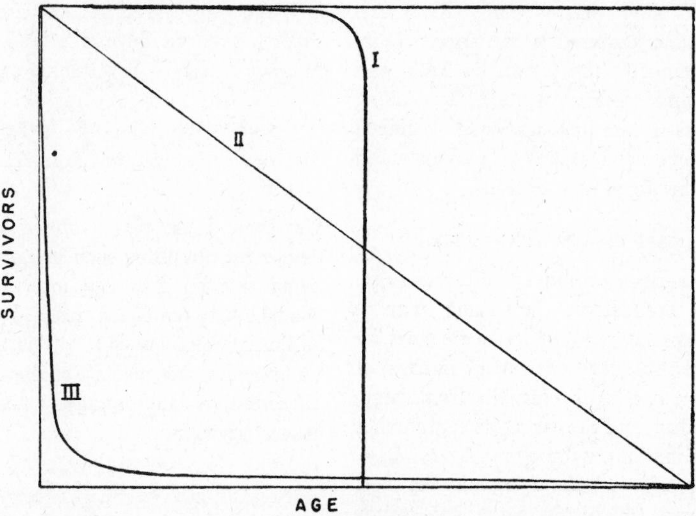

FIG. 1. SCHEMATIC REPRESENTATION OF THEORETICAL TYPES OF SURVIVORSHIP CURVE, ADAPTED FROM PEARL AND MINER (1935)

The survival axis can be graduated either arithmetically or logarithmically, but the logarithmic scale is more instructive, in that a straight line implies equal *rates* of mortality with respect to age.

Nice's table is convenient for ornithologists, since the assumption of constant age-specific mortality rates proves to be approximately true for adult birds. When mortality rates change with age, as they normally do, the table is inapplicable, though of course the age composition computed as percentage will always bear the same relationship to the d_x column. Nice states that her table applies to species breeding at one year of age, but this is not a necessary condition, as Farner (1945) has pointed out: it merely implies that the birth rate cannot be deduced from the life table age composition unless all members of the population breed every year.

The fact that the various life table columns are interconvertible makes it unnecessary to discuss all of them in dealing with a given species. Usually it is sufficient to focus attention on the survivorship curve, since this is most readily comprehensible. Pearl and Miner (1935; see also Pearl, 1940) have made it clear that there are three possible sorts of distribution of survivorship with respect to age, as shown diagrammatically in Fig. 1. Type I, the *negatively skew rectangular*, is shown by members of a cohort which, having been born at the same time, die more or less simultaneously after a life span which is presumably characteristic of the species. Type II is *diagonal* (when the logarithm of the number of survivors is plotted against age), implying a constant mortality rate for all age groups, or no one age as a favored time of dying. Type III, the *positively skew rectangular*, shows extremely heavy mortality beginning early in life, but the few individuals which survive to advanced ages have a relatively high expectation of further life.

Most survivorship curves hitherto published, including those for man, *Drosophila*, *Hydra*, *Agriolimax*, the mouse (Pearl and Miner, 1935), the vole (Leslie and Ranson, 1940), the black widow spider (Deevey and Deevey, 1945), *Tribolium* (Pearl Park, and Miner, 1941), and other laboratory animals, are variants of the diagonal type, or rather are intermediate between Type I and Type II. Type III has never been obtained with a laboratory population, though marine species with pelagic eggs and larvae, such as the oysters, would doubtless fall here if complete data were available. Type I has been observed in the case of adult *Drosophila* which were given no food, but this sort of survivorship is probably to be thought of as a laboratory curiosity.

KINDS OF LIFE TABLES

Life tables for human populations, which differ in certain important respects from animal populations in nature, are calculated by roundabout methods, most of which have little relevance to ecology. Some understanding of them is nonetheless essential. Census data show the number of persons born in a given year living in various political areas. Published vital statistics give the number of deaths in the same areas each year and the ages of those dying. By combining the two sets of figures it is possible to arrive at estimates of the rate of mortality (q_x) suffered by persons of a given age *at the time of the census*. Using a smooth curve fitted with exquisite precision to the q_x data, a life table can be constructed on the assumptions: (1) that a standard cohort (100,000 persons) is born alive uniformly throughout the year of the census; (2) that its members will be exposed throughout life to these particular mortality rates; and (3) that there is no immigration or emigration.

A life table so derived exposes to view a purely theoretical population, one which might have existed at the time of the census, but which ceased to exist even before the census was complete. For human populations are notably subject to immigration and emigration; the best known ones are growing, and their age structure is therefore changing; and what is even more important, the mortality rates observed at the time of the census are certain to change with the passage of time. An example will make clear how ordinary life table procedure crystallizes an imaginary population from a series of "time-specific" death rates.

This example is a paraphrase of Merrell's lucid exposition delivered at the symposium on "Life Tables and Their Application" held at Boston on December 27, 1946.

In 1940 the individuals, born in 1890 and now living in a certain state, were exposed to a risk of death at their current age (50 years) which works out at 12.58 per thousand. By 1950 the survivors of these same individuals, now aged 60 years, will be exposed to a different risk of death, say 27.03 per thousand. Eventually the last survivor will be dead, having been subject, in his last year of life, to a mortality rate of 1000 per thousand, and at that time it will be theoretically possible to construct a survivorship curve for the original group of individuals born in the state in 1890 and suffering age-specific mortality rates which changed systematically throughout their lives. But this will be impossible to do in practice, since (1) the birth records for 1890 are incomplete, and (2) many of those whose births were recorded will have left the state and died elsewhere. Moreover, (3) they will have been replaced by a number (probably a larger number) of persons born elsewhere in 1890, subjected to different mortality risks for varying fractions of their lives, who appear in the death records merely as "born in 1890."

In 1940, however, we also know the mortality rate for individuals born in 1900, and now 40 years of age. By 1950, when these persons are 50 years old, their age-specific mortality rate at age 50 will be obtainable. It will not be 12.58 per thousand, but probably a slightly lower figure. In fact, the mortality rates for all ages will have changed slightly, some more, some less, by 1950, partly because of immigration and emigration and partly because of improvements in public health technique. The same applies, mutatis mutandis, to 1960, when the 1900 year-class are 60 years old. In actuarial practice *this does not matter*. By drawing a vertical line, as it were, through all the age-classes present in 1940, and taking their age-specific mortality rates as the basis of a life table, the actuary seizes the only way out of a troublesome situation. He erects a hypothetical population and tables its survivorship, its mortality rates, its age structure, and the expectation of life of its members, and his figures serve for ordinary purposes. In any case they are the best available until the next census, when they have to be completely revised.

A very different life table would result if, instead of arbitrarily halting the flow of events at some particular time, as 1940, we followed all the individuals born in a certain state in a particular year, and recorded their deaths as they occurred. This would be a "horizontal" life table. Human biologists are less interested in this type, for from their standpoint, life being long and patience short, it is more worth while to be able to predict the future than to describe the past. The life table for persons born in 1840 is not of pressing concern to medical scientists (or to insurance salesmen) in 1940, conditions having meanwhile changed profoundly. The two sorts of life table approach identity as the age structure of the population approaches stability in a uniform environment, but these considerations have no real meaning to the actuary, who deals with expanding populations in which births exceed deaths and which are constantly improving their own environmental conditions. The ecologist, on the other hand, is bound to be interested in both kinds of life table. If there is no change in the environment from year to year, and if the natural population is at equilibrium, with recruitment of each age class always kept exactly balanced by deaths, a horizontal life table for the year-class born in 1940 or any other year will be identical with a vertical life table drawn up for all year-classes present in 1940 or any other year. But normally there will be good years and bad years, both the birth rate and the age-specific death rates will oscillate more or less reciprocally, and the resulting differences in the two sorts of life tables will be large.

Since the data necessary for a vertical life table include both a census of the age distribution of the living members of the population and a record of the deaths by ages, the horizontal life table is easier to construct. The experimental ecologist, in particular, can go at the problem directly, by allowing a large cohort to be born at the same time, keeping its members under observation throughout their lives, and recording deaths as they occur. Thus survivorship (l_x) and deaths (d_x) make up the raw data of his experiment. Mortality rates are then easily obtained as the ratio of the dying to the living at any age, and other life table functions follow just as readily. The environment having been maintained constant artificially, there should be no difference between such a life table and one built up vertically from a census made when the age structure becomes stable.

ECOLOGICAL LIFE TABLES

The field ecologist deals with populations which are by no means so elementary as those inside *Drosophila* bottles. Even the total size of the population of a species cannot be easily ascertained for an area large enough to be representative, and calculations of the birth rate and death rate are uncertain at best, largely owing to immigration and emigration. It is seldom indeed that the ecologist knows anything of the age structure of a natural population. In a few cases, growth rings on the scales or otoliths (fish) or horns (ungulates) make it possible to determine the age of an animal. Moore (1935) has shown that annual growth rings occur in the genital plates of sea-urchin tests, as they do in the shells of some molluscs. Moore checked the validity of the age determination by reference to the size-frequency distribution in his catches, and the separation of modal size classes in a population often affords a clue to age, particularly for younger age groups. The age of adult females can be determined in the case of certain mammals (whales, Wheeler, 1934, Laurie, 1937; seals, Bertram, 1940) by counting the corpora lutea in the ovaries. But for most animals it is possible to find out the ages of individuals only by marking them in some way.

Even when the age of a member of a natural population is known, it is not a simple matter to obtain accurate vital statistics. The source of greatest confusion lies in the impracticability of keeping the individuals under continuous observation. Migratory birds, for example, are easy to band as nestlings, but nearly impossible to find between fledging and the time they leave for winter quarters. Often they can not be found at all unless they return to the same area to breed, when they can be trapped in nest boxes. Their mortality between fledging and breeding can be calculated, but the calculation is rendered uncertain by the tendency of young birds not to return to their birthplaces as breeding adults.

As sources of data for the construction of life tables, the ecological information falls into three groups: (1) cases where the age at death (d_x) is directly observed for a large and reasonably random sample of the population; (2) cases where the survival (l_x) of a large cohort (born more or less simultaneously) is followed at fairly close intervals throughout its existence; (3) cases where the age structure is obtained from a sample, assumed to be a random sample of the population, and d_x is inferred from the shrinkage between successive age classes. It should be noticed that only the second sort of information is statistically respectable, since in so far as the breeding can safely be assumed to be simultaneous, it is comparable to that obtained from a *Drosophila* bottle. The first and third types can be used only if one is prepared to assume that the population is stable in time, so that the actual age distribution and the life table age distribution are identical. This assumption would certainly not be true of a human population; it may be approximately true for many natural populations of animals. When it is definitely not true, e.g., when certain age classes are stronger or weaker than they should be, to take the ages at death or the actual age structure as observed at any "instant" of time will give erroneous estimates of the age-specific mortality rates. In these cases it would be better to construct a series of horizontal life tables, one for each year class. A vertical life table could be constructed from the average age composition observed over many years, if the ages at death were also known. But the ecological information does not yet give both the census by ages and the deaths by ages for any one population.

In making comparisons between species that have widely different life spans, Pearl's device is very useful. This consists in shifting the origin of the age axis from zero to the mean length of life and regraduating the age scale so that age is expressed as percentage deviation from the mean. In this way l_x values (and other life table functions, should they be desired) can be shown on the same graph in equal detail for rotifers, which live for a matter of days, and for birds, which live for many years. In connection with this method it has been customary to work with a fitted curve, the life table functions being calculated for equal percentage deviations, as −80%, −60%, −40%, etc. This procedure, applied to the natural populations considered in this review, would entail an enormous amount of arithmetical labor which does not seem to be justified by the end in view. Curve fitting minimizes observational error and generalizes the sweep of the observations, but in this case the generalization goes too far, in that it seems to confer a universality on the resulting life table which is not supported by the facts. The published life tables for *Drosophila*, the flour beetle, and other lower organisms apply only to the particular experimental conditions under which they were obtained. Under other conditions, e.g., with different population densities, the longevity will be different and different life tables will result. Accordingly, all life tables presented below have been treated simply, and age intervals, though expressed as percentage deviation from the mean longevity, have been entered in the tables only for values corresponding to the original observations. The only exception is the life table for *Balanus balanoides* (see footnote, Table 6).

Age at Death Directly Observed

In the course of his careful investigation of the wolves of Mt. McKinley, Murie (1944) picked up the skulls of 608 Dall mountain sheep (*Ovis d. dalli*) which had died at some time previous to his visit, and an additional 221 skulls of sheep deceased during the four years he spent in the Park. The age of these sheep at death was determinable from the annual rings on the horns. "Time, which antiquates antiquities, and hath an art to make dust of all things, hath yet spared these minor monuments" (Sir Thomas Browne, *Urn Burial*). Most of the deaths presumably occurred directly as a result of predation by wolves. Many skulls showed evidence of a necrotic bone disease, but it is not possible to say whether death was due solely to the disease or whether the disease merely ensured death by predation.

The mean longevity of the later sample is significantly greater (7.83 years) than that of the earlier (7.09 years), but the interpretation of this fact is not clear. The form of the distribution of deaths is sensibly the same in the two samples. As the survival of the members of this population is astonishingly great, it seems best to be conservative, and attention has been focussed on the larger, earlier sample. Except for the "lamb" and "yearling" classes, which are doubtless under-represented in the data owing to the perishability of their skulls, there is no reason to suppose that either group is anything but a fair sample of the total population, i.e., the probability of finding a skull is not likely to be affected by the age of its owner. A life table for the 608 sheep has accordingly been prepared (Table 1). The survivorship curve, plotted logarithmically in Fig. 2, is remarkably "human" in showing two periods of relatively heavy mortality, very early and very late, with high and nearly constant survival ratios at intermediate ages.

TABLE 1

Life table for the Dall Mountain Sheep (Ovis d. dalli) based on the known age at death of 608 sheep dying before 1937 (both sexes combined). Mean length of life 7.09 years Data from Murie (1944)*

x	x'	d_x	l_x	$1000\,q_x$	e_x
AGE (*years*)	AGE AS % DEVIATION FROM MEAN LENGTH OF LIFE •	NUMBER DYING IN AGE INTERVAL OUT OF 1000 BORN	NUMBER SURVIVING AT BEGINNING OF AGE INTERVAL OUT OF 1000 BORN	MORTALITY RATE PER THOUSAND ALIVE AT BEGINNING OF AGE INTERVAL	EXPECTATION OF LIFE, OR MEAN LIFE-TIME REMAINING TO THOSE ATTAINING AGE INTERVAL (*years*)
0–0.5	−100	54	1000	54.0	7.06
0.5–1	−93.0	145	946	153.0	—
1–2	−85.9	12	801	15.0	7.7
2–3	−71.8	13	789	16.5	6.8
3–4	−57.7	12	776	15.5	5.9
4–5	−43.5	30	764	39.3	5.0
5–6	−29.5	46	734	62.6	4.2
6–7	−15.4	48	688	69.9	3.4
7–8	−1.1	69	640	108.0	2.6
8–9	+13.0	132	571	231.0	1.9
9–10	+27.0	187	439	426.0	1.3
10–11	+41.0	156	252	619.0	0.9
11–12	+55.0	90	96	937.0	0.6
12–13	+69.0	3	6	500.0	1.2
13–14	+84.0	3	3	1000	0.7

* A small number of skulls without horns, but judged by their osteology to belong to sheep nine years old or older, have been apportioned *pro rata* among the older age classes.

The adult sheep have two principal methods of defense against wolves, their chief enemies: flight to higher elevations, where wolves can not pursue; and group action or herding. It is clear that these recourses confer a relative immunity to death by predation and that only the very young, which have not learned by experience, and the very old, which are too feeble to escape, suffer heavy losses. This survivorship curve is decidedly not of the positively skew rectangular type.

The second case to be discussed is that of an aquatic invertebrate, the sessile rotifer ***Floscularia conifera***. This species has been studied by Edmondson (1945) under conditions which are fully as natural as those enjoyed by Murie's mountain sheep. *Floscularia* lives attached to water plants, especially *Utricularia*, surrounded by a tube constructed by itself out of pellets of detritus. The tube is added to at the top continuously throughout life, and Edmondson was able to identify all the members of a population living in a pond by dusting the *Utricularia* plant with a suspension of powdered carmine. On subsequent visits the *Floscularia* present at the time of dusting were conspicuously marked by bands of carmine-stained pellets in the walls of their tubes, each band being surmounted by new construction of varying widths. Thus in one operation the stage was set for an analysis of growth, age, birth-plus-immigration, and death in a natural population. Among other spectacular results, Edmondson found that the expectation of life of solitary individuals was only half as great as that of members of colonies of two or more, and he presented separate life tables for each component of the population, calculated from the age at death. To facilitate comparison with other species, however, solitary and colonial individuals have been lumped together (for Edmondson's "Experiment 1") in the life table of Table 2.

The survivorship curve (Fig. 2), like that of the Dall sheep, shows unexpectedly good survival. As Edmondson has pointed out, it is not so good as that of other rotifers reared in the laboratory under standard conditions (*Proales decipiens*, *P. sordida*, *Lecane inermis*), but it is only a little less good, and life tables for these rotifers are notorious (Pearl and Miner, 1935) for their close approach to a Type I distribution.

The case of *Floscularia* is almost above reproach as an example of a life table obtained under natural conditions. It is, of course, open to the objection that only the age at death is known, and the age structure of the living animals must be assumed to be constant. Apart from this deficiency, it should also be realized that the origin of the life table is not at birth. The pelagic larval life of the rotifer, like the larval life of barnacles and insects, is omitted from consideration in such a table.

A life table for a population of herring gulls (*Larus argentatus*) has recently been prepared by Paynter (*in press*). These gulls, banded as chicks at the Bowdoin Scientific Station, Kent Island, Bay of Fundy, have been recovered dead from all over North America. No special effort was made to recover banded gulls at their birthplace, and the colony is a large one (ca. 30,000 birds). The fact remains, however, that the first-year birds are perhaps more likely to be picked up than older birds near the place of banding, and perhaps less likely to be picked up elsewhere, so that some doubt can be cast on the reliability of the first-year recoveries as truly representative of the deaths in the first year. This troublesome point is probably less serious than with the songbirds to be discussed below; moreover, it is overshadowed by another difficulty, the fact that the study is not complete, and many of the banded birds are still alive. Paynter minimized this error by a compensatory adjustment; since banding began ten years ago and is still being carried out, first-year recoveries were divided by 10, second-year recoveries by 9, etc. Birds dying at ages greater than 10 years have naturally not yet been recorded, though a few are to be expected.

That these older birds will probably not change the life table appreciably is shown by Marshall's independent study (1947) of the longevity of the herring gull. Marshall used all available records of American herring gulls banded as young during

TABLE 2

Life table for the sessile rotifer Floscularia conifera based on the known age at death of 50 rotifers, both solitary and colonial. Mean length of life 4.74 days
From Edmondson (1945), Experiment 1

x	x'	d_x	l_x	$1000\ q_x$	e_x
AGE (*days*)	AGE AS % DEVIATION FROM MEAN LENGTH OF LIFE	NUMBER DYING IN AGE INTERVAL OUT OF 1000 ATTACHING	NUMBER SURVIVING AT BEGINNING OF AGE INTERVAL OUT OF 1000 ATTACHING	MORTALITY RATE PER THOUSAND ALIVE AT BEGINNING OF AGE INTERVAL	EXPECTATION OF LIFE, OR MEAN LIFE TIME REMAINING TO THOSE ATTAINING AGE INTERVAL (*days*)
0–1	−100	20	1000	20	4.76
1–2	−78.9	200	980	204	3.78
2–3	−57.8	60	780	77	3.70
3–4	−36.7	0	720	0	2.98
4–5	−15.6	300	720	416	1.97
5–6	+5.4	140	420	333	2.02
6–7	+26.7	60	280	214	1.79
7–8	+47.7	140	220	636	1.14
8–9	+68.8	40	80	500	1.25
9–10	+90.0	20	40	500	1.00
10–11	+111.0	20	20	1000	0.50

the last 25 years and subsequently recovered dead. Thus his data probably include most of the returns from the Kent Island population. Returns before September 1 of the first year of life were excluded, so that the life table refers to adult birds only. It differs from Paynter's chiefly in that it includes birds older than 10 years, one bird having lived as long as 17 years. Despite two factors which might be supposed to enhance the apparent longevity (exclusion of juvenile mortality; inclusion of older birds) the expectation of life is markedly lower than that of the Kent Island colony, 1.5 years on the first September 1 of life as against 2.44 years at banding age.

Probably neither set of data for the herring gull is wholly reliable. Paynter's calculations suggest that the Kent Island population is just replacing its losses, assuming a rather high reproductive potential and a rather low rate of mortality between hatching and fledging, while a similar calculation applied to Marshall's figures implies that the population as a whole must be declining. Several reasons may be suggested for the discrepancy between the two life tables: (1) the mortality of the Kent Island gulls may actually be lower than average; (2) there may have been greater total mortality before 1936, and Marshall's recoveries may have been predominantly from the earlier years, before banding started at Kent Island. The simplest explanation is that (3) an appreciable number of bands are lost by older birds, so that the mean age at death is actually higher than appears from the returns of banded birds.

These questions will doubtless be discussed by Paynter on the basis of direct observation of juvenile mortality, planned for the coming summer (1947) at Kent Island. Meanwhile, taking his life table at face value, the figures have been entered in Table 3, and the survivorship curve is plotted in Fig. 2 for comparison with the Dall sheep and the rotifer. In contrast to those cases, the curve for the gulls is of the diagonal type, the mortality rate being approximately constant throughout life. This feature seems to be characteristic of birds, as will appear below. The causes of death of these birds have been discussed in detail by Paynter, who finds that there is no significant difference in mean length of life between gulls dying through human interference (shooting, trapping, etc.) and those dying through "natural" or unknown causes.

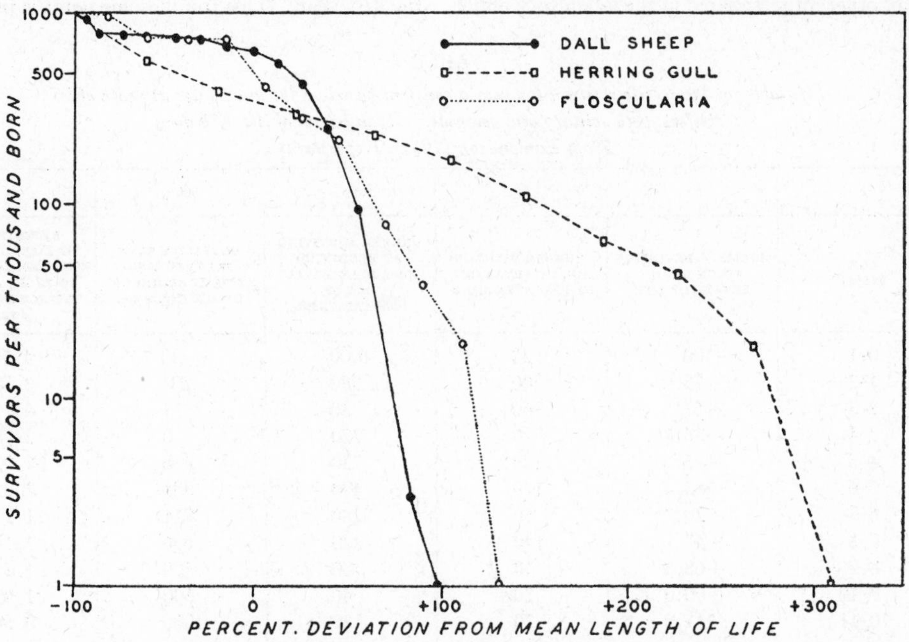

FIG. 2. SURVIVORSHIP (l_x) CURVES FOR THE DALL MOUNTAIN SHEEP, THE SESSILE ROTIFER FLOSCULARIA CONIFERA, AND THE HERRING GULL, AGE BEING EXPRESSED AS PERCENTAGE DEVIATION FROM THE MEAN LENGTH OF LIFE

In his delightful book, *The Life of the Robin* (1943a) and in two admirable papers, Lack (1943b,

c) has investigated the age at death of certain British birds, as obtained by recoveries of individuals banded as nestlings. Because banded nestlings are likely to be picked up near the banding stations or not at all, it is impossible to estimate the whole of the mortality in the first year of life with any accuracy, and Lack begins his life tables on August 1. The proportion of birds banded which are later recovered is small, ranging from 1.0 per cent for the robin to 18.4 per cent for the cormorant; but after August 1 of the first year it is considered that the ages at death of birds recovered are not likely to differ from the ages at death among the total population. The samples are small and of course become progressively smaller with increasing age, they suffer more or less severe depredations from shooting.

The striking feature of these survivorship curves is their diagonal form. The mortality in the first year varies from 380 per thousand for the lapwing to 723 per thousand for the robin, but for a given species the mortality remains approximately constant throughout life, or at least for as long as the data are reliable.

When the ages of these birds are transformed into percentage deviations from the mean, as in Fig. 4, it becomes obvious that the mortality per unit of life span is constant for all the birds studied. This does not tell us anything new, for any series of diagonal lines will become the same when replotted

TABLE 3

Life table for the Herring Gull (Larus argentatus) based on returns of 1252 birds banded as chicks at Kent Island, Bay of Fundy, 1936–1945. Mean length of life 2.44 years
From Paynter (in press)

x	x'	d_x	l_x	$1000\ q_x$	e_x
AGE (*years*)	AGE AS % DEVIATION FROM MEAN LENGTH OF LIFE	NUMBER DYING IN AGE INTERVAL OUT OF 1000 BORN	NUMBER SURVIVING AT BEGINNING OF AGE INTERVAL OUT OF 1000 BORN	MORTALITY RATE PER THOUSAND ALIVE AT BEGINNING OF AGE INTERVAL	EXPECTATION OF LIFE, OR MEAN LIFE TIME REMAINING TO THOSE ATTAINING AGE INTERVALS (*years*)
0–1	−100	419	1000	419	2.44
1–2	−59	181	581	312	2.84
2–3	−18	95	400	238	2.90
3–4	+23	65	305	213	2.65
4–5	+64	69	240	288	2.22
5–6	+105	60	171	351	1.92
6–7	+146	45	111	405	1.68
7–8	+187	21	66	318	1.48
8–9	+228	26	45	578	0.93
9–10	+269	19	19	1000	0.53

so that Lack does not regard the mortality rates and expectation of life as reliable beyond the fourth or fifth year.

Several of Lack's life tables are reproduced in Table 4, and the survivorship curves are shown in Fig. 3. Three of the species are familiar British songbirds belonging to the Turdidae, the robin (*Erithacus rubecula melophilus*), the blackbird (*Turdus m. merula*), and the song thrush (*T. e. ericetorum*). The others are the starling (*Sturnus v. vulgaris*) and the lapwing (*Vanellus vanellus*), taxonomically though not ecologically a "shorebird" (Charadriidae). Lack's remaining species, the woodcock, black-headed gull, lesser black-backed gull, and cormorant, have been omitted, as in this way, but it is helpful none the less. A line fitted by eye to the survivorship points plotted in this figure has a slope corresponding to a mortality of about 320 per thousand per 100 per cent deviation. If the divergence of the points for older ages is ignored as being due to inadequate data, and this line projected, it cuts the age axis at about +560 per cent, implying that if the mortality of birds is really constant throughout life, the oldest bird in a group of 1000 adults should survive about 6.6 times as long as the average bird.

The American robin (*Turdus m. migratorius*), a larger bird than its distant English relative, has been studied by Farner (1945), using U. S. Fish and Wildlife Service data on 855 birds banded as young

TABLE 4

Life tables for several British birds, based on returns from all Britain of birds banded as nestlings and known to be alive on August 1 of their first year. Age reckoned from August 1
From Lack (1943a, b, c)

SPECIES; SIZE OF SAMPLE; MEAN LENGTH OF LIFE AFTER FIRST AUGUST 1	x	x'	d_x	l_x	$1000\ q_x$	e_x
	AGE (*years*)	AGE AS % DEVIATION FROM MEAN LENGTH OF LIFE	NUMBER DYING IN AGE INTERVAL OUT OF 1000 ALIVE ON AUGUST 1	NUMBER SURVIVING AT BEGINNING OF AGE INTERVAL OUT OF 1000 ALIVE ON AUGUST 1	MORTALITY RATE PER THOUSAND ALIVE AT BEGINNING OF AGE INTERVAL	EXPECTATION OF LIFE, OR MEAN LIFE-TIME REMAINING TO THOSE ATTAINING AGE INTERVAL (*years*)
Blackbird (352) 1.58 years	0-1	−100	545	1000	545	1.57
	1-2	−37	170	455	374	1.85
	2-3	+27	142	285	498	1.66
	3-4	+90	57	143	398	1.82
	4-5	+153	34	86	396	1.80
	5-6	+216	20	52	385	1.65
	6-7	+280	17	32	531	1.38
	7-8	+343	9	15	600	1.33
	8-9	+405	0	6	0	1.50
	9-10	+470	6	6	1000	0.50
Song Thrush (374) 1.44 years	0-1	−100	556	1000	556	1.44
	1-2	−31	185	444	417	1.61
	2-3	+39	136	259	525	1.40
	3-4	+108	72	123	585	1.39
	4-5	+178	21	51	411	1.65
	5-6	+245	13	30	433	1.43
	6-7	+316	11	17	647	1.12
	7-8	+385	3	6	500	1.17
	8-9	+455	3	3	1000	0.67
Robin (130) 1.01 years	0-1	−100	723	1000	723	1.03
	1-2	−2	131	277	472	1.41
	2-3	+97	108	146	740	1.23
	3-4	+196	23	38	605	2.29
	4-5	+294	8	15	533	4.0
	5-6	+392	0	15	0	3.0
	6-7	+491	0	15	0	2.0
	7-8	+590	0	15	0	1.0
	8-9	+689	8	7	1000	0.5
Starling (203) 1.49 years	0-1	−100	487	1000	487	1.49
	1-2	−33	261	513	509	1.43
	2-3	+34	113	252	448	1.40
	3-4	+102	89	139	640	1.12
	4-5	+168	25	50	500	1.22
	5-6	+236	20	25	800	0.92
	6-7	+302	0	5	0	1.60
	7-8	+370	5	5	1000	0.60
Lapwing (460) 2.36 years	0-1	−100	380	1000	380	2.37
	1-2	−58	213	620	344	2.51
	2-3	−15	128	407	314	2.56
	3-4	+27	78	279	280	2.50
	4-5	+70	67	201	334	2.28
	5-6	+112	56	134	418	2.17
	6-7	+154	24	78	308	2.37
	7-8	+196	20	54	370	2.20
	8-9	+239	7	34	206	2.20
	9-10	+282	9	27	333	1.63
	10-11	+324	7	18	389	1.17
	11-12	+366	11	11	1000	0.55

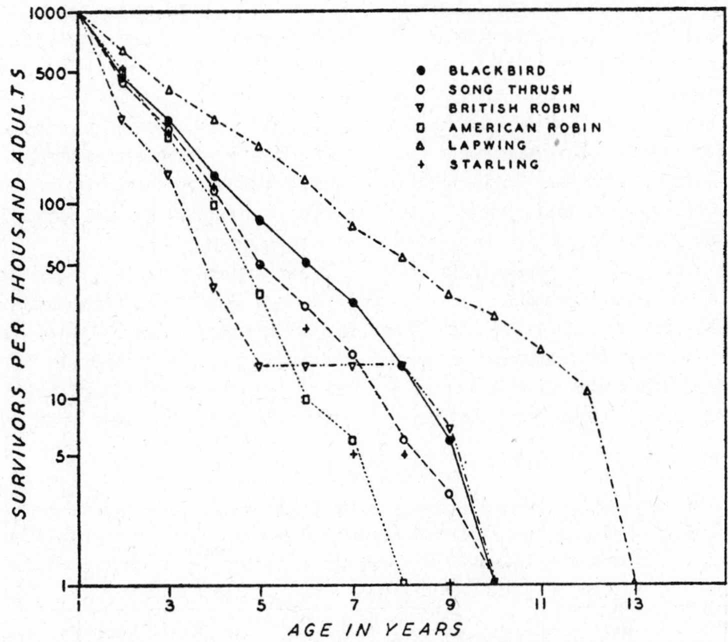

FIG. 3. SURVIVORSHIP (l_x) CURVES FOR THE BRITISH ROBIN, SONG THRUSH, BLACKBIRD, STARLING, LAPWING AND AMERICAN ROBIN, AGE BEING EXPRESSED IN YEARS

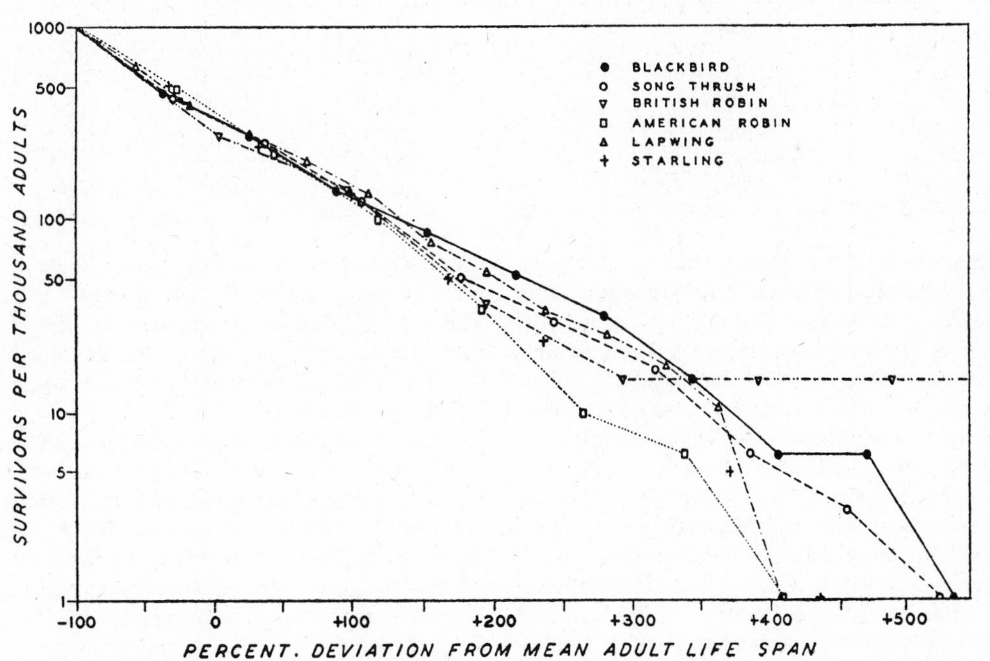

FIG. 4. SURVIVORSHIP (l_x) CURVES FOR THE SAME SPECIES AS IN FIG. 3, AGE BEING EXPRESSED AS PERCENTAGE DEVIATION FROM THE MEAN LENGTH OF LIFE

within the breeding range of the type subspecies between 1920 and 1940, and subsequently recovered dead. Farner's method of treatment of the data is analogous to Lack's, except that November 1 is taken as the starting point for the life table. The figures for the American robin have been entered in Table 5, and Figs. 3 and 4 indicate that this species suffers a mortality which is not only uniform with respect to age but is approximately the same as that of the British birds with respect to units of the mean life span.

Lack (1946) has recently discussed anew the question whether the disproportionately high mortality found among birds in their first year of life is real, or is due to the greater likelihood of their being picked up near the banding station. Analysing the returns between August 1 and January 1 for the blackbird, the song-thrush, the starling, and the lapwing, he found that most of these returns were of first-year birds, but that the proportion of first-year birds is no higher among those found by the bander or found near the banding station than it is among those found at a distance. The annual mortality is greater for first-year birds than for older birds when the calculations begin on August 1, and it remains greater when November 1 is the starting date, but by January 1 the constant level of adult mortality is reached. Calculations of adult mortality should therefore start on January 1, but from a comparative point of view this adjustment is of minor importance. The "disproportionate" mortality in the first year, starting from August 1, is really very little greater than in later years; it is scarcely visible on a logarithmic plot of survivorship (Figs. 3 and 4). The significant differences between juvenile and adult mortality, which would give a marked initial dip on such a plot, have been left out of account altogether, and August 1 is not too early, but too late a starting point.

Additional information on the lapwing is given by Kraak, Rinkel, and Hoogerheide (1940), who studied the age at death of 1333 continental birds banded as juveniles. The life table is not published, but the survivorship curve is reproduced, and is shown to be closely fitted by a line corresponding to a constant mortality rate of 40 per cent per year, reckoned from the first January 1 of life. This value is slightly higher than that found by Lack for the British population, but as the mean length of life is slightly lower, the mortality per unit of life span is the same.

It may be mentioned that the mortality rates for adult song sparrows, dealt with in the next section because the original data give l_x and not d_x, are fully consistent with the picture given by Fig. 4. The same may be said of Paynter's herring gull data, which have been presented separately because juvenile mortality is not specifically excluded, as it is for the other birds. All natural populations of birds so far investigated in any detail appear, therefore, to be alike in suffering a constant annual risk

TABLE 5

Life table for the American Robin (Turdus m. migratorius), based on returns of 568 birds banded as nestlings and known to be alive on November 1 of their first year. Age reckoned from November 1. Mean length of life after November 1—1.37 years

From Farner (1945)

x	x'	d_x	l_x	$1000\,q_x$	e_x
AGE (*years*)	AGE AS % DEVIATION FROM MEAN LENGTH OF LIFE	NUMBER DYING IN AGE INTERVAL OUT OF 1000 ALIVE ON NOVEMBER 1	NUMBER SURVIVING AT BEGINNING OF AGE INTERVAL OUT OF 1000 ALIVE ON NOVEMBER 1	MORTALITY RATE PER THOUSAND ALIVE AT BEGINNING OF AGE INTERVAL	EXPECTATION OF LIFE, OR MEAN LIFE TIME REMAINING TO THOSE ATTAINING AGE INTERVAL (*years*)
0–1	−100	503	1000	503	1.38
1–2	−27	268	497	539	1.26
2–3	+46	130	229	567	1.16
3–4	+119	63	99	636	1.03
4–5	+192	26	36	722	0.94
5–6	+265	4	10	400	1.10
6–7	+338	5	6	1000	0.50

of death from early adult life to the end of the life span, this mortality being constant for birds at about 320 per thousand per hundred centiles of life span. Little is known of the seasonal distribution of these deaths, and it will be very interesting to discover whether non-migratory tropical birds suffer death in similar fashion.

Survivorship Directly Observed

The cases now to be discussed differ from the preceding in the character of the original observations. Instead of a fairly large sample of individuals about which little or nothing can be told except their age at death, we have a group of individuals known to have been born at a particular time and to have been present or absent at some later time. Their presence gives their survivorship, their absence implies death in the interval since they were last observed. This is the best sort of information to have, since it does not require the assumption that the age composition of the population is stable in time. Provided only that the season of birth is a small fraction of the age interval between successive observations, so that births can be assumed to be simultaneous, as in a *Drosophila* bottle, a horizontal life table can be directly constructed from the survivorship data. Unfortunately, most of the species which have been studied in this way have short spans of natural life, and when census data are obtained only once a year the number of points on the survivorship curve is too small to be satisfactory.

The best example of such observed survivorship comes from Hatton's work (1938) with the barnacle, *Balanus balanoides*. This work will be examined in great detail in a later section, and it is here necessary to say only that the case is very nearly ideal. The barnacle settles on rocks during a short time (two to six weeks) in early spring. Test areas were scraped clean one winter, and after new populations had settled, the survival of their members was followed at intervals of one to four months for three years. Barnacles which disappeared from the areas between observations were certainly dead, for emigration does not complicate the problem. Immigration, however, does present

TABLE 6

Life table for a typical population of Balanus balanoides, based on the observed survival of adult barnacles settling on a cleaned rock surface in the spring of 1930. The population is that at Cité, (St. Malo, France), a moderately sheltered location, at Level III, at half-tide level. The initial settling density (2200 per 100 cm²) is taken as the maximum density attained on May 15. Mean length of life 12.1 months

Data from Hatton (1938)

x	x'	d_x	l_x	$1000\ q_x$	e_x
*AGE (*months*)	*AGE AS % DEVIATION FROM MEAN LENGTH OF LIFE	NUMBER DYING IN AGE INTERVAL OF 1000 ATTACHING	NUMBER SURVIVING TO BEGINNING OF AGE INTERVAL OUT OF 1000 ATTACHING	MORTALITY RATE PER THOUSAND ALIVE AT BEGINNING OF AGE INTERVAL	EXPECTATION OF FURTHER LIFE (*months*)
0–2	−100	90	1000	90	12.1
2–4	−83.5	100	910	110	11.3
4–6	−67.0	50	810	62	10.5
6–8	−50.4	60	760	79	9.1
8–10	−33.9	80	700	114	7.8
10–12	−17.4	160	620	258	6.7
12–14	−0.9	80	460	174	6.7
14–16	+16.0	100	380	263	5.9
16–18	+32.2	50	280	179	5.7
18–20	+49.0	40	230	174	4.7
20–22	+65.4	100	190	526	2.4
22–24	+82.0	60	90	667	1.9
24–26	+98.8	20	30	667	1.8
26–28	+115.0	8	10	800	1.4
28–30	+132.0	2	2	1000	1.0

* Survivorship data given graphically by Hatton were smoothed by eye, and values at every other month were then read from the curve. The original observations were made at irregular intervals during three years.

difficulties, though since it is confined to the attachment seasons of subsequent years it should be possible to control it in subsequent work. There is one further disadvantage in that the life tables necessarily start at metamorphosis, leaving out of account mortality during pelagic larval stages. A life table for a typical population of barnacles is presented in Table 6.

The remaining examples suffer from more serious defects, and the data do not justify extended treatment. Green and Evans (1940) in their important study of the snowshoe rabbit (*Lepus americanus*) in Minnesota, followed the survival of marked individuals of several year classes, the total population present on the area and the number in each age-class being obtained by the mark-and-recapture method—also known as the "Lincoln index" (Jackson, 1939). Marking was done during most of the winter, and the annual census was made in February. It is perhaps unnecessary, and certainly uncharitable, to point out two sources of error in this excellent and ingenious work. In the first place, when marked individuals are released into a population and later recaptured, the calculation of the total population from the fraction

$$\frac{\text{size of sample when recapturing}}{\text{number recaptured}} \times \text{number marked}$$

depends on two assumptions, neither of which is likely to be true in this case: that there is no mortality between marking and recapturing; and that the marked individuals disperse at random through the whole population. Secondly, the flow of vital events in this population was so rapid, very few rabbits more than three years old ever having been found, that observations made annually can give only a very rough idea of the life table.

The latter objection applies with equal force to the study of a pheasant population made by Leopold et al. (1943) in Wisconsin. The former objection, though doubtless it could be urged, has less validity here, since the population, as ascertained by trapping, was checked by census drives.

Nice's thoroughgoing work (1937) on the song sparrow (*Melospiza melodia*) included a consideration of the survival of banded birds from year to year. The number of individuals which could be kept under continuous observation was necesarily* small, and to find a sample large enough to use as the basis of a life table, it is necessary to take the 144 males banded in the breeding season between 1928 and 1935. Unfortunately, some of these males were of unknown age when first banded. Even if one assumes, (and the assumption is not far from the truth) that all new males appearing are first-year birds born elsewhere, the survival ratios from year to year will be too low if any adult males were still alive but failed to return to the area. Evidently such emigration is of minor importance with adult male song sparrows. With adult females, however, it is so serious that Nice did not think it worth while to publish the data on their return. Clearly, work on the survival of migratory birds is full of uncertainties, though the same may be said of resident species such as the wren-tit (Erickson, 1938) and the robin (Lack, 1943a).

All of these cases, snowshoe rabbit, pheasant, and song sparrow have one defect in common. This is the necessity of calculating the survival between birth and the first year of adult life from other data than those given by banding. For the snowshoe rabbit, the initial strength of the year-class is calculated from the estimated breeding population present and its known fertility. Leopold et al., lacking observations of their own on the pheasant mortality between birth and the first census period, used the estimates given by Errington for pheasants in another state. Nice calculates the survival of fledged young song sparrows to their first breeding season, by assuming a stable population and combining the estimated mean length of life of adults with their average nesting success. These procedures, while perfectly defensible as approaches to the problem, are inadequate substitutes for direct observation.

The three sets of data, with all their uncertainties, have been used as bases for synthetic life tables, and the survivorship curves are presented in Fig. 5. The snowshoe rabbit curve is that for the 1933 year class, the only one for which data are available on rabbits as old as four years. The juvenile mortality for 1933 is calculated by Green and Evans as 77 per cent between birth and the following February; for most other years it was higher, and for a few it was lower. Adult mortality, amounting to 70 per cent per year, was essentially constant throughout the study. The data for the pheasant are the average survival values for adults (30 per cent per year), combined with Errington's estimate of 84 per cent mortality between hatching and maturity. The song sparrow curve is calculated in two ways, the first including only the estimated mortality between fledging and the first breeding season (80 per cent) and the

* Corrected spelling is: necessarily

second also including the loss (40 per cent) between the laying of the eggs and fledging. The adult part of the life span is taken from the survival of the 144 males banded in 1928–1935.

The three curves show a pronounced diagonality from the adult stage onward. Initially, however, since the juvenile mortality in all cases is greater than the adult mortality, the curves show a dip which is most emphatic for the song sparrow reckoned from the egg, but which is invariably present. Here, then, we have for the first time survivorship curves which approach the positively skew rectangular type expected in theory from animals in nature. It is surprising that the approach is not closer, but it may well be true that the theoretical curve, in its most extreme form, is not to be looked for among terrestrial vertebrates.

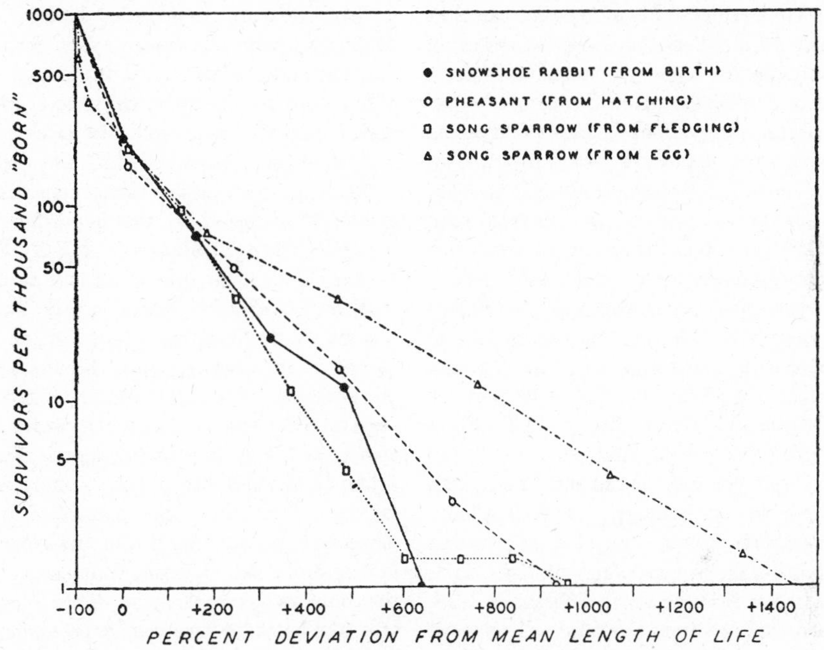

FIG. 5. SYNTHETIC SURVIVORSHIP (l_x) CURVES FOR THE SNOWSHOE RABBIT, THE PHEASANT, AND THE SONG SPARROW, THE LATTER CALCULATED FROM TWO DIFFERENT BIOLOGICAL AGES

Data for different parts of the life spans are derived in different ways, as explained in the text.

Age Structure Directly Observed

Ecological information of a third sort is available for a number of natural populations, principally of fishes and birds. In these cases the investigator has been able to determine how many individuals of each age are living in the population, and the age at death, though calculable from the shrinkage between successive age classes, has not been directly observed. This kind of information lends itself just as well as either of the others to the computation of life tables. As in the group where only the age at death is known, of course, it is necessary to assume the age composition to be unchanged with time. When this assumption is unreasonable, as it often is for fish populations, with their outrageous fluctuation in strength of year-classes, average age compositions obtained from several years' work can often be used. As it happens, however, all the life tables which fall in this third group are incomplete for one reason or another, and the data do not bear close comparison with such examples of natural life tables as those of the Dall sheep and the barnacle.

Kortlandt (1942) has recently given a very elaborate analysis of the Netherlands population of cormorants (*Phalacrocorax carbo sinensis*). Birds banded as nestlings were later observed in their breeding and playing colonies, the numbers on the bands being read with the aid of a telescope. The age distribution of the banded birds being known in 1940 and 1941, it should be possible to infer the age distribution of the total population and from this to compute the annual mortality suffered by each year-class. A number of complicating conditions are present in this case, however, making direct calculation unreliable and necessitating a more circuitous approach: (1) the size of the Dutch cormorant population is not constant, but has been increasing by about 10 per cent per year, as estimated by counts of nests at the breeding colonies; (2) differences between the observed sex ratio among sexually mature birds and the sex ratio predicted on the basis of estimated mortality by sex and age class show clearly that there is some *band mortality*; that is, some birds either lose bands or die because of the band, making estimates of natural mortality too high by a factor of about 2; (3) it is not possible to infer the complete age structure from observations made at breeding colonies, since the one- and two-year-old birds occupy "colonies" elsewhere, returning to their birthplaces to breed no sooner than their third year.

In view of these difficulties, and others which need not be discussed here, Kortlandt's results must be regarded as schematic and preliminary only, and scarcely warrant the construction of a life table. His computations suggest that cormorants suffer mortality somewhat as follows: 17 per cent between fledging and the first May 1; 8 per cent in the first year; 6 per cent in the second year; and about 4 per cent per year in the third to twelfth years. These are astonishingly low figures for a natural population, but it must be remembered that the population is increasing rapidly. It is interesting to find that the slight differential death rate between the sexes from the third year onward appears to favor the female rather than the male sex. It is not known whether this is true of birds generally, in contrast to most other animals (Geiser, 1923, 1924). MacArthur and Baillie (1932) have maintained that there is no evidence that differential mortality is correlated with the sex-determining chromosome mechanism, and that among moths and birds the male longevity is generally lower in conformity with the "rate of living" theory.

Huge numbers of returns of the common tern (*Sterna hirundo*) have been obtained at the Austin Ornithological Research Station on Cape Cod (Austin, 1942), where terns have been banded for over twenty years. Unfortunately the data are inadequately published, and in any case can yield only an incomplete life table, since terns, like other sea birds, scatter widely after birth and do not return to their birthplace until breeding age. Inspection of Austin's table, in which all returns are given by ages for the four years 1938–1941, suggests that the annual mortality is not constant from the fourth year onward, but varies from 178 to 636 per thousand even between the fourth and eighth years, when the numbers are large. It is not clear, however, whether or not the tern population has remained statistically constant during the period of study, i.e., whether the table really reflects the true natural mortality of an average or of any one year-class.

The literature of fisheries biology is full of attempts to estimate the mortality of fishes, to distinguish natural mortality from rate of exploitation, and to determine the rate of exploitation which, given certain mortality rates and certain relationships between age and size, will steadily yield an optimum catch. These complex questions are fully discussed in the important works of Russell (1942), Thompson and Bell (1934), and Ricker (1940, 1944), and by various authors in the *Rapports et Procès-Verbaux of the International Council for the Study of the Sea*, Volume 110, 1939. Little of this information can be directly used for our purpose. The explanation is as simple as it is regrettable: although the age of a caught fish can be ascertained with more or less complete confidence, fishes of all ages can not be caught with equal facility. Inevitably the methods so skilfully developed for catching fish of desirable sizes will fail to catch fish of undesirable sizes. It is true that on various occasions the whole fish population of a lake has been removed by poisoning or drainage. The estimates given by Eschmeyer (1939) for the abundance of large-mouth black bass (*Huro salmoides*) in Howe Lake, Michigan, at the time of its poisoning in 1937, may be cited as an example:

Age	*Number*
0	18,374
0 (cannibals)	229
I	25
II	10
III	105
IV	7
V and older	9
Total	18,759

The implication of enormously greater mortality in the first year of life is plain from these figures, but such data can not be taken as they stand, partly because of very variable annual recruitment, and partly because young of the year were removed from the lake at various times for hatchery purposes.

Lacking satisfactory observations of the complete age structure of the population, and faced with the obstacle of variable yearly recruitment in its most massive form, it is not surprising that fisheries workers have not attempted the construction of life tables, and have so far been content with the estimation of natural mortality among fishes of certain sizes only. This mortality is generally assumed to be constant with respect to age, and it may well be so for middle-aged fishes exposed to fishing; but a life table constructed from the available observations would certainly be lacking both head and tail.

As an example of the kind of information yielded by fisheries statistics, and of the methods used in their analysis, we may first take the data given by Ricker (1945) for the bluegill sunfish (*Lepomis macrochirus*) in Muskellunge Lake, Indiana. This is an especially instructive case, for it shows that despite great technical advantages not enjoyed by students of marine fisheries (a small, isolated, self-contained population; size and character of catch known with certainty by the investigator; age structure of the population checked by tagging methods), the difficulties remaining are still embarrassing.

Ricker first determined the rate of exploitation and the total mortality between one year and the next by what he called (rather inappropriately) the "direct" method, involving marked fish. In 1942, of 140 fish 145 mm. and larger (mostly 3 years old and older) marked prior to the opening of the season, 25 were recaptured by fishermen during the season, giving a rate of exploitation of 18 per cent. Estimated autumn fishing raises this figure to 19 per cent. Of 230 blue-gills 125 mm. and larger, marked prior to the 1942 season, 14 were recaptured in 1943. The rate of exploitation of fish in the same size group (then 155 mm. and larger) in 1943 was 15.1 per cent. It is necessary to calculate the number of 1942-marked fish present at the beginning of the 1943 season; this number is given by dividing the number recaptured in 1943 by the rate of exploitation in 1943, or $\frac{14}{0.151} = 93$. These 93 fish were the survivors of 230 marked fish present before the 1942 season, so the rate of mortality from one season to the next was $\frac{230 - 93}{230} =$ 60 per cent. Subtracting the 19 per cent rate of exploitation leaves 41 per cent as the natural mortality.

Ricker's "indirect" method is the life-table method in a crude form. A collection of scales from 529 blue-gills caught by fishermen in 1942 gave the following as the age structure of the sample:

Age.......	I	II	III	IV	V	VI	VII	VIII
Number...	1	293	151	54	20	7	2	1

The age I fish was presumably caught by accident, and those of age II were not equally vulnerable to fishing during the first part of the season. From age III onward the age structure may be used to yield an estimate of the age-specific mortality rates (assuming uniform recruitment and mortality rates from year to year). These mortality rates in early ages, where the data are more reliable, are nearly constant at about 65 per cent. A weighted geometric mean by Jackson's method gives

$$\frac{1 + 2 + 7 + 20 + 54}{2 + 7 + 20 + 54 + 151} = 36\% \text{ survival}$$

$$= 64\% \text{ mortality.}$$

This is close to the 60 per cent mortality calculated by the "direct" method. However, both methods contain unproved and rather unlikely assumptions, and the agreement merely shows the order of magnitude of the total annual mortality. Moreover, the natural mortality as calculated so far is too low, as some of the fish caught by anglers would have died anyway. By making the additional assumption that the natural mortality is synchronized with the fishing mortality, Ricker calculates the former to be of the order of 50 per cent per year for blue-gills age III and older in four Indiana lakes. This is an important result, and one which will doubtless surprise many fisheries supervisors. It is not sufficient as the basis for a life table, however, since it does not include the mortality from birth to the third year of life, and since the method of weighting underrates the age-specific mortality at advanced ages. Ricker, in fact, thinks it not unlikely that the older fish are subject to a still higher mortality, but his data give no clear answer to the question.

It is a generally accepted conclusion that *adult* fishes, from the time they enter a fishery to the age at which they cease to be caught in significant numbers, suffer a more or less constant mortality with respect to age. Thus for these intermediate ages the survivorship curves, whether constructed vertically for a series of year-classes in any one fishing season, or horizontally for particular year-classes followed through several seasons, tend to fall on straight lines when plotted logarithmically. Such straight lines, with slopes changing according to the rate of exploitation, are implicit in Raitt's treatment of the statistics on the haddock (1939) and are conspicuous in Jensen's review (1939) of data on the cod, haddock, plaice, and herring in the North Sea. Whether the natural mortality, as distinguished from the fishing mortality, also is constant at all adult ages is an open question, but most fisheries workers would probably be prepared to assume that this is the case, in the absence of evidence to the contrary.

Direct observations of *juvenile* mortality in fishes are not easy to make, but a mass of indirect evidence points to the conclusion that it must be very much greater than adult mortality in many species. Some idea of this mortality can be had from Sette's work (1943) on the mackerel. Eggs and larvae of this pelagic species were caught on several systematically conducted cruises over the continental shelf between Martha's Vineyard and the Chesapeake Capes. Several broods spawned at short intervals during the season of 1932 were recognizable at later times and at geographically remote stations as separate modes in the frequency distributions of size and age. Assuming that the technique of plankton sampling gives a reliable estimate of the abundance of eggs and larvae of particular stages in the sea, their reduction in numbers gives a measure of their mortality. Sette's calculations show that the mortality is very great, and is substantially the same per unit time at all egg and larval stages. There is a noticeable rise in mortality rate, from about 10 to 14 per cent per day up to about 30 to 45 per cent per day, at the transition from larval to post-larval stages, when the fins are developing rapidly, but it falls again to the original level. The total mortality from the beginning of development to the 50 mm. stage, when the baby fish school like the adults and seek out their nursery grounds, is 99.9996 per cent. This fantastically high figure refers to a time interval of about *70 days*, and may be compared with values of 50 to 90 per cent *per year* estimated as the total mortality suffered by several species of commercial fishes as adults. Clearly, Pearl was correct in supposing that the survivorship curve for pelagic fishes may be of the J-shaped or positively skew rectangular form.

Though it can not be doubted that survivorship curves for fishes in nature will in general have an initial dip, it would be incorrect to conclude that this dip is invariably as pronounced as in the case of the mackerel. Barnaby (1944), for example, has considered the mortality of the Karluk River population of red salmon (*Oncorhynchus nerka*). Marking experiments suggest a total mortality in the ocean of about 79 per cent, while a calculation based on the reproductive potential yields a figure for the mortality in fresh water, between birth and seaward migration, of 99.55 per cent. The problem is complicated by the fact that the salmon may spend their lives in fresh water and in the ocean in various combinations of years, as 3 + 2 years, 3 + 3 years, 4 + 2 years, etc., so that these mortality rates refer to varying intervals of age. Thus there is no proof that the *annual* mortality rate is other than constant, and while no such deduction should be made from the data, it is evident that the age-specific mortality in fresh water can not be *very much* greater than in the ocean.

The data just presented have been grouped together because they give some conception of the form of the life table for certain species of fish, and the fact has been ignored that some of the information is not based on the age structure of the population, but on other kinds of evidence. This section may logically be concluded with a brief reference to the data for the fin whale, in which, as recent investigations have shown, the age of the female can be determined from the number of old corpora lutea in the ovary. By this method Wheeler (1934) arrived at the following as the age structure, observed over five seasons, 1926–1931, of the catch of female fin whales in the Antarctic:

Age	*Number caught*
3–4 years	130
5–6 years	95
7–8 years	72
9–10 years	53
11–12 years	37
13–14 years	28
15–16 years	10
17–18 years	4
19–20 years	1
21–22 years	1

The data imply (subject to the usual qualifications) a biennial mortality of about 26 per cent, increasing beyond the 15th year to much higher values. The author considers that the increased rate of loss with age is not real, but is due to failure of the older whales to return from their winter quarters in the north. This belief may or may not be well founded, but one suspects it to be predicated on the idea that mortality, at least when it is primarily due to exploitation, is constant among animals with respect to age. Edser (to whom the statistical analysis is credited) assumed, for the purpose of a rough calculation of the necessary rate of replacement, that the mortality between birth and breeding age is also 26 per cent. The improbability of this assumption may be surmised by reference to the life table for the Dall sheep (Table 1). Edser's calculation has the great merit of yielding a minimal estimate of the alarming exploitation being conducted by the whaling industry in the Antarctic. More realistic assumptions would darken the picture even more. In any case the data can not yet be cast into a life table.

Miscellaneous Survivorship Data

By means of the mark-and-recapture method, Jackson (1936, 1939) has given an analysis of the population of a tsetse fly (*Glossina morsitans*) in Tanganyika. Jackson was chiefly interested in determining the size of the population and its fluctuations from season to season. The death of flies in the one-week intervals between marking and recapturing struck at the foundation of the method, which assumes no such mortality. But by taking a geometric average of the survival of marked flies in successive weeks, and extrapolating backward one week, the number theoretically recapturable on the date of marking was calculable. From this figure, the first term in a geometric survival series, the population could be directly calculated for each week during the year over which the study was conducted. But the flies were of unknown ages when first marked, being recognizable simply as adult males (plus a few females) having had their first meal. Evidently the operation was designed to smooth out of existence those systematic changes in age-specific mortality in which we are interested here. A few males were marked *before* their first meal, and the returns of these should permit the construction of a life table beginning at early adult life, but the data are not published separately, and in any case are probably inadequate statistically.

Two other points of interest are raised by this resourceful study. The first deals with the sex ratio in the wild population. Data on the return of marked females are not numerous, but so far as they go they suggest a considerably lower mortality than among males, the calculated survival ratio being 0.716 for females and ranging from 0.307 to 0.622 (depending on the season) for males. Expressed as mortality rates, these values are equal to 284, and between 693 and 378 per thousand flies per week, respectively. As a result, the normal sex ratio among the wild flies must vary from 1.5 to 2.0 in favor of females. Yet the sex ratio at emergence from the pupa is unity. There is no evidence that emigration, though always a complicating factor, is performed differentially by the two sexes, and it is not improbable that here also, as in man and in so many other animals studied in the laboratory, the female is significantly more long-lived than the male. The oldest fly captured lived 13½ weeks after marking, and was a female.

The second point is that Jackson used two methods for the calculation of a, the initial term in a survivorship series. "Instead of considering the survival curve of flies marked in any one week and recaptured in subsequent weeks . . . we can equally well consider the recaptures of flies marked in previous weeks and recaptured in any one week. Subject to sampling errors, both methods should give the same value of a." The difference between the latter "negative" method and the former "positive" method is essentially the difference between a vertical and a horizontal life table. The two methods, while equally applicable to a series of mortality rates assumed to be constant and equal to the geometric mean, as in this case, will give different results for animals of known ages if the age-specific mortality rates change with time. Inasmuch as the smoothed mortality rates for flies of all ages in the population appear to change regularly with the season, being greater in the dry season, real life tables constructed for similar populations would have to be distinguished with care.

An elaborate program of trapping and marking has been carried out with a population of long-tailed field mice (*Apodemus sylvaticus*) by Hacker and Pearson (1946). This sort of work is full of pitfalls, arising mainly from the fact that the traps are attractive to the mice and tend to drain them from distances which are frequently too great to be safely negotiated a second time. As the mice were of unknown ages when first marked, the results need not be summarized in any detail here, but some of the conclusions are of interest in giving an indication of the form of the field mouse life table in nature.

The "standard" survival ratio for mature mice,

as determined from repeated recaptures between December 1938 and April 1939, was 0.879, i.e., the mortality was 121 per thousand per month. But returns of these same mice in December and in March of the following year were much lower than expected from this ratio, implying that the mortality rate increases with age. Data for other years also show that the survival of the winter population is lower in the summer. Moreover, a study of returns of small, middle-sized, and large mice over three winter periods shows that the rates of loss are higher at both ends of the size distribution. Such scanty information can not be cast into a life table, but it is noticeable that a survivorship curve with two inflections fits well with that of the vole (*Microtus agrestis*), as established in the laboratory by Leslie and Ranson (1940).

Survival of Barnacles

Some of the advantages of the life table notation will now be illustrated by an analysis of the survivorship of the barnacle *Balanus balanoides*, as studied at St. Malo by Hatton (1938). The technical advantages presented by intertidal barnacles as objects of population research have been discussed in an earlier section, and a typical example of a barnacle life table has been given in Table 6. The relevant information about the biology of the species, as elucidated by Runnström (1925), Moore (1934), and Hatton, may be briefly summarized:

Balanus balanoides is a typical intertidal species, occurring primarily within the mean range of neap tides, where it often makes dense incrustations on all solid objects. It breeds in the fall, the nauplii being held in the mantle cavity for some time before liberation, while attachment and metamorphosis of the cyprid larvae takes place in the early spring, the exact time doubtless depending on the temperature. The attachment season lasts about six weeks. The intensity of attachment varies with the exposure to surf and the tidal level, being greatest at most exposed localities and at lower levels. The growth rate after attachment is greatest at lower tidal levels in the first year of life, but in subsequent years the growth at higher levels surpasses that at lower levels. Mortality, however, is also greater at lower levels, as shown by survival of barnacles of known ages from year to year, and thus the few barnacles at high levels (up to the mean level of high-water neap tides) are larger after a year's growth and live longer than those lower down. The maximum longevity appears to be about 5 years, but is much less at lower levels.

It is not clear which of these facts are simple responses to the physical ecology of the intertidal zone, and which are biotic effects. It is easy to suppose that the growth rate might be best at lower levels, where the barnacles are more continuously submerged and therefore take food more frequently. It is not so easy to explain the decline of growth rate with age at these levels (or the increase of growth rate with age at higher levels), unless it is in some way related to the population density; yet the growth differences are said to be observable in the absence of crowding. The low attachment densities at high levels presumably reflect the time necessary for a cyprid to attach, for the time available on any one tide decreases with the height. But after attachment the higher levels are exposed for longer periods to desiccation, direct sunlight, and rainwater, and the enhanced survival under these conditions is difficult to understand except as a function of the low population density.

The relation between population density and longevity is well known for certain laboratory animals. In general the length of life is curtailed by overcrowding (Pearl, 1946; Davis, 1945). In certain well-studied cases, however, the mean length of life has been found to increase at densities above the minimum, to decrease at very high densities, and to be greatest at some intermediate density (Pearl, Miner, and Parker, 1927). Pratt's proof of an optimum density for longevity of *Daphnia magna* (1943) is particularly convincing, since the densities were actually maintained constant throughout the life of the animals, and were not permitted to decrease with the gradual extinction of the initial cohort.

It is of considerable importance, therefore, to examine Hatton's data, which fortunately are published in full, for evidence of the relationship between longevity and population density in *Balanus balanoides*. Hatton studied nine different populations, allowed to settle on cleaned areas in 1930, and followed for three years. Three different levels were chosen at each of three localities as follows:

Localities	*Levels*
Décollé Ouest, exposed	II—mean high-water neap tide
Décollé Est, sheltered	III—half-tide
Cité, moderately sheltered	IV—mean low-water neap tide

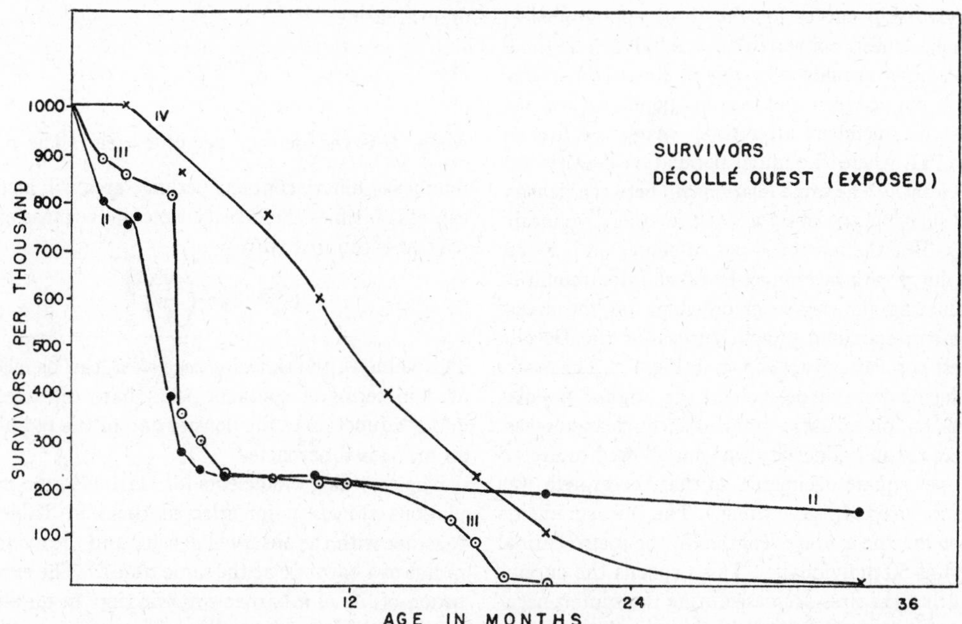

FIG. 6. SURVIVORSHIP (l_x) CURVES FOR THREE OF THE NINE POPULATIONS OF BALANUS BALANOIDES STUDIED AT ST. MALO BY HATTON (1938)

The locality, Décollé Ouest, is exposed to surf. The initial density of attachment, taken as the maximum density attained on May 15, 1930, was as follows: II (at mean high-water neap tide level), 790 per 100 cm²; III (at half-tide level), 2330 per 100 cm²; IV (at mean low-water neap tide level), 1500 per 100 cm².

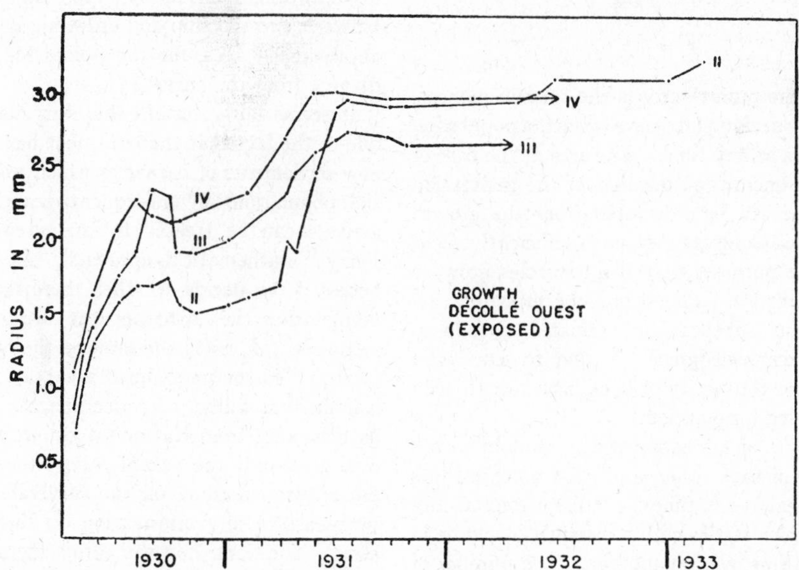

FIG. 7. GROWTH CURVES FOR BARNACLES CORRESPONDING TO THE THREE POPULATIONS OF FIG. 6, BUT OBTAINED FROM UNCROWDED SPECIMENS

The measurements began on April 1, 1930, and the points plotted are the average lengths (at the base, in the rostro-carinal axis), divided by 2. Each point represents an average of about 50 measurements.

Survivorship curves for the three populations at Décollé Ouest, converted to a relative (per thousand) basis, are shown by way of illustration in Fig. 6. It may be seen that the only population having surviving members after three years was that at Level II, where the initial population density was also least. The same relationship between density and survival was observed at the other two localities. But the matter is not so simple as it looks, for the growth rates must be taken into account in evaluating the degree of crowding on the areas. The corresponding growth curves for the Décollé Ouest populations are shown in Fig. 7. The measurements were made, not on the original populations, but on barnacles from adjacent cleaned areas, where the initial density was not allowed to exceed 100 per square decimeter, so that the growth was uninfluenced by crowding. The measurements given are the average lengths (in the rostro-carinal axis) of 50 individuals. This explains the curious fact that the sizes decrease during the winter: negative growth is biologically impossible in this case, and evidently there was a relatively great loss of older barnacles each winter. For purposes of calculation the radius of a barnacle has been taken to equal half the length, and the reasonable growth figures (ignoring negative increments) have been fitted to equations of the form

$$r = at^b$$

where r is the radius and t is the time in months.

Hatton's survivorship curves give the population per unit area at any time. The area at the base of an average uncrowded member of the population at any time can be calculated from the growth curve on the assumption, which is sufficiently accurate for the purpose, that the barnacles grow as expanding circles. The degree of crowding attained at any time can be evaluated as follows: (Grateful acknowledgment is due to Dr. John Ferry, of the University of Wisconsin, for the elegant following formulation.)

If barnacles of radius r settle at random within distance D of each other, and grow as expanding circles, so that at any time the radii r are equal, any barnacle which settles within distance $2r$ will be in contact with or overlap another. The number of binary contacts per barnacle will be given by:

$$\int_0^{2r} \frac{N}{A} \cdot 2\pi D \cdot dD$$

or, evaluating:

$$4\pi r^2 \frac{N}{A}.$$

where $\frac{N}{A}$ is the density per unit area. The total number of binary contacts per unit area will be this expression times the density times $\frac{1}{2}$ (because each contact is counted twice):

$$C = 2\pi r^2 \left(\frac{N}{A}\right)^2$$

This value C, the *crowding coefficient*, can be evaluated in terms of contacts per square centimeter, and is a function of the density and of the radius of an individual barnacle.

The crowding coefficients for Hatton's nine populations are given for selected times in Table 7, together with the observed density and the average radius of a barnacle at the same times. The expectation of life of a barnacle at the time in question is calculated by ordinary life table methods. Plotting C against e_x gives the graph shown in Fig. 8.

Evidently the population density, when considered in this way, has a definite effect on the survival of *Balanus balanoides*. The effect is not linear, but becomes less marked at higher degrees of crowding. Evidently, too, the relationship between survivorship and crowding is less definite at advanced ages, for the points for 18 months diverge from the curve.

It seems fairly certain that this discrepancy is due to the fact that the treatment has ignored the new settlements of barnacles which were added to the populations in subsequent years. The new arrivals can be treated by an extension of Dr. Ferry's mathematical approach, but it becomes necessary to decide whether there is any superincrustation, i.e., whether the area exposed to settlement, A, is (1) the same as the original area, (2) equal to the unoccupied area, or (3) has some intermediate value. No decision can be reached on this point from Hatton's account, which moreover gives only the second-year settlements, without subsequent data on the survival of the 1931 year-class or any information on the 1932 year-class. The data, however, are suggestive in that all the populations which diverge widely at 18 months from the curve of Fig. 8 received high second-year settlements, while the "good" points are from populations which received relatively little recruitment in 1931. Since in general the populations with highest initial densities will receive the most considerable reinforcement in subsequent such as the one drawn in Fig. 8, is an illusion. But only further work will permit a deeper analysis of this exceptionally interesting case.

TABLE 7

Population density, calculated radius, crowding coefficients, and expectation of life at selected times for nine populations of Balanus balanoides at St. Malo
Original data from Hatton (1938)

POPULATION (*Locality and Level*)	t TIME (*months*)*	N/A DENSITY PER CM²	r RADIUS (*mm.*)	C CROWDING COEFFICIENT: *contacts per cm²* = $2\pi r^2(N/A)^2$	e_x EXPECTATION OF FURTHER LIFE (*months*)†	POPULATION (*Locality and Level*)	t TIME (*months*)*	N/A DENSITY PER CM²	r RADIUS (*mm.*)	C CROWDING COEFFICIENT: *contacts per cm²* = $2\pi r^2(N/A)^2$	e_x EXPECTATION OF FURTHER LIFE (*months*)†
Décollé	0	4.0	1.08	1.17	23.1	Décollé	0	15.0	1.74	42.55	12.6
Est II	6	2.4	1.65	0.98	29.6	Ouest IV	6	12.6	2.20	48.41	8.2
	12	2.1	1.92	1.02	27.2		12	7.3	2.40	19.35	5.6
	18	1.9	2.11	1.01	23.7		18	3.0	2.54	3.65	3.7
	24	1.5	2.27	0.73	23.1		24	0.6	2.64	0.16	2.9
	30	1.5	2.39	0.81	17.7		30	0.08	2.73	0.03	2.0
Décollé	0	11.9	1.12	11.24	13.8	Cité II	0	10.0	1.24	9.61	14.3
Est III	6	8.3	1.59	10.87	12.8		6	3.4	1.67	2.03	28.6
	12	5.4	1.80	5.92	12.6		12	2.9	1.89	1.88	27.2
	18	4.2	1.94	4.09	9.1		18	2.8	2.00	1.97	22.5
	24	2.0	2.06	1.07	9.9		24	2.5	2.10	1.73	19.0
	30	1.0	2.16	0.29	12.2		30	2.2	2.19	1.45	15.2
Décollé	0	15.0	1.41	27.91	9.5	Cité III‡	0	22.0	1.32	53.22	12.1
Est IV	6	8.4	1.80	14.35	7.5		6	16.7	1.66	48.05	9.1
	12	4.8	1.97	5.61	4.9		12	10.1	1.80	20.70	6.7
	18	1.8	2.08	0.88	1.2		18	5.1	1.89	5.85	4.7
							24	0.7	1.96	0.11	1.8
Décollé	0	7.9	1.34	7.07	11.0						
Ouest II	6	1.9	1.82	0.75	31.2	Cité IV	0	23.8	1.44	74.10	11.2
	12	1.7	2.03	0.75	28.5		6	12.9	1.71	30.68	12.2
	18	1.5	2.18	0.67	24.5		12	11.0	1.82	25.29	7.9
	24	1.4	2.29	0.65	20.3		18	6.1	1.90	8.41	5.4
	30	1.3	2.38	0.61	15.8		24	2.6	1.95	1.62	2.5
Décollé	0	23.3	1.50	76.28	7.0						
Ouest III	6	6.3	1.94	9.34	8.7						
	12	4.9	2.12	6.81	4.7						
	18	1.2	2.25	0.46	1.0						

* These are the times corresponding to the density figures (read from the survivorship curves), beginning at 0 = 15 May. The growth curves begin on 1 April, and the time values for radius as stated are actually 1.5, 7.5, 13.5, 19.5, 25.5, and 31.5 months.

† Computed on the assumption that those populations still having surviving members after 3 years would have terminated at 5 years.

‡ Life table for this population given in Table 6.

years, it is easy to imagine that over the years the effect of unit change of crowding on survival, $\frac{de_x}{dC}$, will be greatest for these populations. This argument carries the implication that a single curve,

Returning to the original question, whether there is a density above the minimum which is optimal for the longevity of *Balanus balanoides* in nature, Fig. 8 indicates that there is not. The expectation of life is greatest when the crowding coefficient is least, and the curve does not rise before it falls. This negative evidence is probably not conclusive, and a larger body of data, preferably obtained under conditions which are less variable as regards factors other than crowding, might give a different answer. But there is no particular reason to expect that a species such as this one would benefit greatly from mutual support. It is possible to point to another barnacle in which the case may be otherwise. This is *Chthamalus stellatus*, which flourishes best at an intertidal level above that of *B. balanoides*. Here it is exposed to sun and drought for long periods, and Monterosso (1930) has found that it is remarkably hardy, specimens having survived for three years on a laboratory table with only one or two days' immersion in sea water each month. Hatton suggests that the chances of survival of a young *Chthamalus* are improved if it settles in the shade of a larger individual; at any rate, the larvae tend to attach in the shade in greater numbers, when ridges of cement are built upon the rocks. Moreover, while attached and growing *B. balanoides* were frequently found to dislodge each other from the substratum, this phenomenon was never observed with *Chthamalus*.

Hatton's work included survival studies of *Chthamalus* as well as of *B. balanoides*, but as the longevity of the former is greater (see also Moore and Kitching, 1939), few of the populations had run their courses when the experiments were terminated at the end of three years. As a result, the expectation of life cannot be calculated with any confidence. Annual mortality rates for six populations (three at Level I, above the *B. balanoids* zone; and three at Level II, where densities of *B. balanoides* were low) are arranged in Table 8 for direct comparison with the density. The table shows that the populations having very low densities suffered higher mortality rates on the average than those below the dashed line in the table, which had higher densities. The difference is more pronounced when the first year's mortality is omitted, but in neither case is the difference significant statistically. The predicted relation between density and survivorship of *Chthamalus* is therefore not proven, and the question remains open.

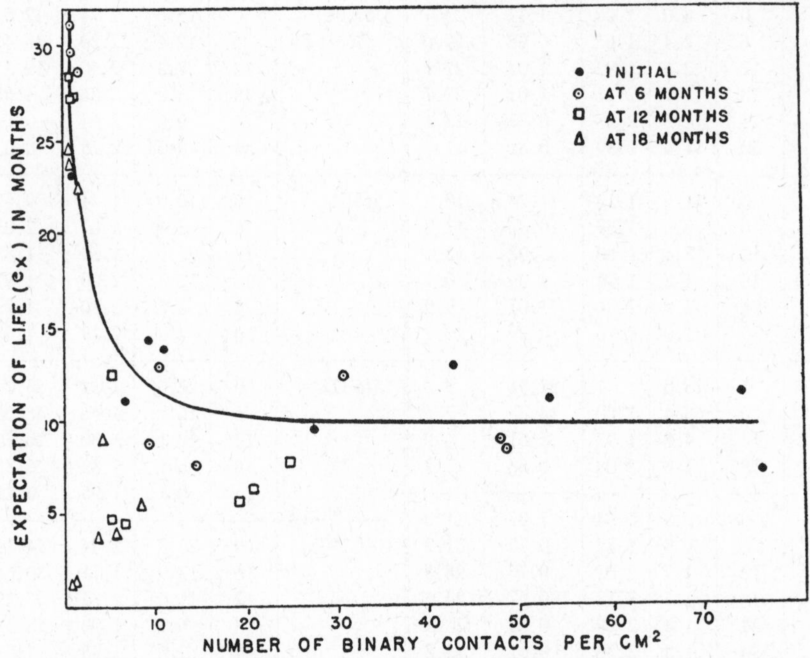

FIG. 8. RELATION BETWEEN EXPECTATION OF LIFE (e_x) OF BALANUS BALANOIDES AT SELECTED TIMES AND THE CROWDING COEFFICIENT (CONTACTS PER SQUARE CENTIMETER) AT THE SAME TIME
Data in Table 7, calculated from data of Hatton.

Mention has been made in an earlier section of a

defect inherent in the life tables calculated from experiments like Hatton's, in that the observations much greater, reaching 95 per cent (survival ratio 0.05) at the greatest densities observed.

TABLE 8

Annual mortality of Chthamalus stellatus at St. Malo in relation to population density
Data from Hatton (1938), Tables XXXVI–XXXVIII

POPULATION (LOCALITY AND LEVEL)	FIRST YEAR		SECOND YEAR		THIRD YEAR	
	Initial density per 100 cm²	Mortality %	Density per 100 cm²	Mortality %	Density per 100 cm²	Mortality %
Décollé Ouest I	21	4.8	20	10.0	18	16.6
Décollé Est II	39	10.3	35	20.0	28	28.6
Cité I	44	9.1	40	17.5	33	9.1
Décollé Est I	48	31.2	33	9.1	30	36.7
Cité II	184	11.4	163	13.5	141	8.5
Décollé Ouest II	270	17.4	223	11.2	198	14.1

start with metamorphosis, and the pelagic larval life is neglected. Some idea of the mortality during the earliest attachment stage, the interval between attachment of the cyprid and its transformation to an adult barnacle, can be gained from the unpublished studies of Weiss at Miami Beach, Florida.

Permission to present these results in advance of publication has been courteously granted by Mr. C. M. Weiss of the Woods Hole Oceanographic Institution.

Weiss observed the daily attachment of cyprid larvae (mainly *Balanus improvisus*) to glass slides exposed each twenty-four hours for more than three years. At the same time, records were kept of the attachment of adult barnacles to glass panels exposed each month at the same locality. The time required for a cyprid to grow into an adult barnacle large enough to be counted varies from one to two weeks according to the season. By summing the daily cyprid attachments over a two- to three-week period, therefore, and comparing the figures with the number of adult barnacles found on the panels at the end of the month, a measure of the survival between cyprid and adult stages was obtained. The results are shown in Fig. 9, the ratio of surviving barnacles to cyprids being plotted against the intensity of cyprid attachment. The curve shows clearly that a cyprid's chances of successful growth to maturity vary inversely with the density of attachment: when few cyprids attach most or all of them survive to become barnacles, but when cyprid densities are high the mortality is

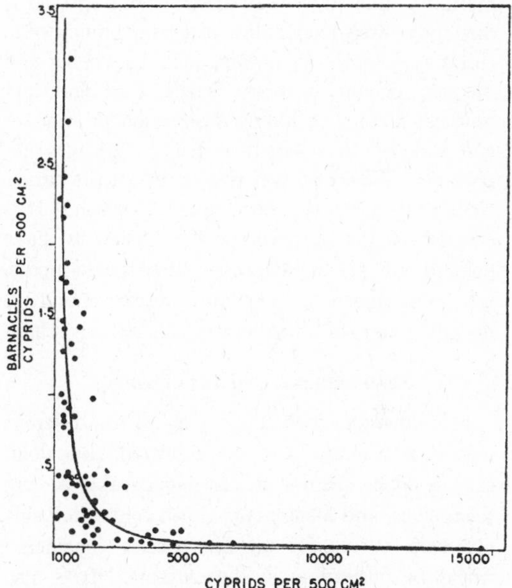

FIG. 9. RELATION BETWEEN SURVIVAL OF BARNACLES TO MATURITY AND THE INTENSITY OF CYPRID ATTACHMENT AT MIAMI BEACH, FLORIDA

Cyprid attachment was observed on glass slides exposed for twenty-four hours; the barnacles were counted on glass panels exposed for twenty-eight days. Daily cyprid attachment figures have been summed over two or three weeks, according to the season, for comparison with the number of surviving barnacles. From unpublished results of C. M. Weiss, Woods Hole Oceanographic Institution.

Inspection of the scale of barnacle:cyprid ratios in Fig. 9 brings out an apparent paradox in that ratios above 1.0 were frequently observed, i.e., in some months more barnacles survived than can be accounted for from the cyprids attaching. Weiss takes this to mean that the longer exposure of the one-month panels made them more suitable for the attachment of barnacles than the twenty-four-hour slides. Such a result of exposure can reasonably be attributed to the facilitating effect of a "slime film" (of diatoms and bacteria) on the attachment of larvae of fouling organisms, an effect of which there is independent evidence. This complication, interesting as it is, makes it impossible to use the data further for an analysis of the mortality of barnacles in early stages. For if in any month more cyprids attached to the panels during certain days than the daily figures show, the barnacle:cyprid ratio will give too low an estimate of the mortality; but such an error is not likely to be systematic, and would have to be evaluated separately.

Although it is abundantly clear that much of the mortality suffered by natural stands of barnacles is directly related to population density, much of it certainly is not. Predators, such as whelks and limpets, account for many deaths at all ages, and physical factors, including desiccation in summer and abrasion by boulders in winter, are also important. We are not yet able to dissect the barnacle life tables to expose the causes of death. It is enough for the purposes of this review to have pointed out: (1) the attraction of barnacle incrustations as objects for population research; and (2) the advantages of life table methods in their study.

COMPARISONS AND CONCLUSIONS

It is now apparent that, owing to the different ways in which data have been collected, all ecological life tables are not strictly comparable among themselves, and a summary graph containing survivorship curves for all the species considered would be misleading in the extreme. It is also true, though not so obvious, that within any one group of life tables, such as the "d_x observed" group or the "l_x observed" group, comparisons are also apt to lead us astray. For the various life tables so far constructed *take their origin at different biological ages*. Is it fair to compare a bird life table, beginning at early adult life, with the Dall sheep life table, which begins at birth, or with the life table of a sessile invertebrate, beginning at attachment or metamorphosis? Evidently not; birth itself is not an age of universal biological equivalence outside the placental mammals, and for a broader view of comparative mortality the only safe point of reference would be the fertilized ovum.

This reservation should perhaps not be applied too literally. Human and insect survivorship curves have been compared in the past, and the comparison is instructive, despite the very different origins and statistical foundations of the life tables. It is possible to compare the survivorship of an insect such as *Drosophila*, beginning at sexual maturity, with that of a laboratory population of black widow spiders (Deevey and Deevey, 1945) which enter their life table at the antepenultimate instar when the sexes become distinguishable. The comparison, which of course is purely qualitative, suggests that organisms are born at different points on their survivorship curves, so to speak, and that heavy juvenile mortality may be carried over into later life as a neotenic character. This is the statistical aspect of that ancient proverb which Cicero quotes disparagingly, "grow old early if you would be old long."

The cognate suggestion has been made that altricial and praecocial birds should be examined in the light of this hypothesis. Unfortunately, such a comparison cannot yet be made. We now have life tables of a sort for several altricial species, (song sparrow, Turdidae, etc.) and for at least one markedly praecocial bird (the pheasant), but the data are lacking for those early ages at which the comparison might have some meaning.

If bird life tables cannot even be compared with one another except from adult ages onward, we can hardly make very enlightening comparisons between birds and other animals. The ecological information is deficient, to a variable degree it is true, but still deficient, for the early ages; and this is the segment of the life curve on which future investigators must concentrate their efforts. The most that can be said at present is that the more nearly complete natural life tables (Dall sheep, barnacle, rotifer) give no ground for supposing that ecological life tables are invariably diagonal, as is so often assumed *faute de mieux* in fisheries work. Increases and decreases in mortality rate must be expected at any age, as the laboratory populations also show.

Related to the paucity of data near the beginning of life is the remarkable absence, among the examples adduced, of life curves approaching Pearl's "Type III" distribution. Only the synthetic survivorship curve for the song sparrow calculated from the egg stage (Fig. 5) shows the pronounced dip in early life associated with this form. But Sette's data for the mackerel show that pelagic fishes actually fall here; the barnacle and the rotifer might also fall here if their life tables were complete, and ecologists will await with interest the construction of a life table for the oyster.

It is pertinent to inquire whether the ecological life tables throw any light on the relation between the different theoretical types of survivorship curve (Fig. 1). It is a well known property of human longevity that while the mean age at death shows extreme variation among different populations, ancient and modern, and has shown a marked increase in Europe and the United States in recent decades, the maximum life span is fixed (Dublin and Lotka, 1935; Pearl, 1946). In other words, the human survivorship curve is like a rubber band, fixed at points corresponding to birth and about the 115th year, and while medical science has succeeded in stretching the band more and more toward the upper side of Fig. 1, the termini have remained fixed as they were in Roman times.

If the maximum life span is fixed for all species by physiological considerations, as it probably is, the mean life span is not. Lack (1943b) points out that a young blackbird in nature can expect to live for but 8 per cent of its potential life span, compared to some 60 per cent for a juvenile human. Evidently there is much room for improvement in the expectation of life of species in the wild, to judge from the known longevity of some of them in captivity. As has been shown, birds as a group seem to have remarkably diagonal survivorship curves, the mortality being constant for a given bird with respect to age, and for all birds so far studied with respect to units of mean life span. This means that experience of life is of no use to a bird in avoiding death, although Farner (1945) raises the question whether the apparent diagonality may not be a result of insufficient data.

The case is quite otherwise with the Dall sheep, with its low mortality during middle life. This species seems to have evolved a mechanism for stretching its mean life span toward the maximum. Whether this has come about because of intimate demographic contact with a single important predator or for some other reason is a "puzzling question." Such an enhancement of survival during the years of maximum reproductive efficiency has important implications for the whole population problem, including the question of the nature of internally generated cycles; but on this matter little more can be said than that the mathematical methods are available for a study of the relation between the fertility schedule and the death rate structure when the data come to hand (Leslie, 1945).

Bodenheimer (1938) has maintained that not only is the maximum life span fixed for a species, but that the potential mean longevity is the same as the maximum. On this view a species has a "physiological life table" of the negatively skew rectangular type, and a more diagonal or positively skew "ecological life table" which is the result of premature mortality. All such mortality is thus regarded as environmentally produced. This position is probably not tenable as a basis for a general theory of mortality, since there appears to be no reason why "endogenous senescence" (in Pearl's phrase) should be strictly confined to the end of the life span. Even in genetically homogeneous populations the members are not identical, and endogenous senescence must have a probability distribution which is not necessarily regular, though it may well be more so than that of "exogenous senescence." In any case, since we can not observe physiological survivorship except in an environment of some sort, Bodenheimer's conception would appear to be non-operational.

The question at issue resolves itself into the relation between the mean and the maximum life span. In theory there is a simple answer: the ratio of the maximum to the mean approaches 1.0 as a limit for Type I, approaches infinity for Type III, and its actual value for Type II depends on the level at which we permit the abscissa of Figure 1 to intersect the ordinate. If we decide to terminate the diagram when a cohort of 1000 individuals has been reduced to 1, a diagonal survivorship line will intersect the age axis at some point above 1.0, but if we start with 100,000 individuals the same line projected will give a higher maximum age for the last survivor. Reference to Figs. 2, 4, and 5 will make the matter plain, when it is realized that an age value of +100 per cent deviation from the mean corresponds to a maximum: mean ratio of 2.0, one of +500 per cent corresponds to a ratio of 6.0, etc. In all cases we have started with 1000 individuals, simply because the samples were of less than 1000 to begin with, and only three places at most can be significant. Had we larger samples available the maximum life span, as shown on the abscissas of Figs. 2, 4, and 5, would have been higher for a given mortality rate.

It should now be clear that we cannot yet formulate the relationship exactly. One stumbling block is that with a cohort of 1000 individuals the 1 per thousand level has lost all semblance of reliability: taking Fig. 4 as an illustration, we might well find that the last hundred birds in a cohort of 100,000 really have gained some benefit from their accumulated experience of life, and die at decreasing rates. This would mean that the true survivorship curve is concave. It is equally possible that these hypothetical survivors of a larger cohort would be found to be decrepit, and to die at greatly accelerated rates, giving a convexity to the tail of the survivorship curve.

The other obstacle to an exact formulation is that the mean length of life is calculated from different starting points in the cases before us, so that an observed relation between maximum and mean has no quantitative significance as a basis of comparison between species. Empirically, it will eventually be possible to divide animals into three groups, somewhat as follows: those in which the maximum length of life is between two and six times the mean may be called "thrifty" (the Dall sheep, rotifer, and barnacle might fall here, along with most of the populations studied in the laboratory); those in which the ratio lies between 6.0 and 15.0 (as perhaps in song birds) might be called "indifferent"; those which on the average realize less than one-fifteenth of their maximum life span might be called "prodigal." These limits would have to be arbitrarily defined by the age (in units of mean life span) attained by the oldest individual in a cohort of 1000. But such limits can not yet be specified, and the values assigned are pure guesses, based on data which we know to be inadequate, and intended simply for illustration.

So far we have confined our attention almost exclusively to the *form* of the life table, and have said very little about the *causes* of death other than to imply that they are suitable subjects for ecological investigation. Authors who have discussed the matter in some detail for particular cases have not reached very satisfactory general conclusions. Thus Ricker (1945) decides that "senile death is an everyday occurrence among bluegills and crappies," and Lack (1943a) says, "Who killed cock robin is, for the most part, still a mystery." Errington (1945, 1946) has argued energetically against the generally accepted view that predation is responsible for the maintenance of population size among vertebrates, believing that intraspecific competition demands more attention than it has received. Predation, in Errington's opinion, falls principally on the very young, the very old, and the diseased, i.e., on the insecure members of the population, who might otherwise have died in any event. Clearly, the task of constructing better life tables for natural populations, though an important prerequisite to the study of mortality, is not a substitute for such a study. Even so interesting a series of life tables as is available for *Balanus balanoides* proves to be unsatisfactory when it is realized that they all start at the same season, and the survivors are exposed to winter conditions at the same ages. What would happen to the survivorship curves if such animals were caused to be born out of season can only be found out by painstaking work. And until such questions, and many others, are answered, we will not be ready to establish a general theory of mortality.

"Sed omnes una manet nox
et calcanda semel via leti."

SUMMARY

Materials for the study of the age distribution of mortality are available from several natural populations of animals. Attempts are made, in most instances for the first time, to condense this information into life tables, showing for each age interval the number of deaths, the number of survivors, the mortality rate, and the expectation of further life of members of an initial cohort of 1000 individuals. These life table functions, especially when age is expressed in terms of units of the mean life span rather than in years, months, or days, should afford the best basis for comparing populations of the same and of different species in respect to their order of dying. Unfortunately, the ecological information is of unequal value in the various cases, and only limited and tentative comparisons can be made.

According to the methods used in collecting the information, the species studied fall into three groups: (a) those in which the *age at death* (d_x) is known, with fair accuracy, at least beyond certain ages (Dall mountain sheep, the sessile rotifer *Floscularia conifera*, and several species of birds); (*b*) those in which the *number of survivors* (l_x) out of a definite initial number has been directly observed at frequent intervals (barnacles, song sparrow, pheasant, snowshoe rabbit); (*c*) those in which the *age structure* (L_x) of the population is observed at a specified time, and the age at death is inferred from the shrinkage between age classes (cormorant, many fish, fin whale). Information of type (*b*) is comparable to that obtainable from a laboratory experiment, provided only that the season of birth is sharply defined, and can be used without qualification for the construction of a life table. Information of types (*a*) and (*c*) can be so used only upon the assumption that the age structure of the population does not change with time.

Both in nature and in the laboratory, animals differ characteristically in their order of dying. When the mortality rate at all ages is constant, the survivorship (l_x) curve is diagonal on semi-logarithmic graph paper. Such a curve is found for many birds from adult stages onward; the mortality of adult birds is about 320 per thousand per hundred centiles of mean life span. If the constant age-specific mortality rate observed for the first few years of adult life is really maintained throughout life, the oldest bird in a cohort of 1000 lives 6.6 times as long as the average bird. Not all animals resemble birds in this respect, however, although many (e.g., fish) are assumed to do so. The Dall sheep, the rotifer, and possibly the barnacle are more like civilized man in that they seem to have evolved a mechanism for stretching the mean life span toward the maximum, so that the survivorship curve is convex. In these cases the maximum life span (among a sample of 1000) is only two or three times the mean. On the other hand there are undoubtedly species in which juvenile mortality is very heavy, but the few survivors to advanced ages die at reduced rates. This J-shaped or concave survivorship line, with the maximum longevity perhaps 15 or more times the mean, is presumed to characterize the oyster and other species, but it has not yet been formally recognized either in the laboratory or in nature. The closest approach to it, so far, is found when the survival of song sparrows is reckoned from the egg stage; but the mackerel will almost certainly provide an even better example.

Detailed comparisons between species cannot yet be made, partly because of the diverse statistical foundations of the life tables and partly because the data begin at different biological ages (birth, hatching, metamorphosis, sexual maturity, etc.) in the different cases. In all cases it is the youngest ages about which we know least, and ecologists should therefore concentrate their efforts on this segment of the life span of animals in nature.

The best examples of ecological life tables come from Hatton's work with the barnacle *Balanus balanoides*, which is a very favorable object for population research. By way of emphasizing the advantages of life table notation, Hatton's data are manipulated so as to show the relationship between longevity and population density. A theory of two-dimensional crowding by radially growing circular objects is first derived from geometric considerations, and it is then possible to relate the expectation of life (e_x) of a barnacle to a factor, called the *crowding coefficient*, which incorporates both the population density and the rate of growth. The number of barnacle populations available for study is limited, and Hatton's experiments were designed for a different purpose, but so far as the data go there is no evidence of an optimum density for survival of *B. balanoides*. Reasons are given for supposing that *Chthamalus stellatus* may prove to have such an optimum density.

ACKNOWLEDGMENTS

This article had its inception as part of a symposium, entitled "Life Tables and Their Application," held at Boston on December 27, 1943, under the joint auspices of the Ecological Society of America and the American Statistical Association. The present version has been completely reworked in the light of other contributions to the symposium. Remarks made at the meeting by Margaret Merrell, C. P. Winsor, and W. E. Ricker have been particularly helpful. Much has been learned also from later conversations with David Lack, G. E. Hutchinson, and Daniel Merriman. The author retains sole responsibility, however, for errors which may still remain.

LIST OF LITERATURE

Austin, O. L. 1942. The life span of the common tern (*Sterna hirundo*). *Bird-Banding*, 13: 159–176.

Barnaby, J. T. 1944. Fluctuations in abundance of red salmon, *Oncorhynchus nerka* (Walbaum) of the Karluk River, Alaska. *U. S. Fish & Wildlife Service, Fishery Bull.*, 50 (39): 235–295.

Bertram, G. C. L. 1940. The biology of the Weddell and Crabeater Seals, with a study of the comparative behaviour of the Pinnipedia. *Brit. Mus.*

(*Nat. Hist.*): *British Graham Land Expedition 1934–37, Sci. Rep.*, 1 (1): 139 pp., pls. 1–10.

BODENHEIMER, F. S. 1938. *Problems of animal ecology.* vi + 183 pp. Oxford Univ. Press, London.

DAVIS, M. B. 1945. The effect of population density on longevity in *Trogoderma versicolor* Creutz. (= *T. inclusa* Lec.). *Ecology*, 26: 353–362.

DEEVEY, G. B., and E. S. DEEVEY. 1945. A life table for the black widow. *Trans. Conn. Acad. Arts Sci.*, 36: 115–134.

DUBLIN, L. I., and A. J. LOTKA. 1935. *Length of life. A study of the life table.* xxii + 400 pp. Ronald Press, New York.

EDMONDSON, W. T. 1945. Ecological studies of sessile Rotatoria, Part II. Dynamics of populations and social structures. *Ecol. Mon.*, 15: 141–172.

ERICKSON, M. M. 1938. Territory, annual cycle, and numbers in a population of wren-tits (*Chamaea fasciata*). *Univ. Calif. Pub. Zool.*, 42 (5): 247–334, pls. 9–14.

ERRINGTON, P. L. 1945. Some contributions of a fifteen-year local study of the northern bobwhite to a knowledge of population phenomena. *Ecol. Mon.*, 15: 1–34.

——. 1946. Predation and vertebrate populations. *Quart. Rev. Biol.*, 21: 144–177, 221–245.

ESCHMEYER, R. W. 1939. Analysis of the complete fish population from Howe Lake, Crawford County, Michigan. *Papers Mich. Acad. Sci. Arts Lett.*, 24 (II): 117–137.

FARNER, D. S. 1945. Age groups and longevity in the American robin. *Wilson Bull.*, 57: 56–74.

GEISER, S. W. 1923. Evidences of a differential death rate of the sexes among animals. *Amer. Midl. Nat.*, 8: 155–163.

——. 1924. The differential death-rate of the sexes among animals, with a suggested explanation. *Wash. Univ. Stud.*, 12: 73–96.

GREEN, R. G., and C. A. EVANS. 1940. Studies on a population cycle of snowshoe hares on the Lake Alexander area. I. Gross annual censuses, 1932–1939. *J. Wildl. Man.*, 4: 220–238. II. Mortality according to age groups and seasons. Ibid., 4: 267–278. III. Effect of reproduction and mortality of young hares on the cycle. Ibid., 4: 347–358.

HACKER, H. P., and H. S. PEARSON. 1946. The growth, survival, wandering, and variation of the long-tailed field mouse, *Apodemus sylvaticus*. II. Survival (By H. P. Hacker). *Biometrika*, 33: 333–361.

HATTON, H. 1938. Essais de bionomie explicative sur quelques espèces intercotidales d'algues et d'animaux. *Ann. Inst. Océanogr.*, 17: 241–348.

HODGE, W. B. 1857. On the rates of interest for the use of money in ancient and modern times. (Part I). *Assurance Mag. & J. Inst. Act.*, 6: 301–333.

JACKSON, C. H. N. 1936. Some new methods in the study of *Glossina morsitans*. *Proc. Zool. Soc. Lond.*, 1936: 811–896, pls. 1–12.

——. 1939. The analysis of an animal population. *J. Anim. Ecol.*, 8: 238–246.

JENSEN, A. J. C. 1939. On the laws of decrease in fish stocks. *Cons. Per. Intern. Explor. Mer, Rapp. Proc.-Verb.*, 110 (8): 85–96.

KORTLANDT, A. 1942. Levensloop, samenstelling en structuur der Nederlandse aalscholver bevolking. *Ardea*, 31: 175–280.

KRAAK, W. K., G. L. RINKEL, and J. HOOGERHEIDE. 1940. Oecologische bewerking van de Europese ringgegevens van de Kievit (*Vanellus vanellus* (L.)). *Ardea*, 29: 151–175.

LACK, D. 1943a. *The life of the robin.* 200 pp. H. F. & G. Witherby, London.

——. 1943b. The age of the blackbird. *Brit. Birds*, 36: 166–175.

——. 1943c. The age of some more British birds. *Brit. Birds*, 36: 193–197, 214–221.

——. 1946. Do juvenile birds survive less well than adults? *Brit. Birds*, 39: 258–264.

LAURIE, A. H. 1937. The age of female blue whales and the effect of whaling on the stock. *Discov. Rep.*, 15: 223–284.

LEOPOLD, A., T. M. SPERRY, W. S. FEENEY, and J. S. CATENHUSEN. 1943. Population turnover on a Wisconsin pheasant refuge. *J. Wildl. Man.*, 7: 383–394.

LESLIE, P. H. 1945. On the use of matrices in certain population mathematics. *Biometrika*, 33: 183–212.

——, and R. M. RANSON. 1940. The mortality, fertility, and rate of natural increase of the vole (*Microtus agrestis*) as observed in the laboratory. *J. Anim. Ecol.*, 9: 27–52.

MACARTHUR, J. W., and W. H. T. BAILLIE. 1932. Sex differences in mortality in *Abraxas*-type species. *Quart. Rev. Biol.*, 7: 313–325.

MACDONELL, W. R. 1913. On the expectation of life in ancient Rome, and in the provinces of Hispania and Lusitania, and Africa. *Biometrika*, 9: 366–380.

MARSHALL, H. 1947. Longevity of the American herring gull. *Auk*, 64: 188–198.

MONTEROSSO, B. 1930. Studi cirripedologici, VI. Sul comportamento di "Chthamalus stellatus" in diverse condizioni sperimentali. *Atti. R. Accad. Naz. Lincei Rend., Ser. 6, Cl. Sci. Fis. Mat. Nat.*, 11 (5): 501–505.

MOORE, H. B. 1934. The biology of *Balanus balanoides*. I. Growth rate and its relation to size, season, and tidal level. *J. Mar. Biol. Ass.*, n. s., 19: 851–868.

Moore, H. B. 1935. A comparison of the biology of *Echinus esculentus* in different habitats. Part II. *J. Mar. Biol. Ass.*, n. s., 20: 109–128.

——, and J. A. Kitching. 1939. The biology of *Chthamalus stellatus* (Poli). *J. Mar. Biol. Ass.*, n. s., 23: 521–541.

Murie, A. 1944. *The wolves of Mount McKinley.* (Fauna of the National Parks of the U. S., Fauna Series No. 5, xx + 238 pp.) U. S. Dept. Int., Nat. Park Service, Washington.

Nice, M. M. 1937. Studies on the life history of the song sparrow. Vol. I. A population study of the song sparrow. *Trans. Linn. Soc. N. Y.*, 4: vi + 247 pp.

Paynter, R. A. (*in press*). The fate of Kent Island herring gulls. *Bird-Banding,* (in press).

Pearl, R. 1940. *Introduction to medical biometry and statistics.* 3rd ed. xv + 537 pp. W. B. Saunders, Philadelphia and London.

——. 1946. *Man the animal.* 128 pp. Principia Press, Bloomington.

——, and J. R. Miner. 1935. Experimental studies on the duration of life. XIV. The comparative mortality of certain lower organisms. *Quart. Rev. Biol.*, 10: 60–79.

——, ——, and S. L. Parker. 1927. Experimental studies on the duration of life. XI. Density of population and life duration in *Drosophila*. *Amer. Nat.*, 61: 289–318.

——, T. Park, and J. R. Miner. 1941. Experimental studies on the duration of life. XVI. Life tables for the flour beetle *Tribolium confusum* Duval. *Amer. Nat.*, 75: 5–19.

Pratt, D. M. 1943. Analysis of population development in *Daphnia* at different temperatures. *Biol. Bull.*, 85: 116–140.

Raitt, D. S. 1939. The rate of mortality of the haddock of the North Sea stock. *Cons. Perm. Intern. Explor. Mer, Rapp. Proc.-Verb.*, 110 (6): 65–79.

Ricker, W. E. 1940. Relation of "catch per unit effort" to abundance and rate of exploitation. *J. Fish. Res. Bd. Canada,* 5: 43–70.

——. 1944. Further notes on fishing mortality and effort. *Copeia,* 1944: 23–44.

——. 1945. Natural mortality among Indiana bluegill sunfish. *Ecology* 26: 111–121.

Runnström, S. 1925. Zur Biologie und Entwicklung von *Balanus balanoides* (Linné). *Bergens Mus. Aarbok* 1924–25, *Naturvid. Raekke,* (5). 46 pp.

Russell, E. S. 1942. *The overfishing problem.* viii + 130 pp. Cambridge Univ. Press, Cambridge.

Sette, O. E. 1943. Biology of the Atlantic mackerel (*Scomber scombrus*) of North America. Part I: Early life history, including the growth, drift, and mortality of the egg and larval populations. *U. S. Fish Wildl. Serv. Fish. Bull.*, 50 (38): 147–237.

Thompson, W. F., and F. H. Bell. 1934. Biological statistics of the Pacific halibut fishery. (2) Effect of changes in intensity upon total yield and yield per unit of gear. *Rep. Intern. Fish. Comm.*, 8: 49 pp.

Trenerry, C. F. 1926. *The origin and early history of insurance, including the contract of bottomry.* xiv + 330 pp. P. S. King & Son, London.

Wheeler, J. F. G. 1934. On the stock of whales at South Georgia. *Discov. Rep.*, 9: 351–372.

THE INTRINSIC RATE OF NATURAL INCREASE OF AN INSECT POPULATION

By L. C. BIRCH*, *Zoology Department, University of Sydney*

CONTENTS

1. INTRODUCTION

The intrinsic rate of increase is a basic parameter which an ecologist may wish to establish for an insect population. We define it as the rate of increase per head under specified physical conditions, in an unlimited environment where the effects of increasing density do not need to be considered. The growth of such a population is by definition exponential. Many authors, including Malthus and Darwin, have been concerned with this and related concepts, but there has been no general agreement in recent times on definitions. Chapman (1931) referred to it as 'biotic potential', and although he does state in one place that biotic potential should in some way combine fecundity rate, sex ratio and survival rate, he never precisely defined this expression. Stanley (1946) discussed a somewhat similar concept which he called the 'environmental index'. This gives a measure of the relative suitability of different environments, but it does not give the actual rate of increase of the insect under these different conditions. An index for the possible rate of increase under different physical conditions would at the same time provide a measure of the relative suitability of different environments. Birch (1945*c*) attempted to provide this in an index combining the total number of eggs laid, the survival rate of immature stages, the rate of development and the sex ratio. This was done when the author was unaware of the relevance of cognate studies in human demography. A sounder approach to insect populations based on demographic procedures is now suggested in this paper. The development of this branch of population mathematics is principally due to A. J. Lotka. From the point of view of the biologist, convenient summaries of his fundamental contributions to this subject will be found in Lotka (1925, Chapter 9; 1939 and 1945). A numerical example of the application of Lotka's methods in the case of a human population will be found in Dublin & Lotka (1925). The parameter which Lotka has developed for human populations, and which he has variously called the 'true' or 'inherent' or 'intrinsic' rate of natural increase, has obvious application to populations of animals besides the human species. The first determination of the intrinsic rate of increase of an animal other than man was made by Leslie & Ranson (1940). They calculated the 'true rate of natural increase' of the vole, *Microtus agrestis*, from age-specific rates of fecundity and mortality determined under laboratory conditions. With the use of matrices Leslie has extended these methods and, as an example, calculated the true rate of natural increase of the brown rat, *Rattus norvegicus* (Leslie, 1945). The author is much indebted to Mr Leslie for having drawn his attention to the possible application of actuarial procedures to insect populations. He has been completely dependent upon him for the methods of calculation used in this paper.

Before proceeding to discuss the reasons for the particular terminology adopted in this paper, it is necessary first to consider the true nature of the parameter with which we are concerned.

* This investigation was carried out at the Bureau of Animal Population, Oxford University, during the tenure of an overseas senior research scholarship from the Australian Science & Industry Endowment Fund.

2. BIOLOGICAL SIGNIFICANCE OF THE INTRINSIC RATE OF NATURAL INCREASE

The intrinsic rate of increase is best defined as the constant 'r' in the differential equation for population increase in an unlimited environment,

$$dN/dt = rN,$$

or in the integrated form $N_t = N_0 e^{rt}$,

where N_0 = number of animals at time zero,
N_t = number of animals at time t,
r = infinitesimal rate of increase.

The exponent r is the difference between the birth-rate (b) and the death-rate (d) in the population ($r = b - d$). In some circumstances it may be more useful to know the finite rate of increase, i.e. the number of times the population multiplies in a unit of time. Thus, in a population which is increasing exponentially, if there are N_t individuals at time t then in one unit of time later the ratio

$$\frac{N_{t+1}}{N_t} = e^r$$
$$= \text{antilog}_e\, r = \lambda.$$

Hence the finite rate of increase (λ) is the natural antilogarithm of the intrinsic (infinitesimal) rate of increase.

Any statement about the rate of increase of a population is incomplete without reference to the age distribution of that population, unless every female in it happens to be producing offspring at the same rate at all ages, and at the same time is exposed to a chance of dying which is the same at all ages. In such an inconceivable population the age of the individuals obviously has no significance. In practice, a population has a certain age schedule both of fecundity and of mortality. Now a population with *constant* age schedules of fecundity and mortality, which is multiplying in an unlimited environment, will gradually assume a fixed age distribution known as the stable age distribution' (Lotka, 1925, p. 110). When this age distribution is established the population will increase at a rate $dN/dt = rN$. Thus the parameter r refers to a population with a stable age distribution. The consideration of rates of increase in terms of the stable age distribution was one of the most important advances in vital statistics. In any other sort of population the rate of increase varies with time until a stable age distribution is assumed. There is, for example, no simple answer to the question: what is the rate of increase of x newly emerged adult insects in an unlimited environment? The rate will vary with time as immature stages are produced until the population has a stable age distribution. The rate of increase in the first generation might be given, but that is a figure of limited value. On the other hand, the maximum rate that it can ever maintain over an indefinite period of time is given by the rate of increase in a population of stable age distribution. That rate is therefore the true intrinsic capacity of the organism to increase. Thompson (1931) rejected the use of the exponential formula in the study of insect populations in preference for a method of dealing with the rate of increase as a 'discontinuous phenomenon'. His paper should be consulted for the reasons why he considers a single index unsatisfactory in relation to the particular problems with which he was concerned.

If the 'biotic potential' of Chapman is to be given quantitative expression in a single index, the parameter r would seem to be the best measure to adopt, since it gives the intrinsic capacity of the animal to increase in an unlimited environment.* But neither 'biotic potential' nor 'true rate of natural increase' can be regarded as satisfactory descriptive titles. The word 'potential' has physical connotations which are not particularly appropriate when applied to organisms. There is a sense in which it might be better used with reference to the environment rather than the organism. Contrary to what it seems to imply, the 'true rate of natural increase' does not describe the actual rate of increase of a population at a particular point in time, unless the age distribution of that population happens to be stable. But it does define the intrinsic capacity of that population, with its given regime of fecundity and mortality, to increase. This point is clearly made by Dublin & Lotka (1925). More recently, Lotka (1945) has dropped the use of 'true rate of natural increase' for the more precise 'intrinsic rate of natural increase'. It would seem desirable that students of populations should adopt the same terminology, irrespective of the animals concerned, and as 'intrinsic rate of natural increase' is more truly descriptive of the parameter r than other alternatives, its use is adopted in this paper.

The intrinsic rate of increase of a population may be calculated from the age-specific fecundity† and survival rates observed under defined environmental conditions. For poikilothermic animals these rates vary with physical factors of the environment such as temperature and humidity. Furthermore, within any

* For a discussion of the relative merits of this and other parameters in human demography reference should be made to Lotka (1945).

† Fecundity rate is used to denote the rate at which eggs are laid by a female. Some eggs laid are infertile and so do not hatch. The percentage 'infertility' is included in the mortality rate of the egg stage. It is usual amongst entomologists to denote the percentage of fertile eggs as the 'fertility rate'. Demographers, on the other hand, use 'fertility rate' to denote the rate of live births. Since 'fertility rate' has this other usage in entomology the term 'fecundity rate' is used throughout this paper as synonymous with the 'fertility rate' of the demographers.

given combination of physical factors, the fecundity and survival rates will vary with the density of the animals. Hence it is possible to calculate an array of values of r at different densities. But particular significance attaches to the value of r when the fecundity and survival rates are maximal, i.e. when density is optimal, for this gives the maximum possible rate of increase *within* the defined physical conditions. *Between* the whole array of physical conditions in which the animal can survive there is a zone where fecundity and survival rates are greatest and where, therefore, the intrinsic rate of increase will be greatest too. The zone within which the intrinsic rate of increase is a maximum may be referred to as the optimum zone. This is an arbitrary use of the word optimum and it does not imply that it is always to the advantage of the animal to increase at the maximum possible rate. The maximum intrinsic rate of increase under given physical conditions has importance from two points of view. It has a theoretical value, since it is the parameter which necessarily enters many equations in population mathematics (cf. Lotka, 1925; Volterra, 1931; Gause, 1934; Crombie, 1945). It also has practical significance. The range of temperature and moisture within which the insect can multiply is defined most precisely by that range within which the parameter exceeds zero. This will define the maximum possible range. In nature the range of physical conditions within which the species may be found to multiply may be less, since it is possible that effects of density and interspecific competition may reduce this range, and also the range of the optimum zone. These considerations are, however, beyond the scope of this paper; some discussion of them will be found in a review paper by Crombie (1947).

There are some important differences in the orientation with which the demographer and the student of insect populations face their problems. In human populations the parameter r varies in different civilizations and at different times in one civilization, depending upon customs, sanitation and other factors which alter mortality and fecundity rates. The maximum possible value of r does not enter into most demographic studies. In a population which is growing logistically the initial rate of increase is theoretically the maximum intrinsic rate of increase, and this latter value can be determined indirectly by calculating the appropriate logistic curve. Lotka (1927) has done this for a human population and so arrived at an estimate of a physiological maximum for man. This has theoretical interest only. In insect populations, on the other hand, the maximum value for the intrinsic rate of increase does assume considerable theoretical and practical significance, as has already been pointed out. The entomologist can readily determine the maximum values and this is his obvious starting-point. But the determination of r at different stages in the population history of an insect, whether in an experimental population or in the field, offers many practical difficulties which have not yet been surmounted for any single species. The values which the entomologist has difficulty in determining are those which are most readily obtained for human populations. The crude birth-rates and crude death-rates of the population at specific stages in its history are precisely those indices with which the demographer works. His census data provides him with the actual age distribution which is something not known empirically for a single insect species. He can have a knowledge of age distribution even at intercensal periods, and under civilized conditions he can also determine the age-specific rates of fecundity and mortality which were in operation during any particular year. In insect populations this is at present impossible; one can only keep a number of individuals under specified conditions and determine their age-specific rates of fecundity and survival, and from these data r can be calculated.

The fact that populations in nature may not realize the maximum value of their intrinsic rate of natural increase, does not negate the utility of this parameter either from a theoretical or a practical point of view. Having determined this parameter, the next logical step is to find out the extent to which this rate of increase is realized in nature. It is conceivable that some species, such as those which infest stored wheat or flour, may increase exponentially when liberated in vast quantities of these foodstuffs. This would imply that the insects could move out of the area in which they were multiplying with sufficient speed to escape density effects and that they had no gregarious tendencies. An exponential rate of increase may also occur in temperate climates in some plant-feeding species which only multiply in a short period of the year in the spring. In seasons with abundant plant growth the insect population may be far from approaching any limitation in the resources of the environment before the onset of summer retards the rate of increase. The population counts of *Thrips imaginis* in some favourable seasons in South Australia suggest such a picture (Davidson & Andrewartha, 1948).

3. CALCULATION OF THE INTRINSIC RATE OF NATURAL INCREASE

(*a*) *Experimental data required*

The calculation of r is based on the female population; the primary data required being as follows:

(1) The female life table giving the probability at birth of being alive at age x. This is usually designated l_x ($l_0 = 1$).

(2) The age-specific fecundity table giving the

mean number of female offspring produced in a unit of time by a female aged x. This is designated m_x.

In the calculation of the stable age distribution the age-specific survival rates (l_x) of both the immature stages and the reproductive stages are required. For the calculation of r the life table of the adult and only the total survival of the immature stages (irrespective of age) are needed. In practice, the age-specific fecundity rates m_x will be established for some convenient interval of age, such as a week. If N eggs are laid per female alive between the ages x to $x+1$ in the unit of time chosen, then m_x simply equals $\frac{1}{2}N$ when sex ratio is unity. It is assumed that this value occurs at the mid-point of the age group.

A numerical example is worked out for the rice weevil *Calandra* (*Sitophilus*) *oryzae* (L.) living under optimum conditions (29° C. in wheat of 14% moisture content). Data for the rates of development and survival of the immature stages, and the age-specific fecundity rates were obtained from Birch (1945*a*, *b*). The life table of adult females has not been determined experimentally, only the mean length of adult life being known. However, an estimate was obtained for purposes of these calculations by adapting the known life table of *Tribolium confusum* Duval (Pearl, Park & Miner, 1941) to *Calandra oryzae*, making the necessary reduction in the time scale. Since the mean length of life of *Tribolium confusum* in this life table was 198 days and the mean length of life of *Calandra oryzae* at 29° was 84 days, one '*Calandra* day' has been taken as equivalent to 2·35 '*Tribolium* days'. To this extent the example worked out is artificial, but, for reasons which will become evident later in the paper, it is unlikely that the error so introduced in the estimate of r is of much significance.

Before proceeding to outline direct methods of estimating r two other parameters must first be mentioned: the net reproduction rate and the mean length of a generation.

(*b*) *The net reproduction rate*

This is the rate of multiplication in one generation (Lotka, 1945) and is best expressed as the ratio of total female births in two successive generations. This we shall call R_0 and so follow the symbolism of the demographers. R_0 is determined from age-specific fecundity and survival rates and is defined as

$$R_0 = \int_0^\infty l_x m_x \, dx,$$

where l_x and m_x are as already defined.

The method of calculating R_0 is set out in Table 1. The values of l_x are taken at the mid-point of each age group and age is given from the time the egg is laid. Since the survival rate of the immature stages was 0·90 the life table of adults reckoned from 'birth', i.e. oviposition, was the product: l_x for adults $\times$ 0·90. Development from the egg to emergence of the adult from the grain lasts 28 days and 4·5 weeks is the mid-point of the first week of egg laying. The product $l_x m_x$ is obtained for each age group and the sum of these products $\Sigma l_x m_x$ is the value R_0. In this particular example $R_0 = 113{\cdot}6$. Thus a population of *Calandra oryzae* at 29° will multiply 113·6 times *in each generation.*

Table 1. *Showing the life table (for oviposition span) age-specific fecundity rates and the method of calculating the net reproduction rate (R_0) for* Calandra oryzae *at* 29° *in wheat of* 14% *moisture content. Sex ratio is equal*

Pivotal age in weeks (x)	(l_x)	(m_x)	($l_x m_x$)
4·5	0·87	20·0	17·400
5·5	0·83	23·0	19·090
6·5	0·81	15·0	12·150
7·5	0·80	12·5	10·000
8·5	0·79	12·5	9·875
9·5	0·77	14·0	10·780
10·5	0·74	12·5	9·250
11·5	0·66	14·5	9·570
12·5	0·59	11·0	6·490
13·5	0·52	9·5	4·940
14·5	0·45	2·5	1·125
15·5	0·36	2·5	0·900
16·5	0·29	2·5	0·800
17·5	0·25	4·0	1·000
18·5	0·19	1·0	0·190
			$R_0 = 113{\cdot}560$

The comparison of two or more populations by means of their net reproduction rates may be quite misleading unless the mean lengths of the generations are the same. Two or more populations may have the same net reproduction rate but their intrinsic rates of increase may be quite different because of different lengths of their generations. Consider, for example, the effect of moving the $l_x m_x$ column in Table 1 up or down by a unit of age, R_0 remains the same but it is obvious that the generation times are now very different. For these reasons the parameter R_0 has limited value and it must always be considered in relation to the length of the generation (T).

(*c*) *The mean length of a generation*

The relation between numbers and time in a population growing exponentially is given by

$$N_T = N_0 e^{rT}.$$

When T = the mean length of a generation, then from the definition of net reproduction rate $N_T/N_0 = R_0$, hence

$$R_0 = e^{rT},$$

and

$$T = \frac{\log_e R_0}{r}.$$

It follows that an accurate estimate of the mean length of a generation cannot be obtained until the value of r is known. For many purposes, however, an approximate estimate of T which can be calculated independently of r may be of use. Thus, although oviposition by the female is extended over a period of time, it may be considered as concentrated for each generation at one point of time, successive generations being spaced T units apart (Dublin & Lotka, 1925). For approximate purposes therefore it may be defined as

$$T=\frac{\Sigma x l_x m_x}{\Sigma l_x m_x}.$$

We may thus consider the figures for the product $l_x m_x$ given in the last column of Table 1 as a frequency distribution of which the individual items are each concentrated at the mid-point of each age group. The mean of this distribution is the approximate value of T. In this particular example

$$T=\frac{943\cdot09}{113\cdot56}=8\cdot3 \text{ weeks.}$$

If this were an accurate estimate of T we could proceed to calculate the value of r since, from the above equation relating R_0, r and T, we have

$$r=\frac{\log_e R_0}{T}$$

$$=\frac{\log_e 113\cdot56}{8\cdot30}=0\cdot57 \text{ per head per week.}$$

It will become evident in what follows that this is an underestimate of r owing to the approximate estimate of T. The procedure does, however, serve to illustrate the nature of the parameter, and in some cases where r is small it may be a sufficiently accurate means of calculation (cf. for example, Dublin & Lotka, 1925). We shall proceed in the next section to an accurate method for the calculation of r.

(*d*) *The calculation of 'r'*

A population with constant age schedules of fecundity and mortality will gradually approach a fixed form of age distribution known as the stable age distribution (p. 16). Once this is established the population increases at a rate $dN/dt=rN$ and the value of r may be calculated from the equation

$$\int_0^\infty e^{-rx} l_x m_x dx=1.$$

For the derivation of this formula reference must be made to Lotka (1925) and the bibliography therein. The usual methods of calculation may be found in Dublin & Lotka (1925, Appendix) or Lotka (1939, p. 68 *et seq.*). For high values of r, these methods may not be particularly satisfactory (Leslie & Ranson, 1940; Leslie, 1945, Appendix), and the computations, moreover, become very tedious. Some approximations to the rigorous procedures are justified in so far as the determination of the primary data which enter the above formula is of course subject to considerable error, arising from the normal variation in the organisms and conditions to which they are subjected in the experiments. It was considered that an estimate of r, calculated to the second decimal place, was sufficient in these circumstances. The following approximate method was therefore adopted. It has the merit of being both simple and fast.

As an approximation we may write

$$\Sigma e^{-rx} l_x m_x=1.$$

Here x is taken to be the mid-point of each age group and the summation is carried out over all age groups for which $m_x>0$. A number of trial values are now substituted in this equation, in each case calculating a series of values e^{-rx} and multiplying them by the appropriate $l_x m_x$ values for each age group. By graphing these trial values of r against the corresponding summation values of the left-hand side of the above expression, we may find the value of r which will make

$$\Sigma e^{-rx} l_x m_x \to 1.$$

The whole procedure is greatly simplified by the use of 4-figure tables for powers of e (e.g. Milne-Thomson & Comrie 1944, Table 9). Since these tables only give the values of $e^{\pm x}$ at intervals of 0·01 in the argument x up to $e^{\pm 6}$, it may be convenient to multiply both sides of the equation by a factor e^k in order to work with powers of e which lie in the more detailed parts of the table. Thus, in the present example, k was taken as 7:

$$e^7 \Sigma e^{-rx} l_x m_x = e^7$$

$$\Sigma e^{7-rx} l_x m_x = 1097.$$

A value of r was now sought which would make the left-hand side of this expression equal to 1097. The actual process of carrying out this simple computation is exemplified in Table 2. The summation of the expression is not carried beyond the age group centred at 13·5 because of the negligible contribution of the older age groups. It has already been mentioned that r is an infinitesimal rate of increase not to be confused with a finite rate of increase λ which equals antilog$_e$ r. In this particular example $r=0\cdot76$ and λ therefore has a value 2·14. In other words the population will multiply 2·14 times *per week*.

By reference to Table 2 it is clear that the relative weights with which the different age groups contribute to the value of r are given by the values $l_x m_x e^{7-rx}$ at each age group. It is of particular interest to observe the relation between values at successive age intervals (Table 3). The value of r is 56% accounted for by the first week of adult life. The first 2 weeks combined contribute 85% towards the final value and the first 3 weeks combined total 94%. The 13·5th week, on the other hand, contributes 0·02%. It should not be inferred that adults 13·5 weeks old are of no importance since their eggs will eventually give rise to adults in the productive age categories. The biological significance of Table 3 is that the intrinsic rate of increase is determined to a much greater extent by the rate of oviposition in the first couple of weeks of adult life than by the total number of eggs laid in the life span of the adult, even although only 27 % of the total number of eggs are laid in the first 2 weeks. With

Table 2. *Showing the method of calculating r for* Calandra oryzae *at* 29° *by trial and error substitutions in the expression* $\Sigma e^{7-rx} l_x m_x = 1097$

Pivotal age group (x)	$l_x m_x$	$r=0{\cdot}76$: $7-rx$	$r=0{\cdot}76$: e^{7-rx}	$r=0{\cdot}77$: $7-rx$	$r=0{\cdot}77$: e^{7-rx}
4·5	17·400	3·58	35·87	3·53	34·12
5·5	19·090	2·82	16·78	2·76	15·80
6·5	12·150	2·06	7·846	1·99	7·316
7·5	10·000	1·30	3·669	1·22	3·387
8·5	9·875	0·54	1·716	0·45	1·5683
9·5	10·780	−0·22	0·8025	−0·32	0·7261
10·5	9·250	−0·98	0·3753	−1·09	0·3362
11·5	9·570	−1·74	0·1755	−1·86	0·1557
12·5	6·490	−2·50	0·0821	−2·62	0·0728
13·5	4·940	−3·26	0·0384	−3·39	0·0337
$\sum_{4\cdot5}^{13\cdot5} e^{7-rx} l_x m_x =$			1108		1047

r lies between 0·76 and 0·77 and by graphical interpretation = 0·762.

Table 3. *The contribution of each age group to the value of r when* $r=0{\cdot}76$

Pivotal age group (x)	$l_x m_x e^{7-rx}$	Percentage contribution of each age group
4·5	624·1	56·33
5·5	320·3	28·91
6·5	95·3	8·60
7·5	36·7	3·31
8·5	17·0	1·53
9·5	8·7	0·78
10·5	3·5	0·32
11·5	1·7	0·15
12·5	0·5	0·05
13·5	0·2	0·02
	1108·0	100·00

each successive week, eggs laid make a lessened contribution to the value of r. In this particular case this can be expressed by stating that for each egg laid in the first week of adult life it would require 2·1 times as many in the second week to make the same contribution to the value of r, $(2{\cdot}1)^2$ in the third week and $(2{\cdot}1)^{n-1}$ in the nth week. The ratio 2·1 : 1 is the ratio between successive weighting values e^{7-rx} (per egg) in Table 2. The importance of the first few weeks is further intensified by the fact that egg laying is at a maximum then. From these considerations it follows that in determining oviposition rates experimentally, the rates in early adult life should be found with the greatest accuracy. Of corresponding importance is the accurate determination of the pivotal age for the first age category in which eggs are laid. In the example being cited an error of half a week causes an error of 8 % in the estimate of r.

The calculations were repeated ignoring the adult life table. The value of r was then 0·77. Since the imposition of an adult life table only makes a difference of 1 % in the value of r it is evident that the life table is of little importance in this example. This is due to the fact already noted that the major contribution to the value of r is made by adults in early life, and during early adult life survival rate is at a maximum. The life table may assume quite a different importance in a species with a different type of age schedule of fecundity or when the value of r is lower.

4. THE STABLE AGE DISTRIBUTION

With a knowledge of the intrinsic rate of increase and the life table it is possible to calculate the stable age distribution and the stable female birth-rate of the population. Thus if c_x is the proportion of the stable population aged between x and $x+dx$, and b is the instantaneous birth-rate

$$c_x = b e^{-rx} l_x,$$

and

$$1/b = \int_0^\infty e^{-rx} l_x dx.$$

For the usual methods of computation reference should be made again to Dublin & Lotka (1925). Mr Leslie has, however, pointed out to me another method of calculation which saves much of the numerical integration involved in the more usual methods. At the same time it is sufficiently accurate for our present purpose. If at time t we consider a stable population consisting of N_t individuals, and if during the interval of time t to $t+1$ there are B_t female births, we may define a birth-rate

$$\beta = B_t / N_t.$$

Then if we define for the given life table (l_x) the series of values L_x by the relationship $L_x = \int_x^{x+1} l_x dx$ (the stationary or 'life table' age distribution of the actuary),* the proportion (p_x) of individuals aged between x and $x+1$ in the stable population is given by

$$p_x = \beta L_x e^{-r(x+1)},$$

$$1/\beta = \sum_{x=0}^{m} L_x e^{-r(x+1)},$$

where $x=m$ to $m+1$ is the last age group considered in the complete life table age distribution. It will be noticed that the life table (l_x values) for the complete

* For a discussion of L_x see Dublin & Lotka (1936).

age span of the species are required for the computation of p_x and β. But where r is high it will be found that for the older age groups the terms $L_x e^{-r(x+1)}$ are so small and contribute so little to the value of β that they can be neglected.

The calculations involved are quite simple and are illustrated in the following example for *Calandra oryzae* at 29° (Table 4). Actually, in the present example, instead of calculating the values of L_x, the values of l_x were taken at the mid-points of each age group. This was considered sufficiently accurate in the present instance. It should also be pointed out that whereas only the total mortality of immature stages was required in the calculation of r, the age specific mortality of the immature stages is needed

Table 4. *Calculation of the stable age distribution of* Calandra oryzae *at* 29° *when* $r=0{\cdot}76$

Age group (x)	L_x	$e^{-r(x+1)}$	$L_x e^{-r(x+1)}$	Percentage distribution $100\beta L_x e^{-r(x+1)}$	
0–	0·95	0·4677	0·4443150	54·740	95·5 % total immature stages
1–	0·90	0·2187	0·1968300	24·249	
2–	0·90	0·10228	0·0920520	11·341	
3–	0·90	0·04783	0·0430470	5·304	
4–	0·87	0·02237	0·0194619	2·398	4·5 % total adults
5–	0·83	0·01046	0·0086818	1·070	
6–	0·81	0·00489	0·0039609	0·488	
7–	0·80	0·002243	0·0017944	0·221	
8–	0·79	0·001070	0·0008453	0·104	
9–	0·77	0·000500	0·0003850	0·047	
10–	0·74	0·000239	0·0001769	0·022	
11–	0·66	0·000110	0·0000726	0·009	
12–	0·59	0·000051	0·0000301	0·004	
13–	0·52	0·000024	0·0000125	0·002	
14–	0·45	0·000011	0·0000050	0·001	
			$1/\beta=0{\cdot}8116704$	100·000	

for the calculation of the stable age distribution. In this example the total mortality of the immature stages was 10 %—and 98 % of this mortality occurred in the first week of larval life (Birch, 1945*d*). Hence the approximate value of L_x for the mid-point of the first week will be 0·95 and thereafter 0·90 for successive weeks of the larval and pupal period (column 2, Table 4). The stable age distribution is shown in the fifth column of Table 4. This column simply expresses the fourth column of figures as percentages. It is of particular interest to note the high proportion of immature stages (95·5 %) in this theoretical population. This is associated with the high value of the intrinsic rate of natural increase. It emphasizes a point of practical importance in estimating the abundance of insects such as *C. oryzae* and other pests of stored products. The number of adults found in a sample of wheat may be quite a misleading representation of the true size of the whole insect population. Methods of sampling are required which will take account of the immature stages hidden inside the grains, such, for example, as the 'carbon dioxide index' developed by Howe & Oxley (1944). The nature of this stable age distribution has a bearing on another practical problem. It provides further evidence to that developed from a practical approach (Birch, 1946) as to how it is possible for *C. oryzae* to cause heating in vast bulks of wheat, when only a small density of adult insects is observed. It is not an unreasonable supposition that the initial rate of increase of insects in bulks of wheat may approach the maximum intrinsic rate of increase and therefore that the age distribution may approach the stable form. Nothing, however, is known about the actual age distribution in nature at this stage of an infestation.

5. THE INSTANTANEOUS BIRTH-RATE AND DEATH-RATE

We have already defined a birth-rate β by the expression

$$1/\beta = \sum_{x=0}^{m} L_x e^{-r(x+1)}.$$

This is not, however, the same as the instantaneous birth-rate (b) where $r=b-d$. In personal communications Mr Leslie has provided me with the following relationship between these two birth-rates.

$$b=\frac{r\beta}{e^r-1}.$$

Thus, in the example for *C. oryzae*, we have $1/\beta=0{\cdot}81167$ (Table 4), $r=0{\cdot}76$ and thus $b=0{\cdot}82$ and the difference between r and b is the instantaneous death-rate (d) $=0{\cdot}06$.

The instantaneous birth-rate and death-rate are widely used by students of human populations. The insect ecologist is more likely to find greater use for the finite rate of increase λ (natural antilog$_e$).

6. THE EFFECT OF TEMPERATURE ON 'r'

As an illustration of the way in which the value of r varies with temperature and the corresponding changes in rate of development, survival and fecundity, an estimate of r for *C. oryzae* has been made for two temperatures (23° and 33·5° C.) on either side of the optimum (29°). The span of adult life at 23° is about the same as at the optimum 29° and so the same life table has been applied. Even although the egg laying is more evenly distributed throughout adult life the life table makes little difference to the value of r. Furthermore, the first 2 weeks of adult life carry a weight of 59 % of the total weight of all age groups in the determination of the value of r. For every egg laid in the first week of adult life it would require 1·5 times as many eggs in the second week to make the same contribution to the value of r, and 2·3 times as many eggs in the third week to have the same effect. The relative weight of each week decreases less with successive weeks at 23° than at 29°. This is associated with the lower oviposition rates and the longer duration of the immature stages at 23°.

At 33·5° egg laying ceases after the fourth week of adult life, the mortality of adults during these 4 weeks is not high and so the estimate of r obtained without a life table may not be very different from the true value.

Table 5. *Showing the values of* l_x, m_x *and the estimate of* r *for* Calandra oryzae *at* 23° *and* 33·5°

23°			33·5°		
Pivotal age in weeks (x)	l_x	m_x	Pivotal age in weeks (x)	l_x	m_x
0·5 … 6·5 Immature stages	0·90	—	0·5 … 8·5 Immature stages	0·25	—
7·5	0·87	9·0	9·5	0·25	6·0
8·5	0·83	11·0	10·5	0·25	3·5
9·5	0·81	11·5	11·5	0·25	3·0
10·5	0·80	12·0	12·5	0·25	1·0
11·5	0·79	11·5			
12·5	0·77	13·0	r=0·12 per head per week		
13·5	0·74	11·5			
14·5	0·66	11·0			
15·5	0·60	10·0			
16·5	0·52	11·0			
17·5	0·45	12·5			
18·5	0·36	10·5			
19·5	0·29	11·5			
20·5	0·25	4·0			
21·5	0·19	2·0			

With adult life table r=0·43 per head per week.
Without adult life table r=0·44 ,, ,,

7. DISCUSSION

In order for a species to survive in a particular environment it may need to have evolved a certain minimum value for its intrinsic rate of natural increase. If its rate of increase is less than this it may succumb in the struggle for existence. It does not necessarily follow that the higher the intrinsic rate of increase the more successful will the species be. Evolution may operate to select species with an intrinsic rate of increase which is both large enough to enable them to compete successfully with other species and small enough to prevent a rate of multiplication which would exhaust the food supply in the environment. Whatever is the minimum necessary value of 'r' it could be attained along more than one route, since r has a number of component variables; the length of development of the immature stages, the survival rate of the immature stages, the adult life table and the age-specific fecundity schedule. These components enter into the value of r with various weights, and it is suggested in the discussion which follows that a knowledge of their relative contributions may provide a clue to the significance of the life patterns characteristic of different species. There is clearly a pattern in the seasonal environment too, which must be considered at the same time. A hot dry period, for example, may necessitate a prolonged egg stage. In an environment which has relatively uniform physical conditions all the year round, these complicating factors are at a minimum, e.g. a tropical forest or the micro-environment of a stack of wheat.

(1) Consider first the length of the immature stages (non-reproductive period) in relation to the span of egg laying and the age schedule of fecundity. The earlier an egg is laid in the life of the insect the greater is the contribution of that particular egg to the value of r. In illustration we may consider the age schedule of fecundity for *C. oryzae* at 29°. Since over 95% of the value of r is determined by the eggs laid in the first 4 weeks of adult life (Table 3) we can, for purposes of illustration, ignore the remaining period.

At 29° the immature stages of *C. oryzae* last 4 weeks and the maximum rate of egg laying is 46 eggs per week (Table 1). Now the same value of r (0·76) is given in a number of imaginary life cycles by reducing the length of the immature stages along with a reduction in the rate of egg laying and alternatively by increasing both the length of the immature stages and the number of eggs laid (ordinary figures, Table 6). In Table 6 the age schedule of fecundity is kept proportionate in each case. In the extreme examples if the immature stages could develop in a week, an oviposition maximum of 5 eggs per week would give the same rate of increase as the imaginary insect which took 6 weeks to develop and had an oviposition maximum of 204 eggs per week. The imaginary life cycles have been calculated from the ratio (2·1:1) for successive weighting values (e^{7-rx}) in Table 2.

The question might now be asked, what determines the particular combination which the species happens to possess? In the specific example in question, if the larva took 6 weeks to develop the adult would need to lay 200 eggs per week. But it now becomes necessary to consider the behaviour pattern, for *C. oryzae* bores a hole in the grain of wheat for every egg which is laid. The whole process of boring and egg laying occupies about 1 hr. per egg. So that with this particular mode of behaviour 24 eggs per day would be an absolute maximum. There must of course also be some physiological limit to egg production. For a larger insect the physiological limit might be less restrictive provided that the size of the egg does not increase proportionately with the size of the insect. In considering this possibility, ecological considerations are important, for *C. oryzae* is adapted to complete its development within a grain of wheat and a size limit is set by the length of the grain. There is, in fact, a strain which is found in maize kernels in Australia and this is considerably larger than the so-called 'small strain' (Birch, 1944). Furthermore, the larger insect would probably require a longer time to complete development (which is actually the relationship observed between the small and large strains) and this would operate to reduce the value of *r*. In considering the possibilities in the opposite direction, there is obviously a limit below which the length of development could not be reduced any further. A species of smaller size could doubtless develop in a shorter time and on this merit might be a more successful mutation. But the question then arises whether a smaller species could command muscles and mandibles of sufficient strength to chew whole grain. Grain-feeding species of beetles which are smaller than *C. oryzae* are in fact scavengers rather than feeders on sound grain. Thus it would seem that a balance is struck somewhere between the minimum time necessary for development and the maximum possible rate of egg laying, and this is conditioned by the behaviour pattern of the insect and the particular ecology of its environment.

For a maximum value of *r* the optimum age schedule of fecundity is one which has an early maximum. In an imaginary schedule for *C. oryzae* a concentration of 71 eggs in the first week of egg laying would give the same value of *r* (0·76) as 141 eggs distributed over 4 weeks.

Age schedule of fecundity of Calandra oryzae *at 29°*

Weeks	1	2	3	4	Total
Actual	40	46	30	25	141
Imaginary	71	0	0	0	71

The relative advantage of this type of fecundity schedule is less, the smaller the value of *r*. At 23° the value of *r* for *C. oryzae* is 0·43 and the eggs laid in the first week of adult life are worth $(1{\cdot}5)^{n-1}$ eggs in the *n*th week (compare this with the value of $(2{\cdot}1)^{n-1}$ when $r=0{\cdot}76$). The actual oviposition time curve at 23° has no distinct peak as at 29° (Tables 1 and 5).

There is a wide variation in the nature of the age schedule of fecundity amongst different species of insects with perhaps the tsetse fly and the lucerne flea illustrating contrasting extremes. Whereas tsetse flies (*Glossina*) deposit single larvae spaced at intervals of time, the 'lucerne flea' (*Smynthurus viridis*) deposits its eggs in one or two batches of as many as 120 at a time (Maclagan, 1932). The particular advantage of this mode of oviposition must be tremendous, and is probably responsible in part for the great abundance of this collembolan and possibly other members of the same order, which, as a whole, are among the most abundant insects in nature. This is of course speculative and much more information is required before any generalizations can be made. Another interesting category are the social insects, since only one female of the population (in termites and the hive-bee) or a few (in social wasps) are reproductives. A theoretical consideration of the relative merits of one queen and many queens might throw more light on the evolution of these systems, especially as they relate to differences in behaviour.

The relation between the length of the pre-reproductive stages and the nature of the age-fecundity schedule is in part dependent upon the nature of the seasonal changes in the environment. Life histories may be timed so that the reproductive and feeding stages coincide with the least hostile season of the year. Diapause, aestivation and hibernation are some of the adaptations which ensure this. They have particular significance too in determining the age distribution of the initial population in the reproductive

Table 6. *Showing the actual relation between the length of the immature stages and the age schedule of fecundity for* Calandra oryzae *at 29° (black figures) and some theoretical possibilities which would give the same intrinsic rate of increase (r=0·76). The length of the immature stages is shown in the left of the table; figures in the body of the table are number of eggs per week*

	Pivotal age in weeks									
0·5	1·5	2·5	3·5	4·5	5·5	6·5	7·5	8·5	9·5	Total
1 week	4	5	3	3	—	—	—	—	—	15
2 weeks		9	10	7	6	—	—	—	—	32
3 weeks			19	22	14	12	—	—	—	67
4 weeks				**40**	**46**	**30**	**25**	—	—	**141**
5 weeks					84	97	63	53	—	297
6 weeks						117	204	132	111	564

season. Consideration of this is left to a later section of the discussion.

(2) For the calculation of the maximum intrinsic rate of increase the life table of the species from deposition of the egg (or larva) to the end of egg-laying life in the adult must be known. The starting-point of this life table is thus the stage which corresponds to the point of 'birth'. Deevey (1947) has noted that the point of universal biological equivalence for animals is doubtless fertilization of the ovum. But, from the point of view of the number of animals in the population and for purposes of calculating r, a knowledge of pre-birth mortality is not required. For the calculation of r the life table beyond the end of reproductive life has no significance, but a knowledge of age-specific post-reproductive survival until the point of death is needed, on the other hand, for the calculation of the stable age distribution and the instantaneous birth-rate. This is evident from a consideration of the method of calculation shown in Table 4. The post-reproductive life assumes negligible significance in this particular example, but its importance in such calculations increases as r approaches a value of zero.

The relative importance of the survival pattern (i.e. the shape of the l_x curve) in determining the value of r is itself a function of r. When r is small its value may be dependent to a significant extent on the oviposition in late adult life, when it is large it is mostly determined by the oviposition rates of adults in early adult life. When the intrinsic rate of increase is high and the life table of the adult follows the typical diagonal pattern (e.g. Pearl *et al.* 1941) with no high mortality in early adult life, consideration of the adult life table is of little importance in calculating r. This is because survival rate is high in the ages which contribute most to the value of r. In species which have a low intrinsic rate of increase the life table may assume more significance in determining the value of that rate of increase. More data are required before the importance of this point can be established. The pattern of survival which gives a maximum value of r has its maxima in the pre-reproductive and early reproductive stages. A knowledge of total survival of the immature stages is of course essential in all cases. More attention might well be given by entomologists to securing life table data than has been given in the past. Without it no true picture of the intrinsic rate of increase can be obtained.

(3) There remains to be considered the age distribution of the population in relation to its capacity to increase in numbers. In a population in an unlimited environment the stable age distribution is the only one which gives an unvarying value of r. For this reason the stable age distribution is the only sound basis on which to make comparisons between different values for rates of increase (whether between different species or one species under different physical conditions). The actual age distribution of a population in nature may be quite different and its consideration is of importance in determining the initial advantage one form of distribution has over another. In an unlimited environment these initial differences in age composition are eventually ironed out. A population which initiates from a number of adults at the peak age of egg laying clearly has a higher initial rate of increase than one which starts from the same number in all different stages of development.

These considerations may be of most importance in temperate climates where there is a definite seasonal occurrence of active stages. The stage in which the insect overwinters or oversummers will determine the age distribution of the population which initiates the seasonal increase in the spring or in the autumn (whichever the case may be). The pea weevil, *Bruchus pisorum*, in California hibernates as an adult. With the first warm days in the spring the adults leave their overwintering quarters under bark and fly into the pea fields (Brindley, Chamberlin & Hinman, 1946). Following a meal of pollen they commence oviposition on the pea crops. This mode of initiating the spring population would be far more effective than one which started with the same number of insects in the egg stage. The overwintering adults begin their reproductive life at a much later age than the adults in the next generation. It would be of interest to know whether the age schedule of fecundity (taking the commencement of egg laying as zero age) is the same for both generations. This is a point which does not appear to have been investigated for insects which hibernate as adults. It is clearly of much importance in determining the intrinsic rate of increase of successive generations.

Overwintering as pupae must theoretically rank as the second most effective age distribution for initiating spring increase. Many species which overwinter as pupae would have a higher mortality if they overwintered as adults. The corn-ear worm, *Heliothis armigera*, for example, can hardly be conceived as overwintering as an adult moth in the North American corn belt. In the northern part of this belt even the pupae which are protected in the soil are unable to survive the winter. Recolonization evidently takes place each year from the warmer south (Haseman, 1931).

Overwintering in the egg stage (in hibernation or in diapause) is common in insects. Here again it is difficult to imagine the other stages of these orders as successfully hibernating. The grasshopper, *Austroicetes cruciata* (Andrewartha, 1944), and the majority of aphids are examples of this. A minority of aphid species are, however, able to overwinter as apterae by finding protection in leaf axils and similar niches (Theobald, 1926), some others are enabled to survive as adults by virtue of their symbiosis with ants (Cutright, 1925). The relatively vulnerable aphids find protection in the nests of ants. The ants not only carry them to their nests, but feed them during the winter months and with the return of spring plant them out on trees again!

Overwintering as nymphs or larvae is a rarer phenomenon except with species which can feed and grow at low temperatures and so are not hibernators. The active stages of the lucerne flea, *Smynthurus viridis*, for example, can be found in the winter in Australia (Davidson, 1934). The seasonal cycle of the reproducing population commences with the first rains in autumn; this population being initiated with oversummering eggs. The eggs are the only stage which are resistant to the dryness and high temperatures of the summer months. Species of insects with hardy adult stages like the weevil, *Otiorrhynchus cribricollis* (Andrewartha, 1933), aestivate as adults. An interesting case of a butterfly, *Melitaea phaeton*, aestivating as a quarter-grown larva at the base of its food plant is described by Hovanitz (1941).

The preceding examples illustrate how the age distributions of initiating populations vary in seasonal species. This depends on the nature of the overwintering or oversummering stage. The particular stage may have been selected in nature not only by virtue of its resistance to unfavourable physical conditions but also in relation to its merits in initiating rapid establishment of a population in the spring and autumn. The calculation of the initial and subsequent rates of increase of populations with these different types of age distribution is considerably more complicated than the calculation of intrinsic rates of increase for populations with stable age distributions. This problem is not dealt with in this paper and the reader is referred to Leslie (1945, p. 207 *et seq.*) for an outline of the principles involved in such calculations.

The length of the developmental stages, the age schedule of fecundity, the life table of the species and the age distribution of initiating populations present a pattern which has adaptive significance for the species. The analytic study of the intrinsic rate of increase of a species (as exemplified by *Calandra oryzae*) may throw light on the evolutionary significance of the life pattern of different species. Such a study must necessarily be related to the behaviour pattern of the insect and the type of environment it lives in. Nor can the importance of effects of density and competition be overlooked. These are, of course, studies in themselves beyond the scope of this paper.

8. SUMMARY

The parameter known as the intrinsic rate of natural increase, which was developed for demographic analyses by A. J. Lotka, is introduced as a useful concept for the study of insect populations. It is suggested that for the sake of uniformity of terminology in population biology and for precision of definition, that the term 'intrinsic rate of natural increase' might be considered more appropriate than an alternative term 'biotic-potential' which is more frequently used in relation to insect populations. The intrinsic rate of natural increase is defined as the exponent 'r' in the exponential equation for population increase in an unlimited environment. The rate of increase of such a population is given by $dN/dt = rN$. The parameter r refers to the rate of increase of a population with a certain fixed age distribution known as the stable age distribution. Both the intrinsic rate of natural increase and the stable age distribution may be calculated from the age-specific survival rates (life table) and age-specific fecundity rates. The methods of calculation are exemplified with data for the rice weevil, *Calandra oryzae* (L.), and some adapted from the flour beetle, *Tribolium confusum* Duval. It is shown in this example that the intrinsic rate of natural increase is determined to a much greater extent by the rate of oviposition in the first 2 weeks of adult life than by the total number of eggs laid in the entire life time. The oviposition rates in the first 2 weeks account for 85% of the value of r whereas only 27% of the total number of eggs are laid in that time. With each successive week in the life of the adult, eggs laid make a lessened contribution to the value of r. The methods of calculation of r provide a means of determining the extent to which the various components—the life table, the fecundity table and the length of the pre-reproductive stages—enter into the value of r. It is suggested that analyses of this sort may provide a clue to the life patterns characteristic of different species.

The importance of the age distribution of populations which initiate seasonal increase in the autumn and spring is discussed. These age distributions depend on the nature of the overwintering or oversummering stage. It is suggested that this particular stage, whether it be adult, larva, pupa or egg, has been selected by virtue not only of its resistance to the unfavourable season, but also in relation to its merits in initiating rapid establishment of a population in the succeeding season.

It is shown how the value of r for *Calandra oryzae* varies with temperature. Four other parameters are also defined: the net reproduction rate, the mean length of a generation, the infinitesimal birth-rate and the infinitesimal death-rate. The methods of calculation of these parameters are also exemplified with data for *C. oryzae*.

9. ACKNOWLEDGEMENTS

Grateful acknowledgement is made to the Director of the Bureau of Animal Population, Oxford University, Mr C. S. Elton, for the facilities of the Bureau which were placed at the author's disposal during his term there as a visiting worker. Mr Elton provided much encouragement during the investigation. It is a pleasure to acknowledge too the inspiration and help of Mr P. H. Leslie of the Bureau of Animal Population. His direction was indispensable in all mathematical and actuarial aspects of the paper and his critical examination of the manuscript was much to its advantage.

REFERENCES

Andrewartha, H. G. (1933). 'The bionomics of *Otiorrhynchus cribricollis* Gyll.' Bull. Ent. Res. 24: 373–84.

Andrewartha, H. G. (1944). 'The distribution of plagues of *Austroicetes cruciata* Sauss. (Acrididae) in relation to climate, vegetation and soil.' Trans. Roy. Soc. S. Aust. 68: 315–26.

Birch, L. C. (1944). 'Two strains of *Calandra oryzae* L. (Coleoptera).' Aust. J. Exp. Biol. Med. Sci. 22: 271–5.

Birch, L. C. (1945*a*). 'The influence of temperature on the development of the different stages of *Calandra oryzae* L. and *Rhizopertha dominica* Fab. (Coleoptera).' Aust. J. Exp. Biol. Med. Sci. 23: 29–35.

Birch, L. C. (1945*b*). 'The influence of temperature, humidity and density on the oviposition of the small strain of *Calandra oryzae* L. and *Rhizopertha dominica* Fab.' Aust. J. Exp. Biol. Med. Sci. 23: 197–203.

Birch, L. C. (1945*c*). 'The biotic potential of the small strain of *Calandra oryzae* and *Rhizopertha dominica*.' J. Anim. Ecol. 2: 125–7.

Birch, L. C. (1945*d*). 'The mortality of the immature stages of *Calandra oryzae* L. (small strain) and *Rhizopertha dominica* Fab. in wheat of different moisture contents.' Aust. J. Exp. Biol. Med. Sci. 23: 141–5.

Birch, L. C. (1946). 'The heating of wheat stored in bulk in Australia.' J. Aust. Inst. Agric. Sci. 12: 27–31.

Brindley, T. A., Chamberlin, J. C. & Hinman, F. G. (1946). 'The pea weevil and methods for its control.' U.S. Dept. Agric. Farmers' Bull. 1971: 1–24.

Chapman, R. N. (1931). 'Animal ecology with especial reference to insects.' New York.

Crombie, A. C. (1945). 'On competition between different species of graminivorous insects.' Proc. Roy. Soc. B, 132: 362–95.

Crombie, A. C. (1947). 'Interspecific competition.' J. Anim. Ecol. 16: 44–73.

Cutright, C. R. (1925). 'Subterranean aphids of Ohio.' Ohio Agric. Exp. Sta. Bull. 387: 175–238.

Davidson, J. (1934). 'The "lucerne flea" *Smynthurus viridis* L. (Collembola) in Australia.' Bull. Coun. Sci. Industr. Res. Aust. 79: 1–66.

Davidson, J. & Andrewartha, H. G. (1948). 'Annual trends in a natural population of *Thrips imaginis* Bagnall (Thysanoptera).' (In the Press.)

Deevey, E. S. (1947). 'Life tables for natural populations of animals.' Biometrics, 3: 59–60.

Dublin, L. I. & Lotka, A. J. (1925). 'On the true rate of natural increase as exemplified by the population of the United States, 1920.' J. Amer. Statist. Ass. 20: 305–39.

Dublin, L. I. & Lotka, A. J. (1936). 'Length of life.' New York.

Gause, G. F. (1934). 'The struggle for existence.' Baltimore.

Haseman, L. (1931). 'Outbreak of corn earworm in Missouri.' J. Econ. Ent. 24: 649–50.

Hovanitz, W. (1941). 'The selective value of aestivation and hibernation in a Californian butterfly.' Bull. Brooklyn Ent. Soc. 36: 133–6.

Howe, R. W. & Oxley, T. A. (1944). 'The use of carbon dioxide production as a measure of infestation of grain by insects.' Bull. Ent. Res. 35: 11–22.

Leslie, P. H. (1945). 'On the use of matrices in certain population mathematics.' Biometrika, 33: 183–212.

Leslie, P. H. & Ranson, R. M. (1940). 'The mortality, fertility and rate of natural increase of the vole (*Microtus agrestis*) as observed in the laboratory.' J. Anim. Ecol. 9: 27–52.

Lotka, A. J. (1925). 'Elements of physical biology.' Baltimore.

Lotka, A. J. (1927). 'The size of American families in the eighteenth century and the significance of the empirical constants in the Pearl-Reed law of population growth.' J. Amer. Statist. Ass. 22: 154–70.

Lotka, A. J. (1939). 'Théorie analytique des associations biologiques. Deuxième Partie. Analyse démographique avec application particulière à l'espèce humaine.' Actualités Sci. Industr. 780: 1–149.

Lotka, A. J. (1945). 'Population analysis as a chapter in the mathematical theory of evolution.' In LeGros Clark, W. E. & Medawar, P. B., 'Essays on Growth and Form', 355–85. Oxford.

Maclagan, D. S. (1932). 'An ecological study of the "lucerne flea" (*Smynthurus viridis*, Linn.)–I.' Bull. Ent. Res. 23: 101–90.

Pearl, R., Park, T. & Miner, J. R. (1941). 'Experimental studies on the duration of life. XVI. Life tables for the flour beetle *Tribolium confusum* Duval.' Amer. Nat. 75: 5–19.

Stanley, J. (1946). 'The environmental index, a new parameter as applied to *Tribolium*.' Ecology, 27: 303–14.

Theobald, F. V. (1926). 'The plant lice or the Aphididae of Great Britain.' Vol. 1. Ashford.

Thompson, W. R. (1931). 'On the reproduction of organisms with overlapping generations.' Bull. Ent. Res. 22: 147–72.

Thomson, L. M. Milne- & Comrie, L. J. (1944). 'Standard four-figure mathematical tables.' London.

Volterra, V. (1931). 'Leçons sur la théorie mathématique de la lutte pour la vie.' Paris.

STUDIES OF THE POPULATION DYNAMICS OF THE SALAMANDER GENUS *DESMOGNATHUS* IN VIRGINIA

JAMES A. ORGAN
Department of Zoology, University of Michigan, Ann Arbor, Michigan

INTRODUCTION

Natural selection operates through differential survival within a species and through net survival between species. Previous work, particularly on the plethodontid salamander genus *Desmognathus,* has indicated some of the directions of evolution within this group of amphibians (Dunn 1926, Noble 1927, and others). For the most part, these studies have demonstrated evolutionary trends by following morphological characters and the modifications thereof, through a series of closely related species.

Populations, on the other hand, are characterized by certain parameters such as birth rates and age-specific mortality rates. There is reason to suspect that these parameters are no less susceptible to natural selection than are the anatomical and physiological characteristics of the organism. Yet evidence for the direction of evolution, in terms of changes in the population structure of several closely related species of a genus, has not been previously presented by vertebrate population ecologists.

The objectives of the present study were threefold: 1) to determine the local distribution, habitat selection, and seasonal changes therein for every plethodontid species occurring within a given area; 2) to determine the population structures and their dynamics for several species of a single genus; and 3) to study the effect of the ecology of the species on its population structure.

Salamanders of the family Plethodontidae are highly suitable for studies of comparative ecology. The species are well known taxonomically and can be identified in the field. Several species of one genus can often be found in the same area and may be collected in sufficient numbers for quantitative study (Hairston 1949).

Previous experience in the southern Appalachian Mountains indicated that the Balsam Mountains of southwestern Virginia were suitable for studies of salamanders at the population level. The region is accessible and the salamander fauna is rich in species with high population densities. The following species occur in the Mount Rogers-Whitetop Mountain area of the Balsams: *Pseudotriton ruber nitidus, Pseudotriton porphyriticus ssp., Eurycea bislineata wilderae, Desmognathus quadramaculatus, Desmognathus monticola monticola, Desmognathus fuscus fuscus, Desmognathus ochrophaeus carolinensis, Desmognathus wrighti, Leurognathus marmorata marmorata, Plethodon yonahlossee, Plethodon glutinosus glutinosus, Plethodon jordani metcalfi, Plethodon welleri ventromaculatus, Plethodon cinereus cinereus, Plethodon richmondi ssp.* (Hereafter, in this report, nominate subspecies will be designated by the binomial form of the name.)

In the course of the present study, 12,000 salamanders were collected, preserved, and subsequently dissected. The local distribution and ecology of all plethodontid species in the area were studied but the resulting mass of information was too extensive to include in one paper; the present report is restricted to the five species of *Desmognathus.* Approximately 7000 specimens of *Desmognathus* were taken during the summer of 1957 and the summer, fall, and spring of 1958-59. None of the five species of the genus, occurring in the study area, is represented by less than 1000 individuals in the collection.

Editor's Note: Sections of this paper not immediately relevant to an analysis of the population dynamics have been omitted. From the section of life histories, Figures 3, 4, and 5 and Table 6 are reproduced because they help clarify the later sections that treat age at transformation, age at sexual maturity, and fecundity of the species.

Reproduced and excerpted with permission from Ecological Monographs, 31: 189, 190, 197-199, 202, 204-220 (only), 1961. Published by The Duke University Press, Durham, North Carolina.

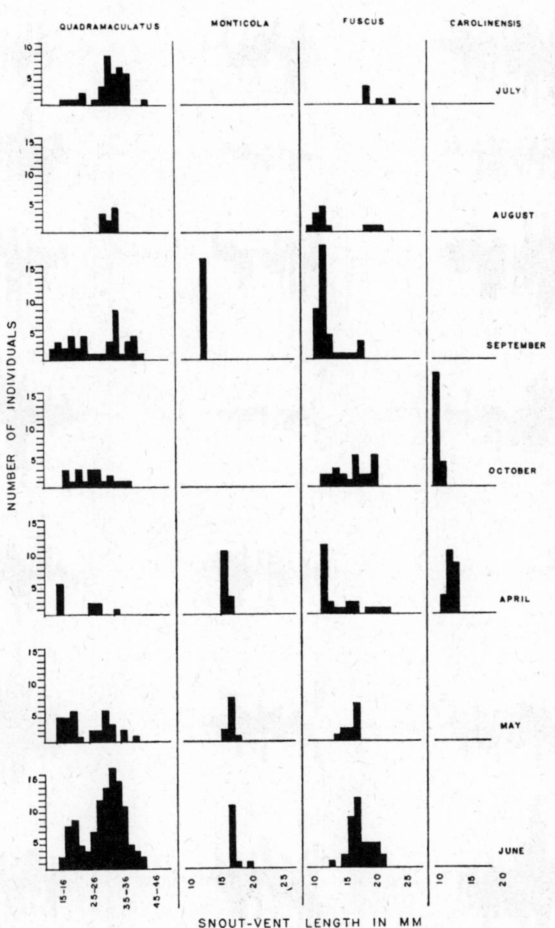

FIG. 3. Monthly size-frequency histograms of larval individuals of four species of *Desmognathus*. The larvae of *D. quadramaculatus* are plotted at intervals of two millimeters but the larvae of the other three species are plotted at intervals of one millimeter. The snout to vent length is the measurement taken from the tip of the snout to the posterior angle of the vent.

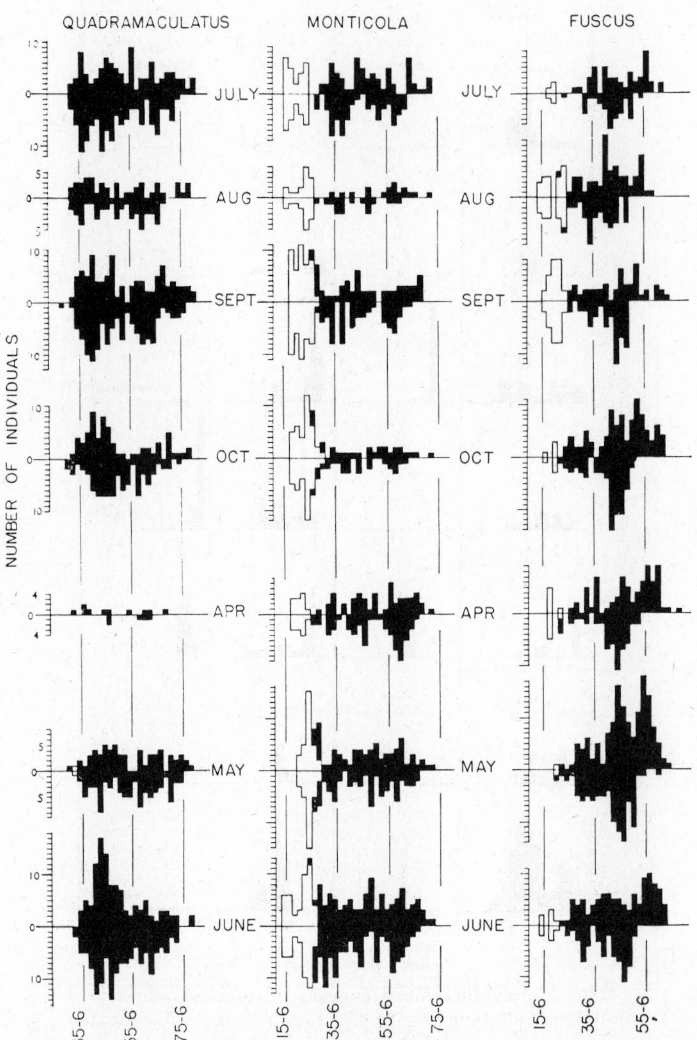

Fig. 4. Monthly size-frequency histograms of transformed individuals of three species of *Desmognathus*. Black squares above each line are males and black squares below each line are females. White squares above each line are the total unsexed individuals and these have been repeated below each line. The vertical guide lines between each histogram are extensions of the sizes indicated at the bottom of the figure. The measurements from the tip of the snout to the posterior angle of the vent are plotted at intervals of two millimeters.

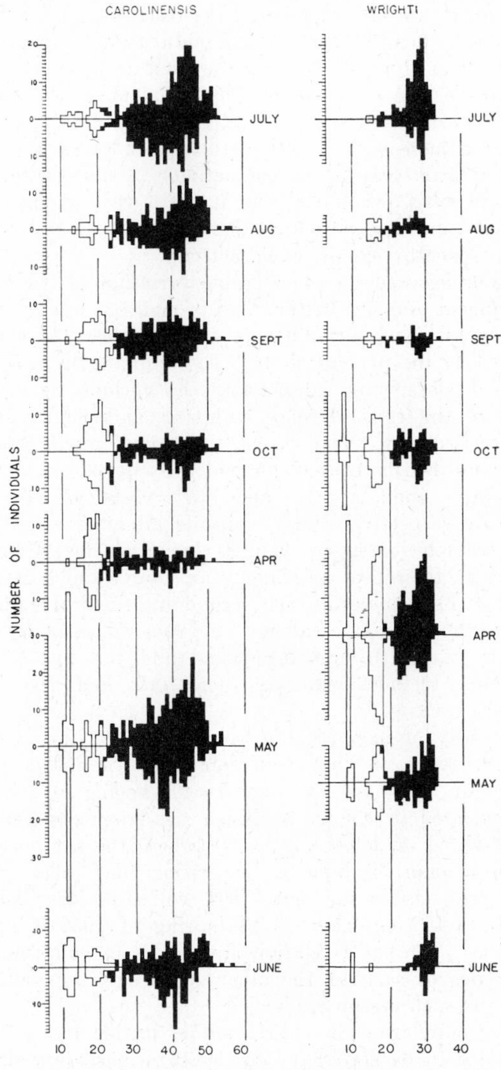

FIG. 5. Monthly size-frequency histograms of transformed individuals of two species of *Desmognathus.* Black squares above each line are males and black squares below each line are females. White squares above each line are the total unsexed individuals and these have been repeated below each line. The vertical guide lines between each histogram are extensions of the sizes indicated at the bottom of the figure. The measurements from the tip of the snout to the posterior angle of the vent are plotted at intervals of one millimeter.

TABLE 6. Egg masses of *Desmognathus* found in the field. The mean clutch size for each species is: *D. quadramaculatus,* 31; *D. monticola,* 27; *D. fuscus,* 23; *D. o. carolinensis,* 10; and *D. wrighti,* 6. Abbreviations as in Table 1.

Species	Date Collected	Stage When Collected	Date Hatched in Captivity	Number of Eggs in Mass
D.q.	22 June 1959	Unsegmented		23
	"	Tail fold		41
	"	"		21
	"	"		23
	"	Early embryo		31
	"	"		43
	"	"		35
D.m.	16 June 1959	Unsegmented		17
	"	"		27
	"	"		17
	22 June 1959	"		36
	"	"		22
	"	"		38
	"	"		29
	"	Early cleavage		29
	15 July 1958	Early embryo		39
	4 Sept. 1958	Hatching	4 Sept.	16
D.f.	19 June 1959	Unsegmented		26
	25 June 1959	"		28
	26 June 1959	"		21
	2 July 1957	Early embryo		26
	10 July 1957	"		28
	"	"	6 Aug.	5
	10 July 1958	"		33
	18 Aug. 1958	Pigmented embryo	27 Sept.	22
	"	Late embryo	5 Sept.	17
D.o.c.	14 June 1959	Being deposited		10
	14 Aug. 1958	Early embryo		9
	"	"		14
	16 Oct. 1958	Late embryo		16
	"	"		9
	"	"	20-21 Oct.	8
	"	"	"	11
	"	"	25 Oct.	3
D.w.	16 Oct. 1958	Late embryo		3
	"	"		8
	"	"	19-20 Oct.	6
	"	"	21 Oct.	8
	"	"	22-23 Oct.	7
	"	"	24-26 Oct.	8

POPULATION DYNAMICS

Deevey (1947) stressed the importance of life table information and particularly of survivorship information in the study of natural populations. In dealing with stationary populations, if one plots the logarithm of the number of individuals in each year class against their age, a survivorship curve is obtained which is characteristic of the population in the environment from which the population was taken.

In referring to theoretical types of survivorship curves, based on the earlier work of Pearl & Minor (1935), Deevey (1947: 286) states:

"Type I, the *negatively skew rectangular,* is shown

by members of a cohort which, having been born at the same time, die more or less simultaneously after a life span which is presumably characteristic of the species. Type II is *diagonal* (when the logarithm of the number of survivors is plotted against age), implying a constant mortality rate for all age groups, or no one age as a favored time of dying. Type III, the *positively skew rectangular,* shows extremely heavy mortality beginning early in life, but the few individuals which survive to advanced ages have a relatively high expectation of further life." Furthermore, Deevey was able to calculate the survivorship curves and life tables for several natural populations from information in the literature.

Size-frequency histograms have been used extensively in herpetological literature to determine the number of year classes present in a given sample. For some groups of Amphibia, this is a successful method of determining the structure of a stationary population. Bannikov was able to determine the population structure of the European Fire-belly Toad, *Bombina bombina* (1950) and of the salamander, *Ranodon sibiricus* (1949) by means of size-frequency data based on large samples taken during a short time interval in the field. Even in these studies, however, it was impossible to determine the number of age groups contained within the size class representing sexually mature adults.

In studies of plethodontid salamanders, size-frequency information is valuable in determining the number of year classes prior to maturity but the adult year classes merge together on a size-frequency histogram. The data presented by Pope & Pope (1949, 1951) and Pope (1950) for three species of the salamender genus *Plethodon* show a considerable number of adults compared with the number of young specimens collected. Some of this discrepancy between the small number of young and the large number of adults collected is doubtlessly the result of being able to find the adults more easily in the field. Much of it, however, is due to a "piling up" of adult year classes on a size-frequency histogram.

The progressive merging of the year classes of *Desmognathus* is striking in the monthly size-frequency histograms based on the collections from the Balsam Mountains (Figs. 3, 4, 5). Since size-frequency information is useless in determining the population structure of adult plethodontid salamanders, some method of separating the year classes contained within the adult sample is needed. For *Desmognathus,* such a method has been available since 1922 but it has never been applied in the study of the structure of salamander populations.

Humphrey (1922) clearly established the relationship between the age of mature males of *Desmognathus fuscus* and the number of lobes on the testes. The smaller, younger males have one lobe on each testis and the larger, older males have 2-5 lobes on each testis with a direct relationship between the number of lobes per testis and the size of the male. Humphrey was able to assign an absolute time interval between the formation of successive lobes of the testis, stating: "In short, the second lobe on the testis of a multiple testis may possibly come to full maturity only after an interval of three years from the time its territory on the testis first matured sex cells—that is, in the animal's third season of sexual activity." (op. cit., p. 56). Thus, a male with 2 full mature lobes per testis is in its third year of sexual activity, a male with 3 mature lobes per testis is in its fifth year of sexual activity, and a male with 4 mature lobes per testis is in its seventh year of sexual activity.

Humphrey found considerable variation in the development and size of the lobes in males at any given season and this variability in size of lobes was confirmed by the present study. To eliminate the necessity of classifying subjectively the various sizes of lobes on the testis, all lobes, both large and small, were counted equally. The second, third, and fourth lobes are known to be present but not fully developed during the second, fourth, and sixth years of sexual activity respectively. By counting all lobes equally, the one-lobe category includes immature males and males in their first breeding year, the two-lobe category includes males in their second and third breeding years, the three-lobe category includes males in their fourth and fifth breeding years, and the four-lobe category includes males in their sixth and seventh breeding years.

By way of example, the relationship of the lobes of the testis to the size-frequency distribution of males of *D. monticola,* taken in the spring of 1959, is indicated in Figure 6. Each size-frequency category based on *lobes per testis* (where the sample is large enough) is bimodal suggesting that there are two year classes in each. The collection of males of *D. monticola* taken in the spring of 1959 is not unique. The same relationship occurs in collections of males of each of the other species of the genus and for each season studied.

The populations of *Desmognathus* in this area were assumed to be stationary, i.e. neither increasing nor decreasing in number. This also assumes that the number of young entering the populations each year is a constant. For many amphibians this assumption would be invalid. For example, in the *Rana p. pretiosa* population studied by Turner (1960), the number of young entering the population fluctuates considerably from year to year. This is due primarily to the instability of the sites utilised by the species for reproductive purposes. In some years, the ponds containing eggs and larvae dry-up completely before the young transform thereby destroying virtually all members of a year class. In other years, the ponds retain water and many, if not most, of the eggs produce transformed young.

In the salamander genus *Desmognathus,* however, the nest sites are located beneath the beds and/or banks of streams and springs below the ground seepage level. These sites provide a relatively non-fluctuating environment, in terms of temperature and moisture. Moreover, some benefit to the eggs probably accrues from the presence of the attending (guarding?) female. It is therefore reasonable to assume

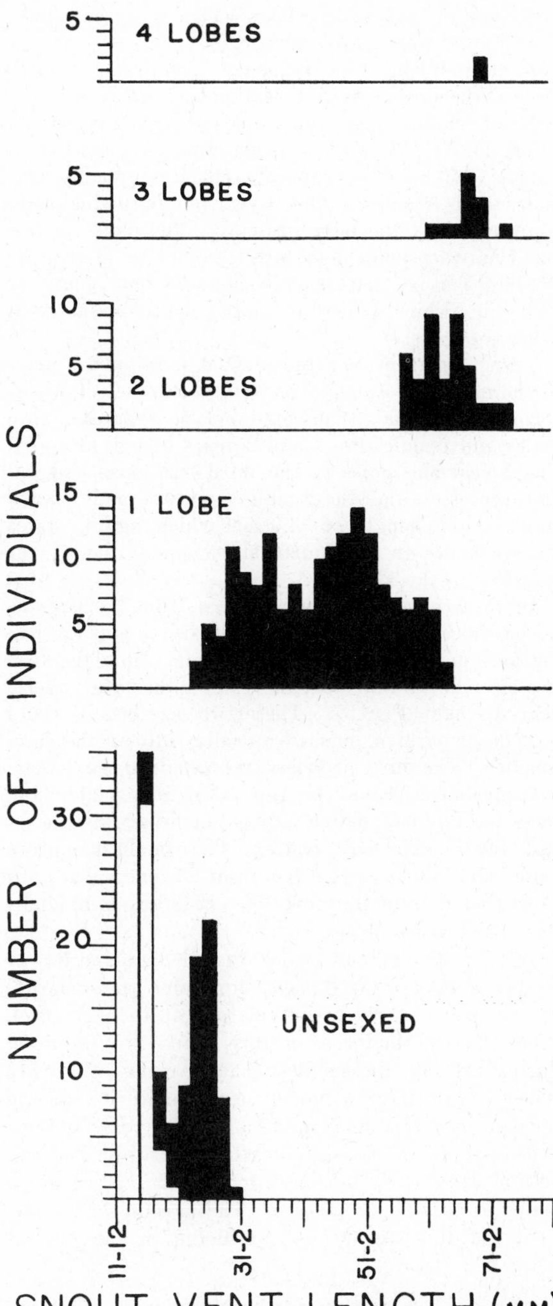

FIG. 6. Relationship of snout-vent length to the number of lobes per testis based on the Spring 1959 collection of males of *D. monticola*. White squares represent larvae and black squares represent transformed individuals.

that egg mortality, resulting from environmental fluctuation (particularly temperature and moisture) is not only relatively constant but also low from year to year in the study area.

AGE AT TRANSFORMATION

Field studies of the reproduction of the five species of *Desmognathus* in the Balsams indicated variation in the egg-laying and hatching periods for each species. All five species, however, have essentially the same reproductive cycle, depositing their eggs in the late spring. Hatching takes place in the late summer and early fall.

In order to express "age" throughout this paper with some degree of consistency, all five species are assumed to lay their eggs during the month of June and the age of the salamanders will be taken from the time at which the eggs are deposited. Thus, a one year old salamander is not one that hatched one year previously but one that entered the population as an egg one year previously.

The larvae of *D. quadramaculatus* are found in the field throughout the year (Fig. 3). Since the age of the individuals is taken from June, the two size classes of larvae of this species that are present in June are 1 and 2 years of age. Recently transformed individuals were collected in August, September, and October (Fig. 4). Transformation in this species, therefore, takes place between the ages of 26 and 28 months.

The larvae of *D. monticola* are found in the field from September through June and form a single size class on a size-frequency histogram (Fig. 3). Recently transformed individuals were taken in June and July (Fig. 4). The smallest group of transformed individuals in June and July have approximately the same snout to vent length as the larvae in June and transformation must occur when the larvae are 12-13 months of age.

In the Balsam Mountains, the observed variation in hatching time for *D. fuscus* was greater than for any other species in the genus. This variation in hatching time is reflected in the size-frequency histograms for the larvae of this species (Fig. 3). The range in larval size is greater than in *D. monticola* but in none of the monthly collections did *D. fuscus* show two distinct size classes of larvae. Recently transformed individuals were taken in July, August, September, and October (Fig. 4) which, again, is a reflection of the variation in hatching time. It is assumed that the larvae represented in the histogram for the month of June (Fig. 3) are 1 year of age and that transformation in *D. fuscus* takes place between the ages of 13 and 16 months. The larval period for this species, therefore, is shorter than that for *D. quadramaculatus* but longer than that for *D. monticola.*

The larvae of *D. o. carolinensis* are found from October through April (Fig. 3) and form a single size class on the monthly size-frequency histograms. Recently transformed individuals were collected in April and May (Fig. 5) and were approximately the same size as the larvae in April. Thus, transformation takes place in *D. o. carolinensis* between the ages of 10 and 11 months.

The five species of *Desmognathus* in the present study have a progressive reduction of the length of the larval period which correlates roughly with the habitat occupied by the species. *D. quadramaculatus,* the most aquatic species in the genus, has the longest larval period, transforming at 26-28 months of age. *D. fuscus,* a stream bank species, transforms at 13-

16 months and *D. monticola,* also a stream bank species, transforms at 12-13 months. *D. o. carolinensis,* which is more terrestrial than *D. quadramaculatus, D. monticola,* and *D. fuscus,* transforms at 10-11 months and finally, *D. wrighti,* the most terrestrial species in the genus, transforms within the egg capsules prior to hatching and has no free-living larval stage.

Age of Males at Maturity

Humphrey (1922) demonstrated by histological studies of the testes of *D. fuscus* that the spermatogenetic wave in this genus results in the formation and release of mature spermatozoa in the fall. Since males, maturing for the first time, are in a transition stage between immaturity and maturity, it is difficult to determine macroscopically whether a particular individual is immature or mature. The use of collections obtained in the fall to determine the age at maturity was further complicated by the fact that some individuals of *D. quadramaculatus* and *D. fuscus* were still transforming from larval to adult stages. In *D. quadramaculatus,* particularly, the size classes merge together on a size-frequency histogram at the age of transformation and there was no clear distinction between individuals that transformed during the previous year and those that transformed during the current year.

The age of males at maturity, therefore, has been based on the spring collections. The distinction between immature and mature males was made more easily in the spring because the mature males had enlarged lobes on the testes and the vasa deferentia were packed with sperm. The single lobe on each testis of immature males was small and the vasa deferentia were neither enlarged nor packed with sperm. Moreover, transformation did not occur in *D. quadramaculatus* during the spring and the largest size-group of larvae were clearly one year younger than the smallest size-group of transformed individuals.

In June, the larvae of *D. quadramaculatus* (Fig. 3) were 1 and 2 years old. Since transformation occurred prior to the age of 3, the smallest transformed individuals in June were 3 years of age (Fig. 4). These 3-year-old individuals could be separated into males and females. The males had one immature lobe on each testis and the smallest mature male had a snout to vent length of 55.0 mm. This places the mature males in the next size group, representing individuals 4 years of age.

Since *D. monticola* transformed during the month of June, the smallest size-group on the size frequency histogram for transformed specimens of this species collected in June (Fig. 4) represents individuals that are 1 year of age. The individuals in this size group and in the next size group, which represents individuals that are 2 years of age, could not be separated into males and females. The third group, individuals that are 3 years of age, could be separated macroscopically into males and females. The males at 3 years of age had small, immature testes. The smallest mature male had a snout to vent length of 47.0 mm and is in the fourth size class which represents individuals that are 4 years of age.

In the spring size-frequency histograms for *D. fuscus,* the larvae were 1 year old (Fig. 3) and the smallest transformed individuals were 2 years old (Fig. 4). As in *D. monticola,* the 2-year-old individuals could not be separated macroscopically into males and females. The 3-year-old individuals are represented by the next size class. The males in this size class had small, immature testes (Fig. 4) and the smallest mature male had a snout to vent length of 41.0 mm, which places it in the next size class at 4 years of age.

Transformation occurred in *D. o. carolinensis* prior to the month of June. The two size classes of transformed individuals that could not be separated into males and females are 1 and 2 years of age (Fig. 5). The 3-year-old males in the third size class had immature testes and the smallest mature male had a snout to vent length of 34.0 mm which, again, places mature males in the fourth size class at the age of 4 years.

In *D. wrighti* the young emerge from the eggs as transformed salamanders. In the size-frequency histograms of this species for May and June the first two size classes represent individuals that are 1 and 2 years of age (Fig. 5). These two size classes could not be separated macroscopically into males and females. The third size class, representing the 3 year-old specimens, could be separated into males and females (Fig. 5). Three year old males of this species had small, immature testes. The smallest mature male had a snout to vent length of 25 mm which indicates that it is in the next size class, i.e., individuals that are 4 years of age.

In the spring, the males of all five species of *Desmognathus* in the Balsam Mountains are immature at the age of 3 years but mature at the age of 4. Since the spermatozoa in this genus are produced during the fall, the smallest mature males of all five species must have attained sexual maturity during the pervious fall at approximately 3.5 years of age.

The size of the species, length of larval period, and habitat apparently have no effect on the age at which males of this genus mature. The age of sexual maturity of the five species considered in the present study is 3.5 years.

Age of Females at Maturity

Females with small ova and lacking the large convoluted oviducts characteristic of spent individuals were assumed to be immature. The collection was divided into a summer (July and August, 1957 and 1958), a fall (September and October, 1958), and a spring (April, May, and June, 1959) collection. The total number of immature females was tested against the total number of males with one lobe per testis by the Chi Square method for each species and for each of the seasons studied. The 0.05 level was selected for acceptance of the null hypothesis that the sex ratio was 1:1. The results were such that the null hypothesis could be accepted at better than the 0.05 level and rejected at the 0.01 level.

Of the fifteen samples thus tested, only four failed to show a 1:1 sex ratio between immature females and males with one lobe per testis (Table 7). With the exception of *D. fuscus,* every species had a 1:1 sex ratio between these females and males for at least two out of the three seasons tested. The immature females, therefore, are considered to be equal in number to the males with one lobe per testis.

TABLE 7. Chi Square Tests of the ratio of immature females to males with one lobe per testis. The null hypothesis is that the sex ratio is one to one. The data were such that this was accepted at better than the 0.05 level and rejected at the 0.01 level (**). Abbreviations as in Table 1.

Species	Season	Number of Males With One Lobe	Number of Immature Females	Chi Square
D.q.	Sm	106	134	3.26
	Fl	126	174	7.68**
	Sp	146	170	1.82
D.m.	Sm	56	72	2.0
	Fl	60	61	0.008
	Sp	164	182	0.936
D.f.	Sm	89	51	10.3**
	Fl	81	86	1.498
	Sp	221	156	11.26**
D.o.c.	Sm	205	215	0.238
	Fl	123	155	3.682
	Sp	264	254	0.193
D.w.	Sm	86	48	10.76**
	Fl	40	30	1.486
	Sp	146	116	3.42

The field studies failed to disclose any difference in habitat or behavior between immature females and either immature or mature males. It is unlikely, therefore, that there is a difference in mortality between the sexes prior to maturity of the females. Since the immature females, as a group, are numerically equal to the males with one lobe per testis, they must be the same age as these males. This, of course, assumes that males and females are produced in equal numbers at hatching.

In the spring males with one lobe per testis are known to be 3 and 4 years of age. The immature females must also be 3 and 4 years of age. Egg laying takes place in the spring but 4 year old females are not sufficiently developed sexually to produce eggs in the spring. Therefore, the mature females in the collection must be 5 years of age or older. Thus, the females of all five species deposit eggs for the first time when they are 5 years old. Since there is a fall as well as a spring courtship, the females probably reached maturity during the previous fall at an age of approximately 4.5 years, exactly one year later in life than the males of this genus. As in males, the size of the species, duration of larval period, and habitat apparently have no effect upon the age at which the females attain maturity.

The Breeding Cycle of Females

In the spring, prior to the beginning of the egg-laying season in June, the females in the collection fall into three distinct groups: 1) those with small, relatively uniform, colorless and/or white ova in the ovaries and with small oviducts; 2) those with large white ova in the ovaries; and 3) those with small white ova and usually with one or two large yellowish spherical bodies (retained and resorbing ova?) in the ovaries and with enlarged convoluted oviducts indicating that they are spent. The first group is composed of immature females and the last two groups are mature females.

The spent females found in the spring prior to the egg-laying season must represent the females that produced eggs during the preceding year. It is highly improbable that the ovaries of these females are capable of forming large yolked ova in time for depositing eggs during the current year. Thus, there must be a biennial breeding cycle in the females of this genus in the Balsam Mountains.

This should not be surprising when the habits of breeding females are considered. After depositing their eggs, the females remain with the eggs in the nest throughout the period of development and hatching. Since the eggs hatch in late summer and fall, the attending females have little opportunity to feed before the onset of winter when, in this area, activity is presumably reduced. From a nutritional standpoint, the spent females have little opportunity to lay down yolk in the ovaries and, at the same time, meet their basic physiological requirements.

Since there is evidence for a biennial breeding cycle in females of this genus, the eggs are presumably deposited for the first time when the females are 5 years old. At 6 years of age, the females are spent but are forming large yolked eggs in the ovaries again. At 7 years of age, the second egg clutch is deposited. At 8 years of age the females again are spent and at 9 years of age, the third clutch is deposited.

The Reliability of Partial Survivorship Curves Based on the Multiple Testis

To test the reliability of those portions of the survivorship curves for males based on the number of lobes per testis, the collection was divided into a summer, fall, and spring sample, as was indicated above in the section on the age of maturity of females. For each species and for each of the three seasons, the number of males in the 1 lobe, 2 lobe, 3 lobe, and 4 lobe categories was determined (Table 8). The number of males with one lobe per testis in each sample was converted to a sample size of 100 and the number of males with 2, 3, and 4 lobes per testis were proportionally converted to the number surviving on the basis of an initial population of 100 males with one lobe per testis. In this way, the survivorship curves for each of the species at each of the seasons studied could be directly compared on a semi-logarithmic graph for seasonal variation (Fig. 7).

In determining that part of the survivorship curve for males that is based on the number of lobes per testis, the season of the year in which the samples were taken apparently is less important than the sample size. In the collections from the Balsam Mountains, the samples of all five species taken in the spring were larger than those taken at any other season. The survivorship curves, based on the spring samples, either agree with those from at least one other season, as in *D. quadramaculatus*, *D. monticola*, and *D. wrighti* (Fig. 7), or are intermediate between two extremes based on the smaller samples, as in *D. fuscus* and *D. o. carolinensis* (Fig. 7). Moreover, the larger the sample, the greater are the chances of collecting individuals in the oldest age category (males with 4 lobes per testis). In the summer and fall samples of *D. fuscus* and *D. wrighti*, this age class was absent but in the larger samples taken in the spring both species had individuals in the 4 lobe category (Table 8). Thus, from the standpoint of sample size and the presence of all known age classes in the sample, the spring collections produced the most reliable partial survivorship curves based on the number of lobes per testis.

Method of Calculating Male Survivorship

To calculate the survivorship in any population, one must know the initial population size or the number of individuals at age 0. The number of eggs produced by the population is usually taken as the number of individuals at age 0 in a stationary population. In the case of the males of

TABLE 8. Seasonal variation in the population structure of males. See text for the method used in obtaining the number of males in the year classes 0-1 and the method used in obtaining the survivorship (l_x) of males from the samples collected in the spring. Abbreviations as in Table 1.

Species	Number of Lobes per Testis	Observed Number of Males: Summer	Fall	Spring	Age in Years (x)	Survivorship Based on the Spring Sample (l_x)
D.q.	0			720	0–1	1.000
	1	106	126	146	3–4	.203
	2	37	26	27	5–6	.0375
	3	8	9	4	7–8	.00555
	4	1	2	1	9–10	.0014
D.m.	0			768	0–1	1.000
	1	56	60	164	3–4	.214
	2	15	17	43	5–6	.C57
	3	7	7	12	7–8	.0156
	4	2	1	2	9–10	.0026
D.f.	0			742	0–1	1.000
	1	89	81	221	3–4	.298
	2	18	44	85	5–6	.114
	3	5	16	14	7–8	.019
	4			1	9–10	.00135
D.o.c.	0			750	0–1	1.000
	1	205	123	264	3–4	.352
	2	130	47	146	5–6	.195
	3	45	16	47	7–8	.063
	4	5	4	5	9–10	.0067
D.w.	0			235	0–1	1.000
	1	86	40	146	3–4	.620
	2	53	21	120	5–6	.510
	3	2	2	10	7–8	.0425
	4			1	9–10	.00425

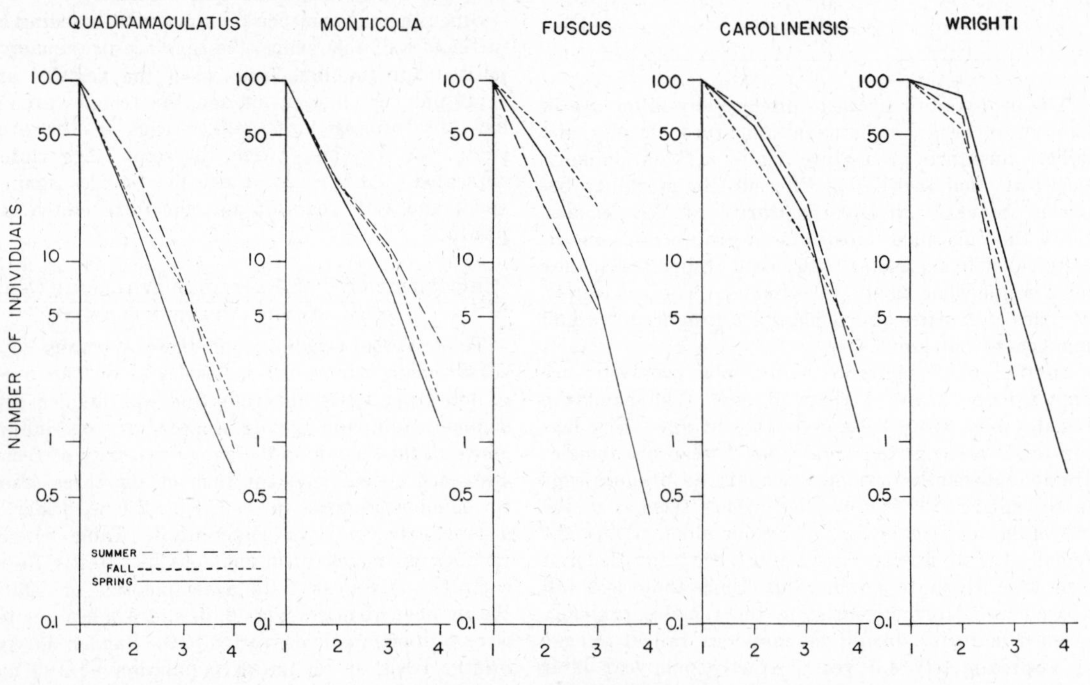

FIG. 7. Seasonal variation in partial survivorship curves based on the number of lobes per testis. The vertical axis is on a logarithmic scale and the points on the survivorship curves were calculated from the data in Table 8 by the method explained in the text.

Desmognathus, however, every point on the male survivorship curve represents not one but two year classes (Table 8). To obtain the initial point on the survivorship curve for males of each species, it is necessary to know the number of males at age 0 and the number surviving to one year of age. The starting point of the survivorship curve for each species will then be the sum of the individuals in age classes 0 and 1.

The number of male eggs produced per year is relatively easy to determine. This is the product of one half the mean clutch size times the number of females producing eggs during the current year. The mean clutch size for each species was based on the egg masses found in the field (Table 6). The number of females producing eggs during the current year is nearly impossible to determine from collections taken in the summer and fall because it is difficult to distinguish between females that were spent during the previous year and those spent during the current year unless the latter are actually taken in the nest with their eggs. In collections taken in the spring, prior to egg-laying in mid-June, it is a simple matter to distinguish between females that produced eggs during the previous year and those producing eggs during the current year. The former have spent ovaries and the latter have large ripe ovarian eggs ready for deposition. From mid-June to the end of June, all spent females taken in association with eggs in the nests were added to the number of ripe females collected in the spring and all spent females not taken in association with eggs in the field were added to the number of spent females that had produced eggs during the previous year. By this method, the total number of females in the spring sample known to be producing eggs during the current year for each species was: *D. quadramaculatus,* 30; *D. monticola,* 37; *D. fuscus,* 42; *D. o. carolinensis,* 99; and *D. wrighti,* 46 (Table 11).

Assuming a 1:1 sex ratio at this age and assuming that the one year old individuals were collected in proportion to their relative numbers in the population, the number of males surviving to the age of one year is equal to one half of the unsexed one year old specimens collected in the spring. Unfortunately, the small size and secretive habits of the larvae and of the transformed one and two year old salamanders makes the sampling error greater for these age groups than for any other (Figs. 3, 4, 5). Even if there were no mortality between the ages of one and two, which is unlikely, one would expect the number of one year old individuals to equal the number of two year old individuals. In every collection, however, the individuals one year old were fewer in number than the individuals in the two year old group. The latter were also fewer in number than had been expected. The sampling error for two year old specimens, however, appears to be less than that for the one year old specimens.

The number of males in the age groups 0 and 1 can be estimated by two methods. Twice the number of male eggs produced per year would give the number of male eggs for two successive years. This is an overestimation of the number in the year classes 0 and 1 because it assumes that there is no mortality between the ages of 0 and 1 year. The number of male eggs produced per year plus one half the number of individuals in the two year old class, collected in the spring, would give an estimation of the males in the year classes 0 and 1. This would be an underestimation because, whereas the sampling error for two year olds is less than that for one year olds, the number of two year old specimens is still deficient. Since the number of males in the age classes 0 and 1 lies somewhere between the overestimation and the underestimation, the mean of the two estimates was selected as the number in the initial population. This, admittedly, is a source of error in the calculations of survivorship and population structure for each species but it is an error that cannot be avoided.

The number of males in the year classes 0 and 1 for each species, based on the spring sample and estimated by the method indicated above, was: *D. quadramaculatus,* 720; *D. monticola,* 768; *D. fuscus,* 742; *D. o. carolinensis,* 750; and *D. wrighti,* 235 (Table 8). The estimated number of males in the year classes 0 plus one were then converted to a sample size of 1.000 and the males in the 1, 2, 3, and 4 lobe categories were proportionally converted to the number of males surviving out of an initial population of 1.000 (Table 8). For each species, this represents the survivorship column (l_x) of the male life table.

Survivorship of Males

A direct comparison of the survivorship curves for males of the five species of *Desmognathus* shows a striking trend (Fig. 8). *D. quadramaculatus* and *D. monticola* males both have curves close to the theoretical Type II curve; a straight line indicating a constant rate of survivorship for all age classes. Moreover, the curve for males of *D. monticola* is less steep than that for *D. quadramaculatus* indicating that the former has a higher rate of survival than the latter. The survivorship curves for males of *D. fuscus, D. o. carolinensis,* and *D. wrighti* respectively show a progressive shift from a Type II curve to a Type I curve. The Type I curve, it should be remembered, "is shown by members of a cohort which, having been born at the same time, die more or less simultaneously after a life span which is presumably characteristic of the species." (Deevey 1947: 286). No species of *Desmognathus* actually shows a true Type I curve, nor should it be expected to do so. Mortality in the field is not merely the result of old age but rather of accidents, predation, etc. The species of *Desmognathus,* however, show an unmistakable trend towards a Type I survivorship curve. This trend in the survivorship of the species of *Desmognathus* is analogous to the survivorship trend of man from early primitive populations to modern populations (Deevey 1950).

This range of survivorship for five closely related species of a single genus is truly remarkable but it should be remembered that the range of habitat in this genus is no less remarkable. The series: *D. quadra-*

maculatus, D. monticola, D. fuscus, D. o. carolinensis, D. wrighti is not only one of progressively greater terrestrialism but it is also one of progressive increase in survivorship through the early years of sexual maturity.

D. quadramaculatus shows little difference in habitat between the larvae and the transformed individuals. At all ages, this species is essentially aquatic and the mortality rates of the larvae and transformed individuals are similar. Since most of the specimens of this species were taken from the water of large and small streams and the slope of the survivorship curve is steep, it may be concluded that mortality is not only constant but also high in these habitats (Fig. 8).

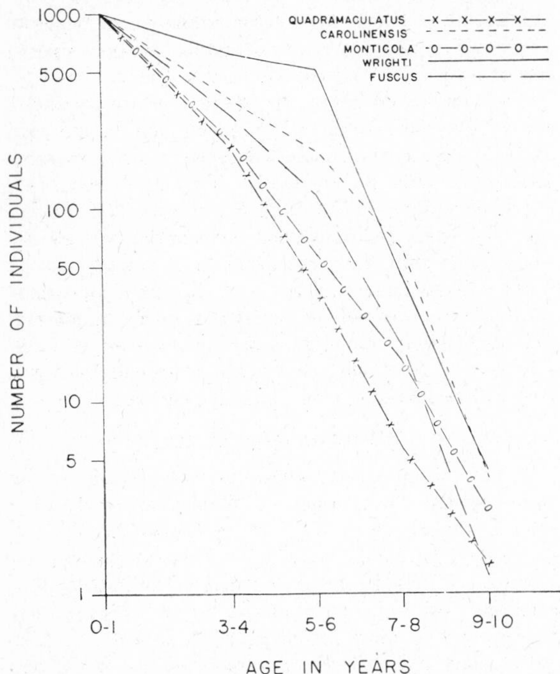

FIG. 8. Survivorship curves of males of five species of *Desmognathus.* The points on the survivorship curves were calculated from the data in the survivorship column (l_x) of Table 8 by multiplying each quantity in the column by 1000. The vertical axis is on a logarithmic scale.

In *D. monticola,* the larvae are aquatic and the transformed individuals are found in the stream banks. The larval period of this species is shorter than that of *D. quadramaculatus* but the survivorship for the early years of life for both species is essentially the same (Fig. 8). For the later years of life, at least during the early years of maturity, the slope of the survivorship curve of *D. monticola* is less steep than that of *D. quadramaculatus.* Thus, in terms of survivorship, whatever benefit accrues from a shift in habitat from stream to stream banks does not manifest itself until the salamanders have attained a certain size. The survivorship of *D. monticola* is a reflection of the survivorship in the banks of large and small streams at lower elevations since most of the specimens of this species came from these habitats. Whereas the mortality within these habitats is lower than in the habitats occupied by *D. quadramaculatus,* it is higher than the mortality in habitats occupied by *D. fuscus, D. o. carolinensis, and D. wrighti* (Fig. 8).

The larval period of *D. fuscus* is apparently longer than that of *D. monticola* and the transformed individuals are found within seepage areas and in the banks of the headwaters of streams. The mortality for the early years of life is lower for this species than for both *D. quadramaculatus* and *D. monticola* and this low rate of mortality extends into the early years of sexual maturity. Thus, the length of the larval period, in itself, does not influence survivorship but the habitat occupied by recently transformed individuals has a considerable effect on survivorship. Since most of the specimens of *D. fuscus* were taken within seepage areas and the headwaters of streams, mortality in these sites is lower than in either the streams or the banks of mountain streams (Fig. 8).

The larval period of *D. o. carolinensis* is short; transformation occurs at an age of 10-11 months. The recently transformed individuals are found in the banks of aquatic sites during the spring of the year. Shortly thereafter, during the summer, the young are found in the forest. The mortality for the young of this species is lower than that for the young of *D. quadramaculatus, D. monticola,* and *D. fuscus,* the three more aquatic species of the genus. This low rate of mortality extends into the early years of maturity for males of *D. o. carolinensis* and since most of the specimens of this species were taken in the forest, the mortality in terrestrial habitats is considerably lower than that in any of the aquatic habitats (Fig. 8).

Finally, *D. wrighti,* which has no free-living larval stage, has the lowest mortality in the early years of life of the species studied (Fig. 8). All specimens of the one-year class and many of the two-year class were found during the fall and spring in underground seepage areas but some two-year-old specimens were taken in the forest during the summer, thus indicating that the young abandon aquatic sites at an early age. As was true of *D. o. carolinensis,* the low mortality rate of the young extends into the early years of sexual maturity. If the survivorship of *Desmognathus* is directly related to terrestrialism, one would expect the most terrestrial species to show the highest survival rate. This is exactly the case. *D. wrighti,* the most terrestrial species, shows the highest rate of survival during the early years of life (Fig. 8).

In this genus, therefore, the more terrestrial the species, the greater becomes the survivorship of the individuals. The reduction of the larval period, *per se,* does not lead to increased survivorship unless the transformed individuals leave the aquatic sites. As a corollary, therefore, it may be said that the earlier the aquatic sites are abandoned, the greater the proportion of individuals attaining sexual maturity.

SURVIVORSHIP OF FEMALES

Through the use of size-frequency information and the number of lobes per testis, it has been possible to determine the survivorship of males. But what of the survivorship of females? No character comparable to the number of lobes per testis in males could be found to give the relative ages of adult females.

If the sex ratios of total females to total males were one to one for each species, it could be assumed that the survivorship of the females was similar to that of the males of their species. Spring collections indicate, however, that this ratio is not one to one for all five species (Table 9). The total sex ratio is one to one in *D. quadramaculatus* and *D. monticola* but not in *D. fuscus, D. o. carolinensis,* and *D. wrighti.* It might be valid to assume that the survivorship of *D. quadramaculatus* and *D. monticola* females was the same as that of the males but this assumption would clearly be invalid for *D. fuscus, D. o. carolinensis,* and *D. wrighti.*

TABLE 9. Chi Square Tests of the ratio of total females to total males based on the spring sample. The null hypothesis is that the sex ratio is one to one. The data were such that this was accepted at better than the 0.05 level and rejected at the 0.01 level (**). Abbreviations as in Table 1.

Species	Total Males	Total Females	Chi Square
D.q.	178	212	2.96
D.m.	221	230	0.18
D.f.	321	203	26.50**
D.o.c.	460	383	7.02**
D.w.	277	171	25.08**

In the sample from the spring, for all of the species except *D. fuscus,* the ratio of immature females to males with one lobe per testis is one to one (Table 7). When the ratio of mature females, both spent and ripe, to males with two or more lobes per testis is tested, *D. quadramaculatus* and *D. monticola* show a one to one ratio but *D. fuscus, D. o. carolinensis,* and *D. wrighti* do not (Table 10). The latter three species are all consistently deficient in mature females.

TABLE 10. Chi Square Tests of the ratio of mature females to males with two or more lobes per testis based on the spring sample. The null hypothesis is that the sex ratio is one to one. The data were such that this was accepted at better than the 0.05 level and rejected at the 0.01 level (**). Abbreviations as in Table 1.

Species	Number of Males With Two or More Lobes	Number of Mature Females	Chi Square
D.q.	32	42	1.35
D.m.	57	48	0.772
D.f.	100	47	19.1**
D.o.c.	196	129	13.8**
D.w.	131	55	31.0**

This indicates that the survivorship of the females of all five species, with the possible exception of *D. fuscus,* is similar to that of the males up to the time that the females become sexually mature. Thereafter, the survivorship of the females is not similar to that of the males of their species at the same ages. This difference is insignificant in *D. quadramaculatus* and *D. monticola* but in *D. fuscus, D. o. carolinensis,* and *D. wrighti,* the mortality of mature females is considerably higher than that of the males of their species at comparable ages. What factors, operating in the environment, would lead to the greater mortality of the mature females of *D. fuscus, D. o. carolinensis,* and *D. wrighti* than of the males of these species?

From the studies on survivorship of males of this genus, the habitat occupied by a population has been shown to have considerable influence on survivorship. The more terrestrial the population, the higher is the survivorship through the early years of maturity (Fig. 8). Do mature females occupy habitats that are different from those of males and immature individuals of both sexes?

During the late spring, summer, and early fall, the brooding females are in aquatic nesting sites with their eggs. These nests are so similar in physical conditions that brooding females of all five species may be said to have the same habitat at this time of the year.

The nesting sites, utilized by brooding females of *D. quadramaculatus* and *D. monticola* are not a great departure from the habitats occupied by the males and survivorship is similar for the two sexes. In *D. o. carolinensis* and *D. wrighti,* however, the aquatic nesting sites are a great departure from the habitats occupied by the males during the late spring, summer, and early fall inasmuch as the males of these two species are terrestrial at those times of the year. If the mortality in aquatic habitats is higher than in terrestrial habitats, any part of an otherwise terrestrial population that returns to an aquatic habitat will be subject to a higher mortality rate than the part that does not. In *D. o. carolinensis* and *D. wrighti* the brooding females, as a group, represent a part of the population that returns to an aquatic site and, as a group, they have a higher rate of mortality than that part of the population that remains terrestrial during the brooding season.

In *D. fuscus,* however, the nesting sites are not a great departure from the habitat occupied by the males of this species and yet the mature females have a higher mortality than the males. Clearly, habitat alone is insufficient to explain the higher mortality of mature females of *D. fuscus, D. o. carolinensis,* and *D. wrighti.* It should not, however, be minimized as one of the factors operating against the females.

The brooding females apparently remain in the nest with their eggs throughout the period of development and hatching. The interval between egg laying and hatching is unknown for any of the species of the genus but it must certainly be a matter of months. During this time the brooding females apparently do not forage for food but may feed on organisms entering the nest. Since hatching occurs during the late summer and fall, the females that have been brooding eggs have little opportunity to feed before the onset of winter when reduced activity or hibernation takes place. One of the results of this lack of opportunity for brooding females to feed has been a biennial reproductive cycle in the females. Another result may well be increased mortality among the females due to malnutrition.

One final consideration of the factors operating against the females is the behavior of brooding females in the nest. They do not react to danger by fleeing as readily as nonbrooding females and males. Even when the nest is completely uncovered, the brooding females remain with their eggs. Brooding females, therefore, are probably more susceptible to predation than nonbrooding adults of their species. Since the most likely predators in this area are other salamanders such as *Pseudotriton,* and the larger species of *Desmognathus,* the smaller the female, the more likely is it to be eaten by another salamander. The large size of brooding females of *D. quadramaculatus* and *D. monticola* may give them some immunity from this type of predation.

All these factors: size of the female, lack of food while brooding, hesitancy to flee from danger, and habitat occupied while brooding doubtlessly contribute to the higher mortality observed in mature females. The effect is greatest in the smaller species where the habitat occupied by brooding females is strikingly different from that of the males and nonbrooding females of the species.

No differences in behavior or habitat of nonbrooding females and males were noted in the course of the field studies. Since there is evidence for a biennial reproductive cycle in the females, mature females survive at one rate in the years that they are brooding eggs and at another rate in the years that they are not. If these two rates of survival are known, it is possible to calculate the survivorship of mature females from the number of immature females which are known to be 3 and 4 years of age.

The mean annual rate of survival of brooding females is the number of females that produced eggs during the previous year divided by the number of females producing eggs during the current year. As was indicated in the section on the method of calculating male survivorship, it is relatively easy to distinguish between these two categories of mature females in collections taken in the spring. The mean annual rates of survival of brooding females, based on the spring sample, are given in Table 11.

Since no differences were noted in the behavior and habitat of nonbrooding females and males, the mean annual rate of survival of nonbrooding females is assumed to be equal to that of males. In males of *D. fuscus, D. o. carolinensis,* and *D. wrighti,* there is considerable difference between survivorship during the early years of life and survivorship in the later years of life (Fig. 8). Therefore, it is necessary to estimate a mean rate of survival for the early years of life and another rate or the later years of life.

The best estimate of the mean rate of survival for males in their early years of life is the number of males with 2 lobes per testis divided by the number of males with 1 lobe per testis. Since the lobes are added to the testis at intervals of 2 years, this is actually a mean *biennial rate* of survival. To determine the mean *annual rate* of survival, it is necessary to take the square root of the mean biennial rate of survival (Table 12).

The best estimate of the mean rate of survival of males in their later years of life is the number of males with 3 lobes per testis divided by the number of males with 2 lobes per testis. Again, this is a mean biennial rate of survival and the mean annual rate of survival is the square root of the mean biennial rate (Table 13).

Assuming that the sex ratio is one to one at the egg stage of the life history, the number of females in age classes 0 and 1 is the same as that of the males of each species (Table 8). This number was converted to 1.000 as it was in males. The number of immature females of each species was then proportionally converted to the number of females surviving from an initial population of 1.000 in the survivorship

TABLE 11. The mean annual rates of survival for brooding females based on the spring sample. The mean annual rate of survival for brooding females is the number of females that produced eggs during the previous year divided by the number of females producing eggs during the current year. See text for the method used in determining to which category individual mature females belonged. Abbreviations as in Table 1.

Species	Females That Produced Eggs During the Previous Year	Females Producing Eggs During the Current Year	Mean Annual Rate of Survival for Brooding Females S
D.q.	12	30	.40
D.m.	11	37	.30
D.f.	5	42	.11
D.o.c.	30	99	.30
D.w.	9	46	.19

TABLE 12. The mean annual rates of survival for males and nonbrooding females in the early years of life and estimates of the mean age of immature females based on the spring sample. The mean annual rate of survival for nonbrooding females is assumed to be equal to that for males. This is the square root of the quotient of the number of males with two lobes per testis divided by the number of males with one lobe per testis. The mean age of immature females is equal to:

$$\frac{3+4S}{1+S}$$

where "S" is the mean annual rate of survival for immature females. Abbreviations as in Table 1.

Species	Number of Males With Two Lobes per Testis	Number of Males With One Lobe per Testis	Mean Biennial Rate of Survival S^2	Mean Annual Rate of Survival S	Mean Age of Immature Females in Years
D.q.	27	146	.185	.43	3.3
D.m.	43	164	.262	.51	3.3
D.f.	85	221	.385	.62	3.4
D.o.c.	146	264	.553	.74	3.4
D.w.	120	146	.823	.91	3.5

TABLE 13. The mean annual rates of survival for males and nonbrooding females in the later years of life based on the spring sample. The mean annual rate of survival for nonbrooding females is assumed to be equal to that for males. This is the square root of the quotient of the number of males with three lobes per testis divided by the number of males with two lobes per testis. Abbreviations as in Table 1.

Species	Number of Males With Three Lobes per Testis	Number of Males With Two Lobes per Testis	Mean Biennial Rate of Survival S^2	Mean Annual Rate of Survival S
D.q.	4	27	.148	.38
D.m.	12	43	.279	.53
D.f.	14	85	.165	.40
D.o.c.	47	146	.322	.57
D.w.	10	120	.0835	.29

column (l_x) of each life table (Tables 14, 15, 16, 17, 18). These immature females are known to be 3 and 4 years of age but since the survivorship of each species is different in the early years of life (Fig. 8), the proportion of 3 year old females to four year old females in each of the samples of immature females will be slightly different. Thus, the mean age of the immature females of each species will also be slightly different. In *D. quadramaculatus* and *D. monticola,* both of which have a low survivorship in early years, this mean age will be closer to three years than to four years. On the other hand, in *D. wrighti,* which has a high survivorship in early years, the value of the mean age of immature females should be almost midway between three and four years. The mean age for immature females of each species is given in Table 12, as is the method used in determining this value.

TABLE 14. The life table for females of *D. quadramaculatus* based on the spring sample. See text for the method used in obtaining the life table.

Age in Years x	Observed Survivorship	Survivorship l_x	Survival Rates S	Interpolated Survivorship l_x	Female Eggs per Female m_x	l_xm_x
0.0. . . .						
0.5. . . .	720	1.000				
1.0. . . .						
2.0. . . .						
3.0. . . .						
3.3. . . .	170	.236	.43			
4.0. . . .				.130		
4.3. . . .		.1015	.40			
5.0. . . .				.053	15.5	.8515
5.3. . . .		.0406	.43			
6.0. . . .				.023		
6.3. . . .		.0175	.40			
7.0. . . .				.0088	15.5	.1364
7.3. . . .		.0066	.38			
8.0. . . .				.0035		
8.3. . . .		.00264	.40			
9.0. . . .				.00135	15.5	.0209
9.3. . . .		.00100	.38			
10.0. . . .						
10.3. . . .		.00038				
					R_o=SUM OF l_xm_x=	1.01

Since the mean age of immature females of each species is slightly different, only one species, *D. wrighti,* will be used as an example of the method used in determining the survivorship of females in this genus. The mean age of immature females of *D. wrighti* is 3.5 years (Table 12). To obtain the pro-

TABLE 15. The life table for females of *D. monticola* based on the spring sample. See text for the method used in obtaining the life table.

Age in Years x	Observed Survivorship	Survivorship l_x	Survival Rates S	Interpolated Survivorship l_x	Female Eggs per Female m_x	l_xm_x
0.0. . . .						
0.5. . . .	768	1.000				
1.0. . . .						
2.0. . . .						
3.0. . . .						
3.3. . . .	170	.221	.51			
4.0. . . .				.140		
4.3. . . .		.113	.30			
5.0. . . .				.049	13.5	.6615
5.3. . . .		.034	.51			
6.0. . . .				.021		
6.3. . . .		.017	.30			
7.0. . . .				.0075	13.5	.1012
7.3. . . .		.0052	.53			
8.0. . . .				.0033		
8.3. . . .		.0027	.30			
9.0. . . .				.0012	13.5	.0162
9.3. . . .		.00082	.53			
10.0. . . .						
10.3. . . .		.00044				
					R_o=SUM OF l_xm_x=	.78

TABLE 16. The life table for females of *D. fuscus* based on the spring sample. See text for the method used in obtaining the life table.

Age in Years x	Observed Survivorship	Survivorship l_x	Survival Rates S	Interpolated Survivorship l_x	Female Eggs per Female m_x	l_xm_x
0.0. . . .						
0.5. . . .	742	1.000				
1.0. . . .						
2.0. . . .						
3.0. . . .						
3.4. . . .	156	.210	.62			
4.0. . . .				.156		
4.4. . . .		.130	.11			
5.0. . . .				.034	11.5	.3910
5.4. . . .		.0143	.62			
6.0. . . .				.011		
6.4. . . .		.00887	.11			
7.0. . . .				.0024	11.5	.0276
7.4. . . .		.000976	.40			
8.0. . . .				.00056		
8.4. . . .		.000390	.11			
9.0. . . .				.00010	11.5	.0011
9.4. . . .		.000043	.40			
10.0. . . .						
10.4. . . .		.000017				
					R_o=SUM OF l_xm_x=	.42

TABLE 17. The life table for females of *D. o. carolinensis* based on the spring sample. See text for the method used in obtaining the life table.

Age in Years x	Observed Survivorship	Survivorship l_x	Survival Rates S	Interpolated Survivorship l_x	Female Eggs per Female m_x	$l_x m_x$
0.0....						
0.5....	750	1.000				
1.0....						
2.0....						
3.0....						
3.4....	254	.339	.74			
4.0....				.285		
4.4....		.251	.30			
5.0....				.120	5	.600
5.4....		.0753	.74			
6.0....				.062		
6.4....		.0557	.30			
7.0....				.027	5	.135
7.4....		.01671	.57			
8.0....				.0118		
8.4....		.00952	.30			
9.0....				.0046	5	.023
9.4....		.002856	.57			
10.0....						
10.4....		.0016				
					R_0=SUM OF $l_x m_x$=	.76

TABLE 18. The life table for females of *D. wrighti* based on the spring sample. See text for the method used in obtaining the life table.

Age in Years x	Observed Survivorship	Survivorship l_x	Survival Rates S	Interpolated Survivorship l_x	Female Eggs per Female m_x	$l_x m_x$
0.0....						
0.5....	235	1.000				
1.0....						
2.0....						
3.0....						
3.5....	116	.495	.91			
4.0....				.470		
4.5....		.450	.19			
5.0....				.200	3	.600
5.5....		.0855	.91			
6.0....				.081		
6.5....		.0778	.19			
7.0....				.035	3	.105
7.5....		.0148	.29			
8.0....				.006		
8.5....		.0028	.19			
9.0....				.0012	3	.004
9.5....		.00053	.29			
10.0....						
10.5....		.000154				
					R_0=SUM OF $l_x m_x$=	.71

portion of females surviving at 4.5 years, the proportion of females in the survivorship column (l_x) of the life table (Table 18) at age 3.5 years was multiplied by 0.91, the mean annual rate of survival for younger nonbrooding females (Table 12). The proportion of females at age 4.5 years was multiplied by 0.19, the mean annual rate of survival for brooding females (Table 11), to obtain the proportion of females surviving at 5.5 years. The proportion of females at age 5.5 was multiplied by 0.91, as before, to obtain the proportion surviving at 6.5 years. The proportion at age 6.5 was multiplied by 0.19, as before, to obtain the proportion of females surviving at 7.5 years. The proportion of females at age 7.5 was then multiplied by 0.29, the mean annual rate of survival for nonbrooding females in later years of life (Table 13), to obtain the proportion surviving at 8.5 years. The proportion at age 8.5 was multiplied by 0.19, as before, to obtain the proportion surviving at 9.5 years. Finally, the proportion at age 9.5 was multiplied by 0.29, as before, to obtain the proportion surviving at 10.5 years of age. Thus, the survival rate for brooding females is constant, but two different rates of survival for nonbrooding females are used in order to be consistent with the assumption that the survival rate for nonbrooding females must be the same as that for males of comparable ages.

The log of the proportion of females surviving at 3.5, 4.5, 5.5, 6.5, 7.5, 8.5, 9.5, and 10.5 years was plotted against age, and the proportion of females surviving at 4, 5, 6, 7, 8, and 9 years was obtained by interpolation between the calculated points (Table 18). By this method, the survivorship of females of *D. wrighti* was obtained for each year class rather than in units of two year classes as it was in the males (Table 8).

The same method was used in obtaining the survivorship column (l_x) of the life tables of females of the other species. In *D. quadramaculatus* and *D. monticola,* the survivorship of females prior to interpolation on a semilogarithmic graph was in time units of 3.3, 4.3, 5.3, 6.3, 7.3, 8.3, 9.3, and 10.3 years (Tables 14, 15). In *D. fuscus* and *D. o. carolinensis* the survivorship of females prior to interpolation on a semilogarithmic graph was in time units of 3.4, 4.4, 5.4, 6.4, 7.4, 8.4, 9.4, and 10.4 years (Tables 16, 17).

LIFE TABLES OF FEMALES

Now that the survivorship (l_x) of females has been determined, it is possible to use the life table as a method of checking the accuracy of the assumptions made in determining the survivorship of the females and the sampling error in the collections taken in the field during the spring of the year.

Since the populations of all five species of *Desmognathus* have been assumed to be stationary (exactly replacing themselves), the proportion of eggs produced by each population (Net Reproductive Rate) should be equal to the proportion of individuals in the 0 and 1 year class. For each species, the proportion of individuals in the 0 and 1 year class has the value of 1.000 in the survivorship column (l_x) of the life table. Thus, the net reproductive rate for each species should also have a value equal to 1.000. The net reproductive rate for each species is the total number of female eggs produced per female or the sum of the $l_x m_x$ column of the life table. The sum of the $l_x m_x$ column or net reproductive rate is usually designated by the symbol R_0 in life table studies.

The m_x column of the life table is based on the

number of female eggs produced per female. Assuming a one to one sex ratio in the egg stage of the life history, the number of female eggs produced per female is one half the mean clutch size of the species. The mean clutch size for each species is based on the data given in Table 6. Finally, since the females of all five species deposit eggs at the ages of five, seven, and nine years, the m_x value can apply only to these three age classes and is zero for all other age classes because the females are not depositing eggs.

The life tables for each species of *Desmognathus,* based on the females collected in the spring, are given in Tables 14, 15, 16, 17, and 18. None of the species has a net reproductive rate (R_0) equal to the expected value of 1.000. In *D. quadramaculatus, D. monticola, D. o. carolinensis,* and *D. wrighti,* the net reproductive rate is between 0.5 and 2.0, which is a reasonable range of error for field studies on life tables. In *D. fuscus,* the net reproductive rate (R_0) is not between the values of 0.5 and 2.0 and is not considered to be close to the expected value of unity. Thus, in every species except *D. fuscus,* the errors contained in the assumptions made in determining the survivorship of the females and the sampling error in the collections taken during the spring were apparently small.

The range of error of 0.5 to 2.0 for the net reproductive rate, at first glance, may appear to be a wide range but it should be remembered that, in calculating a life table based on a sample from the field, any sampling error in the collection will be compounded throughout the life table and will appear in a highly expanded form in the net reproductive rate (R_0).

For example, the life table for each of the species of *Desmognathus* is based on a sample collected in the spring of a single year. The relationship between the net reproductive rate and the sampling error for a collection taken in a single year is such that $R_0 = (\%\text{ error per year})^T$, where the exponent "T" is the mean generation time for the population. The mean generation time (T) for a population is the sum of the xl_xm_x column of the life table divided by the sum of the l_xm_x column of the life table; where "x" is the age in years; "l_x" is the survivorship; and "m_x" is the number of female eggs per female. The mean generation time (T) for each species, based on the life table of the females, is: *D. quadramaculatus,* 5.35 years; *D. monticola,* 5.56 years; *D. fuscus,* 5.14 years; *D. o. carolinensis,* 5.46 years; and *D. wrighti,* 5.31 years.

In other words, the sampling error in the spring collection was multiplied by itself more than five times and this compounded error is contained in the net reproductive rate (R_0) for each species in the life tables (Tables 14, 15, 16, 17, 18).

As a check on the accuracy of the samples collected in the spring, it is necessary to determine the percent error per year. In the equation $R_0 = (\%\text{ error per year})^T$, the net reproductive rate, R_0, and the mean generation time, T, are known for each species. Solving for the percent error per year in the collection, the formula is % error per year=

$$\left(1 - \text{antilog}\left[\frac{\log R_0}{T}\right]\right)(100)$$

The percent error per year for each species, obtained by the above formula, is *D. quadramaculatus,* 0.0%; *D. monticola,* 2%; *D. fuscus* 16%; *D. o. carolinensis,* 5%; and *D. wrighti,* 6%. Thus, with the exception of the collection for females of *D. fuscus,* the sampling errors contained in the spring collections for the five species of *Desmognathus* are within a reasonably small range.

The most striking difference between the collection of *D. fuscus* and the collections of the other four species of the genus was in the sex ratio between immature females and males with one lobe per testis. *D. fuscus* was the only species in which this ratio was not one to one in the spring sample. If the sampling error in this species is as large as was indicated above, then it is certainly in the direction of collecting immature females in insufficient numbers. On the other hand, the females of *D. fuscus* may conceivably attain sexual maturity at an earlier age than the females of the other species. There is even the possibility that some females of *D. fuscus* may reproduce annually instead of biennially. The last suggestion is based on the observed hatching time for the young of this species (Table 6). In *D. fuscus,* at least one egg mass hatched in early August. The females that brood egg masses hatching in early August may resume active feeding for a long enough period prior to winter to develop large ovarian eggs which may be deposited in successive years rather than biennially.

Of the five species of *Desmognathus* in the study area, *D. fuscus* is the least typical of mountainous areas. It attains high altitudes at Whitetop Mountain and Mount Rogers and also is found above 5000 ft in the Great Smoky Mountains National Park (King 1939). Throughout most of its geographical range, however, it is a piedmont and lowland species. At the present state of our knowledge, the life table for females of *D. fuscus* must remain in doubt. It is hoped that more attention will be focused upon this species in future field studies of the population structure and dynamics of salamanders.

DISCUSSION

The series *D. quadramaculatus, D. monticola, D. fuscus, D. o. carolinensis,* and *D. wrighti* has long been considered to represent successive stages of evolution within the genus *Desmognathus* (Dunn 1926, Hairston 1949, and others). This series is usually based on certain morphological characters that are generalized or primitive in *D. quadramaculatus* and become progressively more specialized, reaching an extreme in *D. wrighti.* The morphological characters and their changes have been dealt with in detail by Dunn (1926), Noble (1927), and King (1936).

Dunn (1926) envisioned speciation within *Desmognathus* as the result of the presence of various ecological barriers. Evidence of considerable overlap in habitat and in ecology of the species of the genus, however, has been presented by Hairston (1949) and confirmed by the present study. Moreover, the ecological barriers between the species tend to break down even further during the critical courtship and reproductive stages of the life histories. It is difficult to visualize speciation within the genus without the presence of some other kinds of barriers. This aspect of speciation within the genus has been discussed in detail by Hairston (1949).

Conservatism of Reproductive Habits

Prior to a discussion of the many aspects of the five species that show progressive trends in the genus *Desmognathus,* it should be noted that the reproductive habits of the species are relatively devoid of such trends. Males of all five species reach maturity at 3.5 years of age. With the possible exception of *D. fuscus,* females reach maturity at 4.5 years of age, deposit their first eggs at 5 years of age, and have a biennial reproductive cycle. Courtship takes place in all 5 species during the fall and spring. The courtship patterns of the 4 species observed were similar as were the aggressive responses of males towards other males during the courtship seasons. All of the species deposit their eggs in the late spring and early summer and the eggs hatch in late summer and early fall. The females remain with the eggs and brood them until the young have hatched. The nesting sites utilized by the 5 species are aquatic and so similar that the eggs and brooding females of two different species can be found in the same site at the same time.

Evolutionary Trends in the Genus *Desmognathus*

Dunn (1926) postulated that the Plethodontidae evolved as a group that was adapted for life in the mountain streams of the southern Appalachians. He suggested that these mountain streams had originally been occupied by the ancestral form and were still occupied by the more generalized species of the family. From the ancestral mountain stream habitat many lines of radiation are evident. Some plethodontids are completely aquatic, others are completely terrestrial, etc. Moreover, several groups within the family have followed similar lines of adaptation independently. *Desmognathus* is one of the groups with an evolutionary trend towards terrestrialism.

In the following discussion, the various species of the genus will be referred to as "representative of stages of evolution of *Desmognathus.*" This does not imply that each "stage" gave rise to the next "stage" in terms of one contemporary species giving rise to another. It merely indicates that the pathway taken during the change of habitat from aquatic to terrestrial in the course of the evolution of the genus was more probably from stream to stream-bank to forest rather than directly from stream to forest. Since some of the species still occupy these habitats, they should be indicative of some of the results of natural selection within each habitat. In short, the evolutionary trends in the genus, resulting from changes in ecology, should not be confused with the details of the mechanisms of speciation. Indeed, the pattern of speciation within the genus, in terms of the presence or absence of past geographical barriers as indicated by Hairston (1949), in no way conflicts with the above suggestion as to the sequence in which successive habitats were occupied during the evolution of the genus.

Hairston (1949) demonstrated that *D. quadramaculatus, D. monticola, D. o. carolinensis,* and *D. wrighti* formed an aquatic to terrestrial ecological series. This has not only been confirmed by the present study but it has also been supplemented by the insertion of *D. fuscus* in the series.

D. quadramaculatus, the most generalized species in the genus, is essentially an aquatic form. It is found both in the water and in the banks of streams but the highest percentage of specimens are taken in the water. *D. monticola,* which is closely related to *D. quadramaculatus,* is representative of the next stage of evolution within the genus. It occupies the banks of streams and is found in seepage areas. The stream bank and seepage area habitats are more terrestrial than the habitats occupied by *D. quadramaculatus.*

D. fuscus is representative of the next stage of evolution within the genus. Typically, it is a lowland and piedmont species, but in the Balsam Mountains it occupies the headwaters of streams and is found in seepage areas. Since these sites are more subject to fluctuation in water level than are the sites usually occupied by *D. monticola, D. fuscus* may be considered to be slightly more terrestrial than *D. monticola.* There is, however, some overlap in habitat between the two species, particularly in seepage areas, and the implied difference between the two species may be greater than actually exists.

D. o. carolinensis, which is representative of the next stage of evolution within the genus, is unquestionably more terrestrial than *D. fuscus.* With the exception of the winter season, when many, if not most, of the individuals aggregate in aquatic sites for hibernation, this species is typical of the forest habitats. Even during the summer, spring, and fall, however, some individuals, other than breeding females, can be found in aquatic sites.

D. wrighti is considered to represent the terminal species within the series (Hairston, 1949). During the summer, fall, and spring, with the exception of breeding females in aquatic nesting sites, virtually all of the individuals of this species are in the forest. Like *D. o. carolinensis,* many, if not most, of the individuals return to aquatic sites for hibernaation. In spite of this, there is little doubt that *D. wrighti* is the most terrestrial species in the genus.

There are many other trends within the genus that parallel this ecological trend. The most obvious of these is the progressive reduction in body size. In decreasing order from the largest to the smallest species, the series is: *D. quadramaculatus, D. monticola, D. fuscus, D. o. carolinensis,* and *D. wrighti.* The reduction in body size has been accompanied by a progressive reduction in the number of eggs produced per female in each of the species. The series in decreasing order of mean clutch size from the largest to the smallest clutch is the same as that for size reduction.

Terrestrialism has also been accompanied by a progressive reduction in the length of the larval period in the five species. The series in decreasing order from the longest to the shortest larval period is: *D. quadramaculatus, D. fuscus, D. monticola, D. o. carolinensis,* and *D. wrighti.* The last species has no free-living larval stage. It should be noted that the expected positions of *D. monticola* and *D. fuscus* in the series are reversed.

The most striking effect of the terrestrial trend in this genus has been on survivorship. The more terrestrial the population, the greater is the proportion of individuals surviving up to, and through, the early years of maturity. This has been demonstrated both at the interspecies and intraspecies level. The series in increasing order from the species with the lowest proportion of individuals reaching maturity to the highest is: *D. quadramaculatus, D. monticola, D. fuscus, D. o. carolinensis,* and *D. wrighti.* Even within a single species, when one sex has been shown to occupy an aquatic habitat whereas the other sex occupies terrestrial habitats, the sex with the aquatic habitat has a higher rate of mortality than that with a terrestrial habitat. This is particularly evident in *D. o. carolinensis* and *D. wrighti,* in which breeding females are aquatic and nearly all males and nonbreeding females are terrestrial during the late spring, summer, and early fall.

In terms of population dynamics, the direction taken by evolution within this genus has been the gradual transformation of a population with a high egg production and low survival into a population with a low egg production and a high survival to maturity. Most of the other trends observed in the species of *Desmognathus* are directly related to this change in the population structure and its dynamics. For example, the age of maturity in females is stable in this genus and the reduction of the size of the species through the series would be detrimental to the species unless there was a corresponding increase in survival to maturity. Since there is probably a minimum egg size, below which a hatchling cannot be produced, any reduction in size of the female would also result in a reduction of the clutch size deposited by the female. If the clutch size is reduced without a corresponding increase in survivorship to maturity, the species would become extinct.

Terrestrialism has yet another effect on the population structure within the genus. The more terrestrial the species, the higher the proportion of mature males to mature females in the species. This is attributed directly to the higher death rate of mature breeding females as a result of their aquatic nesting behavior.

Whereas no quantitative studies were made on the population density in the various habitats utilized by the species of *Desmognathus,* the subjective impression gained in the course of this study was that the density is high in the aquatic sites and low in the terrestrial sites. Assuming random movement of the individuals, the encounters between the sexes in the terrestrial habitats are probably less frequent than in the aquatic habitats. The surplus of mature males in the terrestrial species may actually counterbalance the high mortality of breeding females by increasing the probability of successfully encountering and fertilizing the available mature females in that habitat. This, of course, does not imply that the high mortality of mature females of the terrestrial species has a selective advantage but it does imply that the low mortality of mature males of these species has a selective advantage. The alternative to this suggestion is that the presence of surplus males in the more terrestrial species, such as *D. o. carolinensis* and *D. wrighti,* has no selective advantage at all.

The population dynamics of the five species of *Desmognathus,* based on the collections from the Balsam Mountains in Virginia, are not expected to have universal validity for any of the species over their entire geographical range. The population structures and their dynamics, in this genus, are so obviously the result of various environmental pressures and of the interrelationships between the species of this genus and those of other salamander genera that they could only be duplicated in regions where the conditions were similar to, if not identical with, those existing in the Balsam Mountains. For example, the survivorship of *D. fuscus* in the northern part of its range, where it is the only species of *Desmognathus* present in the environment, is probably different from that in the Balsam Mountains where four other species of this genus are present. The same can be said for each of the other species.

When the population dynamics of a single species is known for different competitive situations under different ecological conditions throughout its geographical range, ecologists will begin to have some insight into the relationship of that species to its environment. This information can be derived only from studies in the field. It is hoped that more attention will be directed towards this problem in the future.

SUMMARY

Intensive field studies have been made on five species of the salamander genus *Desmognathus* in the Balsam Mountains of southwestern Virginia. Of 12,000 plethodontid salamanders collected, preserved, and subsequently dissected in the course of this study, 7000 were of the genus *Desmognathus.* None of the five species of this genus is represented by less than 1000 individuals in the collection.

The local distributions of the five species were determined by vertical transects made along a continuous slope at intervals of 100 vertical feet. Horizontal transects were made at each vertical stop along transects of large streams. The seasonal variation in the local distributions of the five species was determined by repeating the transects at different seasons of the year.

The aquatic to terrestrial ecological series in this genus, described by Hairston, was confirmed. In addition, *D. fuscus,* like *D. monticola,* was shown to be a stream bank species in large streams in this area.

D. o. carolinensis and *D. wrighti,* both of which are found in the forest up to 250 ft from open water in the summer, showed a seasonal shift towards the aquatic sites in the fall and spring. Excavations in aquatic habitats revealed that these two species aggregate and presumably hibernate in these sites during the winter.

The transects revealed considerable overlap in the vertical distributions of the five species. Studies in different kinds of aquatic sites revealed that *D. monticola* and *D. fuscus* are altitudinally separated along large mountain streams. *D. fuscus* occupies the banks at the headwaters and *D. monticola* occupies the banks at the lower elevations along the streams. These two species, however, occur together in small streams and in seepage areas at lower elevations. *D. quadramaculatus* is present in large and small mountain streams but is absent from seepage areas.

The life histories of all five species were studied in detail. The courtship seasons and the reproductive seasons of these species were found to be the same. The females of *Desmognathus* utilize aquatic nesting sites for egg-laying and apparently remain with the eggs through the period of development to hatching. The eggs are deposited in the late spring and early summer and hatching takes place in late summer and fall. Courtship takes place in the fall and spring.

Courtship behavior and aggressive behavior were described for four out of the five species studied. The courtship patterns of the species of this genus are similar and the patterns observed in the fall were the same as those observed in the spring. The aggressive behavior of males towards other males during the courtship season was suggested as the method by which sex recognition takes place in this genus.

The role of secondary sexual characters in *Desmognathus* is explained on the basis of either courtship behavior or aggressive behavior in connection with courtship. Most of the secondary sexual characters of males of this genus were found to have a function either directly or indirectly related to courtship.

The series *D. quadramaculatus, D. fuscus, D. monticola, D. o. carolinensis,* and *D. wrighti* has been shown to be one of progressive reduction of the length of the larval period. The last species has no free-living larval stage in its life history.

The age at maturity was determined for each species by dissections and by size-frequency information. The males of all five species become sexually mature and engage in their first courtship in the fall at 3.5 years of age. The females of the five species also become mature in the fall, one year later than the males, and deposit their first clutch of eggs in the following spring or summer at 5 years of age. The size of the species, length of larval period, and habitat occupied have been shown to have no effect on the age of maturity in this genus.

On the basis of dissections, particularly of females collected in the spring, the five species were shown to have a biennial reproductive cycle in the Balsam Mountains. Moreover, the females were shown to deposit eggs at 5, 7, and 9 years of age.

The population structures and survivorship curves for males of each species were determined by means of size-frequency information and the number of lobes on each of the testes. The lobes per testis are known to increase with the age of the individual. The series *D. quadramaculatus, D. monticola, D. fuscus, D. o. carolinensis,* and *D. wrighti* was shown to be one of increasing survivorship through the early years of sexual maturity. This sequence of species was identical to that in the aquatic to terrestrial ecological sequence.

The population structures and life tables for the females of the five species were also determined. When balanced, four out of the five life tables were found to be within a reasonable range of error for field studies of stationary life tables. The life table for females of *D. fuscus* did not fall within this range of error. Either the assumptions used in determining the survivorship of females of this species were invalid or the sampling error in *D. fuscus* was larger than in the other species studied.

The survivorship of females of *D. quadramaculatus* and *D. monticola* was found to be similar to that of the males of these species, both before and after the females became mature. In *D. fuscus, D. o. carolinensis,* and *D. wrighti,* the survivorship in females was the same as that in the males until the females reached maturity, but mature females were found to have a higher mortality than males of comparable ages.

The relationship of habitat to survivorship in this genus has been demonstrated and discussed both at the interspecific and intraspecific levels. It has been shown that, in the genus *Desmognathus,* the more terrestrial the population, the higher is the proportion of individuals reaching sexual maturity and the lower is the number of eggs produced per female.

The direction of evolution in this genus has been indicated by various trends shown by the species within it, such as: size of the species, mean clutch size, length of larval period, habitat, and survivorship.

Finally, the effect of natural selection on the population structure and its dynamics within the genus *Desmognathus* has been indicated and discussed.

LITERATURE CITED

Bailey, J. R. 1937. Notes on plethodontid salamanders of the southeastern United States. Occas. Papers Mus. Zool. Univ. Mich. **364**: 1-10.

Bannikov, A. G. 1949. Notes on the biology of *Ranodon sibiricus.* Doklady Akademiia Nauk USSR **65** (2): 237-240 (Zoology). Translated by Elaine Levi, Dept. Zool., Univ. Calif. Los Angeles. Edited by F. B. Turner, Dept Zool., Univ. Calif. Los Angeles.)

———. 1950. Age composition of a population and its dynamics in *Bombina bombina* L. Doklady Akademiia Nauk USSR **70** (1):101-103. (Translated by A. Starrett, Univ. Mich. Mus. Zool., January, 1957. Edited and prepared for duplication by F. B. Turner, Wayne State Univ.)

Barbour, R. W. & L. Y. Lancaster. 1946. Food habits of *Desmognathus fuscus* in Kentucky. Copeia 1946 (1): 48-9.

Bishop, S. C. 1941. The salamanders of New York. New York State Mus. Bull. **324**: 1-365.

Bogert, C. M. 1952. Relative abundance, habitats, and normal thermal levels of some Virginia salamanders. Ecology **33** (1): 16-30.

Brady, M. K. 1924. Eggs of *Desmognathus phoca* (Matthes). Copeia **127**: 29.

Cagle, F. R. 1956. An outline for the study of an amphibian life history. Tulane Studies in Zool. **4** (3): 79-110.

Deevey, E. S., Jr. 1947. Life tables for natural populations of animals. Quart. Rev. Biol. **22**: 283-314.

———. 1950. The probability of death. Sci. Amer. **182** (4): 58-60.

Dunn, E. R. 1926. The salamanders of the family Plethodontidae. Smith College Anniversary Publ.: 1-441.

———. 1928. The habitats of Plethodontidae. Amer. Nat **62**: 236-248.

Hairston, N. G. 1949. The local distribution and ecology of the plethodontid salamanders of the southern Appalachians. Ecol. Monog. **19**: 47-73.

———. 1951. Interspecies competition and its probable influence upon the vertical distribution of Appalachian salamanders of the genus *Plethodon*. Ecology **32** (2): 266-274.

Humphrey, R. R. 1922. The multiple testis in urodeles. Biol. Bull. **43** (1): 45-67.

Hutchison, V. H. 1959. Aggressive behavior in *Plethodon jordani*. Copeia 1959 (1): 72-73.

King, W. 1936. A new salamander (*Desmognathus*) from the southern Appalachians. Herpetologica **1** (2): 56-60.

———. 1939. A survey of the herpetology of the Great Smoky Mountains National Park. Amer. Midl. Nat., **21** (3): 531-582.

Martof, B. S. 1956. Three new subspecies of *Leurognathus marmorata* from the southern Appalachian Mountains. Occ. Papers Mus. Zool. Univ. Mich. **575**: 1-17.

Martof, B. S. & D. C. Scott. 1957. The food of the salamander *Leurognathus.* Ecology **38** (3): 494-501.

Noble, G. K. 1927. The plethodontid salamanders; some aspects of their evolution. Amer. Mus. Novitates **249**: 1-26.

———. 1929. The relation of courtship to the secondary sexual characters of the two-lined salamander, *Eurycea bislineata* (Green). Amer. Mus. Novitates **362**: 1-5.

Noble, G. K. & M. K. Brady. 1930. The courtship of the plethodontid salamanders. Copeia 1930 (2): 52-54.

Organ, J. A. 1958. Courtship and spermatophore of *Plethodon jordani metcalfi.* Copeia 1958. (4): 251-259.

———. 1960. The courtship and spermatophore of the salamander *Plethodon glutinosus.* Copeia 1960 (1): 34-40.

Pearl, R. & J. R. Minor. 1935. Experimental studies on the duration of life. XIV. The comparative mortality of certain lower organisms. Quart. Rev. Biol. **10**: 60-79.

Pope, C. H. 1950. A statistical and ecological study of the salamander *Plethodon yonahlossee.* Bull. Chicago. Acad. Sci. **9** (5): 79-106.

Pope, C. H. & S. H. Pope. 1949. Notes on growth and reproduction in the slimy salamander *Plethodon glutinosus.* Fieldiana **31** (29): 251-261.

———. 1951. A study on the salamander *Plethodon ouachitae* and the description of an allied form. Bull. Chicago Acad. Sci. **9** (8): 129-152.

Schmidt, K. P. 1936. Guatemalan salamanders of the genus *Oedipus.* Zool. Series Field Mus. Nat. Hist. **20** (17): 135-166.

Stebbins, R. C. 1949. Courtship of the plethodontid salamander *Ensatina eschscholtzii.* Copeia 1949 (4): 274-281.

———. 1954. Natural history of the salamanders of the plethodontid genus *Ensatina.* Univ. Calif. Pubs. Zool. **54** (2): 47-124.

Turner, F. B. 1960. Population structure and dynamics of the western spotted frog, *Rana p. pretiosa* Baird & Girard, in Yellowstone Park, Wyoming. Ecol. Monog. **30** (3): 251-78.

Wilder, I. H. 1913. The life history of *Desmognathus fusca.* Biol. Bull. **24** (4): 251-292; (5) 293-342.

———. 1917. On the breeding habits of *Desmognathus fusca.* Biol. Bull. **32** (1): 13-20.

———. 1923. Spermatophores of *Desmognathus fusca.* Copeia **121**: 88-92.

EXPERIMENTAL METHODS IN POPULATION DYNAMICS: A CRITIQUE

FREDERICK E. SMITH
Department of Zoology, University of Michigan, Ann Arbor, Michigan

INTRODUCTION

Until very recently, deterministic theory has been the source of mathematical models for population dynamics. Simple equations have been proposed as suitable representations of sigmoid growth, competition, predation, etc., and these have been fitted to various data. The studies of Gause (1934) epitomize this field.

Stochastic theory provides a kind of model that expresses, not only the general sequence of events, but also the inherent variability of the system. While the deterministic function may represent the "pure" curve of maximum likelihood, the stochastic function permits an evaluation of the actual, observed curve, regardless of its irregularities. Since this ability to handle chance variations and their sequential effects during dynamic processes is relatively new, one must conclude that its future effect upon the approach to population dynamics will be one of progressive increase.

As the theoretical approach is shifting its base, it would be well to look closely to the experimental methods that are in use. The intent of such a critique is two-fold: to determine what has actually been accomplished by such methods, as opposed to what is supposed to have been accomplished, and to launch the newer theoretical approach upon a somewhat better methodology.

Only a few aspects of the experimental techniques are discussed, serving to emphasize phenomena that may well be extended to other aspects. Those discussed fall into the following sections: the mechanisms of culture, the responses of the population, certain properties of deterministic theories, and the application of theories to data. It is the methods that are criticized; such criticisms as occur on the usefulness of particular theories are more or less incidental.

While this paper represents the views of one individual, its existence is very much a result of discussions with E. S. Deevey, G. A. Riley, L. B. Slobodkin, D. W. Calhoun, and especially with G. E. Hutchinson, all at Yale University. Later developments reflect the influence of many others in several places.

THE EXPERIMENTAL ENVIRONMENT

Experiments in population dynamics are accomplished in cultures, and associated with these cultures are specific environments. One advantage of an experiment over field studies is the possibility of simplifying the environment through appropriate manipulation of the culture.

The culture can be treated in many ways, producing various qualitative effects in the environment and hence upon the population. If the experiment is designed as a test of some theory, the manipulations should be such as to simulate the conditions implied by the theory. Thus, if one were to test the

Reproduced with permission from Ecology, 33: 441-450, 1952. Published by the Ecological Society of America and The Duke University Press, Durham, North Carolina.

predation theory of Lotka (1925) and Volterra (1928), the environment would have to be such that the growth of the prey were in no way inhibited by prey density.

Surprisingly little attention has been paid to the possibility that a given theory, under investigation, defines certain properties for the experiment. In an attempt to emphasize such relationships, a very crude system of classification is given for several culture techniques that may be used in the laboratory. To these will be related the corresponding environments, and the latter will be associated with particular theories.

From the standpoint of ease of interpretation, the simplest culture technique is the *unlimited* culture. Either the population is continually so rarefied or the culture is so rapidly enriched that the organisms never suffer any inhibitive effects upon each other, at least not during the course of study.

Among culture techniques that have limited capacities for growth, the *unrenewed* culture is most frequently used, especially in bacteriology and protozoology. The culture is innoculated, and the subsequent history of the population is recorded. Nothing is added or subtracted by the experimenter.

A variant of this technique is the *periodically renewed* culture. At regular intervals, either the entire population is transferred to a new culture (as is done with flour beetles) or the culture is given booster shots of concentrated medium (as has been done with protozoa).

A still further refinement is the *continuously renewed* culture. The intervals between renewals are so small as to be ineffective, and the system can be treated as though fresh medium is being flushed through at a constant rate all of the time.

While these are but a few techniques, they are simple, and adequate for the present purpose.

Associated with each culture, and determined by the particular factors that are limiting, is a corresponding environment. In the unlimited culture, of course, since nothing is limiting, the environment is of the same type, an unlimited environment.

If the limiting factor is an expendable component of the medium, such as sugar or amino acid, the environment will follow the pattern of the culture.

If the limiting factor is non-expendable, such as space, the environment will in all cases follow the continuously renewed pattern, since the factor is resupplied automatically by the death of individuals. If spatial organization is involved, however, the rhythmic disturbance of the periodically renewed environment may produce a significant effect.

If the limiting factor is a freely diffusable substance like oxygen or carbon dioxide, again the system will in all cases regulate toward the continuously renewed pattern.

If the limiting factor is a noxious metabolite, the environment will follow the pattern of the culture, except that adding booster shots accomplishes little, and this type of culture will be modified toward the unrenewed type.

While these are but a few possibilities, they are enough to indicate some patterns that may occur. Combinations of limiting factors will complicate these patterns, so that, for example, it is not unlikely for an unrenewed culture to be temporarily regulated toward a continuously renewed environment by the supply of oxygen, only to revert to type later as the food is exhausted.

If we now examine some of the published theories, the implied environmental types (extrinsic to the interspecies relation when two populations are involved) are as follows:

1. Unlimited environment: exponential growth (Malthus 1798), predation (Lotka 1925; Volterra 1928), and the host-parasite relation

(Nicholson and Bailey 1935; Thompson 1939).

2. Unrenewed environment: sigmoid growth (Klem 1933).
3. Periodically renewed environment: none.
4. Continuously renewed environment: sigmoid growth (Verhulst 1838; Pearl and Reed 1920; Gompertz and Wilson, both in Wilson 1934) and indirect competition (Volterra 1928; Gause 1934).

In experiments on exponential growth, the culture has usually been so manipulated as to provide the proper environment. This is not known to be so for any of the experiments on predation; in those of Gause (1934, 1935) and of Gause, Smaragdova, and Witt (1936) the prey definitely reached densities that inhibited their own rate of growth. The same is true for most of the experiments on the host-parasite relation. Only one, an experiment by DeBach and Smith (1947), specifically eliminated self-inhibition in the growth of the prey population.

Klem's theory of sigmoid growth was developed for his experiments on yeast. The event appears to be unique, since no one else has applied a theory of growth in an unrenewed environment to data from an unrenewed environment.

While no theories have been developed to include the rhythmic effects of periodic renewal, many experiments have been recorded in which such effects probably existed. This would apply especially to studies of flour insects.

No ecological experiment has been conducted in a continuously renewed culture, although such techniques can be adapted from the work of Novick and Szilard (1950) or of Myers and Clark (1944). No experimental environment has ever been proved to be continuously renewed. While the chances are very good that in some experiments the unrenewed or periodically renewed culture technique that was used was modified by the limiting factors toward a continuously renewed type, this cannot be said with assurance for any particular case.

In summary, from the point of view that an experiment should simulate the conditions of the theory to which it is compared, very few of the published comparisons are known to be suitable. It is known for only one experiment on sigmoid growth (in which the theory did not fit the data well), one experiment on the host-parasite relation (in which the fit of theory to data is fair), and for many experiments on exponential growth. All of the remaining comparisons are open to question.

The Experimental Population

While theories developed in population dynamics are admittedly oversimplified, a general awareness of this in experimental terms seems to be deficient. For, again, if the data are to be used as a "test" of a theory, they should be derived from an appropriate ecological system.

An almost universal simplification in theories is that the unit of the population, the organism, always bears the same relation to the environment. While this is never true, if the distribution of (qualitative) variations among the units is always similar, the approximation is satisfactory.

But stability or constancy of such properties as size-distribution, age-distribution, sex-ratio, etc. is surprisingly rare. Even in the most simple case of population dynamics, exponential growth, marked changes in the population during a recorded phase of such growth are frequent. Demonstrations of such changes are relatively infrequent, since more than one measure of the population has to be taken if a change is to be discerned.

Hershey (1938) demonstrated that, during the period that the cell count was increasing along a good exponential curve, the rate of nitrogen uptake in the population was increasing along a different curve, having a rate function at least 30% smaller. Obviously some character of the population was changing with time; the organism did not stay the same.

The most striking demonstration of this phenomenon was found by Richards (1932) in yeast. During the thirty hours of exponential increase in cell count, the percentage of budding cells increased steadily from 10 to 25, the percentage of moribund cells fell exponentially from 7 to 1, and the surface-volume ratio increased from about 2.9 to 3.4. Richards remarked that the sigmoid growth of yeast was too complicated for comparison to "formulae with arbitrary constants which over simplify the various influences that determine the extent of natural unlimited growth of the cells"; this remark applies equally well to the exponential phase of growth.

Finally, it is a commonplace in bacteriology that cell-count curves and colorimetric curves do not agree.

The conclusion from these demonstrations is that, although the culture is mechanically of the proper type, insufficient time is allowed for the population to adjust to exponential growth. Before the population is able to "settle down," it becomes crowded and passes into plateau. This may be avoided (Hershey 1939) by subculturing from very young cultures. Effectively the period of exponential growth is prolonged, and a steady state of population characteristics is able to develop. In an adjusted culture, all estimates of the growth rate (number, total volume, nitrogen uptake, etc.) must be the same. Most of the published observations of exponential growth are probably inaccurate estimates of the "true" rate of increase.

The concept of unchanging population characteristics in sigmoid growth or in other ecological relations is absurd. This has been recognised, and such "simple" organisms as yeast, protozoa, and bacteria have been used with the assumption that, here, at least, qualitative changes are minimal. It would now appear that such an assumption is unwarranted. The reactions of yeast to environmental stress, as recorded by Richards (1932), are fully as complicated from a mathematical point of view as those of any higher organism.

It is unfortunate that just those species which culture easily (yeast, flour insects, fruit flies, etc.) come from naturally unstable environments. Their complex adaptabilities, which facilitate culture, are precisely what complicate the population experiment. A simpler system would be one using species (not necessarily simple) from stable, uniform environments—species that usually are difficult to culture. Another possible solution is to present the traditional laboratory species with totally new limiting factors, and gamble that the population response will be relatively simple.

It is possible that in some experiments physiological adaptation to stress has combined with an unsuitable environmental type to produce a deceptive result. This is especially likely in comparisons of sigmoid growth with the Verhulst-Pearl theory. In many yeasts and bacteria, as growth proceeds in the unrenewed culture, the population shifts progressively to an inactive state. In an unrenewed environment one would expect the upper part of the sigmoid curve to be small, since it is curtailed by a falling capacity in the culture. After the peak of growth the population, if it could not adapt, would fall, perhaps along a negative exponential. But in these cases, the sum of inactive and active cells enlarges the upper portion of the growth curve and postpones the fall almost indefinitely.

While the result may be described closely by the mathematical form of the Verhulst-Pearl logistic, such a description is not useful. Either the combination of two errors has produced a fortuitous result, or their interaction is regulated by a process as yet unsuspected. In either case the theory does not describe the underlying biology.

Other complications that may be introduced by the organisms cannot be treated lightly. These include environmental conditioning, changes in the age structure of the population, and mutation with a complete replacement of the population (as occurs frequently in the chemostat of Novick and Szilard 1950). Whatever the specific complications, they must be reconciled in any comparison of theory and experiment.

Properties of Deterministic Theories

Any equation in population dynamics has specific properties, properties which are obvious to the mathematician, but which seem to have escaped any degree of experimental application. Many of these properties are useful, in that some of them may show immediately that the theory has limitations, while others may provide tools for study. These properties will be discussed by examples.

The theory of Verhulst (1838) and Pearl and Reed (1920) has the following form:

$$\frac{dN}{dt} = rN\left(1 - \frac{N}{K}\right)$$

where N = population size,

t = time,
r = intrinsic (net, maximum, exponential) rate of increase,
K = saturation level or plateau,

expressing the rate of change of the population (dN) with respect to change in time (dt). The equation can also be written as the average rate of change for the individual (dN/N) with respect to the change in time:

$$\frac{dN}{Ndt} = r\left(1 - \frac{N}{K}\right).$$

In this latter form, the average growth rate is seen to be a linear function of the degree of saturation (N/K). Thus, when this ratio is nearly zero, the growth rate is maximal (r), when it is one-half, the growth rate is one-half, and when the system is just saturated, the growth rate is zero.

In unrenewed environments, and in competitive and predative relationships, the possibility of a population level exceeding the current saturation level must be considered. In the Verhulst-Pearl theory, the linear relation continues; when the system is twice saturated, the growth rate is minus r, when it is ten times saturated, the rate is minus $9r$. Thus, the rate of decrease is not a limited function. Lotka (1925) indicated that this property may not be suitable for some situations.

The Verhulst-Pearl theory stands up under this kind of analysis better than most. In the Gompertz theory (Wilson 1934), the equation can be stated:

$$\frac{dN}{dt} = rN \log_e\left(\frac{K}{N}\right)$$

or:

$$\frac{dN}{Ndt} = r \log_e\left(\frac{K}{N}\right).$$

This equation has the same limitation as the Verhulst-Pearl theory, setting no limit to the rate of decrease. It has the more serious fault, however, of setting no limit to the rate of increase. When the ratio, N/K, is small, the rate of growth approaches infinity. It is only between about one-third saturation (where $\log_e K/N$ is 1.0) and full saturation (where $\log_e K/N$ is 0.0) that the constants of the equation can be interpreted biologically.

As a final example, the predation equations of Lotka (1925) and Volterra (1928) are:

$$\frac{dN_1}{dt} = r_1N_1 - k_1N_1N_2$$

$$\frac{dN_2}{dt} = k_2N_1N_2 - d_2N_2$$

where N_1 = prey population,
N_2 = predator population,
r_1 = intrinsic rate of increase for the prey,
d_2 = exponential death rate of the predators,
k_1,k_2 = predation constants.

If the predation constants are taken as simple, as they were in the development of an intrinsic cyclic relation, some of the properties are as follows:

$$\frac{dN_1}{N_1dt} = r_1 - k_1N_2,$$

$$\frac{dN_2}{N_2dt} = k_2N_1 - d_2.$$

1. Neither species enters in its own average growth function; hence, neither ever inhibits its own growth; the environment extrinsic to the relation is unlimited.
2. Prey density has no effect upon the likelihood of a prey being eaten; there is no safety in numbers.
3. Predator density has no effect upon the likelihood of a predator catching a prey; there is no competition for food.
4. The predators have an unlimited rate of increase.

While (1) can be arranged mechanically, and (2) may be true if the predators are certain filter-feeders, (3) and especially (4) are biologically unknown. These simple interpretations of the predation constants must be considered useless. To do so at once invalidates the predation "laws" of Volterra and the regular intrinsic cyclic relation developed by both Lotka and Volterra.

A more complex interpretation of the predation constants is that:

$$k_1 = a + bN_1 + cN_2 + \ . \ . \ .$$

$$k_2 = a' + b'N_1 + c'N_2 + \ . \ . \ .$$

defining each as a power series (Lotka 1925). If we consider only the second function, k_2, it is evident that a power series is most inept for its purpose.

For the growth function of the predators to be satisfactory, the average rate of growth (dN_2/N_2dt) must rise to some asymptote (r_2) as the prey are made more numerous. To describe such a curve by a power series that will handle all values of prey up to infinity, an infinite number of terms and constants are needed. Even to handle the numbers of prey that are likely to develop in an experiment requires several terms of the series. Furthermore, the function fails markedly should the prey density exceed that expected and allowed for. The use of exponential functions, as suggested by Gause (1934), offers a much higher efficiency in terms of the number of constants that would be required to describe this relation.

So far in this section only the deficiencies of theories have been emphasized. The second use of such an analysis of equations is to develop experimental tools. These will be discussed at the end of the following section.

The Application of Theories to Data

Actually, little can be said in favor of the fitting of deterministic theoretical curves to empirical data. The technique, as a means of "testing" theories, is indefensible on at least three independent counts:

(1) Judgment has to be subjective. Deviations from the best-fit curve always occur, and statistical methods for evaluating these deviations are lacking.

(2) The prior probability of the method is high. This aspect of probability is too often ignored; regardless of the calculated probability of a particular fit, if it is likely to be good before the fit is made, the test itself is inefficient. The method is uncritical; while it may exclude extreme misfits, it fails to discriminate among a host of similar but basically different situations.

Kavanagh and Richards (1934), among others, demonstrated that a variety of theoretical curves could be fitted to the same data on sigmoid growth, and with equal felicity. An even more powerful criticism of this weak method is the fact that the theory of Verhulst and Pearl, for example, has been accepted as a satisfactory fit to a remarkably heterogeneous set of ecological situations. The heterogeneity emphasizes, not the generality of the theory, as is usually assumed, but the weak method of application. The problems discussed in the preceeding sections have not caused difficulty in the past because the established method of fitting theories is not powerful enough to discriminate them.

This weakness is related to the number of constants fitted in the process of comparing a curve to data. With more than two such constants, the prior probability of a "nice" fit (a subjective term to match the subjective basis of judgment) is already high, and with more than four constants to be fitted to one population curve it is hardly necessary to make the comparison.

(3) The method centers attention on the whole rather than on the parts. A direct result has been a general satisfaction with the wholes, without the realization that at least some of the parts in the comparison are not of the right kind. If the overall fit is "nice," a prejudice is established against a rejection of the comparison through some particular fault.

The best fit of a theory to data has been said to be that of the Verhulst-Pearl theory to the growth curve of a yeast culture (Allee *et al.* 1949). The data were gathered by Carlson (1913), and the fit was made by Pearl (1930). In spite of this belief, the culture was unrenewed, the limiting factors were probably at first the food supply (sugar) and the waste accumulation, shifting later to the lower usefulness of the wastes as foods and the re-use of material from burst cells; the culture ended by converting to resting cells!

These three arguments are an unfortunate combination. A high prior probability leaves one at a loss in subjective judgement; the usual standards are not adequately strict. The lack of objective evaluation in whole comparisons, which has been accepted as a necessary evil, has forestalled any degree of partial analysis, in which objective methods are indeed possible. The lack of partial analyses has in turn promoted the habit of fitting all constants, whether some can be calculated independently or not, thus pushing the prior probability to its maximum.

For the comparison of whole theories to the history of a culture, the developing field of stochastic processes offers the only reasonable approach.

But whole comparisons may not be the best way to test theories. The danger still remains that the whole need not be the sum of the right parts. Rigorous testing of the separate aspects of the theories would not only simplify the mathematics, but would eliminate, at least to some degree, this last criticism.

In the Verhulst-Pearl theory, two basic concepts are combined. One is that the exponential rate of growth has a maximum (r), and the other is that the degree of saturation (N/K) is a linear depressant of the rate of growth (dN/Ndt).

The first concept is well supported and established. To measure it in a particular case, however, may be difficult. If there is to be any assurance of its accuracy it should be obtained from at least two kinds of measures in the growing population. Such estimates can be made "deterministic," in the sense that the average of many observations of a constant will approach its deterministic value. Furthermore, the empirical range of error would, with a suitable distribution, provide a means of probability evaluation. The two measures can be tested for the absence of trend and for agreement with each other.

The second concept has never been analysed. Rate curves derived from growth curves are not adequate, since they contain the same stochastic processes as the original data. But the problem can be handled in a different way. In the equation:

$$\frac{dN}{Ndt} = r\left(1 - \frac{N}{K}\right) = r - \frac{r}{K}(\mathrm{N})$$

a graph of the rate of change (dN/Ndt) plotted against the population size (N) shows a straight line, with a y-intercept of r, and x-intercept of K, and a slope of $-r/K$.

Points for this graph could be obtained from a modified chemostat. Keeping the composition of the inflow constant, its rate (the washing-out rate, V/W) can be set at various levels between r and zero. At r, the system will be unstable, but for any rate of flow less than this the population will increase until its growth rate is density-depressed to the rate of flow ($dN/Ndt = V/W$). At each level of this flow, after the system comes to a steady state, a series of observations can be made on the population size (N). The data can then be put through the standard statistical test (again, if a suitable distribution is found) to determine whether the regression of population size (N) upon the rate of growth (dN/Ndt) is linear. This would be a first test of the basic principle of the theory.

Needless to say, this method will apply to other theories of sigmoid growth. In the Gompertz curve, the linear plot becomes:

$$\frac{dN}{Ndt} = r \log_e K - r \log_e N.$$

The procedure can be turned about, to use the methods of partial analysis as a means of finding simple functions for theories. If, for example, none of the functions in established theories worked, a search with the aid of these partial systems may produce suitable relationships. Any experimental technique which will produce a steady state should yield information that can be used in deterministic theory.

The Lotka-Volterra predation theory indicates that:

1. A plot of dN_1/N_1dt against N_2 is a straight line, with a y-intercept of r_1 and a slope of $-1/k_1$.
2. A plot of dN_2/N_2dt against N_1 is a straight line, with a y-intercept of $-d_2$ and a slope of $1/k_2$.
3. dN_1/N_1dt, for one value of N_2, is constant for all values of N_1.
4. dN_2/N_2dt, for one value of N_1, is constant for all values of N_2.

Even these partial analyses, however, are not foolproof. Straight lines are easier to obtain than most people believe. If the data conform to a straight line "except at one end," or if they conform to two straight lines with a "break" in the middle, a linear relation is probably absent. Furthermore, small deviations toward one end of a curve may reflect large discrepancies in the dynamic processes of growth. For the faith that is put into population theories, the experimental examination will have to be rigorous.

Discussion

The preceding sections point to one conclusion: very little in this field of population dynamics is beyond the hypothetical stage. With the possible exception of the concept of exponential growth, it is a misuse of terms to refer to any of the interpretations as "theories." Almost all of the evidence used in support of various interpretations is, at best, inconclusive.

Yet, the field has provided a considerable fund of interesting material, enough to have profound effects upon allied areas. Perhaps, more than anything else, this influence urges an intense and cautious re-examination of our concepts.

The degree of acceptance of such concepts as, for examples, the Verhulst-Pearl logistic and the Lotka-Volterra equations, is astonishing.

Concepts do not appear easily. Although logic teaches that an infinite number of curves can be fitted to data on sigmoid growth, very few such equations have been set down, and of these only two, the Verhulst-Pearl and the Klem equations, have been expressed adequately in ecological terms. We have only one well-known theory of predation, one of competition, and two or three for parasitism. Sparse as it may be, this collection is the accumulated work of many people for many years.

Hence, even though the present stock of concepts is but a collection of hypotheses, it is a valuable collection. It contains what must be considered progress of the most difficult kind. For the future, also, the continued development of hypothetical relationships will be useful; the armchair is still a necessary piece of equipment.

The experimental side of population dynamics is in a different situation. In spite of the many curves recorded, the many fits made, the work will have to be largely discounted as evidence in support of any particular theories. A repetition of all of it, with more appropriate and more carefully detailed designs, will have to be initiated.

Regardless of the use to be made of stochastic processes, deterministic theory will continue to play a major role. It is a way of thinking; inevitably one considers, not the sequential range of values, but the most likely course of events. Most important, thinking in deterministic terms is a way of producing concepts.

Summary

The methods for experimental verification of deterministic theories in population dynamics are criticized from several points of view.

The mechanism of control in the culture should conform to the conditions implied in the theory. This is often not the case; the most notable instance of disagreement concerns the Verhulst-Pearl logistic, which has never been supported by an experiment known to be made in an appropriate environment. Several kinds of culture control are classified.

The reactions of the population should be limited to those provided in the theory. Most equations are admittedly simplified, but such an admission should be coupled with a much more successful restriction to simplified responses by the organisms. Many laboratory species are highly complex in their reactions to environmental control; physiological adaptation is especially common. A simple response is probably unrelated to evolutionary complexity. Two possible means of finding ideally simple reactions are indicated.

Theoretical equations are manipulated to show various of their properties. The method is useful as a means of "*a priori*" evaluation of equations, especially of their limitations. It is also useful as a means of discovering more simple but vital aspects of theories for specific analysis.

The common method of fitting deterministic curves to data is criticized from three points of view, any one of which raises a serious objection. One solution to the problem in the use of stochastic theory is mentioned, but methods are also discussed for the application of sound experimental techniques to deterministic theory.

The general conclusion is that we have a useful and valuable stockpile of concepts, but that up to the present little of the experimental work is at all conclusive. Most of the ideas in this field should be regarded as hypotheses, not theories.

References

Allee, W. C., A. E. Emerson, O. Park, T. Park, and K. P. Schmidt. 1949. Principles of animal ecology. Phila. and London: Saunders.

De Bach, P., and H. S. Smith. 1947. Effects of parasite population density on the rate of change of host and parasite populations. Ecology, **28**: 290–298.

Carlson, T. 1913. Über Geschwindigkeit und Grösse der Hefevermehrung in Würze. Biochem. Ztschr., **57**: 313–334.

Gause, G. F. 1934. The struggle for existence. Baltimore: Williams & Wilkins.

——. 1935. Vérifications expérimentales de la théorie mathématique de la lutte pour la vie. Actual. Sci. Industr., **277**: 1–61.

Gause, G. F., N. P. Smaragdova, and A. A. Witt. 1936. Further studies of interaction between predators and prey. J. Anim. Ecol., **5**: 1–18.

Hershey, A. D. 1938. Factors limiting bacterial growth. II. Growth without lag in *Bacterium coli* cultures. Proc. Soc. Exp. Biol. Med., **38**: 127–128.

——. 1939. Factors limiting bacterial growth. IV. The age of the parent culture and the rate of growth of transplants in *Escherichia coli.* J. Bact., **37**: 285–299.

Kavanagh, A. J., and O. W. Richards. 1934. The autocatalytic growth curve. Amer. Nat., **68**: 54–59.

Klem, Alf. 1933. On the growth of populations of yeast. Norske Vetensk.-Akad., Oslo, Hvalrådets Skrifter, **7**: 55–91.

Lotka, A. J. 1925. Elements of physical biology. Baltimore: Williams & Wilkins.

Malthus, T. R. 1798. An essay on the principle of population. London.

Myers, J., and L. B. Clark. 1944. Culture conditions and the development of the photosynthetic mechanism. II. An apparatus for the continuous culture of *Chlorella.* J. Gen. Physiol., **28**: 103–112.

Novick, A., and L. Szilard. 1950. Experiments with the chemostat on spontaneous mutations of bacteria. Proc. Nat. Acad. Sci., **36**: 708–719.

Nicholson, A. J., and V. A. Bailey. 1935. The balance of animal populations. Part I. Proc. Zool. Soc. London, **1935**, Part III: 551–598.

Pearl, Raymond. 1930. The biology of population growth. New York: Knopf.

Pearl, Raymond, and L. J. Reed. 1920. On the rate of growth of the population of the United States since 1790 and its mathematical representation. Proc. Nat. Acad. Sci., **6**: 275.

Richards, O. W. 1932. The second cycle and subsequent growth of a population of yeast. Archiv Protistenkunde, **78**: 263–301.

Thompson, W. R. 1939. Biological control and the theories of the interaction of populations. Parasitology, **31**: 299–388.

Verhulst, P. F. 1838. Notice sur la loi que la population suit dans son accroissement. Corr. Math. et Phys., **10**: 113.

Volterra, Vito. 1928. Variations and fluctuations of the number of individuals in animal species living together. J. du Conseil intern. pour l'explor. de la mer III vol. I, reprinted in: Animal Ecology, by R. N. Chapman, McGraw-Hill, New York, 1931.

Wilson, E. B. 1934. Mathematics of growth. Cold Spring Harbor Symp. on Quant. Biol., **2**: 199–202.

PART III

RELATIONSHIPS BETWEEN SPECIES: COMPETITION AND PREDATION

BEHAVIOR OF MIXED POPULATIONS AND THE PROBLEM OF NATURAL SELECTION

DR. G. F. GAUSE AND DR. A. A. WITT
Zoological Institute and Physical Institute
University of Moscow

The splendid development of genetic theories of natural selection, dealing with the problem on the exact quantitative basis, is well known. Starting with the consideration of two types or species which do not cross each other and making certain simple assumptions, they enable us to calculate the rate at which the better fitted type is displacing (and will expel to the very last) the less fitted one. But when we approach the conditions of competition in nature, take into account the ecological situation, make certain experimental investigations and write the equation of interaction between the competing species in a more general form, the complexity of the problem under consideration is obvious. It is hardly to be questioned, therefore, that the problem of the growth of a mixed population of two species is worthy of a very careful study so that it could give a sound basis for the development of complicated genetic theories of natural selection.

In the last two years the growth of species competing or helping each other was discussed by several authors. We can mention a book by Lotka (1934) and Kostitzin (1934), a paper by Winsor (1934), and two books by Gause (1934, 1935). The present paper gives an account of our recent theoretical investigations of the problem and summarizes the whole theory of growth of mixed populations, pointing out those conclusions that have already been confirmed by experimental investigations of one of the authors.

Reproduced with permission from The American Naturalist, LXIX: 596-609, 1935. Published by The Science Press, New York, New York.

(1) Equation of Interaction Between Species

The interaction between two competing species was expressed by Volterra (1926), Lotka (1932) and Gause (1932) in the form of a differential equation:

$$dN_1/dt = b_1N_1 \frac{K_1 - N_1 - \alpha N_2}{K_1}$$
$$dN_2/dt = b_2N_2 \frac{K_2 - N_2 - \beta N_1}{K_2} \quad \text{.......... (1)}$$

It was discussed in detail by Gause (1934), and there is no need to repeat it here. Let us only note that (1) this expression is generally true only for very simple populations of yeast cells, (2) the coefficients α and β often change in the course of the growth of the mixed population, and (3) according to Gause (1935) this equation has certain serious limitations. It is supposed in it that in the process of displacing one species by another from the saturating population the properties of these species (coefficients b, α, β) are practically the same as in the initial stages of growth taking place in almost unoccupied microcosm. In biological associations, however, this condition is often unfulfilled, as the properties of individuals of a certain species undergo considerable alterations under the influence of crowding. To avoid this difficulty in experimental investigations, it is sometimes convenient to perform regular and small dilutions of saturating population, keeping it continuously in the process of active growth (such variations in density often take place in field conditions):

$$dN_1/dt = b_1N_1 \frac{K_1 - N_1 - \alpha N_2}{K_1} - mN_1$$
$$dN_2/dt = b_2N_2 \frac{K_2 - N_2 - \beta N_1}{K_2} - mN_2 \quad \text{.......... (2)}$$

where $m < b$.

(2) Strong Mutual Depression of Species

An analysis of the properties of the equations (1) and (2) gives us the possibility of discussing certain essential types of the struggle for existence between species.

The consideration of properties of "singular points" and of the movement of integral curves between these points shows that when $\alpha > K_1/K_2$ and $\beta > K_2/K_1$ (equation 1) or $\alpha/1 - \frac{m}{b_1} > \frac{K_1}{K_2}/1 - \frac{m}{b_2}$ and $\beta/1 - \frac{m}{b_2} > \frac{K_2}{K_1}/1 - \frac{m}{b_1}$ (equation 2) either the first species will entirely displace the second, or the second entirely displace the first, depending on numerical relations between species at the beginning of their competition (Fig. 1). The biological

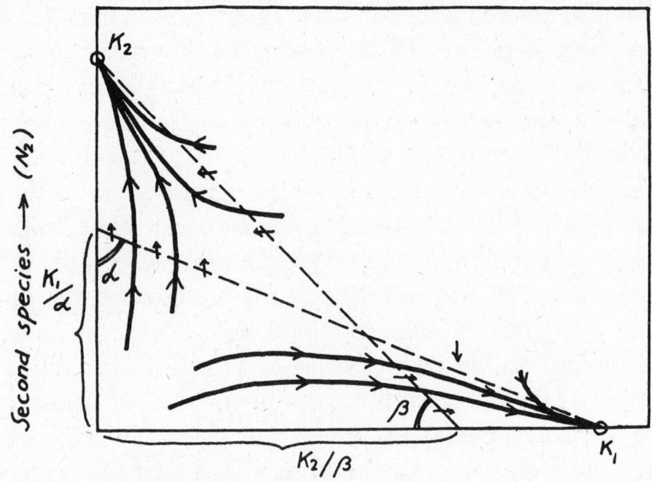

FIG. 1. Curves of interaction in the case of strong mutual depression of species. The coefficients α and β are the tangents of the corresponding angles.

meaning of this conclusion consists in the fact that if the mutual depression of two species is strong the *less numerous* species (whose concentration lies below a certain separatriss) will always disappear in the population. This conclusion has not yet been confirmed by direct experimental methods.

(3) COMPETITION BETWEEN TWO SPECIES BELONGING TO THE SAME ECOLOGICAL NICHE

Let us admit that two species consume one and the same single foodstuff or, if they consume a mixed diet, that the proportion of each ingredient of the diet which they consume is the same for both species. Then if an individual of second species consumes per unit of time twice as much food as the first, it will influence the unutilized opportunity for the growth of the first species twice more than the first species decreases in its growth (α will be equal to 2). But the reverse action of the first species upon the second will be here twice feebler than the action of the second species upon itself ($\beta = \frac{1}{2}$). Under such circumstances the following condition could be fulfilled: $\alpha < K_1/K_2$ and $\beta > K_2/K_1$ (equation 1) or $\alpha/1 - \frac{m}{b_1} < \frac{K_1}{K_2}/1 - \frac{m}{b_2}$ and $\beta/1 - \frac{m}{b_2} > \frac{K_2}{K_1}/1 - \frac{m}{b_1}$ (equation 2) and, theoretically, only N_1 survives in the mixed population independently of initial concentrations of the species (Fig. 2). When $\alpha > K_1/K_2$ and $\beta < K_2/K_1$ survive N_2,

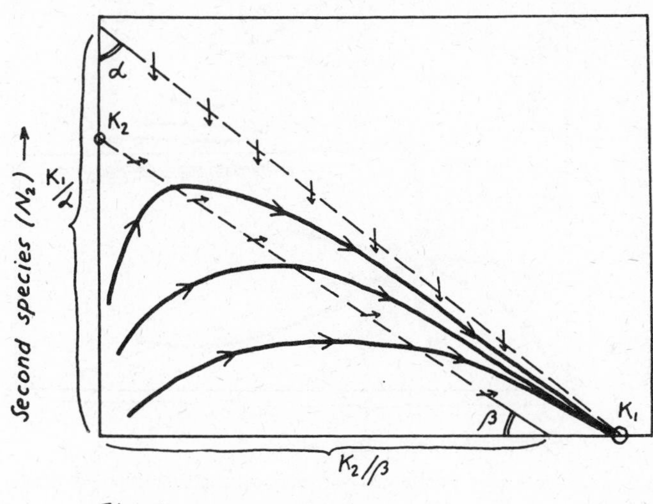

FIG. 2. Curves of interaction in the case of competition between two species belonging to the same ecological niche.

or always the "better adapted" species. A similar conclusion was reached by Haldane (1924), Volterra (1926) and Lotka (1932), and an experimental demonstration of the entire displacing of one species by another in a mixed population of this kind was given by Gause (1934, 1935).

(4) Slight Mutual Depression of Species

When two species belong to different ecological niches in the microcosm and, for instance, in addition to common food for each of the species a special kind of food is available that can not be so effectively obtained or consumed by another species, the mutual depression of these species will be less. Here the following condition may be fulfilled: $\alpha < K_1/K_2$ and $\beta < K_2/K_1$ (equation 1), or $\alpha/1-\frac{m}{b_1}<\frac{K_1}{K_2}/1-\frac{m}{b_2}$ and $\beta/1-\frac{m}{b_2}<\frac{K_2}{K_1}/1-\frac{m}{b_1}$ (equation 2). Theoretical analysis shows that in this case the competition leads to a certain stable population consisting of both species instead of the entire displacement of one of them by another (Fig. 3). An important feature here

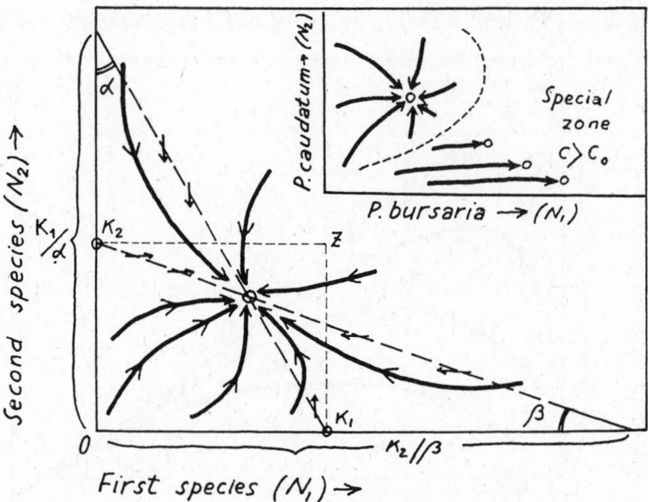

Fig. 3. Curves of interaction in the case of slight mutual depression of species.

also is the "regulation" of composition of the stable population: the disturbance of the stable combination of species leads automatically to the reestablishment of stable combination, in which each of the species is driven into its "niche." Theoretical possibility of an infinite survival of both species in a mixed population (or of a "knot" on the surface N_1N_2) was mentioned by Lotka (1932) and more definitely by Winsor (1934), who put the condition for it in the form: $\alpha\beta < 1$. However, this condition shows only that *if a "singular point" exists* it will be a "knot" (but there also can be no singular point when $\alpha\beta < 1$). Our conditions $\alpha < K_1/K_2$ and $\beta < K_2/K_1$ guarantee both the existence of the singular point and the fact that it is a "knot." For instance, if $\alpha = 5{,}5$; $\beta = 0{,}12$; $K_1 = 75$; $K_2 = 15$, then $\alpha\beta = 0{,}66$ and is < 1, but there is no singular point in the center of the map of integral curves because $5{,}5 > 5$ ($K_1/K_2 = 5$) and $0{,}12 < 0{,}2$ ($K_2/K_1 = 0{,}2$).

An experimental demonstration of the existence of a stable mixed population of two species was given by Gause (1935) in the case of two protozoa, one of which (*Paramecium caudatum* or *P. aurelia*) consumes more effectively bacterial components of a mixed diet suspended in the upper layer of the liquid, whereas the other (*P. bursaria*) prefers yeast cells sedimenting on the bottom.

(5) Special Zones

Experiments show that a definite type of the struggle for existence is often observed only in a certain part of the map of integral curves or, in other words, only under certain concentrations of N_1 and N_2. For instance, in the case of *P. caudatum* and *P. bursaria* (Gause, 1935) the reestablishment of a disturbed stable combination of species is not possible from *all* the points on the surface N_1N_2. If we make the concentration of *P. bursaria* too high, *P. caudatum* is not in a position to drive it out into its former place, and we obtain a stable population with the decreased concentration of *P. caudatum* (Fig. 3, above). In short, when *P. caudatum* enters a young biocoenose with the low concentration of *P. bursaria* the situation for its development appears to be much more favorable than in the case of an older biocoenose. Experiments have shown that this is due to the fact that

P. caudatum is much more sensitive than *P. bursaria* to the waste products accumulating in the daily renewed medium.

Let us consider briefly how the equation of the struggle for existence changes in this particular case. We know (Gause, 1935) that the coefficient of multiplication of *P. caudatum* (b_2) is inhibited by waste products of N_1 and N_2 (let us denote them C), and the expression of the biotic potential will be: $b_2 f(C) N_2$. The accumulation of C will be given by the difference of two factors, one of which depends on their production by N_1 and N_2, and another which represents their removal by washing the cultures in the experiment:

$$dN_1/dt = b_1 N_1 \frac{K_1 - N_1 - \alpha N_2}{K_1}$$

$$dN_2/dt = b_2 f(C) N_2 \frac{K_2 - N_2 - \beta N_1}{K_2}$$

$$dC/dt = f(N_1 N_2) - nC$$

Here $f(N_1 N_2)$ depends more on N_1 than on N_2. When the concentration of C rises above a certain threshold value C_0 the value $b_2 f(C)$ becomes zero and *P. caudatum* (N_2) ceases growing. The growth of N_1 continues until $K_1 - N_1 - \alpha N_2 = 0$. By introducing *P. caudatum* into even more and more dense cultures of *P. bursaria* we obtain a series of stable populations with even lower and lower levels of *P. caudatum.* But when the concentration of C is below C_0 the interaction between the species leads to the "classical" stable population. The general appearance of the curves is shown on Fig. 3, above.

It is to be remarked that we have here three equations with three unknowns, and therefore the integral curves ought to be reproduced in space, instead of surface. However, the structure of our equations enables us to represent their solutions in the region of singular points on surface $N_1 N_2$. Indeed, the stationary states are given by the equations: $dN_1/dt = 0$, $dN_2/dt = 0$, $dC/dt = 0$. The last expression gives C if N_1 and N_2 are known, and the first two N_1 and N_2 independently of C (when $C < C_0$).

If $C > C_0$ the growth of N_2 stops and N_1 is obtained independently of C.

In our real experiments the situation is somewhat more complicated in connection with diurnal rhythm of accumulation of waste products and dilutions of both species. We attempt here to give only a general idea of separate zones introducing new complicating circumstances and changing differential equations of competition.

(6) Symbiosis

Certain symbiotic equations have recently been considered by Kostitzin (1934). Let us analyze here briefly the properties of the basic equation (1) in the case of mutual aid of two species to each other:

$$dN_1/dt = b_1N_1 \frac{K_1 - N_1 + \alpha N_2}{K_1}$$

$$dN_2/dt = b_2N_2 \frac{K_2 - N_2 + \beta N_1}{K_2} \qquad (3)$$

Three following stationary states ought to be mentioned: (1) $N_1 = 0$, $N_2 = 0$; (2) $N_1 = 0$, $N_2 = K_2$; (3) $N_2 = 0$, $N_1 = K_1$. The fourth $N_1 = K_1 + \alpha K_2/1 - \alpha\beta$, $N_2 = K_2 + \beta K_1/1 - \alpha\beta$ will exist only when $\alpha\beta < 1$. Investigation shows that the properties of the singular points are as follows: (1) "unstable knot," (2) "saddle," (3) "saddle" and (4) "stable knot" when $1 - \alpha\beta > 0$. Fig. 4 (above) gives the curves of interaction between species for the case of symbiosis. We have here a certain natural extension of the principle included in Fig. 3. There, with the slight mutual depression of species, the position of the stable "knot" corresponding to a stationary population was determined by intersection of isoclines of horizontal with that of vertical tangents which took place within the tetragon OK_2ZK_1. In the case of mutual aid this intersection lies outside of tetragon and in the mixed population both species together attain larger biomasses than separately. As coefficients of mutual aid α and β increase the "knot" continuously moves up and right-

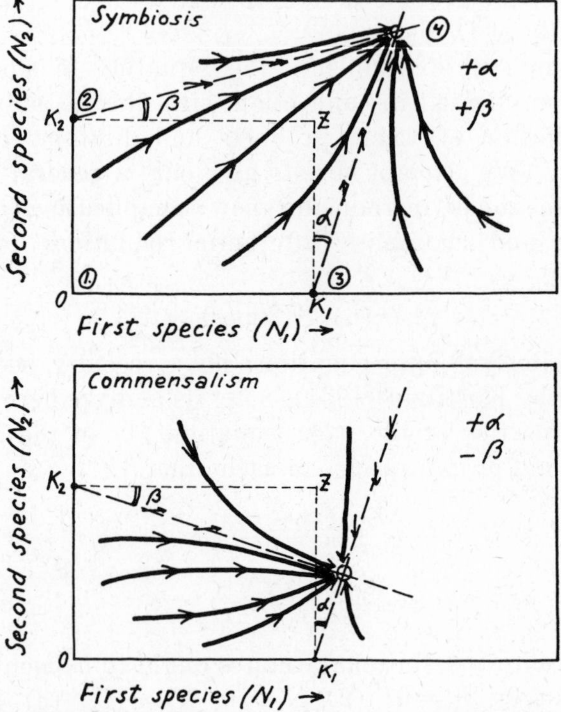

FIG. 4. Curves of interaction between species in the case of symbiosis and of commensalism.

wards and finally with $\alpha\beta = 1$ passes into infinity. It is evident that in a limited microcosm we can not expect infinite populations, and certain observations (Gause, 1934) indicate that the coefficient of mutual aid can considerably decrease in the course of growth of the culture. The case of symbiosis awaits its exact experimental investigation (the experiments of Gause referred to deal with one-sided symbiosis or commensalism and are not complete). Recent studies on artificial symbiosis (Buchsbaum, 1934) open here a new way for attack.

(7) COMMENSALISM

When the first species has a gain due to the presence of the second ($+\alpha N_2$) and in its turn slightly depresses the second ($-\beta N_1$) we have, speaking biologically, commensalism. The corresponding curves of interaction are reproduced on Fig. 4, below. Here the first species in a mixed population attains larger, and the second lower level than separately. As the degree of depression (β) increases the "knot" corresponding to the stable population gradually sinks, and with it the biomass of both species. Finally, the isocline of horizontal tangents crosses K_1 and subsequently remains the pure population of the first species only ($K_2 < K_1\beta$). In this way the system of equations of interaction gives a definite idea of the continuous passage from mutual depression to commensalism and symbiosis of species which is sometimes observed in biological investigations (Yonge, 1934). It is to be hoped that the accumulation of the experimental material will give us the possibility of adopting these equations as the basis of classification of the corresponding biological systems.

(8) The Action of External Factor on Mixed Population

Let us assume that the process of interaction between two competing species (equation 2) depends on a certain external factor, for instance, on temperature, attaining these or those fixed values. With the alteration of temperature the curves of the struggle for existence will continuously change. But at certain special or *bifurcation* values of temperature they will change *qualitatively;* in other terms, will change their topological structure—character and number of basic elements or "singular points." The *change of stability* of the system will take place. At temperatures *below* the bifurcation we can observe one type of the struggle for existence (for instance, strong mutual depression) with the typical stable pure population, and *above* the bifurcation slight mutual depression with the corresponding stable mixed population.

Let us analyze the case of the system (2) where the

conditions of the four types of the struggle for existence will be:

$$1^\circ\ \alpha/1-\frac{m}{b_1} > \frac{K_1}{K_2}/1-\frac{m}{b_2} \text{ and } \beta/1-\frac{m}{b_2} > \frac{K_2}{K_1}/1-\frac{m}{b_1} \text{ (strong depression)}$$

2°	"	<	"	and	"	>	" (remains N_1)
3°	"	>	"	and	"	<	" (remains N_2)
4°	"	<	"	and	"	<	" (slight depression)

We can admit that with the increase of temperature the coefficient of multiplication (b) in each species increases, but in the first species more rapidly. To simplify the calculations let us express this relation by a straight line, although every exponential relation will not change the essence of our conclusions: $b_1 = B_1 + \lambda_1 t$, $b_2 = B_2 + \lambda_2 t$, where $\lambda_2 < \lambda_1$ and $B_1 = B_2 = 0$. Since the calculation represents the very first approximation to the actual state of affairs, we neglect the action of temperature upon all other parameters. We assume also the dilution (m) less than the multiplication (b), so that $1-\frac{m}{b_1} > 0$ and $1-\frac{m}{b_2} > 0$. To separate variables from constant values we put $1-\frac{m}{b_2}/1-\frac{m}{b_1} = F(t)$, where t is temperature, and obtain the conditions of the four types of the competition:

$$1^\circ\ F > K_1/K_2\,\alpha \text{ and } F > \beta\,K_1/K_2$$

2° "	<	"	and "	> "
3° "	>	"	and "	< "
4° "	<	"	and "	< "

Denoting $F(t) = y$ and analyzing the curve of this function we can conclude that as y passes certain critical values, y_1, y_2 . . . etc., defined by non-equalities written above, the type of the stable system undergoes a change. Since $y = t-\frac{m}{\lambda_2}/t-\frac{m}{\lambda_1}$ we can easily calculate a simple example of temperature bifurcation (Fig. 5), which shows how one type of competition is transformed into another.

Summarizing the essence of theoretical calculations we

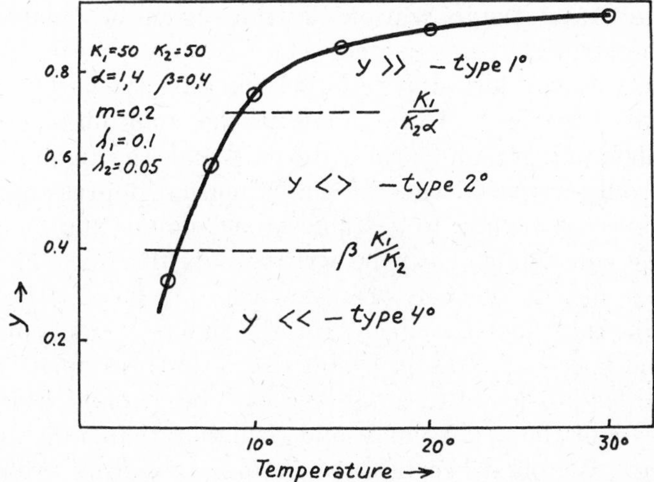

FIG. 5. A theoretical example of the action of temperature upon a mixed population of two species.

note that according to our admissions both species can separately dwell in the habitat and in both the rate of multiplication increases with temperature, but only in a different degree. As a result above a certain threshold one of them can not withstand competition, and bitypic system (4°) is transformed into monotypic (2°). This takes place with the fixed value of dilution and is due to purely biocoenotic (competition) and not physiological (temperature threshold) causes. From the above the conclusion may be drawn that *under the influence of temperature* (and of any other) *gradient a mixed population separates into a number of distinct types.* This conclusion can be confirmed experimentally (Gause, in press) and it is to be remarked that under the complicated conditions of actual habitats we often meet an interplay of biocoenotic and physiological causes of bifurcation. The history of previous temperature changes in the system may also be very important.

(9) RATE OF NATURAL SELECTION

The problem of the rate of natural selection in a population of two species may be reduced to the calculation of the "rate of stabilization" of the system of equations of the struggle for existence (1). In other words, how rapidly is the mixed population purified from the less adapted species? Unfortunately, the solution of this problem in a general form is difficult, and we can analyze here only a special case of slight mutual depression of two species leading to a stable mixed population.

The equation (1) can be written: $dx/dt = Ax(1 - ax + by)$ and $dy/dt = By(1 - cy + dx)$. If $b = d = 0$ we obtain usual logistic curves for the independent growth of the species. Now if b and $d \neq 0$ and are small the solutions of logistic equations can be expanded into series and the orders of b and d higher than first neglected. We obtain certain corrections inhibiting growth (since b and d are negative): $x = x_0 - x_1$. If $A \neq B$ the solutions can be obtained in the form of integrals which can not be taken in simple functions, but if $A = B$ we obtain:

$$x = x_0 - x_1 = \frac{\bar{x}_0}{a\bar{x}_0 + (1 - a\bar{x}_0)e^{-At}} - \frac{b}{ac} KK_1 \frac{e^{-At}}{(e^{-At} + K)^2} \left[\frac{K - K_1}{K^2} \lg \frac{e^{-At} + K_1}{e^{-At}(1 + K_1)} - \frac{K}{K_1} (e^{At} - 1) \right]$$

and an analogous expression for y, where $K = x_0 a / 1 - a\bar{x}_0$, $K_1 = \bar{y}_0 c / 1 - c\bar{y}_0$, and $\bar{x}_0 = x_{t=0}$, $\bar{y}_0 = y_{t=0}$.

From the view-point of the theory of natural selection it would be particularly interesting to obtain a solution for the case of the strong competition, which would help to connect the method of Volterra (1926) with that of Haldane (1924) and Ludwig (1933). It is to be hoped that further analysis will complete this investigation.

(10) Conclusions

The theory of the growth of mixed population of two species is already confirmed in many points by direct experimental investigations, and it can be discussed from two different angles. Firstly, it is directly connected with the problem of natural selection. We distinctly see here how the evolutionary process of expelling the less adapted species by a better adapted one changes with the stage of growth of the population, the relation in concentrations of the competing types ("special zones") and their "ecological niches." In other words, this theory demonstrates that the relative adaptability of two types is a rather variable feature.

Secondly, the results of our analysis ought to be connected with the problems of modern biocoenology. Regulation of the stable combination of species (a system with the slight mutual depression, commensalism and symbiosis) and the separation of the mixed population into a number of distinct types under the action of temperature (and of any other) gradients sheds a new light on the problem of organization of a biological unit—biocoenose.

LITERATURE CITED

(The references of literature prior to 1934 may be found in Gause, 1934.)

Buchsbaum, R. and M.
1934. *Science*, 80: 408.

Gause, G. F.
1934. "The Struggle for Existence." Baltimore: Williams and Wilkins.

Gause, G. F.
1935. Verifications expérimentales de la théorie mathématique de la lutte pour la vie. Actualités Scientifiques. Paris: Hermann (No. 277.)

Kostitzin, V. A.
1934. Symbiose, parasitisme et évolution (Etude mathématique). Actualités Scientifiques. Paris: Hermann.

Lotka, A. J.
1934. Théorie analytique des associations biologiques. Actualités Scientifiques. Paris: Hermann.

Winsor, C. P.
1934. Cold Spring Harbor Symp. Quantit. Biol., 2: 181.

Yonge, C. M.
1934. *Nature*, 134: 12.

COACTIONS IN LABORATORY POPULATIONS OF TWO SPECIES OF *DAPHNIA*

Peter W. Frank
Department of Zoology, University of Missouri, Columbia, Missouri

The simple mathematical formulations of Volterra (1926) and Lotka (1932), and a substantial body of evidence concerning the effects of inter-specific competition on experimentally regulated populations, have strengthened the impression among ecologists that existing patterns of distribution are, in part and perhaps largely, governed by this interaction. Both theory and role of such competition in natural populations have recently been questioned by Andrewartha and Birch (1953, 1954). Although their particular criticism of the competition equations as mathematical models has been answered (Philip 1955), there is no doubt about the limited applicability of the theory in its original form. The most intensive investigation of competition, by Park (1948, 1954) using *Tribolium,* emphasizes that the laboratory model itself presents complexities not inherent in Volterra's theory, which, for example, implies logistic growth for single-species populations. Extinction of one of the two competing species observed invariably resulted, but no a priori prediction as to which one would persist was possible in several of the laboratory environments that were chosen.

More important, the question of the significance of inter-specific competition among animals in natural communities is largely unresolved, nor does the present study bear directly on this point. The type of evidence that exists has been reviewed by Crombie (1947). Direct proof that a species is, in fact, restricted in its prevalence by the presence of competitors is hard to come by. Nevertheless, Elton and Miller (1954), who provide valuable perspective on the problem, feel optimistic about the prospect of gaining meaningful information from community surveys, while maintaining that, at present, the circumstantial nature of the facts, although they are extensive, usually permits alternative explanations.

In an earlier study (Frank 1952) it was observed that members of two genera of Cladocera did not coexist under the experimental conditions provided; in isolation from each other they sustained relatively high densities. The present investigation provides an attempt to apply a similar regime to two species that are more likely to compete in nature. The species *Daphnia magna* and *Daphnia pulicaria* were chosen since they met this requirement and because, unlike most members of their genus, they were relatively easily distinguishable for purposes of census.

The species live in similar habitats, small ponds with high organic content, and have overlapping ranges. Moreover, examination of locality records indicates that they seem not to occur together in one pond. There is, however, a notable scarcity of explicit information on the distribution of Daphnia in small ponds and about the general range of *Daphnia magna.* Thus, as a result of

Reproduced with permission from Ecology, 38: 510-519, 1957. Published by The Ecological Society of America and The Duke University Press, Durham, North Carolina.

lack of published species lists, it was possible for a European worker to reach the erroneous conclusion that *Daphnia magna* does not occur on the American continent (Wagler 1936). Granting that the role of competition in the natural distribution of these species is unknown, it seemed that they were highly suitable for a preliminary investigation intended not only to provide another laboratory model, but to define differences in population physiology and behavior that could conceivably influence their relative success in natural habitats.

The present study was supported by grants of the University of Missouri Research Council, which supplied constant-temperature equipment and provided some financial aid. It is a pleasure to thank Thomas Park and Marian B. Frank, who read the manuscript and suggested a number of improvements.

Materials and Methods

As in the past, only pure clones of the experimental animals were employed. The stock of *Daphnia pulicaria*, originally from an Illinois pond, was the same as in an earlier study (Frank 1952). *Daphnia magna* were collected in 1952 by Prof. G. E. Hutchinson from a pond near Pasadena, California. The culture methods described in the earlier paper were modified; certain of the techniques used by Slobodkin (1954) in particular proved advantageous. Only the essentials of the methods will be mentioned here, since husbandry of the animals has been significantly improved. More detailed description of present conditions of culture will be presented elsewhere.

All animals in the main set of tests were subjected to a routine of census and simultaneous removal to fresh medium at 72 hour intervals. This period, rather than the shorter one of previous experiments, was adopted because it proved better for *Daphnia magna*, which tended to die, apparently from clogging of the filtering appendages, when the medium was changed more often. Animals were cultured in charcoal-filtered tap water, to which was added either (a) 1.2 mg per cc of commercial baker's yeast, or (b) 1.8 million cells per cc of *Chlamydomonas moewusi* Gerloff from pure cultures 15-31 days old. Yeast and algae were estimated photometrically after an initial calibration by weighing or haemocytometer count. The following six types of populations were observed for 69 days:

a. In yeast
    D. pulicaria — 8 replicates
    D. magna — 8 replicates
    Both species — 14 replicates
b. in algae
    D. pulicaria — 8 replicates
    D. magna — 8 replicates
    Both species — 14 replicates

All populations were started with two animals, aged 10-12 days, per species, and were maintained in baby-food jars 4.5 cm in diameter containing 50 cc of medium. Temperature throughout the experimental period was held at 20° C. Cultures were kept in constant light from 40-watt fluorescent fixtures 24 cm above the water surface. Since not all replicates were begun on the same date, it is possible to check on effects of fluctuations in supposedly constant factors. No obvious correlations between time and populational events were noted.

Before census, animals were separated into two size categories by first passing them through a screen of No. 00 bolting cloth, and then visually separating the few animals that clearly did not fit into the groups so established. Census involved complete count of all live animals, ephippia, and parthenogenetic eggs shed prematurely from the mother's brood pouch. Repeated tests showed that both ephippia and such dropped eggs were inviable. Sex ratios were determined at 15-day intervals in single-species replicates. In mixed populations, sex ratios in *Daphnia magna* were observed at every census after Day 30. Immediately prior to census and change of medium, oxygen tension was estimated with a dropping mercury electrode.

Aside from this main set of tests, mass populations in battery jars containing 8 liters of water were observed somewhat more casually. Two replicates of each of the single species and of the mixed species were maintained in constant light and at relatively constant temperature for a period of 18 months. All cultures were fed a mixture of yeast and algae at weekly intervals. No attempt was made to regulate the amount of food except on a visual basis. The water was not changed during the course of the test, but distilled water was added periodically to keep volume constant. It proved impossible to sample the populations quantitatively. In mixed species replicates, the ratio of the two organisms was estimated monthly by dipping out 600 cc of medium after first stirring the contents of the jar vigorously, but in irregular fashion. If the sample so obtained did not yield at least 100 animals, another was drawn. Because of differential behavior of the two species and of different age classes, the observed ratios provide only a very gross estimate of species

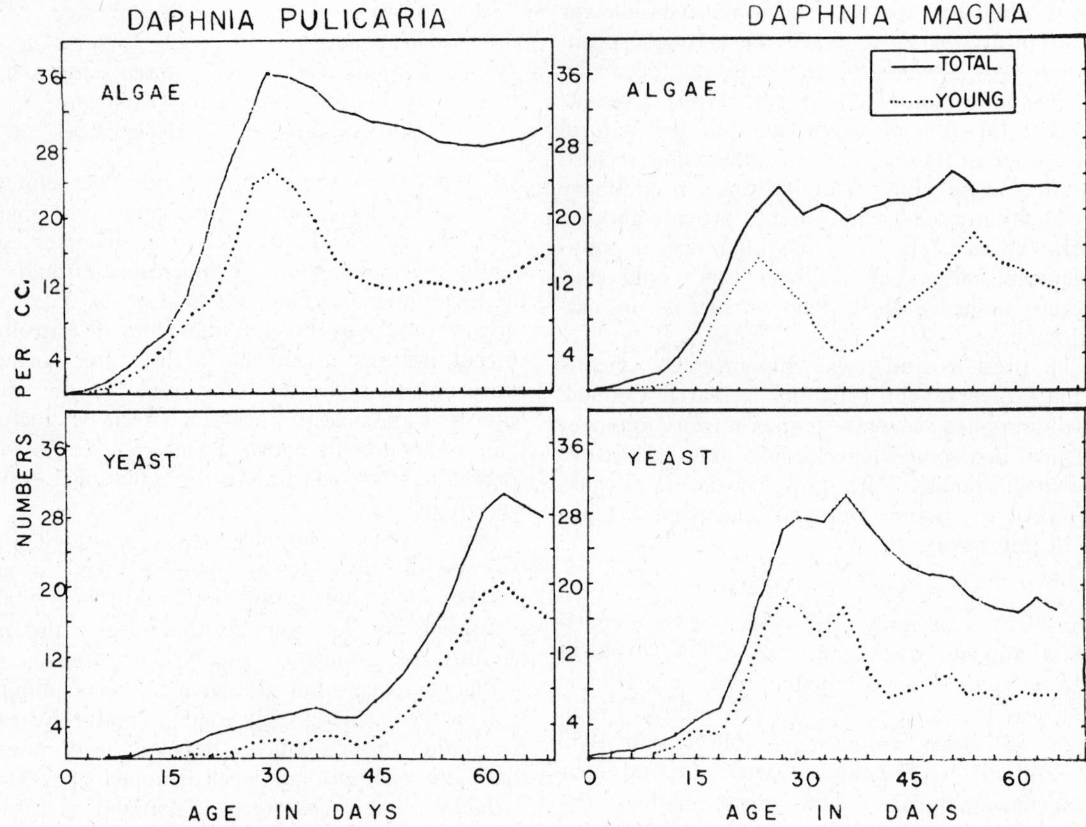

Fig. 1. Average single-species growth form of *Daphnia magna* and *Daphnia pulicaria* in yeast and *Chlamydomonas* cultures.

composition. Contamination of these cultures by other organisms could not be controlled, so that many other interactions besides competition must have existed. Of these complications, availability of bacteria growing in the medium, and growth of epibionts on the Daphnia may certainly have had significant effects.

Experimental Result

The single-species control replicates, besides being a necessary adjunct for demonstration of the existence of interspecific competition, are of considerable interest in themselves. They provide a descriptive norm of growth form of the organisms under the selected conditions, and may be subjected to further causal analysis. Figure 1 illustrates average population growth, and presents some crude indication of age distribution. If one limits himself to examination of major trends, it is at once apparent that, as in previous investigations of Daphnia populations (Pratt 1943; Frank 1952; Slobodkin 1954), an initial rise culminates in a distinct peak, followed by a more gradual decrease. Growth form was not observed for a sufficient time to determine whether a second peak would ensue.

Comparison between foods reveals first that the level of population peaks attained by each species shows surprisingly little difference between algae and yeast. This similarity in maximum density is, however, an artifact in the sense that food concentrations were chosen deliberately, from indications of preliminary tests, to equate these points as much as possible. Nevertheless, within species, it appears that algae sustained denser average populations than did yeast. A more striking contrast may be noted in *Daphnia pulicaria,* where rapid population growth commences almost at once in algae, but not until about Day 42 in yeast. The true relations are somewhat obscured by averaging the replicates, as will be seen below.

Comparison between species indicates greater average numbers for *Daphnia pulicaria* than for *Daphnia magna* once the initial growth phase is passed. On the basis of biomass, however, *Daphnia magna,* a larger species, would clearly be superior.

With respect to age distribution the number of young, consisting aproximately of animals from the first to the fourth instar, gives a modified measure of natality similar to that of a moving average. It differs from such a statistic, since some mortality occurs during this age interval, and an increased period of time is occupied by each instar as density increases. With the exception of *Daphnia pulicaria* in yeast, the populations are predominantly composed of young animals during the initial growth phase, or for the first 24 to 36 days. Even in this exceptional case, once rapid growth is established, young animals form about two thirds of the total. After the peak is reached there is a decline in the proportion of young, reflecting greatly decreased birth rate. During this period, many of the adults die and are replaced by recruitment of young (Slobodkin 1954). Unfortunately, determination of death rates did not prove feasible, and the phenomenon can not be fully documented in the present instance. The total effect is a slow decline in numbers, and an increase in average age of individuals. Only in *Daphnia magna* growing in algae was population development sufficiently advanced when the experiments had to be terminated to show good evidence of another cycle of reproductive activity. This difference in behavior of *Daphnia magna* populations in the two types of media suggests a shorter average life span in algae than in yeast. This is supported by the observation at times of census that algal cultures contained a greater amount of debris during this period. Lacking objective data on death rates, it is easy to overstress this point.

The use of averages in describing the experiments is, of course, of limited value, since significant departures from synchrony will be obscured. In Figure 1, moreover, two of the replicates of *Daphnia pulicaria* in yeast were not included in the average; these two cultures became extinct on Days 33 and 57 respectively, without ever having reached a peak comparable to that of other populations. Extinction further emphasizes the precarious condition of this species in yeast, so long as population size is small. Although most cultures eventually grew well, all exhibited a notable initial lag. Total population numbers for alternate replicates of each of the four species and food combinations are graphed in

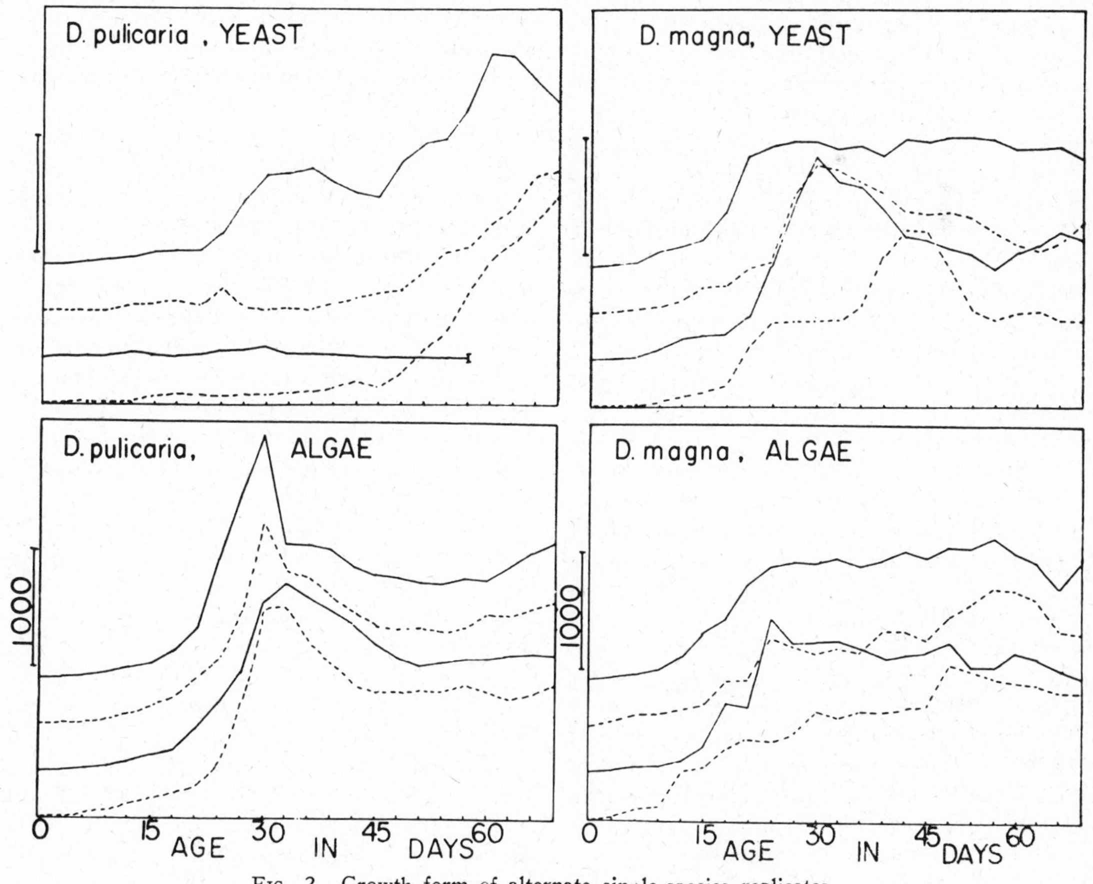

FIG. 2. Growth form of alternate single-species replicates.

Figure 2, in an attempt to give some insight into relative variability. To increase legibility, the vertical scale for successive replicates has been displaced by 400 animals, so that absence of variation would result in parallel families of curves.

By this criterion, *Daphnia pulicaria* in algae grow more consistently than do cultures under other conditions. In yeast, the same species shows great variability. This is stated perhaps in more detail by Table I, which indicates the coefficients of variation at nine-day intervals for each series of replicates. After their extinction, the two previously mentioned *Daphnia pulicaria* cultures are excluded from the calculations. Differences between the species and culture media can be explained only in part. With respect to *Daphnia pulicaria* in algae, culture conditions apparently leave little to be desired, and compare, in terms of variability, with *Tribolium confusum* in a favorable environment (Park 1954). Yeast for these animals clearly is a poor food, at least initially. Those replicates that persisted throughout the experimental period exhibit a variable phase during which populations grew sporadically. Only after approximately one average life span (Frank 1952) were the animals capable of overcoming the deleterious effect of the environment. After densities of about eight Daphnia per cc. were attained, there was no indication that they were still adversely affected. A longer period of observation would have been necessary to discover the permanence of this state. It is likely that yeast causes death selectively of young animals, so that age distribution as well as population density would be significant determinants. Probably bacterial contamination of the yeast is responsible, although perhaps this food organism has itself such an unfavorable influence. No equivalent difficulty is manifested by *Daphnia magna;* they appear to do as well or better in yeast than in algae. In neither medium, however, are their growth curves as congruous as those of *Daphnia pulicaria* in algae.

Certain of the contrasts between species can be established in more detail. Changes in natality are separable into four distinct causes: 1. change in the number of parthenogenetic eggs produced; 2. number of inviable parthenogenetic eggs shed before hatching (referred to hereafter as egg loss); 3. number of adults with ephippial rather than parthenogenetic eggs; 4. number of males in the culture. The number of young animals in populations reflects a compounding of the effects of the first three of these categories. The fourth, however, differs in that mere census yields no estimate of the magnitude of its consequences.

No separate estimate of egg number is available

TABLE I. Coefficients of variation (C.V. per cent) for selected censuses of single species cultures

	DAPHNIA PULICARIA		DAPHNIA MAGNA	
Age in days	Algae	Yeast	Algae	Yeast
9..........	14.3	37.1	24.6	26.2
18..........	20.4	59.0	20.7	18.9
27..........	31.6	55.4	30.7	27.6
36..........	17.8	140.5	25.9	42.0
45..........	20.1	185.4	28.8	35.3
54..........	11.5	81.1	28.2	29.0
63..........	12.9	55.6	39.4	31.5

from the present experiments; a marked decrease with density may be expected (Pratt 1943). The other three elements are presented in Figure 3 as percentages of the total adult populations. In both species egg loss occurred as certain times, particularly during early stages of population development. In regard to food, the species behave in opposite ways, *Daphnia magna* having significantly greater loss in algae than in yeast, with the reverse true for *Daphnia pulicaria.* During the active growth period neither species dropped eggs. The number of ephippia, highest in *Daphnia pulicaria* in yeast, increases quite generally as the initial maximum is reached, and declines thereafter. This finding agrees with data from a different species under somewhat similar conditions (Slobodkin 1954). No obvious relation exists between egg loss and production of ephippia.

The sex ratio strongly suggests a significant species difference that is independent of the type of food. At 30 days, and in the two later censuses for which number of males was observed, *Daphnia magna* cultures averaged 19.6 per cent males, with a range in individual replicates of from 8 to 31 percent. *Daphnia pulicaria* replicates were not found to contain more than 2 per cent males. This difference may perhaps account for the greater variation in development of populations of the former species in contrast to *Daphnia pulicaria* in algae.

To a limited extent it is possible to correlate these events with other variables in the cultures. Measurements of oxygen tensions and egg loss imply some sort of association (Figs. 3, 4). It should be pointed out that since oxygen determinations were made only immediately before census and change of medium, the data do not reflect the entire set of changes that may prove significant. Additional short-term tests show that at moderate densities (to 10 animals per cc) water in the jars attains a minimum oxygen content within four to eight hours after introduction of animals. This low value, usually of the order of

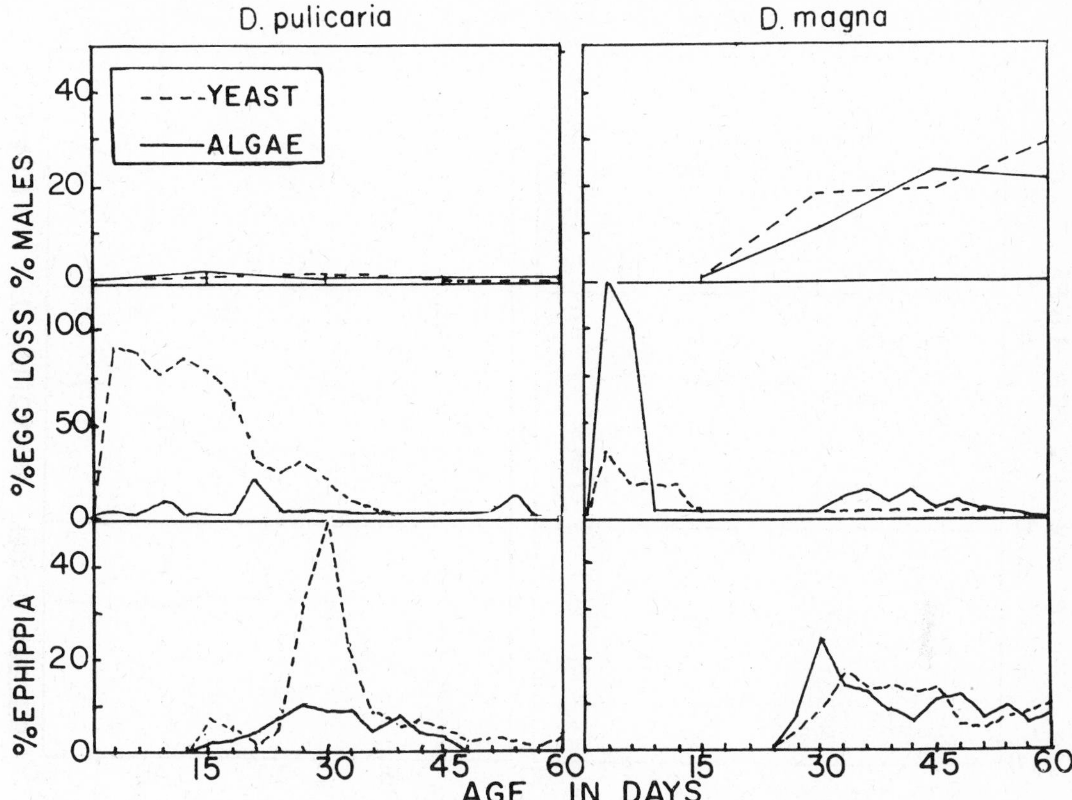

Fig. 3. Average production of males and of ephippia, and egg loss in single-species populations.

0.5 cc of O_2 per liter, is followed by a slow increase. What seems to occur is that at the beginning food contributes a large part of the respiratory loss, not all of which is compensated by entry of air from the surface. As the Daphnia diminish the food supply, less oxygen is consumed by the culture. In algal medium there may be active photosynthesis for a time. This is suggested because it was noted that values of dissolved oxygen increased more quickly and became higher than in yeast cultures. From the data of Figure 4 it may safely be concluded that oxygen lack initially exercises a depressing effect on both species. This could result not only in egg loss, but also in a decline of egg number and of individual growth and feeding rates, as noted by others (Fox, Gilchrist and Phear 1951; Green 1956). However, except when *Daphnia pulicaria* is grown on yeast, such low oxygen concentrations soon rise. During the remainder of the experimental period, food may be assumed to be the major limiting factor.

Ephippia and males show no apparent relation to oxygen concentration, but both seem affected, probably indirectly, by changes in density. It is possible to interpret the present results in the light of a recently proposed hypothesis (von Dehn 1955), according to which lipids in food affect sex determination and sexual egg production, but older theories fit equally well.

In so far as generalization is possible from this limited analytical extension, it seems that the species have similar growth form despite the presence of underlying differences in mechanism of growth limitation. The full significance of such differences cannot be assessed. Its sex composition should presumably confer a decided reproductive advantage to *Daphnia pulicaria,* especially in algal medium. The essentials of single-species behavior were known from preliminary experiments not described here. The present conditions were chosen to demonstrate interspecific competition in the belief that *Daphnia magna* would be favored in yeast, while in algae *Daphnia pulicaria* would be the more successful.

Data from mixed-species replicates, observed concurrently with the cultures just described, are not entirely in accord with this prediction (Fig. 5). In algal medium *Daphnia pulicaria,* as expected, persisted in all 14 replicates, whereas *Daphnia magna* invariably did not. There can be little doubt that extinction was the direct result

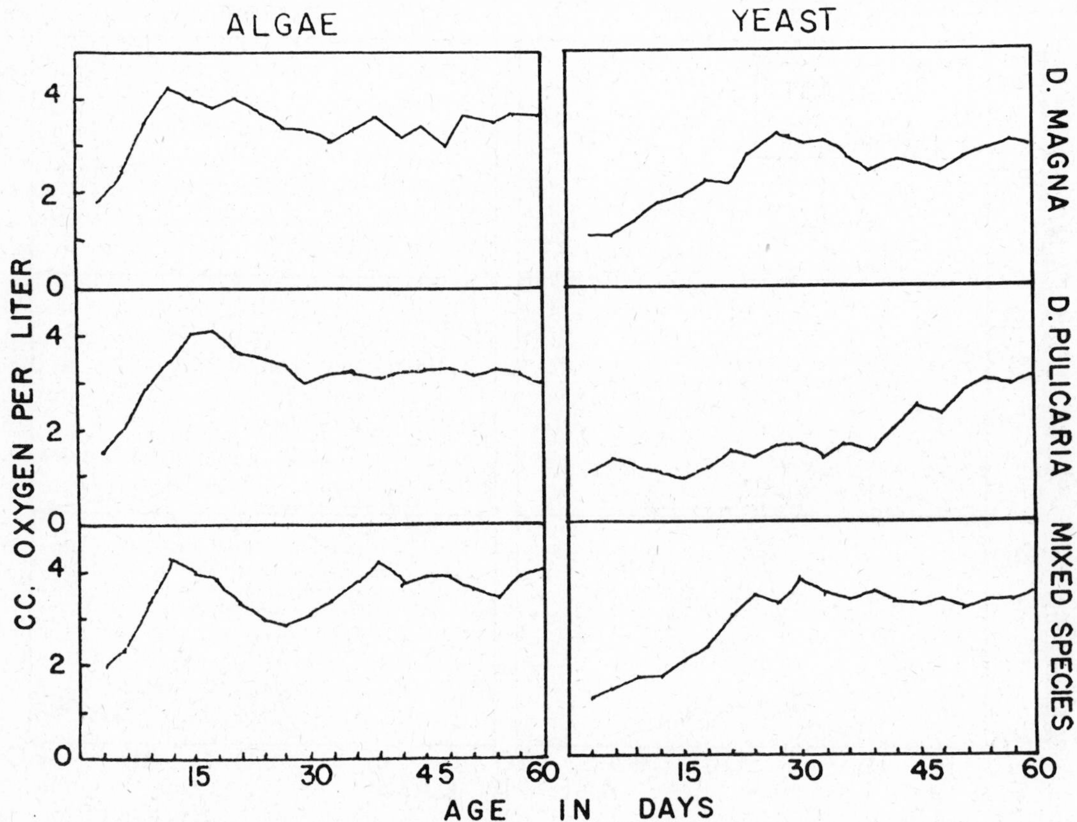

FIG. 4. Dissolved oxygen in single- and mixed-species populations at the end of sucessive census intervals.

of interspecies competition. The analytical data on single species populations suggest the observed outcome: male production, number of ephippia and egg loss all tended to be higher in *Daphnia magna;* moreover, its total population numbers averaged lower than those of the species successful in competition.

In yeast, where *Daphnia magna* might be expected to persist, this result was not realized. During initial stages of population growth, this species does have the faster rate of increase, so that its numbers exceed those of *Daphnia pulicaria.* After Day 27, on the average, *Daphnia magna* starts to decline, and invariably its extinction follows.

More detailed examination shows that, in algae, the populations of the ultimately successful species are inhibited at the outset, when compared to single-species controls. The mean time of occurrence of the population peak is Day 48 rather than Day 30. However, aside from this initial retardation, there seems to be little effect of interspecific competition on *Daphnia pulicaria* here. What causes the major and rapid decline of *Daphnia magna* is not certain, although sex ratio measurements are indicative (Fig. 6). Males predominated during the period of population decline, and formed a greater fraction of the total population than in single-species cultures. In most mixed-species replicates, the last few survivors were entirely males. Since males have, if anything, a shorter life span than do females, it may be conjectured that the immediate cause of extinction is an increase in the proportion of male-determined eggs. Presence of the other species must be assumed as the cause.

In yeast, *Daphnia pulicaria,* far from being inhibited by interspecies competition, increases at a greater rate than in single-species culture. As early as Day 15 its populations in mixed cultures averaged 3.84 per cc as compared with 1.72 for the controls. The difference is significant above the 0.1 per cent level. *Daphnia magna* possibly competes with the other species at this stage, but any such effect is overshadowed by a positive interaction. This, most likely, consists of some sort of detoxification; the simplest explanation is that *Daphnia magna* removes part of the excess food. Thereafter *Daphnia pulicaria* possesses an advantage that may have the same explanation as in mixed-species culture in algae (Fig. 6). Although extinction appears to occur more slowly

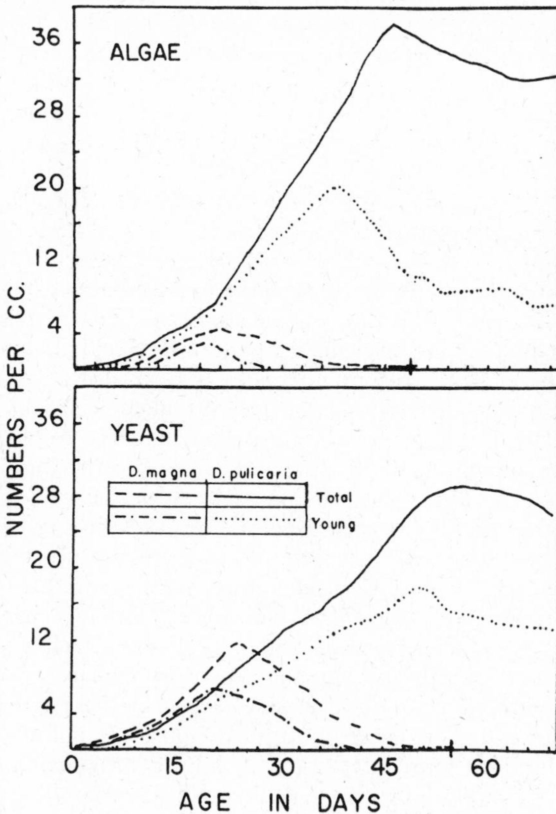

FIG. 5. Average density in mixed-species populations.

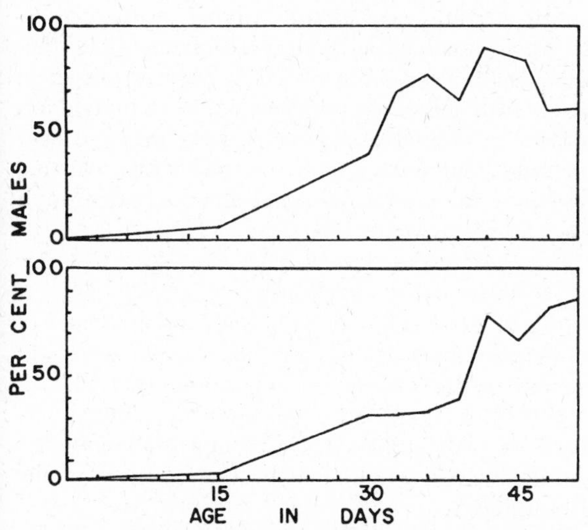

FIG. 6. Percentage of male *Daphnia magna* in mixed-species populations (as per cent of total adult *Daphnia magna*); upper diagram, in yeast; lower diagram, in algae.

in yeast than in algae, the difference is not statistically significant. Time of extinction ranged from Day 33 to 57 in algal medium, with a mean of 45.2 days. In yeast, the first population disappeared on Day 39, the last on Day 66, with an average of 55.3 days.

Information from mass cultures provides a valuable qualifying note to generalization of the foregoing results. This is true despite the facts that sampling of the populations was quite inadequate and that no good estimate of the environmental conditions to which the animals were exposed can be established. However, the major value of these tests is to a considerable extent independent of the demonstration of inter-specific competition as an effective determinant. At least one instructive point emerges whether one considers the difference between single- and mixed-species behavior attributable to such interaction or not. In the jars initially seeded with equal numbers of both species, *Daphnia pulicaria* could not be recovered at the 11th and 18th months respectively (Table II). Single-species populations under otherwise similar conditions persisted well past this period. After *Daphnia pulicaria* had disappeared, the contents of the jars were allowed to dry. Subsequent addition of fresh water caused hatching of ephippial eggs. As neonates were produced, they were removed and counted. After 15 days, when no more ex-ephippial females were observed to emerge, *Daphnia pulicaria* surpassed *Daphnia magna* in hatch by a ratio of 2.3 : 1 and 8.6 : 1 in the two replicates. Certainly, under natural conditions, an apparent result of coexistence of the two species might not be permanent, nor would it necessarily reveal long term trends. *Daphnia pulicaria,* at an apparent disadvantage when the short-range results are examined, may nevertheless be favored if environmental fluctuation, in this case drying, enters as an additional component of competition.

TABLE II. Per cent *Daphnia pulicaria* in samples from mixed-species mass cultures

Month	0	1	2	3	4	5	6	7	8	9
Replicate 1.....	50.0	39.5	55.6	60.6	18.4	15.2	1.7	0.9	1.8	0.3
Replicate 2.....	50.0	46.2	58.8	43.1	46.7	21.0	56.3	32.4	26.4	18.5

Month	10	11	12	13	14	15	16	17	18
Replicate 1.....	0.2	...	...	...	...	...	...	...	..
Replicate 2.....	12.2	3.4	1.0	2.1	1.3	0.6	0.2	0.4	..

DISCUSSION

If the results of the present study are viewed in terms of their relevance as another experimental model of competition, they demonstrate first that, as in all other such cases for which data have been published, two species forced to live together in a simple environment, in which niche diversification is minimal, do not both persist. The case of these organisms in yeast medium presents a departure from the usual model. There is added a type of coaction which leads to a result more akin to succession than to interspecific competition *per se*. Since there is evidence that a limiting factor, oxygen, operates at low densities, but declines in significance as populations increase, the result, although it was unexpected, is not altogether surprising. *Daphnia magna,* under these conditions, is a model of what Hutchinson (1951) has termed a fugitive species.

When one attempts to compare the present experiments with those concerning competition between *Daphnia pulicaria* and *Simocephalus vetulus* (Frank 1952), the shorter time span during which the losing species survives in the present set of tests is striking. Unfortunately, the conditions under which the studies were conducted differ in a number of respects: amount of medium, type and quantity of food, and period between feedings all are not comparable. However, there are indications that the mechanisms by which competition produces its main result, extinction, are quite distinct in the two cases. In the earlier investigation, a direct density effect was demonstrated; in the present series it seems likely that the primary influence of competition between the species is to be found in its effect on male production of *Daphnia magna.* It is not necessary to postulate that *Daphnia pulicaria* exercises a different type of interference from that produced by equivalent densities of *Daphnia magna.* Possibly there are periods during population growth of this species when by itself, during which reproduction may be limited almost entirely to males. If this happens, population decline followed by resumed generation of females could be expected to follow. It appears that in mixed culture when the decline of total population occurs, relatively few females of *Daphnia magna* remain, and most of these may be past their reproductive peak.

At the present stage of analysis, there is no reason to belive that effective competition is for anything except food. As emphasized by Slobodkin (1954), direct density effects in Daphnia cannot be demonstrated under most conditions. Thus it may prove possible eventually to equate severity of competition with population structure, amount of food supplied, and filtering rate of the population. If other sources of competition should prove negligible, the model would be relatively simple. Nevertheless, except in end result, it would not correspond to Volterra's mathematical model, nor do other mixed laboratory populations approach the latter more closely. Since extinction through competition has repeatedly been demonstrated, it may be suggested that less restrictive theoretical formulations might be instructive. It is encouraging that the problem has recently been revived at this level in two quite diverse ways (Nicholson 1954; Neyman, Park and Scott, 1956).

Speculations about extension of the present results to natural populations can be entertained only at considerable risk of proving wrong. In laboratory culture food quantity appears to be limiting. Whenever populations are dense, no food remains suspended in the open medium by the end of a census interval. If food also limits natural populations, which seems likely (Brooks 1946), concentration rather than amount would be significant, so that a markedly different situation results. The experimental model has several other highly artificial aspects. Mass culture tests were conducted primarily to indicate the proper context of the other laboratory experiments. In small ponds the final outcome of interspecific competition between Daphnia, if it exists, is related more directly to the number of ephippial eggs produced than to vegetative stages in the population. The latter must bear some relation to this long-term interaction, if only in providing a source of ephippia; but there is no reason to think this relation must be direct. One species could exist at relatively low densities, yet leave more resting eggs than another with greater average numbers. It thus seems possible that two events are superimposed: a short-range effect leading to decreased numbers of active individuals during a single season, but perhaps rarely if ever causing apparent extinction; and another, lasting over a number of seasons and ultimately determining species composition.

Summary

1. Single- and mixed-species populations of *Daphnia pulicaria* and *Daphnia magna* were observed in the laboratory for a 69-day period.

2. When alone, both species usually persist in each of two food media, although *Daphnia pulicaria* is severely inhibited by one of these in the beginning.

3. In mixed species cultures that were fed on algae, *Daphnia pulicaria* consistently persisted and may be presumed to cause the observed extinction of the other species. The result could have been predicted from study of the isolated species.

4. With yeast as food, *Daphnia pulicaria* increased more rapidly in mixed- than in single-species replicates, and again caused the extinction of *Daphnia magna.*

5. The presence of two limiting factors, oxygen

and food, at different stages of population history can account for the observed results.

6. The major competitive effect causing extinction of *Daphnia magna* in both foods appears to be increased male production of this species.

7. Mass-culture experiments emphasize that in competition between natural populations of these species, numbers of ephippia rather than of active individuals may be more significant.

References

Andrewartha, H. G., and L. C. Birch. 1953. The Lotka-Volterra theory of interspecific competition. Austral. J. Zool., **1**: 174-177.

———. 1954. The distribution and abundance of animals. Chicago, Illinois: University of Chicago Press.

Brooks, J. L. 1946. Cyclomorphosis in Daphnia I. An analysis of *D. retrocurva* and *D. galeata.* Ecol. Monogr., **16**: 409-447.

Crombie, A. C. 1947. Interspecific competition. J. Anim. Ecol., **16**: 44-73.

von Dehn, M. 1955. Die Geschlechtsbestimmung der Daphniden. Die Bedeutung der Fettstoffe, untersucht an *Moina rectirostris* L. Zool. Jahrb., Abt. allg, Zool. Physiol., **65**: 334-356.

Elton, C., and R. S. Miller. 1954. The ecological survey of animal communities: with a practical system of classifying habitats by structural characters. J. Ecol., **42**: 460-496.

Fox, H. M., B. M. Gilchrist, and E. A. Phear. 1951. Functions of haemoglobin in *Daphnia.* Proc. Roy. Soc. (B), **138**: 514-528.

Frank, P. W. 1952. A laboratory study of intraspecies and interspecies competition in *Daphnia pulicaria* (Forbes) and *Simocephalus vetulus* O. F. Müller. Physiol. Zool., **25**: 173-204.

Green, J. 1956. Growth, size and reproduction in *Daphnia* (Crustacea: Cladocera). Proc. Zool. Soc. Lond., **126**: 173-204.

Hutchinson, G. E. 1951. Copepodology for the ornithologist. Ecology, **32**: 571-577.

Lotka, A. J. 1932. The growth of mixed populations: two species competing for a common food supply. J. Wash. Acad. Sci., **22**: 461-469.

Neyman, J., T. Park, and E. L. Scott. 1956. Struggle for existence. The *Tribolium* model: biological and statistical aspects. Proc. 3rd Berkeley Symp. on Math. Stat. and Prob., **4**: 41-79.

Nicholson, A. J. 1954. An outline of the dynamics of animal populations. Austral. J. Zool., **2**: 9-65.

Park, T. 1948. Experimental studies of interspecies competition. I. Competition between populations of the flour beetles *Tribolium confusum* Duval and *Tribolium castaneum* Herbst. Ecol. Monogr., **18**: 265-308.

———. 1954. Experimental studies of interspecies competition. II. Temperature, humidity, and competition in two species of Tribolium. Physiol. Zool., **27**: 177-238.

Philip, J. R. 1955. Note on the mathematical theory of population dynamics and a recent fallacy. Austral. J. Zool., **3**: 287-294.

Pratt, D. M. 1943. Analysis of population development in *Daphnia* at different temperatures. Biol. Bull., **85**: 116-140.

Slobodkin, L. B. 1954. Population dynamics in *Daphnia obtusa* Kurz. Ecol. Monogr., **24**: 69-88.

Volterra, V. 1926. Variazioni e fluttuazioni del numero d'individui in specie animali conviventi. Mem. Accad. Lincei, **2**: 31-113.

Wagler, E. 1936. Die Systematik und Verbreitung des Genus *Daphnia* O. F. Müller mit besonderer Berücksichtigung der Südafrikanischen Arten. Arch. f. Hydrobiol., **30**: 505-556.

Beetles, Competition, and Populations

An intricate ecological phenomenon is brought into the laboratory and studied as an experimental model.

Thomas Park

Let us begin with two seemingly unrelated words: *beetles* and *competition*. We identify competition as a widespread biological phenomenon and assume (for present purposes at least) that it interests us. We view the beetles as an instrument: an organic machine which, at our bidding, can be set in motion and instructed to yield relevant information. If the machine can be properly managed, and if it is one appropriate to the problem, we are able to increase our knowledge of the phenomenon. Unfortunately, however, this does not necessarily mean that the concept is thereby clarified. This could happen of course. But, alternatively, the problem as now enlarged could emerge as being more complicated—that is to say, broader and deeper than first imagined. And the machine itself could prove to be more intricate, even recalcitrant. Obviously there exists an intimate marriage between the machine, its operator, and the phenomenon. Ideally, this marriage is practical, intellectual, and esthetic: practical in that it often, though not immediately, contributes to human welfare; intellectual in that it involves abstract reasoning and empirical observation; esthetic in that it has, of itself, an intrinsic beauty. Perhaps these rather pretentious reflections seem far removed from the original words—beetles and competition. But I do not think this is the case.

We develop the story further. First, I offer some general remarks about competition—the phenomenon. Then, I say something about the beetles—the organic machine. Finally, I attempt to put the two together in a certain way—to pry, discreetly I trust, into the intimacy of their marriage (*1*).

Competition in the Abstract

Biological competition has been the subject of controversy and debate among those who have given it serious study (*2*). Considerable disagreement exists about its essential character and its significance. Such difficult questions as these inevitably arise: How can competition be formally defined? What are its component elements? How can its presence in a natural ecological situation be detected—that is, what constitutes adequate proof? When it does operate, what is the consequence of this for the competitors themselves? Is it a pervasive process, one always effectively in command, or rather, is it a safety valve, something called into account only after a certain threshold is reached? This is not the place to deal systematically with these matters, important as they are. That would be inappropriate and, I fear, tiresome. It is necessary, however, to establish a point which bears on later discussion.

The author is professor of zoology at the University of Chicago, Chicago, Ill. This is the text of his address as retiring president of the AAAS, delivered 28 December 1962 at the meeting in Philadelphia.

It is often held that competition is mediated by two component, but different, processes. The first is called "exploitation"; the second, "interference." Exploitation operates when the organisms draw upon a particular resource (food, say) which is present in limited supply. The more limited this resource, and the larger the population draining it, the greater is the intensity of competition. Interference operates when interactions between organisms affect their reproduction or survival. For example, imagine two populations one of which is small and the other crowded. Assume further that more food is available for both populations than can be used (exploited). The small group readily obtains adequate nourishment but the crowded group does not, for the reason that its members so disturb each other that the *opportunity* to feed is restricted. If this causes a decrease in birth rate, or an increase in death rate, interference can be said to be functioning.

These points are shown schematically in Fig. 1. We see there four squares, each representing a physical habitat. The habitat is occupied by the populations of two species. We denote these as *X* (the closed circle) and *Y* (the broken circle). *R-1* and *R-2* refer to two different resources. The interference of *X* on *Y*, and of *Y* on *X* is indicated below each square as being absent (0) or present (+). We can now examine in the light of the preceding comments what should hold true when competition between *X* and *Y* is indeed a reality.

In situation I we note that although species *X* and *Y* are living together in space and in time they are actually exploiting quite different resources and are not interfering with each other's reproduction and survival. We therefore conclude, a priori, that the biological stage is arranged in such a way as to make it impossible for interspecies competition to exist. This is the null case. Situation II depicts the two species as drawing upon different sources of capital but interfering with each other. Situation III is the opposite of situation II: here, *X* and *Y* are withdrawing their capital from a joint account but interference is zero. We conclude that competition is operating in both situations II and III, but for diverse reasons. In situation IV, *X* and *Y* are utilizing the same resource, but, since they are also engaged in interference, we deduce that competition, thus doubly assured, is intense. These arguments seem logical. Later we shall ask whether indeed they are biological.

Competition Experimentally Viewed

Let me be less formal, less academic. It is not difficult to imagine local populations of two species which share a common geography; which exploit, at least in part, certain of the same resources; and which interfere with each other's reproduction and survival in a manner that is neither haphazard nor frankly predatory. Under such conditions we infer that competition should be operating. But how can the inference be proved? Suppose we find it feasible to count both groups and thereby record the changes in their numbers generation after generation. Suppose, further, that there is no appreciable immigration and emigration. We graph the accumulated data (species *X* and species *Y* against time) and search for *pattern*.

To illustrate the difficulty of the problem, I have generated two artificial patterns, making use of a table of random numbers. These appear in Fig. 2 and are there referred to as case 1 and case 2, respectively. Despite the fact that, biologically speaking, the curves are quite fraudulent, they do bear a seductive resemblance to the behavior of real populations! In case 1 the only relation between the two "species" is purely coincidental, by definition. In case 2, on the other hand, matters have been so contrived that *X* is more abundant than *Y* for most of its recorded history, but there is an intermediate interval during which *Y* exceeds *X*.

Let us pursue the point. We now pretend that the graphs before us are actual rather than synthetic, and also that no information is available other than the census data themselves. Our question remains the same: Is competition operating in either instance? Regrettably, the question cannot be answered on the basis of the knowledge available. All we can do is to draw the following two, rather barren, conclusions:

1) Case 1 does not support an inference of competition. There is no consistent relation between the curves. However, the inference is *not disproved* because competition could be operating but its effect obscured by such extrinsic factors as, say, those variations of climate which characterize each year and which affect the reproduction and survival of both species.

2) Case 2 does support an inference of competition. *X*, characteristically the abundant species, declines significantly (though transiently) when *Y* increases markedly. However, the inference is *not proved* because the visual suggestion of competition could be illusory and the cause, again, could be extrinsic, such as, for example, a particular sequence of seasons more favorable for the increase of *Y* than of *X*.

But there is another point, essential for the argument, that emerges from our brief consideration of Fig. 2. It is this: the information contained therein is retrospective and descriptive rather than prospective and based on experimentation. The curves illustrate the abundance of *X* and *Y* through time. But conditions extraneous to the presumed competition were not controlled, and, as I have tried to show, these could have played a causative role. In addition, we have been able to record the history of only one population of each species; our experience is limited. Traditionally, ecological findings are based on the chronicle of events which have taken place in an environment unmolested by the observer and varying according to its own natural right. Such retrospective studies attempt to explain what has happened on the basis of a single case history, and the derived data are candidates for some form of correlation analysis. Although I am in no sense contemptuous of this method, I am persuaded that progress in an area so complex as population ecology will be greatly facilitated by increased experimentation in the field. There is nothing original in this view. Certain workers consistently find it rewarding to manipulate the natural conditions. But I urge that this approach should accelerate, gain wider adoption, and perfect its techniques. In principle, if not always in practice, the method is limited by neither the taxonomy nor the habitat of the organisms being studied. Parenthetically, I believe it can even contribute to the solution of such pressing problems as conservation and the social biology of man. When a prospective plan is used, the dividends are agreeable. Time is saved; more questions are asked; appropriate treatments are replicated by design; and the data lend themselves to powerful methods of analysis.

There is, however, a different way to study populations and to do so prospectively and experimentally. That is to move a field problem into the laboratory. To do this one must find an organism which is conceptually and technically adapted to investigation of the phenomenon under consideration. In other words, we strive to erect an indoor *model* of an outdoor experience. Such models, though not simple, are simplified; they enjoy a regimen of planned control; their intrinsic interactions are likely to be intensified. To this extent they are unrealistic. But they remain, nonetheless, quantitative *biological* systems, and their unrealistic aspects often prove to be a virtue rather than a vice. Let us explore this matter.

Beetles: The Experimental Material

About 2500 B.C., a Pharaoh died and was entombed. When the site was studied various curios were found, including an urn which contained milled grain. Within the grain were the corpses of small insects known commonly as "flour beetles" and technically as *Tribolium* (*3*). Thus this genus, at least so far as one of its 26 known species is concerned, was apparently preadapted to living in flour in early historical times. As everyone knows, such beetles are important pests of cereals; in fact, large bureaus exist which are zealously engaged in searching for effective ways to destroy them and limit their dispersal. As everyone does *not* know, however, the same creatures are elegantly suited for certain types of ecological and genetic research; in fact, a few small "bureaus" exist which, with equal zeal, are dedicated to the beetles' welfare and conservation. Why should this be so? I shall attempt a brief answer to the question by introducing you to the organism; to the "organic machine," as I referred to it earlier.

A note of history: To the best of my knowledge, the flour beetles were first used experimentally by W. P. Davey, who, in 1917, reported on the relation between x-irradiation and the life duration of the adult stage (*4*). It was R. N. Chapman, however, who studied *Tribolium* as populations; who recognized its potential for this sort of research. That was in 1928 (*5*). Since that time a handful of ecologists have continued, and expanded, this tradition. And only recently, I am happy to report, the geneticists have discovered that the beetles have advantages for their own work (*6*).

In order to perform efficiently, a laboratory population model must satisfy certain requirements. The major, technical ones are these. First, it must be possible to enumerate the population by accurate census. Second, it must be possible to reconstitute the population after each census without appreciable trauma to its membership. And third, it must be possible to control the environment in various ways and to manipulate it in various ways. The precise meaning of "environment" poses a problem of heroic magnitude, and I have no desire to involve you, or myself, in this polemic. But I do think that a certain clarification can be achieved by means of the following assertions. The environment can be viewed as being *spatial*; it has a geometric configuration. It can be viewed as being *climatic*; it has a definition, say, in terms of temperature, moisture, and light. It can be viewed as being *nutritive*; it is a reservoir of food, both in quality and quantity. It can be viewed as being *biotic*; it has a component evoked by interaction among living things. Finally, it must be viewed as being *temporal*; its other attributes are relentlessly influenced by the passage of time.

The technical utility of *Tribolium* stems from the simple natural-history fact that the beetles (and their immature stages) spend their life, and multiply, in finely milled flour. In other words, flour is the spatial, climatic, and nutritive environment neatly bundled into one convenient package. Space can be controlled merely by choosing a container of desired shape into which a known weight of flour is introduced. Climate can be controlled by maintaining unlighted cabinets at prescribed values of temperature and humidity and allowing the flour to come to equilibrium at these values. Food can be partially controlled by using flour which is always prepared in a certain way (quality) and apportioned in a certain amount (quantity). The biological and temporal aspects of the *Tribolium* environment are more effectively introduced somewhat later in this article.

For every population study there is one type of basic datum. This is a record of the number (or weight) of organisms inhabiting a defined space at a particular time. But frequently such records are amazingly difficult to come by; in fact, it is sometimes possible to achieve nothing more than a shrewd guess. With the flour beetles, as I have suggested, we do not encounter this difficulty. A census can be readily taken, and though this is laborious and in itself unexciting, we can take pride in the accuracy of the results. Also, the beetles have given us no compelling reason to think that they are harmed by the procedure. I illustrate by describing a typical sort of census; one where a population is counted each 30 days (30 days is the approximate length of a generation at a temperature of 29°C). The method is diagrammed in Fig. 3. Populated flour is gently poured from its glass container through a series of silk sieves with meshes of different dimensions. This segregates the stages by size and accumulates for disposal the old, but now uninhabited,

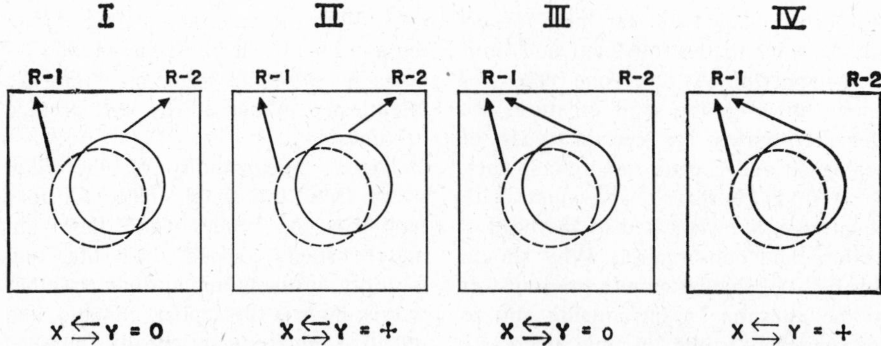

Fig. 1. Abstract representation of interactions that produce competition. *R-1* and *R-2*, two different resources; *X* and *Y*, the interference of one species population with the other (see text). In case I, competition is absent; in case II, competition exists, owing to the presence of interference (+); in case III, competition exists, owing to exploitation by both species (*X* and *Y*) of a shared resource; in case IV, competition is intense, owing to the fact that there is both exploitation and interference.

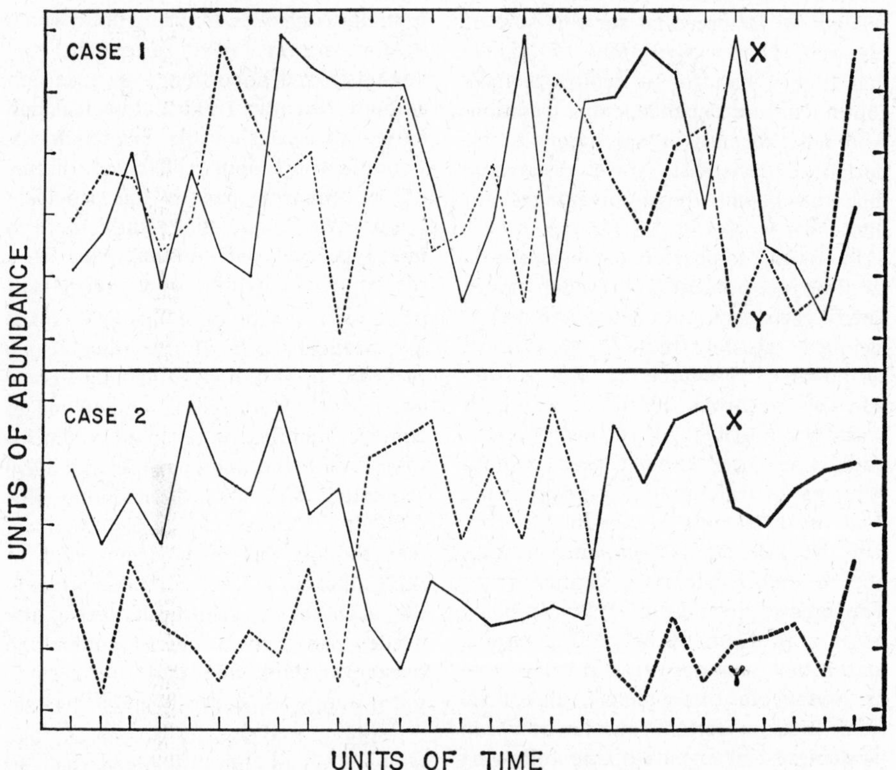

Fig. 2. Fabrication of two population case histories by means of a table of random numbers. There are two species, *X* and *Y*. In case 1 all assocation between the species is coincidental. In case 2, species *X* is permitted to exceed species *Y* except during the intermediate time intervals during which *Y* exceeds *X* (see text).

flour. After counting, and recording of the numbers, the total population is placed in another vial containing fresh flour and returned to the incubator, where, for an additional 30 days, the processes of death, survival, and reproduction go on.

A further point needs making. For studying interspecies competition in the laboratory, at least two distinct species are obviously required. And each of these must satisfy the requirements outlined earlier. The genus *Tribolium* provides such material; there are two satisfactory species. One goes by the quaint name of *Tribolium confusum,* while the other has been christened *Tribolium castaneum.* For convenience, I retain the notations used earlier and refer henceforth to the former as X and to the latter as Y. Both X and Y are husbanded in exactly the same way and censused in exactly the same way, and both dwell in flour. Thus, for any predetermined (prospective) set of climatic, spatial, and nutritive conditions, X can be studied as a single-species population; the same holds true for Y; and X plus Y can be combined as a competition model. The significance of this statement should be fully appreciated because, in many ways, it lies at the heart of our story. Its meaning is this. If we measure what X does and what Y does when both are *alone,* we thereby are able to detect and evaluate what is *new,* or competitive, when both are together. Extrinsic factors, being controlled, no longer mask the data. The intrinsic factors remain, but now they are under surveillance. They constitute the biological and temporal aspects of the environment. This is the intellectual advantage of the model—an advantage very difficult to achieve outside the laboratory. It is, in part, what was meant earlier by the comment that such models, though not simple, are simplified. Gratifying as all this is, however, it does entail an element of risk: the risk that the investigator may be hypnotized by the data as such, concern himself only with the model, and forget the general phenomenon. Since there is a reasonable chance of answering the questions asked, why not shed the burden of theory? That is to say, instead of speculating about such matters as exploitation and interference, why not claim (quite cogently) that competition has been invoked if the behavior of X and Y together differs demonstrably from the behavior of X and Y alone? This is indeed a comforting position when one is immersed in analysis of a particular investigation. But, even though I take it, I do not applaud it. It is purely an operational convenience which, in the long run, may restrict one's contemplation of the phenomenon as a whole. The model should be more than an edifice in its own right.

We return to Fig. 1, there to refresh our memory about situation IV. This is the case for which the deck is stacked in such a way as to maximize the intensity of competition. Both species are exploiting a common resource, and both are engaging in interference. We now transfer this situation to *Tribolium.* The abstraction can be put to empirical test. X and Y are obviously competing for food, and for space in which to live. They are also interfering with each other. Some types of interference have been experimentally studied. Among these may be mentioned the relation of crowding to egg production, to rate of development, and to adult longevity, and a special sort of behavior [which overlaps predation (*1*)] involving the cannibalism of eggs and pupae by larvae and adults. It is probable that still other patterns of interference are as yet undetected (*7*).

To recapitulate briefly, I have suggested that there exists in organic nature a phenomenon known as "competition." I have presented, in terse form, something about the difficulties that arise in its serious study. Finally, this led me from outdoors to indoors, to the introduction of a laboratory organism which has certain properties, both conceptual and technical, that can be adapted to investigation of the problem at hand. I now wish to summarize some results in order to illustrate what happens when the "machine" is put to work.

An Empirical Illustration

A number of reports dealing with *Tribolium* competition have been published, and others are being written (*8*). I select one which illustrates some of the matters discussed earlier—specifically, a study concerned with the relation of six different climates to the population performance of *X* alone, *Y* alone, and *X* interacting with *Y* (*9*). Climate, now under supervision, remains an extrinsic factor but one no longer capricious. The response of each of the two species to climate is a quantitative measure of *intra*species competition. The response of the two species in association measures whatever additional impact arises from *inter*species competition. Owing to the fact that the research is prospective, the treatments can be chosen in such a way as to favor the chance that the phenomenon will be illuminated. It is also mandatory to initiate, not one population per treatment, but just as many as manpower, stamina, and patience permit, in the context, of course, of the demands made by the experimental design. Let me comment on the last point. Somewhere there may lurk a person who holds the view that laboratory population studies (unlike their field counterparts) are easy and quickly consummated. The facts are just the opposite. Maintaining the laboratory and collecting the data is drudgery. I cite some statistics. During the next few paragraphs I summarize a certain investigation in an abbreviated way. In point of fact it required over 4 years to do nothing more than obtain the observations necessary for the analysis: 400 individual populations were sifted and examined every 30 days, and some 3 million beetles were counted. Basically, however, this is irrelevant and immaterial though, I hope, not incompetent. The *real* point is that the opportunity to work prospectively with such a machine as the *Tribolium* model creates, in itself, an obligation to operate that machine at high capacity. But I digress. Let us return to the issue at hand.

We establish six constant climates defined in terms of temperature and moisture and, for convenience, name them as follows: hot-moist, hot-arid, temperate-moist, temperate-arid, cool-moist, and cool-arid (*10*). Into each of the climates we introduce a set of control cultures (*X or Y*) and a set of experimental cultures (*X and Y*) (*11*). The procedures involving husbandry and census have already been described (Fig. 3).

In reporting the findings it is essential to gain some knowledge about the single-species populations before examining the mixed-species groups. A simplified summary appears in Table 1 in which the averaged total densities for both species are ranked within each column in relation to the climate the species inhabit. I draw three conclusions from Table 1: (i) both species persist successfully under the various climatic conditions (*12*); (ii) the *levels* of numerical abundance are affected by temperature and moisture; and (iii) *X* and *Y* do not respond in the same way to the environments in which they live. Thus, *X* is most productive in the hot-moist climate, while the density rank for *Y* in that climate is 3; *X* is least productive in the hot-arid climate, while the rank for *Y* is 5; and so on. In different words, the interaction between climate and *intra*species competition is reflected in the numbers observed.

When we examine what occurs when the two species are required to live together we are immediately confronted with a new, and qualitatively different, fact. It is this. One species is always eliminated and the other survives! Since it has been demonstrated that *X* and *Y* persist successfully when they are alone, it now follows that elimination of one species in the presence of the other is the result of sustained competition. But the matter is more complicated, more interesting. It can be pursued with the aid of Table 2. There, the six climates are listed in column 1; the single-species events are reviewed in column 2, but this time arrayed in a different way; and the competitive outcomes, in terms of percentage of contests won, are summarized in column 3.

Let us first consider column 3 of Table 2. We see there are two different

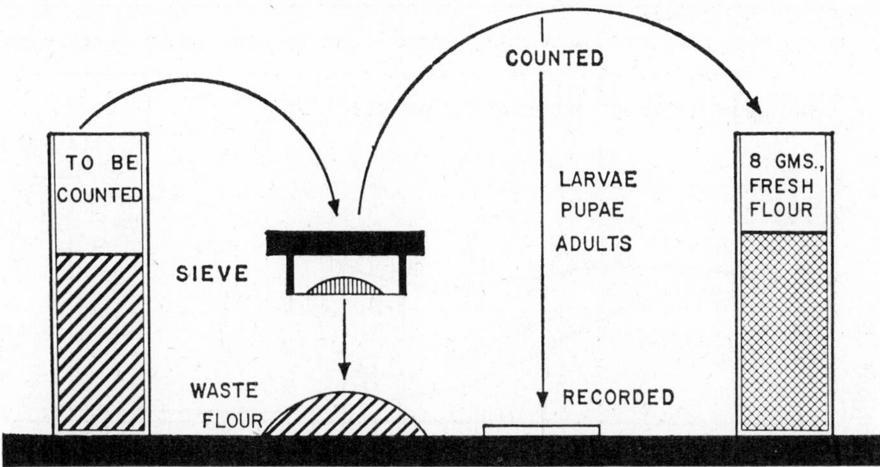

Fig. 3. Schematic diagram showing the technique of censusing a *Tribolium* population (census procedures at 30 days).

Table 1. Average numerical abundance of single species *X* and *Y* ranked in relation to six different climates (rank 1, densest population).

Climate	Rank of *X*	Rank of *Y*
Hot-moist	1	3
Hot-arid	6	5
Temperate-moist	2	1
Temperate-arid	3	4
Cool-moist	4	2
Cool-arid	5	6

patterns. One is unidirectional; the other, alternative. Let me explain. In the hot-moist climate *Y* always wins and *X* always loses. In the cool-arid climate *X* always wins and *Y* always loses. These end results are unidirectional. In the four other climates one species is always the *usual* winner ("usual" being defined as significantly greater than 50 percent), but for each case the other species wins *occasionally*. These results are alternative and can be thought of theoretically as being "stochastic." Thus, the consequences of competition are multifarious—multifarious in respect of climate, of species, and of frequency of success and failure.

Now let us approach Table 2 in a different way. A glance down column 2 reveals that in one climate *X* is equal to *Y*, in three climates *X* exceeds *Y*, and in two climates *Y* exceeds *X*. If no other facts but these were available it might be amusing to attempt an extrapolation—to predict which species, in which climate, would survive in competition. A common-sense hypothesis immediately comes to mind: The species superior by itself should retain that superiority when with its rival. But, paradoxically, this prediction is rarely entirely fulfilled, as column 3 of Table 2 clearly shows. It is completely (see *12*) realized only in the cool-arid climate. It is usually, though not totally, fulfilled in hot-arid, temperate-moist, and temperate-arid climates. No rational guess can be made for the hot-moist climate, since there *X* is equal to *Y*. In the cool-moist climate it is actually the less successful single species, *X*, which usually wins the contest. I advance these points not

Table 2. The outcomes of competition between species *X* and *Y* contrasted with the individual performances of the two species in each of the six different climates.

Climate	Single species (numbers)	Mixed-species outcomes (% of contests won)
Hot-moist	$X=Y$	*Y* (100), *X* (0)
Hot-arid	$X>Y$	*X* (90), *Y* (10)
Temperate-moist	$Y>X$	*Y* (86), *X* (14)
Temperate-arid	$X>Y$	*X* (87), *Y* (13)
Cool-moist	$Y>X$	*X* (71), *Y* (29)
Cool-arid	$X>Y$	*X* (100), *Y* (0)

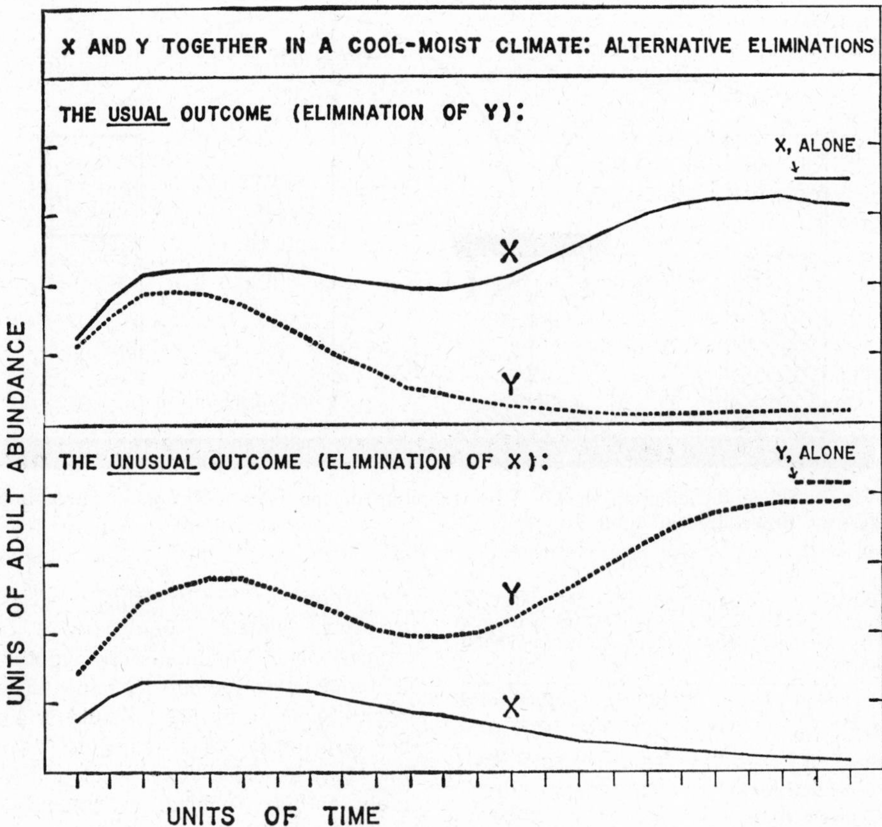

Fig. 4. Smoothed curves showing alternative outcomes for species *X* and *Y* when in competition in the cool-moist climate.

to be mystical but rather to stress the fact that competition, even under supervision, is an extremely complex phenomenon. It is clear from what has just been said that *intra*species processes can be deeply modified by those new types of interference and exploitation which emerge as a consequence of togetherness. And it is becoming increasingly evident that such issues can be studied through a combined empirical and statistical approach, as P. H. Leslie has made abundantly clear (*13*). I think, also, that two points suggested at the beginning of this article here find illustration; the problem as now extended proves to be broader in scope than was at first imagined, and, in a sense, the machine has behaved in a more intricate fashion.

It is appropriate to illustrate one of the six competitive situations in a bit more detail. For this I choose the events seen in the cool-moist climate. This is a complicated case but an interesting one. The outcomes are alternative, but in large measure they fail to conform to an expectation based (a priori) on the performances of single-species populations. Let us examine Fig. 4. There, as smoothed curves, the numbers of adult beetles of species *X* (solid line) and species *Y* (broken line) are plotted against census time. The upper graph depicts the frequent outcome, or elimination of *Y*; the lower graph, the infrequent outcome, or elimination of *X*. In both instances there is an initial competitive period during which the two species are increasing. This is followed, again in both instances, by a period during which one species is progressively declining while the other is increasing. The increase eventually leads the successful species to a level of abundance which is statistically similar to that displayed by single-species populations of the same age, suggesting that the travail of competition has not (in this case at least) left a permanent scar on the victor.

A new perspective is now possible. With the research finished, the curves of Fig. 4 obviously become retrospective, historical documents. But at this stage, I think, we enjoy an added confidence and an added understanding. We know that while climate has played an extrinsic role in determining the abundances of *X* and *Y* it has not caused population extinction. The latter results from interaction between the species—"the biotic and temporal aspects of the environment." We know, further, that the data have a certain generality. Instead of reporting an isolated circumstance they are based on the performance of 70 separate populations (20 of *X*; 20 of *Y*; 30 of *X* + *Y*). In short, we have advanced to a new status: a tentative inference of competition has become a fact, and the outcomes of the process have been established. There are of course many things we do not know. For example, why does *Y* sometimes eliminate *X*? Is the stringent competition here described a reality of outdoor nature or is it purely a consequence of keeping the species in confinement? There are other such questions, and all are difficult. But the mere phrasing of a proper question is a signpost toward its answer.

At this juncture the investigator plays a more active part. It becomes his responsibility to pose the next question, to run the machine differently. As has just been suggested, numerous opportunities confront him. He could proclaim an analytical interest in the competitive events that characterize, say, the cool-moist climate. Investigation in this direction leads to a study of mechanism; to an exploration of ecological and genetic causation. By increasing the understanding of how parts of the machine work together, the phenomenon is enlarged in *depth*. Alternatively, the investigator might proclaim a greater interest in *breadth*. He complicates the model in such a way as to make it biologically more realistic and by this means searches for further ramifications of the phenomenon. He might assert, for example, that climates do not really exist in six tidy packets of temperature and moisture but, rather, are characterized by their variability. Therefore, the promising thing to do is to program the research in such a way that climate becomes cyclic and what is measured is the added impact of *this* on *X* alone, *Y* alone, and *X* with *Y*. Or again, the investigator might proclaim that his work had yielded additional insight—insight about the phenomenon itself, about methods, about new items to observe and record. Therefore (he might argue) the time has come to forsake the model, move outdoors, and there start afresh. The course finally chosen is to a considerable extent subjective. Although the choice must be mediated by practical and intellectual values, nevertheless it does involve an element of taste. And it is here that an esthetic, an intuitive, quality insinuates itself into the domain which I have called "beetles, competition, and populations."

Conclusion

I have essentially finished my story. Its message has been a simple one. The population is difficult to study with rigor and even more difficult to understand. Populations can be investigated in a number of ways, several of which I have tried to suggest. Each way has its strengths and its limitations. I have concerned myself primarily with one method, the use of laboratory models. Because of conviction I have been careful neither to say nor to imply that this is the most rewarding approach. But it is the approach I know best, and one I find agreeable. There is, however, a new and exciting prospect that is emerging from the experimental study of populations—the prospect that mathematical theory may be able to attack even such intricate problems as competition. I have earlier pointed out how a certain generality is derived from a series of replicated experiments. But if mathematics can grasp data such as these, a greater abstract generality may ultimately result. There is a passage from A. N. Whitehead which precisely summarizes what I mean. In tracing the historical development of the science of electromagnetism Whitehead says (*14*): "This rapid sketch . . . illustrates how, by the gradual introduction of the relevant theoretic ideas, suggested by experiment and themselves suggesting fresh experiments, a whole mass of isolated and even trivial phenomena are welded together into one coherent science, in which the results of abstract mathematical deductions, starting from a few simple assumed laws, supply the explanation to the complex tangle of the course of events."

I am expected to close, I presume, with a remark about the "population explosion." I oblige. I am against it! I do not wish, however, to draw direct parallels between insects and men. But despite this reluctance, several facts have emerged from the study of beetles in their flour which seem to have general currency. One of these is that overexploitation and intense "interference" are perilous and that the peril increases as the population increases.

And there is another fact, one illustrated earlier: The largest population, if exposed to stress, does not necessarily enjoy the best prospect of survival. Man, as we all know and pontificate, has the intellectual talent and the technical skill to avoid such coleopterous hazards. In short, he has the capacity to manage his own population and (of equal importance) to conserve those myriad other populations on which he depends. But one thing is certain. If man does not manage *his* biology *it* will manage him. (*15*, *16*).

References and Notes

1. There are other common ecological relations between species in addition to competition. These are the interaction between plant and herbivore, between predator and prey, and between parasite and host. The three differ from competition, however, in that they all share a built-in behavior such that one population is the attacked and the other is the attacker, with obvious consequences for both. Thus, horses "attack" grass; lynxes attack rabbits; tapeworms attack swine. Still other ecological relations are mutually beneficial, while at the pinnacle of specialization are those end products of convergent evolutions, populations which are socially structured.
2. Many of the points that I have raised here, and elsewhere, are of course not original with me. Several general references which pertain to various aspects of the problem of competition are as follows: G. F. Gause, *The Struggle for Existence* (Williams and Wilkins, Baltimore, 1934); A. C. Crombie, *J. Animal Ecol.* **16**, 44 (1947); E. Mayr, *Proc. Am. Phil. Soc.* **93**, 514 (1949); A. J. Nicholson, *Australian J. Zool.* **2**, 9 (1954); L. C. Birch, *Am. Naturalist* **91**, 5 (1957); C. Elton, *The Ecology of Invasions by Animals and Plants* (Methuen, London, 1958); M. S. Bartlett, *Stochastic Population Models* (Methuen, London, 1960); L. B. Slobodkin, *Growth and Regulation of Animal Populations* (Holt, Rinehart and Winston, New York, 1961).
3. A. Andres, *Bull. Roy. Soc. Entomol. Egypt* **24**, 74 (1931).
4. W. P. Davey, *J. Exptl. Zool.* **22**, 573 (1917).
5. R. N. Chapman, *Ecology* **9**, 111 (1928).
6. I. M. Lerner and F. K. Ho, *Am. Naturalist* **95**, 329 (1962).
7. Cannibalism, a special case of interference, has been recently studied by E. R. Rich [*Ecology* **37**, 109 (1956)], F. J. Sonleitner [*Physiol. Zool.* **34**, 233 (1961)], and J. L. Brereton [*Ecology* **43**, 63 (1962)].
8. T. Park, *Ecol. Monographs* **18**, 265 (1948); ———, D. B. Mertz, K. Petrusewicz, *Physiol. Zool.* **34**, 62 (1961).
9. T. Park, *Physiol. Zool.* **27**, 177 (1954); J. Neyman, T. Park, E. L. Scott, *Third Berkeley Symposium on Mathematical Statistics and Probability* (Univ. of California Press, Berkeley, 1956), vol. 4, p. 41.
10. The actual temperature and humidity values, in degrees centigrade and percentage of relative humidity, are as follows: 34°, 70 percent; 34°, 30 percent; 29°, 70 percent; 29°, 30 percent; 24°, 70 percent; and 24°, 30 percent.
11. All cultures were started with eight young adult beetles per vial; sex ratio, unity. Control cultures received four males and four females of species *X* or four males and four females of species *Y*. Experimental cultures received two males and two females each of species *X* and *Y*.
12. There is one exception to this statement. Single-species populations of *Y* eventually became extinct in the cool-arid climate (temperature, 24°C; humidity, 30 percent). However, they persisted for a longer time than they did when in competition with *X* in the same climate.
13. P. H. Leslie, *Biometrika* **49**, 1 (1962).
14. A. N. Whitehead, *An Introduction to Mathematics* (Holt, New York, 1911).
15. H. F. Dorn, *Science* **135**, 283 (1962).
16. I am deeply grateful to the following friends who read the manuscript and gave me the benefit of their advice: P. P. H. DeBruyn, P. H. Leslie, D. B. Mertz, and Philip Wylie. I am also greatly indebted to the late Sydney Hadfield for a color slide used in connection with the lecture.

POPULATION ECOLOGY OF SOME WARBLERS OF NORTHEASTERN CONIFEROUS FORESTS[1]

ROBERT H. MACARTHUR
Department of Zoology, University of Pennsylvania

INTRODUCTION

Five species of warbler, Cape May (*Dendroica tigrina*), myrtle (*D. coronata*), black-throated green (*D. virens*), blackburnian (*D. fusca*), and bay-breasted (*D. castanea*), are sometimes found together in the breeding season in relatively homogeneous mature boreal forests. These species are congeneric, have roughly similar sizes and shapes, and all are mainly insectivorous. They are so similar in general ecological preference, at least during years of abundant food supply, that ecologists studying them have concluded that any differences in the species' requirements must be quite obscure (Kendeigh, 1947; Stewart and Aldrich, 1952). Thus it appeared that these species might provide an interesting exception to the general rule that species either are limited by different factors or differ in habitat or range (Lack, 1954). Accordingly, this study was undertaken with the aim of determining the factors controlling the species' bundances and preventing all but one from being exterminated by competition.

LOGICAL NATURE OF POPULATION CONTROL

Animal populations may be regulated by two types of events. The first type occurs (but need not exert its effect) independently of the density of the population. Examples are catastrophes such as storms, severe winters, some predation, and some disease. The second type of event depends upon the density of the population for both its occurrence and strength. Examples are shortages of food and nesting holes. Both types seem to be important for all well-studied species. The first kind will be called density independent and the second density dependent. This is slightly different from the usual definitions of these terms which require the effects upon the population and not the occurrence to be density independent or dependent (Andrewartha and Birch 1954).

When density dependent events play a major role in regulating abundance, interspecific relations are also important, for the presence of an individual of another species may have some of the effects of an individual of the original density dependent species. This is clearly illustrated by the generalized habitats of the few species of passerine birds of Bermuda contrasted with their specialized habitats in continental North America where many additional species are also present (Bourne 1957).

If the species' requirements are sufficiently similar, the proposition of Volterra (1926) and Gause (1934), first enunciated by Grinnell (1922), suggests that only one will be able to persist, so that the existence of one species may even control the presence or absence of another. Because of this proposition it has become customary for ecologists to look for differences in food

[1] A Dissertation Presented to the Faculty of the Graduate School of Yale University in Candidacy for the Degree of Doctor of Philosophy, 1957.

or habitat of related species; such differences, if found, are then cited as the reason competition is not eliminating all but one of the species. Unfortunately, however, differences in food and space requirements are neither always necessary nor always sufficient to prevent competition and permit coexistence. Actually, to permit coexistence it seems necessary that each species, when very abundant, should inhibit its own further increase more than it inhibits the other's. This is illustrated in Figure 1. In this figure, the populations of the two species form the coordinates so that any point in the plane represents a population for each species. Each shaded area covers the points (*i.e.,* the sets of combined populations of the species) in which the species corresponding to the shading can increase, within a given environment. Thus, in the doubly-shaded area both species increase and in the unshaded area both species decrease. The arrows, representing the direction of population change, must then be as shown in the figure for these regions. In order that a stable equilibrium of the two species should exist, the arrows in the singly shaded regions obviously must also be as in the figure; an interchange of the species represented by the shading would reverse the directions of these arrows resulting in a situation in which only one species could persist. Thus, for stability, the boundaries of the shaded zones of increase must have the relative slope illustrated in the figure with each species inhibiting its own further increase more than the other's. The easiest way for this to happen would be to have each species' population limited by a slightly different factor. It is these different limiting factors which are the principal problem in an investigation of multispecific animal populations regulated by density dependent events.

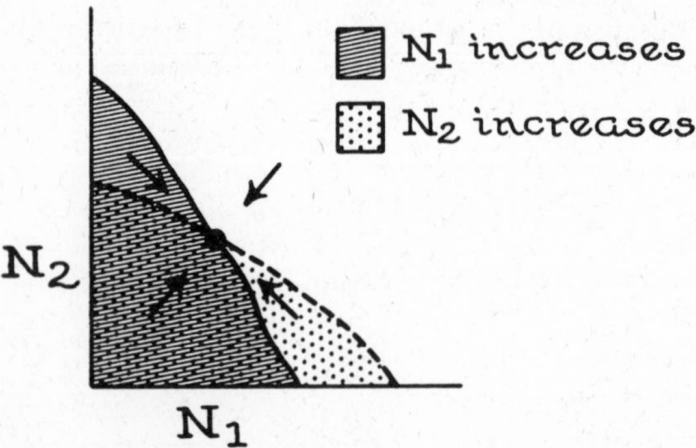

FIG. 1. The necessary conditions for a stable equilibrium of two species. The coordinate axes represent the populations of the species.

An example which has not received sufficient attention is competition in a heterogeneous environment. As has often been pointed out (Kluijver and Tinbergen 1953, Lack 1955, Hinde 1956) birds may emigrate or disperse from the most suitable areas where reproduction is successful into marginal habitats. Consider such a species which will be called A. Let B be a species that lives only in the area that is marginal for species A. Now, even if in an unlimited environment of this type, species B would eliminate species A by competition, in the heterogeneous environment species B may be eliminated from its own preferred habitat. For, if there is sufficient dispersal by species A, it may maintain, partly by immigration, such a high population in the marginal habitat that species B is forced to decrease. This process is probably very important in considering the environmental distributions of birds and implies that small areas of habitat typical for one species may not contain that species.

The study of limiting factors in nature is very difficult because ideally it requires changing the amount of the factor alone and observing whether this change affects the size of the population. Theoretically, if more than one factor changes, the analysis can still be performed, but in practice, if more changes of known nature occur, more of an unknown nature usually also occur. Limiting factors have been studied in two ways. The best way is artificially to modify single factors in the environment, observing the effect upon the birds. MacKenzie (1946) reviews some experiments of this type. The most notable was the increase from zero to abundant of pied flycatchers (*Muscicapa hypoleuca*) when nest boxes were introduced in the Forest of Dean. This showed conclusively that lack of nesting sites had limited the population. Such simple modifications are not always feasible. For instance, changing the food supply of an insectivorous bird is nearly impossible. The most feasible approach in such a case is to compare the bird populations in two regions which differ in the abundance of the factor being considered. Ideally, the two regions should differ only in this respect, but this is very improbable. A good example of this method of study is the work of Breckenridge (1956) which showed that the least flycatchers (*Empidonax minimus*) were more abundant in a given wood wherever the wood was more open.

The present study of the factors limiting warblers was conducted by the second approach. This is slightly less accurate than the first method, but permits studying more factors and requires less time. There are actually four parts to the study. First, it is shown that density dependent events play a large role in controlling the populations of the species. Second, a discussion of the general ecology of the species (food, feeding zones, feeding behavior, territoriality, predators, and mortality) is presented. The observations were made in the summers of 1956 and 1957. Third, the habits of the different species in different seasons are compared to see what aspects of the general ecology are invariant and hence characteristic of the species. Some observations on the species' morphology are discussed in the light of these characteristics. This was the project of the fall and winter of 1956 and the spring of 1957. Finally, a wood-to-wood comparison of species abundances, relative to the important constituents of their niches as determined in the earlier stages, is presented. This work was done in the summers of 1956 and 1957.

Density Dependence

It is the aim of this section to demonstrate that the five species of warbler are primarily regulated by density dependent events, that is, that they increase when rare and decrease when common (relative to the supply of a limiting factor). The strongest argument for this is the correlation of abundances with limiting factors discussed later. However, to avoid any risk of circularity, an independent partial demonstration will now be given.

If density independent events do not occur randomly but have a periodic recurrence, then a population controlled by these events could undergo a regular oscillation nearly indistinguishable in form from that of a population regulated by density dependent events. The distinction can be made, however, by observing the effect of the presence of an ecologically similar species. Here it will first be shown that increases and decreases are not random; then an argument will be given which renders the density independent explanation improbable.

If increases, I, and decreases, D, occur randomly, the sequence of observed I's and D's would have random order. A run of I's (or D's) is a sequence (perhaps consisting of one element) of adjacent I's (or D's) which cannot be lengthened; *i.e.*, the total number of runs is always one greater than the number of changes from I to D or D to I. If more runs of I's or D's are observed than would be expected in a random sequence, then an increase makes the following change more likely to be a decrease and conversely. This is what would be expected on the hypothesis of density dependent events.

There have been very few extensive censuses of any of the five species of warbler that are studied here. The longest are reproduced below from the data of Smith (1953) in Vermont, Williams (1950) in Ohio, and Cruickshank (1956) in Maine. The populations of myrtle, black-throated green, and blackburnian are listed; only those species are mentioned that are consistently present.

Myrtle													
Maine	7	5	7	7	6	7	8	10	9	8	10	10	10
			8	10	7	10							
Black-throated green													
Ohio	3	3	5	3	4	3	2	4	0	1	-	3	3
			3	4	3	3	4	3					
Vermont	7	7	7	6	8	5	6	6	7	8	8	6	8
			8	3	6	3							
Maine	8	9	11	10	10	10	11	11	11	10	11	9	8
			9	8	9								
Blackburnian													
Vermont	11	11	10	7	8	7	7	10	10	8	5	6	3
			3	6	6	5							
Maine	2	4	3	3	5	5	7	5	6	5	7	5	5
			7	6	6	3							

The increases, I, and decreases, D, of these censuses, in order are as follows:

Myrtle

D I D I I I D D I D I D I

Black-throated green

I D I D D I D I I I D I D

D I D I I I D I D I D

I I D I D I D D I D I

Blackburnian

D D I D I D D I D I D

I D I I D I D I D I D D

In this form the data from different censuses are perfectly compatible and, since censuses end or begin with I or D in no particular pattern, all the censuses for a given species may be attached:

Myrtle

D I D I I I D D I D I D I (10)

Black-throated green

I D I D D I D I I I D I D D I D

I I I D I D I D I I D I (27)

D I D D I D I

Blackburnian

D D I D I D D I D I D I D I I D I

D I D I D D (19)

Here the groups of letters underlined are runs and the number of runs is totalled in parentheses. From the tables of Swed and Eisenhart (1943), testing the one-sided hypothesis that there are no more runs than would be expected by chance, each of these shows a significantly large number of runs (the first less than 5% significance, the others less than 2.5%). That is, each species tends to decrease following an increase and to increase following a decrease, proving population control non-random. The mean periods of these fluctuations can easily be computed. For a run of increases followed by a run of decreases constitutes one oscillation. Thus, the periods of the oscillations of the three species are $13/5 = 2.6$, $70/27 = 2.6$, and $46/19 = 2.4$ years respectively. These fluctuations would require an unknown environmental cycle of period approximately 2.5 years if a regularly recurring density independent event were controlling the populations. Thus, from these data alone, it seems very probable that the three species (myrtle, black-throated green, blackburnian) are primarily regulated by density dependent events.

A species may be regulated by density dependent events and yet undergo dramatic changes in populations due to changes in the limiting factor itself. In this case tests by the theory of runs, used above, are likely to be useless. However, if a correlation can be made of the population with the environmental factor undergoing change, then not only can density dependence, *i. e.* existence of a limiting factor, be established, but also the nature of the limiting factor. For, if an increase in one environmental variable can be established, an experiment of the first type described above has been performed. That is, the habitat has been modified in one factor and a resulting change in bird population has been observed. Therefore, because the population changes, that one factor has been limiting.

This is apparently what happens in populations of Cape May and bay-breasted warblers. Kendeigh (1947), examining older material, established the fact that these species are abundant when there is an outbreak of *Choristoneura fumiferana* (Clem.), the spruce budworm. More recent information confirms this. To correlate with the fact (Greenbank 1956) that there have been continuously high budworm populations since 1909, there is the statement of Forbush (1929) that the Cape May warbler became more common about 1909, and the statement of Bond (pers. comm.) that the winter range of the species has been increasing in size. An outbreak of spruce budworms started in northern Maine in the late 1940's, and Stewart and Aldrich (1951) and Hensley and Cope (1951) studied the birds during 1950 and 1951. Cape May and bay-breasted warblers were among the commonest birds present, as in the earlier outbreaks, although both species were formerly not common in Maine (Knight 1908). The outbreak has continued through New Brunswick, where current bird studies (Cheshire 1954) indicate that bay-breasted is again the commonest bird, although for unknown reasons the Cape May has not been observed.

In conclusion, it appears that all five species are primarily regulated by density dependent events, and that a limiting factor is food supply for bay-breasted and Cape May warblers.

General Ecology

The density dependence tentatively concluded above implies that the presence of individuals of a species makes the environment less suitable for other individuals of that species. It would also be expected then that the presence of individuals of one species may make the environment less suitable for individuals of a different species. This is called interspecific competition. As mentioned above, this seems to mean that two sympatric species will have their populations limited by different factors so that each species inhibits its own population growth more than it inhibits that of the others. The factors inseparably bound to a species' persistence in a region are, then, its relation to other species and the presence of food, proper feeding zone, shelter from weather, and nesting sites (Andrewartha and Birch 1954, Grinnell 1914). In this section these factors as observed during the breeding season of the five species of warbler will be discussed.

The summer of 1956 was devoted to observations upon the four species, myrtle, black-throated green, blackburnian, and bay-breasted warblers, on their nesting grounds. The principal area studied was a 9.4 acre plot of mature white spruce (*Picea glauca*) on Bass Harbor Head, Mt. Desert Island, Hancock County, Maine. On 7 July 1956 the site of observations was changed to the town of Marlboro in Windham County, Vermont, where a red spruce (*P. rubens*) woodlot of comparable structure was studied. In the summer of 1957 more plots were studied. From 30 May until 5 June, eighteen plots of balsam fir (*Abies balsamea*), black spruce (*P. mariana*), and white spruce near Cross Lake, Long Lake, and Mud Lake in the vicinity of Guerette in Aroostook County, Maine, were studied. The remainder of the breeding season was spent on Mt. Desert Island, Maine, where five plots were censused. These will be described later.

Feeding Habits

Although food might be the factor for which birds compete, evidence presented later shows that differences in type of food between these closely related species result from differences in feeding behavior and position and that each species eats what food is obtainable within the characteristic feeding zone and by the characteristic manner of feeding. For this reason, differences between the species' feeding positions and behavior have been observed in detail.

For the purpose of describing the birds' feeding zone, the number of seconds each observed bird spent in each of 16 zones was recorded. (In the summer of 1956 the seconds were counted by saying "thousand and one, thousand and two, . . ." all subsequent timing was done by stop watch. When the stop watch became available, an attempt was made to calibrate the counted seconds. It was found that each counted second was approximately 1.25 true seconds.) The zones varied with height and position on branch as shown in Figure 2. The height zones were ten foot units measured from the top of the tree. Each branch could be divided into three zones, one of bare or lichen-covered base (B), a middle zone of old needles (M), and a terminal zone of new (less than 1.5 years old) needles or buds (T). Thus a measurement in zone T3 was an observation between 20 and 30 feet from the top of the tree and in the terminal part of the branch. Since most of the trees were 50 to 60 feet tall, a rough idea of the height above the ground can also be obtained from the measurements.

There are certain difficulties concerning these measurements. Since the forest was very dense, certain types of behavior rendered birds invisible. This resulted in all species being observed slightly disproportionately in the open zones of the trees. To combat this difficulty each bird was observed for as long as possible so that a brief excursion into an open but not often-frequented zone would be compensated for by the remaining part of the observation. I believe there is no serious error in this respect. Furthermore, the comparative aspect is independent of this error. A different difficulty arises from measurements of time spent in each zone. The error due to counting should not affect results which are comparative in nature. If a bird sits very still or sings, it might spend a large amount of time in one zone without actually requiring that zone for feeding. To alleviate this trouble, a record of activity, when not feeding, was kept. Because of these difficulties, non-parametric statistics have been used throughout the analysis of the study to avoid any *a priori* assumptions about distributions. One difficulty is of a different nature; because of the density of the vegetation and the activity of the warblers a large number of hours of watching result in disappointingly few seconds of worthwhile observations.

The results of these observations are illustrated in Figures 2-6 in which the species' feeding zones are indicated on diagrammatic spruce trees. While

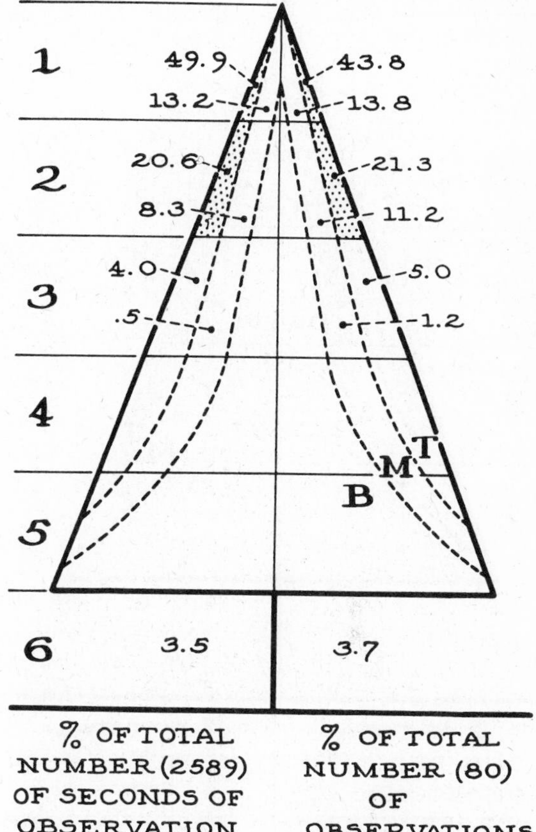

FIG. 2. Cape May warbler feeding position. The zones of most concentrated activity are shaded until at least 50% of the activity is in the stippled zones.

the base zone is always proximal to the trunk of the tree, as shown, the T zone surrounds the M, and is exterior to it but not always distal. For each species observed, the feeding zone is illustrated. The left side of each illustration is the percentage of the number of seconds of observations of the species in each zone. On the right hand side the percentage of the total number of times the species was observed in each zone is entered. The stippled area gives roughly the area in which the species is most likely to be found. More specifically, the zone with the highest percentage is stippled, then the zone with the second highest percentage, and so on until at least fifty percent of the observations or time lie within the stippled zone.

Early in the investigation it became apparent that there were differences between the species' feeding habits other than those of feeding zones. Subjectively, the black-throated green appeared "nervous," the bay-breasted slow and "deliberate." In an attempt to make these observations objective, the following measurements were taken on feeding birds. When a bird landed after a flight, a count

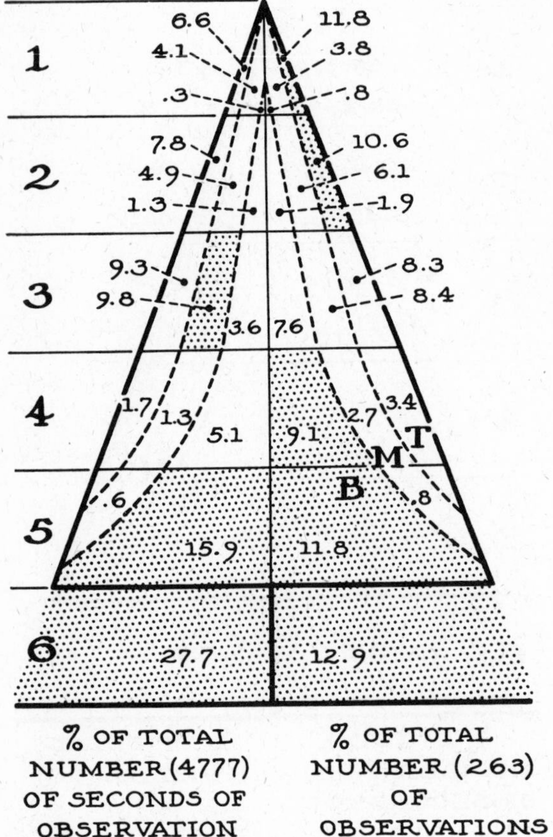

FIG. 3. Myrtle warbler feeding position. The zones of most concentrated activity are shaded until at least 50% of the activity is in the stippled zones.

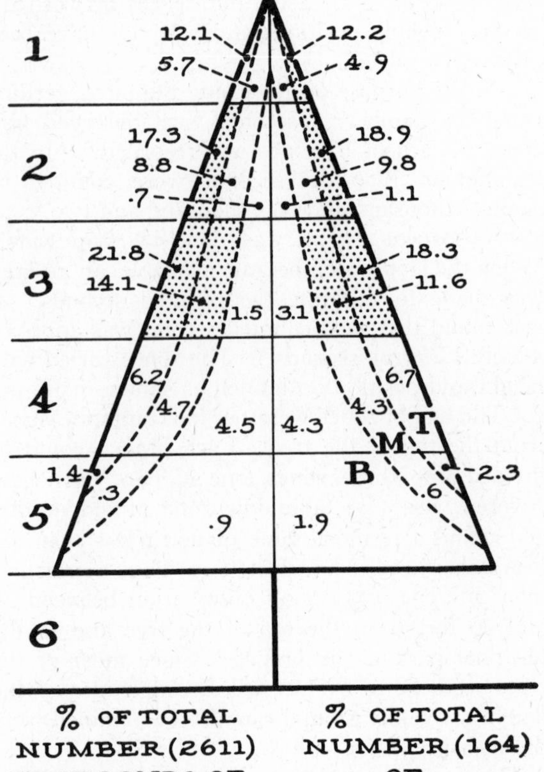

FIG. 4. Black-throated green warbler feeding position. The zones of most concentrated activity are shaded until at least 50% of the activity is in the stippled zones.

of seconds was begun and continued until the bird was lost from sight. The total number of flights (visible uses of the wing) during this period was recorded so that the mean interval between uses of the wing could be computed.

The results for 1956 are shown in Table I. The results for 1957 are shown in Table II. Except for the Cape May fewer observations were taken than in 1956.

By means of the sign test (Wilson, 1952), treating each observation irrespective of the number of flights as a single estimate of mean interval between flights, a test of the difference in activity can be performed. These data are summarized in the following inequality, where $\overset{95}{<}$ is interpreted to mean "has smaller mean interval between flights, with 95% certainty."

$$\text{Black-throated green} \overset{95}{<} \left\{\begin{matrix}\text{Blackburnian}\\ \text{Myrtle}\end{matrix}\right\} \overset{99}{<} \left\{\begin{matrix}\text{Cape May}\\ \text{Bay-breasted}\end{matrix}\right\}$$

The differences in feeding behavior of the warblers can be studied in another way. For, while all the species spend a substantial part of their time searching in the foliage for food, some appear to crawl along branches and others to hop across branches. To measure this the following procedure was adopted. All motions of a bird from place to place in a tree were resolved into components in three independent directions. The natural directions to use were vertical, radial, and tangential. When an observation was made in which all the motion was visible, the number of feet the bird moved in each of the three directions was noted. A surpringing degree of diversity was discovered in this way as is shown in Figure 7. Here, making use of the fact that the sum of the three perpendicular distances from an interior point to the sides of an equilateral triangle is independent of the position of the point, the proportion of motion in each direction is recorded within a triangle. Thus the Cape May moves predominantly in a vertical direction, black-throated green and myrtle in a tangential direction, bay-breasted and blackburnian in a radial direc-

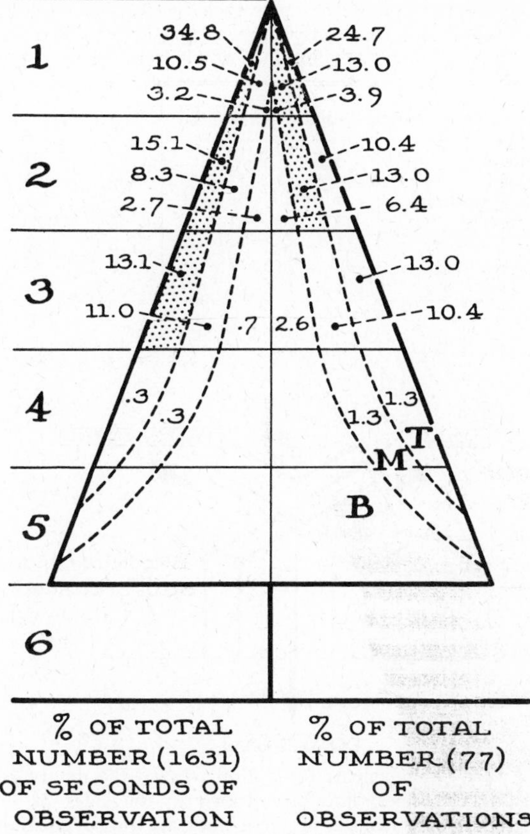

FIG. 5. Blackburnian warbler feeding position. The zones of most concentrated activity are shaded until at least 50% of the activity is in the stippled zones.

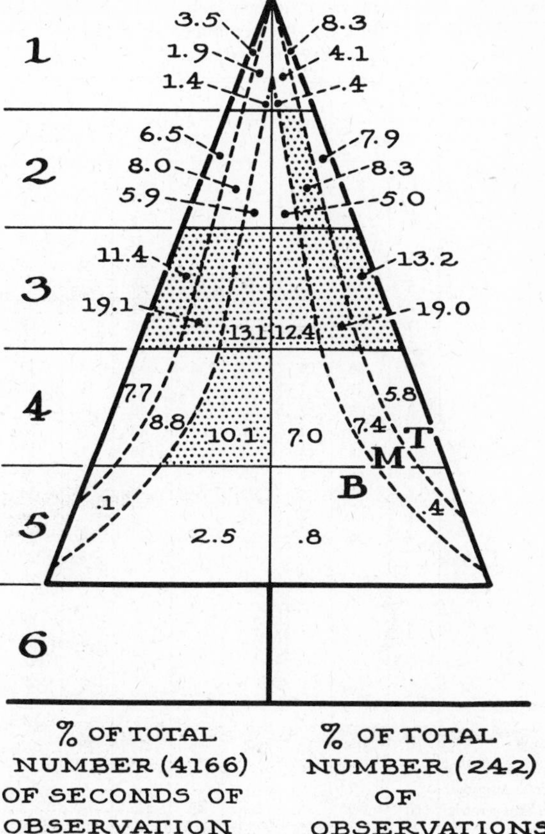

FIG. 6. Bay-breasted warbler feeding position. The zones of most concentrated activity are shaded until at least 50% of the activity is in the stippled zones.

tion. To give a nonparametric test of the significance of these differences Table III is required.

Each motion was classified according to the direction in which the bird moved farthest. Thus, in 47 bay-breasted warbler observations of this type, the bird moved predominantly in a radial direction 32 times. Applying a χ^2 test to these, bay-breasted and blackburnian are not different but all others are significantly ($P<.01$) different from one another and from bay-breasted and blackburnian.

There is one further quantitative comparison which can be made between species, providing additional evidence that during normal feeding behavior the species could become exposed to different types of food. During those observations of 1957 in which the bird was never lost from sight, occurrence of long flights, hawking, or hovering was recorded. A flight was called long if it went between different trees and was greater than an estimated 25 feet. Hawking is distinguished from hovering by the fact that in hawking a moving prey individual is sought in the air, while in hovering a nearly stationary prey individual is sought amid the foliage. This information is summarized in Table IV.

Both Cape May and myrtle hawk and undertake long flights significantly more often than any of the other species. Black-throated green hovers significantly more often than the others.

At this point it is possible to summarize differences in the species' feeding behavior in the breeding season. Unfortunately, there are very few original descriptions in the literature for comparison. The widely known writings of William Brewster (Griscom 1938), Ora Knight (1908), and S. C. Kendeigh (1947) include the best observations that have been published. Based upon the observations reported by these authors, the other scattered published observations, and the observations made during this study, the following comparison of the species' feeding behavior seems warranted.

Cape May Warbler. The foregoing data show that this species feeds more consistently near the top of the tree than any species expect blackburnian, from which it differs principally in type

TABLE I. The number of intervals between flights (I) recorded in 1956 and the total number of seconds (S) of observation counted

	Myrtle		Black-throated green		Blackburnian		Bay-breasted	
	I	S	I	S	I	S	I	S
	1	40	4	45	1	5	5	55
	4	32	8	20	13	77	3	22
	4	13	6	60	2	11	2	33
	4	17	5	35	5	18	1	7
	2	10	5	23	5	24	3	37
	1	10	3	7	3	16	2	20
	5	25	9	35	3	18	1	7
	5	10	8	25	3	15	4	10
	5	11	1	12	4	11	11	60
	6	30	7	20	3	12	5	41
	3	10	7	39	4	46	3	50
	1	5	13	25	2	26	1	17
	13	68	5	10			1	3
	1	5	5	12			1	49
	1	7	2	37			4	42
	4	26					5	60
							5	35
							5	26
							3	14
							4	38
							3	14
							1	11
							3	22
							2	29
Total	60	319	88	405	48	279	78	702
Total Adjusted to True seconds	60	399	88	506	48	349	78	876

TABLE II. Intervals between flights and seconds of observation in 1957

	Cape May		Myrtle		Black-throated green		Black-burnian		Bay-breasted	
	I	S	I	S	I	S	I	S	I	S
	3	47	4	18	3	18	1	22	7	110
	12	35	1	62	5	22	3	22	2	115
	5	50	5	47	3	15	9	110	1	18
	2	15	3	17	13	89	7	26	1	22
	1	15	1	5	23	40	3	8	2	19
	1	45	12	86					2	47
	1	20							3	27
	4	29							8	112
	11	129							7	46
	6	47								
	1	15								
	4	50								
	3	20								
	21	122								
	1	12								
	1	34								
	4	20								
	10	79								
Total	91	782	26	235	47	184	24	188	33	576
Adjusted 1956 Total			60	399	88	506	48	349	78	876
Grand Total	91	782	86	644	125	690	72	537	111	1392
Mean Interval Between Flights		8.59		7.48		5.52		7.47		12.53

TABLE III. Number of times each species was observed to move predominantly in a particular direction. (Numbers ending in .5 result from ties)

Species	Radial	Tangential	Vertical	Total
Cape May	5.5	1.5	25	32
Myrtle	4.5	11.5	9	25
Black-throated green	4	21	5	30
Blackburnian	11	1	3	15
Bay-breasted	32	7	8	47

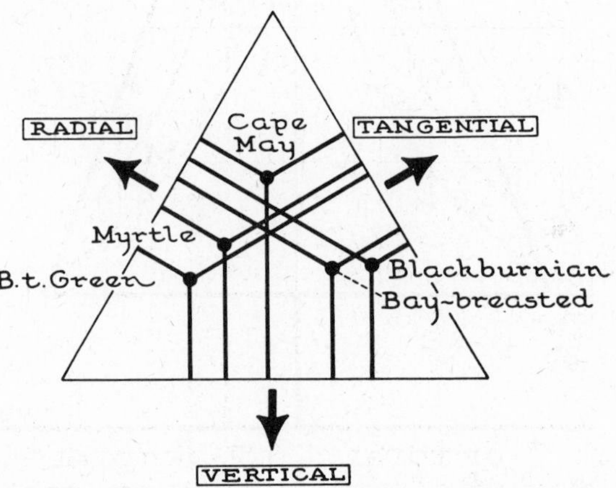

FIG. 7. Components of Motion. From the dot representing a species, lines are drawn to the sides of the triangle. The lengths of these lines are proportional to the total distance which the species moved in radial, tangential, and vertical directions, respectively.

TABLE IV. Classification of the flights observed for each species

Species	Long Flights	Hawking	Hovering	No. of Observ.
Cape May	35	12	0	53
Myrtle	25	9	0	62
Black-throated green	1	0	7	42
Blackburnian	0	1	0	35
Bay-breasted	4	2	2	57

Applying χ^2 tests to pairs of species, the following conclusions emerge.

of feeding action. It not only hawks far more often than the blackburnian, but also moves vertically rather than radially in the tree, causing its feeding zone to be more restricted to the outer shell of the tree. Myrtle warblers when feeding in the tips of the trees nearly duplicate the feeding behavior of the Cape May. During rainy, windy, and cold weather Cape Mays were not found in the tree tops, but were instead foraging in the low willows (*Salix* sp.) and pin cherries (*Prunus pensylvanica*). Here they often fed among the flowers, for which their semitubular tongue (Gardner 1925) may be advantageous.

Because of this species' irregular breeding distribution, both in space and time, and its former rarity, there are very few published descriptions of its feeding behavior. Knight (1908), although he lived in Maine, had never seen one. Brewster (Griscom 1938) wrote that:

> "It keeps invariably near the tops of the highest trees whence it occasionally darts out after passing insects. . . . In rainy or dark weather they came in numbers from the woods to feed among the thickets of low firs and spruces in the pastures. Here they spent much of their time hanging head downward at the extremity of the branches, often continuing in this position for nearly a minute at a time. They seemed to be picking minute insects from under the surface of the fir needles. They also resorted to a thicket of blossoming plum trees directly under the window, where we were always sure of finding several of them."

He also said that it was more active than the bay-breasted. Bond (1937) stated that all feeding was done more than twenty feet above the ground. Kendeigh (1947) said males tend to sing about seven feet from the tops of the trees, and that feeding is done at the same level. He also mentions that the birds sometimes hawk after passing insects. The rainy weather observations indicate behavior very much like that of winter and migration to be discussed later.

Myrtle Warbler. This species seems to have the most varied feeding habits of any species. Although it moves slightly more in a tangential direction than any except black-throated green, it is probably more correct to think of the myrtle as having the most nearly equal components (radial, tangential, and vertical) of any species. This is shown by its most nearly central location in Figure 7. It is also seen to have the most widely distributed feeding zone, although the ground feeding was nearly, but not completely, restricted to the gathering of emerging Tipulids for newly hatched young. Sometimes a substantial amount of this is hawking for flying insects; at other times it is largely by rapid peering (Grinnell 1921) amid the thick foliage near the tree tops. Myrtle, along with Cape May, makes a much higher proportion of flights to other trees than do the other species, often flying from one side of its territory to the other with no apparent provocation. The other three species tend to search one tree rather thoroughly before moving on. Further evidence of the plasticity of the myrtle warbler's feeding habits will be presented when the other seasons are considered. Grinnell and Storer (1924) stated that the Audubon's warbler (which often hybridizes with the myrtle and with it froms a superspecies (Mayr 1950)) also feeds in peripheral foliage and does a greater amount of hawking than other species. Kendeigh (1947) said that birds fed from ground to tops of trees, and also that two males covered two and four acres respectively in only a few minutes. Knight (1908) said "Many of the adult insects are taken on the wing, the warblers taking short springs and flights into the air for this purpose. The young for the first few days are fed on the softer sorts of insects secured by the parents, and later their fare is like that of the parents in every way."

Black-throated Green Warbler. Compared to the myrtle warbler this species is quite restricted in feeding habits. As seen in Figure 4, it tends to frequent the dense parts of the branches and the new buds, especially at mid elevations in the tree. Most of its motion is in a tangential direction, keeping the bird in foliage of a nearly constant type. It has the shortest interval between flights of any of the five species and thus appears the most active. Almost all feeding seems to be by the method of rapid peering, necessitating the frequent use of the wings which the observations indicate. The foliage on a white spruce is a thick, dense mat at the end of the branch, changing to bare branch rather more sharply than in the red spruce. The black-throated greens characteristically hop about very actively upon these mats, often, like the other species, looking down among the needles, and just as often, unlike the myrtle and bay-breasted, peering up into the next mat of foliage above. When food is located above, the bird springs into the air and hovers under the branch with its bill at the point whence the food is being extracted. While other species occasionally feed in this fashion, it is typical only of the black-throated green. After searching one branch, the black-throated green generally flies tangentially to an adjacent branch in the same tree or a neighboring one and continues the search. Only rarely, during feeding, does it make long flights. While it occasionally hawks for flying insects (missing a substantial proportion), this is not a typical behavior and the birds seldom sit motionless watching for flying insects in true hawking behavior. During its feeding, this species is very noisy, chipping almost incessantly, and, if it is a male and if it is early in the season, singing frequently. The other species are very quiet. A portion of this behavior can be confirmed from the literature. Knight (1908) said "Only rarely do they take their prey in the air, preferring to diligently seek it out among the branches and foliage" and Stanwood (Bent 1953) said "The bird is quick in its movements, but often spends periods of some length on one tree." Like the myrtle, this species enlarges its feeding zone while gathering food for its young. This is similar to the results of Betts (1955) indicating that the young tits eat different food from the adults.

Blackburnian Warbler. This species generally feeds high in the trees but is otherwise more or less intermediate between black-throated green and bay-breasted in its feeding behavior. This is true both of its flight frequency and its preferred feeding position on the limb (Figure 5). It is also intermediate in its method of hunting, usually moving out from the base to the tip of the branches looking down in the fashion of the bay-breasted and occasionally hopping about rapidly upon the mat of foliage at the branch tips looking both up and down for insects and even hovering occasionally. They seem to use the method of rapid peering, only occasionally hawking after a flying insect. As further evidence, Knight (1908) wrote "As a rule they feed by passing from limb to limb and examining the foliage and limbs of trees, more seldom catching anything in the air." Kendeigh (1945) said "It belongs to the treetops, singing and feeding at heights of 35 to 75 feet from the ground."

Bay-breasted Warbler. The usual feeding habits of this species are the most restricted of any of the species studied. All of the observations in the T1 zone and most in the T2 zone refer to singing males. This species uses its wings considerably less often than the other species, although it still appears to use the method of rapid peering in its hunting since it moves nearly continuously. These motions are, however, predominantly radial and seldom require the use of wings. The bird regularly works from the licheny base of the branches well out to the tip, although the largest part of the time is spent in the shady interior of the tree. It frequently stays in the same tree for long periods of time. This species very rarely hovers in the black-throated green fashion, and appears much less nimble in its actions about the tips of the branches, usually staying away from those buds which are at the edge of the mat of foliage. When it does feed at the edge of the mat, it is nearly always by hanging down rather than peering up. Other observers have emphasized the slowness. Brewster (Griscom 1938) called this warbler "slow and sluggish," and Kendeigh (1947) said "The birds do not move around much, but may sing and feed for long periods in the same tree." Forbush (1929) stated that it spends most of its time "moving about deliberately, after the manner of vireos."

Food

Two species may eat different food for only three reasons: 1. They may feed in different places or different times of day; 2. They may feed in such a manner as to find different foods; 3. They may accept different kinds of food from among those to which they are exposed. (Of course, a combination of these reasons is also possible.)

In the previous section it was shown that the warblers feed in different places and in a different manner, thus probably being exposed to different foods for the first and second reasons mentioned above. It is the aim of this section to show that the five warbler species have only small differences of the third kind. Theoretically, such differences, unaccompanied by morphological adaptations, would be disadvantageous, for, lacking the adaptations required to give greater efficiency in food collecting, and suffering a reduction in the number of acceptible food species, a bird would obtain food at a lesser rate. When the necessary adaptations are present, they usually consist of quite marked differences in bill structure such as those reported by Huxley (1942), Lack (1947), and Amadon (1950). As Table V shows, the mean bill measurements in millimeters of the five species of warbler considered in this study are quite similar. Twelve specimens of each species from the Peabody Museum of Natural History at Yale University were measured for each of the means given.

TABLE V. Mean dimensions of the bills of 12 specimens of each species

Species	Bill Length	Height at Nares	Width at Nares	Width 2.5mm from tip
Cape May	12.82	2.85	2.93	0.96
Myrtle	12.47	3.26	2.12	1.33
Black-throated green	12.58	3.38	3.15	1.34
Blackburnian	12.97	3.24	3.36	1.17
Bay-breasted	13.04	3.69	3.58	1.43

The Cape May alone has a noticeably different bill, it being more slender, especially at the tip. This bill houses a semi-tubular tongue as mentioned above, which is unique in the genus. These may be useful adaptations for their rainy weather flower feeding, but would seem ill-adapted for the characteristic flycatching of the breeding season (Gardner 1925). It is doubtless useful in other seasons, as will be discussed later. Aside from the Cape May, all other species differ in bill measurement by only a small fraction of a millimeter. Thus, for theoretical reasons, no pronounced differences of the third kind would be expected. Empirically, there is evidence to support this belief.

McAtee (1932) reported upon the analysis of eighty thousand bird stomachs, in an effort to disprove mimicry. Although his results were not conclusive, he claimed that insects appeared in bird stomachs about proportionately to their availability. Kendeigh (1945) agreed with this conclusion. Although McAtee (1926) said that no detailed studies of warbler food habits had been made, and no general ones seem to have appeared since, two very suggestive sets of analyses covering the five species have been published. Kendeigh (1947) reported upon the stomach contents of a collection made near Lake Nipigon, and Mitchell (1952) analyzed the stomachs of many birds taken during a budworm infestation in Maine. These data show, first, that most species of warbler eat all major orders of local arboreal arthropods. Furthermore, although there are differences in proportion of types of foods eaten by various species, these differences are most easily explained in terms of feeding zone. Thus, black-throated green and blackburnian which are morphologically the most similar of the five species have quite different foods. Kendeigh's table shows that black-throated green eats 4% Coleoptera, 31% Araneida, and 20% Homoptera, which blackburnian eats 22% Coleoptera, 2% Araneida, and 3% Homoptera. Dr. W. R. Henson has pointed out (pers. comm.) that Coleoptera can reasonably be assumed to come from inner parts of the tree where blackburnian has been shown to feed, whereas the Homoptera and most of the Araneida would be caught in the current year's growth where the black-throated green feeds more often, thus explaining the observed difference. Black-throated green and bay-breasted, with the most vireo-like bills (high at the nares), seem to eat more Lepidoptera larvae which are typical vireo food, but Mitchell's table shows that the other species too can eat predominantly Lepidoptera larvae when these are abundant. Otherwise, the food of the bay-breasted is more like that of the blackburnian, the feeding habits of which are similar. There are not sufficient data to analyze Cape May in this fashion. The myrtle warbler's feeding behavior is so flexible that no correlation between insects caught and a specific feeding zone or behavior is expected. This is shown by its having the most even distribution of food of any of the species considered. Thus, these correlations show that the differences in warbler food can be readily explained by morphological and zonal characteristics of the species.

Nest Location

The position of the nest is quite characteristic in warbler species. Nearly all species of the genus *Dendroica* nest off the ground. Figure 8 shows heights of the nests of the five species of warbler studied here. These data result from a combination of the records of Cruickshank (1956), the information in the egg collection of the American Museum of Natural History in New York, and that gathered in this study. Since the distributions are skewed and irregular, the median and confidence intervals for the median (Banerjee and Nair 1940) are appropriate measurements. As the figure shows, the Cape May, with 95% confidence interval for the median of 40-50 feet, and the blackburnian, whose interval is 30-50 feet, have quite similar nest heights, probably reflecting their tendency to feed at high elevations. The Cape May's nest is virtually always near the trunk in the uppermost dense cluster of branches in a spruce or occasionally a fir. The blackburnian may nest in a similar location or may nest farther out toward the branch tips. Myrtle and black-throated green have similar nesting heights, both species having 95% confidence interval for the median nest height of 15-20 feet. The black-throated green seems to prefer smaller trees for its nest, and is thus more likely to place its nest near the runk, but, in keeping with its other characteristics, the myrtle seems quite varied in this respect. Finally, the bay-breasted, which has the lowest feeding zone, has the lowest nest position, the median height being between 10 and 15 feet (95% confidence). Thus, the nest positions of the five species of warbler reflect their preferred feeding zones.

Territoriality

Defining territory as any defended area, warbler territories in the breeding season are of what Hinde (1956) called type A ("Large breeding area within which nesting, courtship, and mating and most food-seeking usually occur"). He pointed out that, since the behavioral mechanisms involved in defending a territory against others of the same species are the same as those involved in defending it against other species, this distinction need not be specified in the definition. From the ecological point of view, the distinction is of very great importance, however, for, as G. E. Hutchinson pointed out in conversation, if each species has its density (even locally) limited by a territorial behavior which ignores the other species, then there need be no further differences between the species to permit them to persist together. A weaker form of the same process, in which territories were compressible but only under pressure of a large population, would still be effective, along with small niche differences, in making each species inhibit its own population growth more than the others'—the

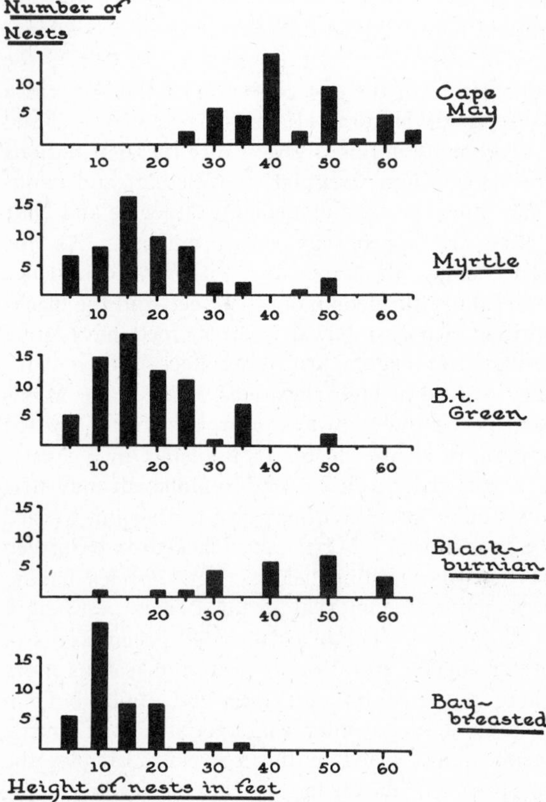

FIG. 8. Nesting heights of warblers.

necessary condition for the persistence of sympatric species.

Two further conditions make territory important for regulating populations. First, to have density dependent regulation, a species' regulating mechanism must have information of its own population density. Second, a predator ideally should keep its prey at that population level which permits the greatest rate of production. This means that the prey would not normally be particularly scarce. This, combined with the varied prey of the birds and the varied predators of the insects, would make food density a poorer criterion of a given bird species' density than size of territory. Thus, competition for food would be reduced from a "scramble" to a "contest" (Haldane 1955).

While the true nature of birds' territories has proved very elusive (Lack 1954, Hinde 1956), two separate lines of evidence suggest strongly that territories contribute to the regulation of local densities in warbler populations. Stewart and Aldrich (1951) and Hensley and Cope (1951) removed adult birds from their territories in 1949 and 1950 respectively, in a 40 acre plot in a budworm-infested area of Maine. The vacated territories were always filled by new pairs, the males singing the vigorous song of a bird setting up a territory. It seems nearly inescapable that these were part of a large floating population of birds only prevented from breeding by the absence of unoccupied territories. Since this was in a budworm outbreak, there seems little doubt that there would have been adequate food for a larger breeding population.

In a study over a series of years on the birds in New Brunswick, Cheshire (1954) recorded the populations and territory sizes of the various species as a budworm outbreak began and progressed. He showed that while the bay-breasted warbler (the commonest bird during the outbreak) underwent a five- to seven-fold increase as the outbreak began, their mean territory sizes remained constant instead of decreasing correspondingly. That is, there had been unoccupied interstices between territories initially; these were filled in by the incoming birds but territory sizes were left unchanged.

The facts suggest that the territory size is more or less fixed in this region (although, of course, it may vary from region to region) and that if territorial compression occurs during high population densities, it only does so during higher population densities than those observed. Of course, if high population densities persisted, natural selection might be expected to reduce territory size, but this is a different situation.

As for interspecific territoriality, there is no exclusion of the kind found in intraspecific territoriality, as is clearly shown in Kendeigh's (1947) territory maps. It is very difficult to distinguish a mild repulsion of other species by territorialism from a preference for slightly different habitats. Adequate information does not exist to make the distinction at present. However, it seems quite certain that interspecific territoriality is weaker than intraspecific and, therefore, that the effect of a large density of one species is greater on that species than on the others. It is thus probable that, in the warblers, territoriality helps reduce competition and acts as a stabilizing factor (as well as performing the well-known functions of pair formation and maintenance).

Natality and Mortality

In a population which has reached an equilibrium size, abundance is independent of birth and death rates. For species in equilibrium, then, a study of birth and death rates is not necessary to understand the control of the equilibrium abundance. However, as Darwin (1859) said, "A large number of eggs is of some importance to those species which depend upon a fluctuating amount of food, for it allows them rapidly to increase in numbers."

The five species of warbler studied here are very interesting in this respect. Table VI is a summary of the nesting data of the Museum of Comparative Zoology at Harvard, the American Museum of Natural History in New York, and the data of Harlow published by Street (1956).

TABLE VI. Mean clutch sizes for the 5 species

Species	No. of Nests	Clutch Size					Mean	St. Dev.
		3	4	5	6	7		
Cape May	48		4	11	24	9	5.792	.850
Myrtle	24	1	19	4			4.125	.449
Black-throated green	45	2	39	4			4.044	.366
Blackburnian	44	7	32	5			3.955	.526
Bay-breasted	49		5	21	20	3	5.429	.752

Cape May and bay-breasted warblers' nests were enough of a prize that it is quite certain that all found were kept and that the collections do not reflect any bias. There is a possibility of slight bias, collectors perhaps prizing larger clutches, in the other three species in the museum collections, but their clutch sizes are so constant that this seems improbable. The data of Harlow are not subject to his criticism, since he recorded all nests found.

While the sources of these collections vary in latitude from that of the Poconos of Pennsylvania to that of northern New Brunswick, there appears to be very little change in clutch size in this range of latitude. Thus the mean clutch size of 16 nests of the black-throated green in the Poconos is 4.06, while for the combined collections from Nova Scotia and New Brunswick (12 nests) the mean clutch is 4.17. The nests of the other species are from a narrow range of latitude and would not be expected to vary. Thus it was felt permissible to combine the data from different latitudes.

It is immediately apparent that Cape May and bay-breasted, the species which capitalize upon the periodic spruce budworm outbreaks, have considerably larger clutches than the other species, as Darwin would have predicted. It is of interest that the only other warbler regularly laying such large clutches is the Tennessee warbler (*Vermivora peregrina*) which is the other species regularly fluctuating with the budworms (Kendeigh 1947). Thus it seems that Darwin's statement provides an appropriate explanation for the larger clutches. It is also interesting that the standard deviation of the Cape May and bay-breasted warblers' clutch sizes is greater. This suggests a certain plasticity which can be verified, for the bay-breasted at least, as follows. If the time of the budworm outbreak in New Brunswick is taken as 1911-1920 (Swaine and and Craighead 1924), and other years from 1903 until 1938 are called non-budworm years, the bay-breasted warbler clutches from northeastern New Brunswick can be summarized as follows:

	Clutch Size			
	4	5	6	7
Budworm Years	1	5	15	3
Non-budworm Years	4	8	5	0

The U test (Hoel 1954) shows this to be significant at the .0024 level; that is, bay-breasted warblers lay significantly larger clutches during years of budworm outbreaks. There are not sufficient data to make a corresponding comparison for Cape May warblers. It is known (Wangersky and Cunningham 1956) that an increase in birth rate is likely to lead to instability. The easiest way to increase the stability, while still maintaining the large clutch which is desirable for the fluctuating food supply, is to have the clutch especially large when food is abundant. This is apparently the solution which the bay-breasted warbler, at least, has taken.

Mortality during the breeding season is more difficult to analyze. Disease is not normally important as a mortality factor in passerines (Lack, 1954) and this appeared to be the case for the warblers under observation. Predation may be important, however. Saw-whet owls (*Aegolius acadica*), Cooper's hawks (*Accipiter cooperii*), goshawks (*A. gentilis*), ravens (*Corvus corax*), crows (*C. brachyrhynchos*), and herring gulls (*Larus argentatus*) all occasionally were noted in the Maine woods, but no evidence was obtained of their preying upon the warblers. In fact, none of the established pairs of birds were broken up by predation of this type. Red squirrels (*Tamiasciurus hudsonicus*) were continually present in all plots and were frequently observed searching for nests. They certainly destroyed the nest of a black-throated green and of a brown creeper (*Certhia familiaris*) and were quite probably responsible for plundering one myrtle warbler nest which was robbed soon after eggs were laid. The most common evidence of mortality, however, was the frequent observation of parents feeding only one or two newly fledged young. Thus two pairs of myrtle warblers in 1956 and one in 1957 were observed the day the young left the nest feeding four young. One of the 1956 pairs succeeded in keeping all four young alive for at least three days, at which time they could no longer be followed. The remaining two pairs were only feeding two young on the day following the departure of the young from the nest. Similarly, of two black-throated green pairs (one in 1956, one in 1957) where young could be followed, one kept all four young alive and the second only raised two of the fledged four. It was difficult to determine the number of young the parents were feeding. It was also difficult to be at the nest site when the young left the nest to determine the number of fledged young. Consequently, no more observations suitable to report were made. When the young leave the nest, they fly to nearby trees quite independently of one another and apparently never return to the nest. The result is that within a few hours the young are widely scattered. In this condition they are very susceptible to predators and exposure, and should one fly when its parents were not nearby, it would rapidly starve. Normally, the young only fly or chatter loudly when a parent with food is calling nearby, and the parents seem remarkably good at remembering where the young have gone. At best, however, this is a very dangerous period. It is of some interest to note that adult warblers will feed not only young of other birds of their own species but also of other species. Skutch (1954) reviewed several published cases of this. Hence, when a wood is densely settled with warblers, the members of a large clutch might have a better chance of surviving, the straying young being fed by neighbors. This high density is, of course, the situation which obtains during a budworm outbreak when bay-breasted and Cape May warblers are so successful.

Time of Activities

So far, the nature and position of the species' activities during the breeding season have been compared. The time of these activities would also be a potential source of diversity. There could either be differences in the time of day in which feeding took place, or there could be differences in the dates during which eggs were laid and the young fed. The first type of difference (time of day) seems inherently improbable since, at least while feeding the fledged young, the parents are kept busy throughout the daylight hours gathering food. Record was taken of the time at which the various warbler species began singing in the morning of 19 June 1956. The results (Eastern Daylight Time) are: 0352, first warbler (magnolia, *D. magnolia*); 0357, first myrtle; 0400, both myrtle and magnolia singing regularly; 0401, first black-throated green; 0402, first parula warbler (*Parula americana*); 0403, first bay-breasted; 0405, all warblers singing regularly. Thus, within 13 minutes after the first warbler sang all species were singing regularly. The sequence of rising corresponds to the degree of exposure of the usual feeding zones for that date (see Figures 2-6), and therefore probably depends only upon the time at which the light reaches a certain intensity.

As for the breeding season, there is good evidence of differences in time of completion of clutches. Since date of completion can be expected to change from place to place, comparisons must be made at one fixed locality. Of 15 nests of black-throated green warbler found by Harlow in the Poconos of Pennsylvania, the mean date of clutch completion was June 3, and of 21 blackburnian the mean date of clutch completion was June 1. Thus, for this region, and there is no reason to think that the relative dates are different in other regions, there is little difference in time of nesting between blackburnian and black-throated green warblers. From the extensive collections of P. B. Philipp near Tabusintac, N. B., now in the American Museum of Natural History, and from a smaller number collected in the same region by R. C. Harlow, now in the Museum of Comparative Zoology, bay-breasted and Cape May warbler nest dates can be compared (Figure 9). It is quite clear that the bay-breasted with the median date of nest discovery of 25 June (95% confidence interval for the median 23-27 June) nest substantially later than the Cape May whose median date is 17 June (95% confidence interval for the median of 16 June-20 June). As the figure shows, the small number of nests of black-throated green and myrtle from the same region show a fairly wide spread but strongly suggest median dates intermediate between Cape May and bay-breasted. (The dates recorded by Palmer (1949) for Maine give a roughly similar sequence; myrtle, 30 May-6 June; black-throated green, 26 May-20 June; bay-breasted, after 7 June.)

It might be expected that the insects caught by the species which feed in the T zones and near the tree tops would reach peak abundance sooner thus making it desirable for those species to nest earlier. The sequence of nesting dates just presented seems to be consistent with this hypothesis.

Evidence from Winter Season

The five species of warbler migrate out of the coniferous forest through the deciduous forest and cultivated land in eastern North America and, mostly, into the West Indies and Central and South America. Therefore, any behavioral char-

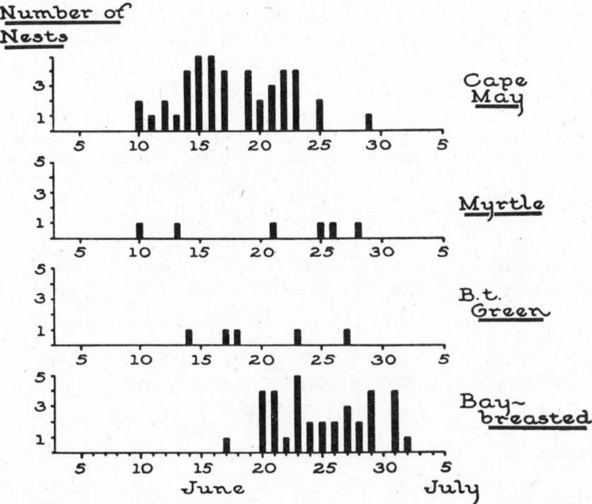

FIG. 9. Nesting dates of warblers in the Tabusintac, N. B., region.

acteristics that remain the same throughout the year must be nearly independent of the specific environment (at least within the range of environmental variation to which the bird is normally exposed). If any aspects of the breeding season behavior are retained throughout the year, these would be expected to be more fundamental than those aspects that varied with the local environment. This would be especially likely if the retained aspects of the behavior were controlled by morphological characteristics. The varying aspects would be interpreted as the result of interaction between the fundamental characteristics and the environment, as direct results of stimuli particular to that environment, or as seasonal aspects of birds' physiology. Thus it is of interest to compare behavior in different seasons.

Winter Distribution

Although Salomonsen (1954) said that species which breed in the same place tend to winter in different geographic regions, there is no evidence for this in the five warblers. More precisely, Salomonsen's statement suggests that a certain amount of competition might be avoided by having allopatric wintering grounds. Probably the most satisfactory way to test this is to determine whether the five warblers' ranges show less winter overlap than a randomly chosen group of five eastern warblers (Western warblers tend to winter in a different region and hence should not be included). To make definitions precise, two species of warbler were said to have a significant overlap in winter ranges if at least half of one species' winter range is included in the other's. From the winter range data of Bent (1953) the twenty-three species of warbler breeding in Maine (Palmer, 1949) show 253 significant overlaps, i.e., an average of 11 per species. Therefore, the probability that a randomly chosen pair of species of Maine warblers will show significant winter range overlap is 11/23 or .478. Considering the five species of warbler in the present study, Cape May overlaps with myrtle and possibly black-throated green; myrtle overlaps with Cape May, black-throated green, and blackburnian; black-throated green overlaps with Cape May (possibly), myrtle, and blackburnian; blackburnian overlaps with myrtle, black-throated green, and bay-breasted; and bay-breasted overlaps with blackburnian. There is thus a total of 10 certain overlaps among the 5 species, or 2 per species. There is thus a mean overlap per pair of species of 2/5 or .400 which is quite near the expected 0.478 suggesting that the five species overlap about randomly. It might be argued that the 23 species of Maine warblers themselves show a mutual repulsion in the winter ranges and hence are a poor standard of comparison. That this is not so can be seen as follows. The 23 species have a total of 315 significant summer overlaps in range, or 13.7 per species; *i.e.,* 13.7/23 or 0.596 is the probability that a randomly chosen pair of species will overlap in summer. As discussed above, the probability is 0.478 that a randomly chosen pair will overlap in winter. Therefore, if winter range is chosen independently of summer, 0.478 x 0.596 = 0.285 would be the expected probability of significant overlap in both winter and summer. Significant summer and winter overlaps were recorded in 164 cases, giving 7.1 per species, or a probability of 7.1/23 = 0.309, which is even a very slightly higher figure than expected, showing a slight tendency for birds which summer together to winter together. Therefore, the Maine warblers do not repel one another in over-all winter range and they are therefore suitable for the comparison made earlier. It can be concluded that the five species show about the amount of overlapping of winter range that would be expected on a random basis.

This does not prove that the species occupy the same habitat in the winter, of course. Although there are no adequate data to investigate the problem, it is quite possible that because of habitat selection, wintering populations of the five species are isolated.

Winter Feeding Behavior

The period of 22 December 1956 until 9 January 1957 was spent in Costa Rica observing winter behavior of warblers. Although myrtle, black-throated green, and blackburnian warblers include Costa Rica in their winter range (Skutch, in Bent 1953, and pers. comm.), only black-throated green of the five were found during the author's study. However, many other species of warbler were present, and detailed notes were taken on them for comparison with summer behavior. Measurements of interval between flights were made for each species. These should be comparable with those made in other seasons. No strictly comparable measurement of feeding position could be made, however. In view of the great variety of tree heights in tropical forests, measurements of feeding height could not reasonably be made in terms of distance from the top of the tree. Instead, height above the ground was used, usually gauged by eye and occasionally checked by camera viewfinder. Zones such as base, middle, and tip of branch were not reasonable, but general reference to large limbs or leaves could be made. The actual behavior while gathering food is probably comparable with other seasons; it is fairly subjective, however, so that the comparison should be confirmed by the various other measurements. A general comparison of winter and summer behavior of warblers wintering in Costa Rica will be given first; this will be followed by a more detailed analysis of two species.

Thirteen species of Parulidae were observed in Costa Rica. Of these, nine, black and white (*Mniotilta varia*), Tennessee, golden-winged (*Vermivora chrysoptera*), yellow, black-throated green, sycamore (*Dendroica dominica albilora*)[2], chestnut-sided (*Dendroica pensylvanica*), Wilson's (*Wilsonia pusilla*), and redstart (*Setophaga ruticilla*), breed in northeastern United States and/or adjacent Canada. Their summer behavior has been observed, somewhat casually, by ornithologists for many years. These observations are summarized in a general way by Bent (1953) and are part of the common knowledge of most ornithologists. It is therefore of great interest that Skutch, who has made very careful observations of Central American birds, has stated (pers. comm.) that he thinks all warblers wintering in Costa Rica (except perhaps chestnut-sided which he feels spends more time in high trees in the winter) have the same general feeding behavior and feeding height in both seasons. Table VII summarizes general results of this study and helps confirm Skutch's impression.

Tennessee and black-throated green were observed in greater numbers than the others. Hence, a detailed comparison of their winter behavior in relation to their summer behavior is possible. Tennessee warblers often hopped along branches, while black-throated green more often hopped

[2] Rare in Costa Rica.

TABLE VII. Summary of observations in Costa Rica

Species	Costa Rica			Breeding Grounds	
	Approx. Number Observed	Principal Feeding Height	Principal Feeding Activities	Principal Feeding Height	Principal Feeding Activities
Black and White	5	0-35′	creeps on trunk and branches	same	same
Golden-winged	1	5-25′	hops	same	same
Tennessee	200	10-50′*	hops, esp. along branches*	0-40′	same*
Yellow	20	4-40′	hops	same	same
Black-th. green	50	10-50′*	hops, esp. across branches*	same*	same*
Sycamore	1	8-30′	creeps and hops	?	same
Chestnut-sided	15	0-50′	hops	0-30′	same
Wilson's	15	0-25′	hops	same	same
Amer. redstart	10	5-50′	hawks for flying insects	same	same

*See text for further information.

across branches. To measure this tendency, the following procedure was adopted. A count was made of the number of changes of feeding branch which required hopping or flying over a gap. The number of seconds of observation was also recorded. If Tennessees moved along branches, they should have had significantly fewer hops per second than black-throated greens which moved across branches. In the table below H stands for the number of hops or flights across an air gap in S seconds.

	Black-throated green H	S	*Tennessee* H	S
			4	30
	8	90	3	48
	5	38	6	105
	7	43	4	54
	1	14	6	100
	12	85	11	74
	12	60	8	83
	14	70	8	82
	59	400	50	576
Mean No. of Seconds per hop	6.78		11.52	

Black-throated greens thus hopped 59 times in 400 seconds for a mean number of seconds per hop of 6.78. Tennessees hopped 50 times in 576 seconds for a mean number of seconds per hop of 11.52. By an extended sign test (Dixon and Massey 1951) this difference is well within the 5.5% level of significance. Hence, it is clear that black-throated greens hop across branches more often than Tennessees, partially confirming the subjective impression described above.

Strictly comparable measurements cannot be made in the breeding season since black-throated green feeds in coniferous and Tennessee in deciduous trees. However, the black-throated green has been shown to move principally in a tangential direction in the summer, while of eleven Tennessee warbler observations in the summer of 1957 all showed the hopping along branches which characterized the winter feeding behavior.

From these data, it is evident that the general aspects of warbler behavior are nearly the same in winter and summer. For warblers wintering in the West Indies the same situation obtains; namely, the winter habitats bear no obvious similarity to those chosen in the breeding season, but the feeding behavior and height are roughly the same (Eaton 1953). Cape May and myrtle warblers are particularly interesting and a little atypical in this respect. Both Bond (1957) and Eaton mention that Cape May frequents gardens and plantations, where it is often near the ground. This behavior parallels that observed by Brewster in the summer and reported earlier. In the winter it spends much of its time feeding upon flowers, a fact which will be used later. Bond (1957) and Skutch (in Bent 1953) both mention that myrtle warblers, in their West Indian and Central American wintering grounds, are found from beaches to forests, frequenting open ground especially. This variety of feeding location combined with its enormous winter range confirms the summer observation of great flexibility of behavior.

These observations on the flexibility of myrtle warblers can be extended by including observations made on their wintering grounds in the United States. It is well known (Pettingill 1951) that myrtles winter in the northeast wherever there are extensive patches of bayberry (*Myrica pensylvanica*). Montauk Point on Long Island, which is such a place, was visited on January 26, 1957. Here myrtles were the commonest bird in the habitat in which the bayberry is abundant. The myrtles were moving about in flocks, frequently, as in the summer, making long flights. They fed principally while hopping upon the fallen leaves under bayberries. (There was no snow.) This behavior was very similar to that observed in the summer while they were catching emerging crane flies. Some were feeding upon the "wax" coat of the berries which is readily digestible and contains nodules which are rich sources of proteins and carbohydrates (Hausman 1927).

Population Control

Any factor that can control a local population has a space distribution. Examples of such factors are food, nesting sites, and predators. Thus all populations are limited by the amount of suitable space. The meaning of "suitable" for a given species is the interesting problem. Within a given environment each necessary activity requires a certain amount of space. That activity which requires the greatest amount of space is likely to be limiting. Thus, animals such as barnacles which wait for moving food to pass by and require very little space to catch it are likely to be limited by amount of surface on which to rest. Here "suitable space" means "space adequate for barnacle attachment." Similarly, for some insects the suitable space may be the space with sufficient food supply within easy dispersal distance; for some birds, suitable nest holes may be scarcer than adequate food and suitable space will mean proper nest hole. This section will be devoted to the nature of suitable space for the five species of warbler under consideration.

The five warblers do not seem to have special nesting space or nesting material requirements which would necessitate a larger amount of space than food gathering. Territory defence is probably the only activity of the warblers that requires an area of comparable size to that needed for food gathering. As discussed earlier, territoriality may exert a limiting effect upon populations under conditions of abundant food supply, thus acting as a stabilizing factor. However, if territory requirements limit populations under normal conditions, it may be inquired why natural selection has not reduced territory sizes thus permitting larger populations. Furthermore, variation in warbler population density from plot to plot suggests that more than an incompressible territory is responsible for population regulation. Therefore, like nesting space and nesting material requirements, territories probably require less space for warblers in normal years than does food gathering. Consequently, suitable space is probably the amount of space with an adequate food supply in which the bird is adapted to feed. Direct measurement of the food supply would require a very elaborate sampling scheme. However, measurement of the amount of foliage of the type in which the species has been shown to feed is quite feasible. If the density of breeding pairs of a species is proportional to the amount of foliage in a certain zone, then a census of a plot with twice the volume of this foliage should have twice the number of birds of corresponding species. Since the five species under consideration feed above 20 feet, only foliage above 20 feet was measured.

Five areas on Mt. Desert Island were censused and measured with this view in mind. All were in predominantly spruce forest, but except for this they were chosen to be as different as possible in order to exhibit as great a range of variation as possible. The volume of foliage above twenty feet was measured as follows. The volume of a cone is proportional to the product of its basal area with its height. The foliage of a spruce tree is roughly a hollow cone with walls of approximately constant thickness. The inner cone may be considered to begin ten feet below the outer. Finally, the basal area of the foliage is proportional to the trunk area. Consequently, the product of the height of foliage in the crown with the basal area of the trunks of the trees will give a figure proportional to the volume of the outer cone. A similar figure for the volume of the inner cone is calculated and the volume of foliage in the hollow shell is obtained by subtraction. The proportion of the volume lying above twenty feet of either the inner or the outer cone is the square of the proportion of the height lying above twenty feet, so that this adjustment is easily made. The number obtained is thus proportional to the desired volume. In practice, the height of foliage in the crown was measured with a rangefinder and the basal area was measured with a "Bitterlich reloscope" (Grosenbaugh 1952).

Plot A was a 3.8 acre section of an open sphagnum bog, the "Big Heath" on Mt. Desert Island. The only trees present were black spruce and tamarack (*Larix laricina*). Trees were very scattered and the highest were between 15 and 20 feet. While typical bog warblers were common, none of the five species considered here was present.

Plot B was a 4 acre strip along the edge of the bog. Red spruce largely replaced black in this plot, the trees occasionally reaching 50 feet in height. The strip was bordered on one side by a road and on the other by the open bog.

Plot C was a 9 acre area along the Hio Truck trail near Seawall on Mt. Desert Island. The forest here was quite mature, trees reaching 70 feet, and was predominantly composed of red spruce, white spruce, and balsam fir, with a higher proportion of white birch than occurred in the other plots.

Plot D was a dense, 4 acre stand of red spruce of moderate age near Southwest Harbor, Maine. Trees reached a height of 60 feet in some places, and had been thinned in part of the plot.

Plot E was the 9 acre stand of white spruce at Bass Harbor Head on Mt. Desert Island in which the observations of 1956 were made. Here the trees reached a height of 70 feet quite frequently, although the mean was nearer 60. This plot apparently originated as an old field stand with numerous, large, low branches. These have died and become covered with a layer of lichens, especially *Usnea*.

For each plot the composition of the warbler population and the volume of the foliage above 20 feet are indicated in figure 10. Here "others" refers to other tree-nesting warblers which fed above 20 feet. It is quite clear that the total tree-nesting warbler population is very nearly proportional to the foliage volume. The abundance of the myrtle warbler is evidently quite constant, only increasing slowly as the volume of foliage increases. This is probably due to its flycatching and ground feeding habits which help to make it less dependent upon the foliage.

Black-throated green warblers were the dominant birds in all mature spruce forest habitats on Mt. Desert Island. As the figure indicates, their abundance was nearly proportional to the foliage volume above 20 feet. Their abundance did fall off slightly in the two plots, C and E, in which very tall trees were present. Black-throated greens seldom use these tall tree tops for feeding, so that the amount of foliage suitable for black-throated greens should be slightly reduced from the amount calculated for plots C and E.

Blackburnians, which require foliage near the tops of the trees, were present in small numbers in both plots which had trees of height greater than 60 feet. A true understanding of their population control on Mt. Desert Island probably cannot be acquired without considering competition with other species. It is reasonable that the blackburnian can only persist where the forest is sufficiently old that the feeding zone of the dominant black-throated green stops well before the tree tops in which the blackburnian prefers to feed.

On Mt. Desert Island, bay-breasted warblers are only common where there are dense growths of lichen-covered lower branches of spruce in the shade of the forest crown. It is in this zone that a large part of their activity takes place and here their sluggish, radially moving, feeding behavior is well suited. This habitat appears when the forest becomes dense and has large trees. Consequently, the bay-breasted warblers only remained permanently in plots D and E. (Two set up territories in plot C but had apparently left by June 8.) Again it appears that this habitat is occupied by the bay-breasted partly because it is not occupied by the black-throated green. In the budworm infested spruce and balsam stands near Ft. Kent, Maine, the bay-breasted warbler was the dominant bird; here they occupied the dense young stands of conifers and black-throated greens were forced to occupy the ridges covered with mixed growths of hemlock and hardwoods. The type of competition in heterogeneous regions mentioned in the first section provides an appropriate explanation for the change in dominance; the forest composition of the whole region is more important than the very local conditions.

Although Cape May warblers did not occupy any of the census plots, observations on their feeding behavior suggest that they would be quite similar to the myrtle warbler as far as dependence on tree foliage is concerned. This is partially confirmed by the fact that of the 18 stations studied in northern Maine, Cape Mays were present in all the lowland ones and dominant only in the fairly open stands with mature trees—a habitat which is unsuitable for the bay-breasted but is quite satisfactory for both myrtle and Cape May.

Discussion and Conclusions

In this study competition has been viewed in the light of the statement that species can coexist only if each inhibits its own population more than the others'. This is probably equivalent to saying that species divide up the resources of a community in such a way that each species is limited by a different factor. If this is taken as a statement of the Volterra-Gause principle, there can be no exceptions to it. Ecological investigations of closely-related species then are looked upon as enumerations of the divers ways in which the resources of a community can be partitioned.

For the five species of warbler considered here, there are three quite distinct categories of "different factors" which could regulate populations. "Different factors" can mean different resources, the same resources at different places, or the same resources at different times. All three of these seem important for the warblers, especially if different places and times mean very different—different habitats and different years.

First, the observations show that there is every reason to believe that the birds behave in such a way as to be exposed to different kinds of food. They feed in different positions, indulge in hawking and hovering to different extents, move in different directions through the trees, vary from active to sluggish, and probably have the greatest need for food at different times corresponding to the different nesting dates. All of these differences are statistical, however; any two species show some overlapping in all of these activities. The species of food organisms which were widespread in the forest and had high dispersal rates would be preyed upon by all the warblers. Thus, competition for food is possible. The actual food eaten does indicate that the species have certain foods in common. The slight difference in habitat preference resulting from the species' different feeding zones is probably more important. This could permit each species to have its own center of dispersal to regions occupied by all species. Coexistence in one habitat, then, may be the result of each species being limited by the availability of a resource in different habitats. Even although the insects fed upon may be basically of the same type in the different habitats, it is improbable that the same individual insects should fly back and forth between distant woods; consequently, there would be no chance for competition. The habitat differences and, equivalently, the feeding zone differences, between blackburnian, black-throated green, and bay-breasted are sufficiently large that this explanation of coexistence is quite reasonable.

The myrtle warbler is present in many habitats in the summer but is never abundant. It has a very large summer and winter range, feeds from the tree tops to the forest floor, and by rapid peering or by hawking. It makes frequent long flights and defends a large territory. Probably it can be considered a marginal species which, by being less specialized and thus more flexible in its requirements, manages to maintain a constant, low population (Figure 10).

The Cape May warbler is in a different category, at least in the region near the southern limit of its range. For here it apparently depends upon the occasional outbreaks of superabundant food (usually spruce budworms) for its continued existence. The bay-breasted warbler, to a lesser degree, does the same thing. During budworm outbreaks, probably because of their extra large clutches, they are able to increase more rapidly than the other species, obtaining a temporary advantage. During the years between outbreaks they suffer reductions in numbers and may even be eliminated locally. Lack's hypothesis, that the clutch is adjusted so as to produce the maximum number of surviving offspring, provides a suitable explanation of the decrease during normal years of these large-clutched species. It may be asked why, if Lack's hypothesis is correct, natural selection favored large clutches in Cape May and bay-breasted. Cheshire's (1954) censuses suggest a tentative answer. During his years of censusing, increases in the bay-breasted warbler population reached a figure of over 300% per year. This probably far exceeds the maximum possible in-

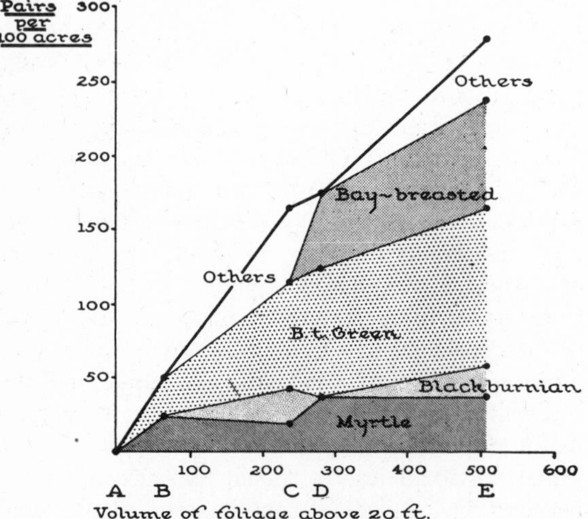

FIG. 10. Composition of the warbler population in plots A, B, C, D, and E. "Others" refers to other warbler species which feed at greater heights than 20 feet above the ground. The units of volume measurement are only proportional to the volume, but each unit roughly equals 1500 cubic feet per acre.

crease due to survival of nestlings raised in that place; probably immigration is the explanation. But if the species with large clutches search for areas in which food is superabundant and immigrate into these regions, then, for the species as a whole, the large clutch may be adapted to the maximum survival of offspring. Cape May and bay-breasted warblers may therefore be considered to be good examples of fugitive species (Hutchinson 1951).

Thus, of the five species, Cape May warblers and to a lesser degree bay-breasted warblers are dependent upon periods of superabundant food, while the remaining species maintain populations roughly proportional to the volume of foliage of the type in which they normally feed. There are differences of feeding position, behavior, and nesting date which reduce competition. These, combined with slight differences in habitat preference and perhaps a tendency for territoriality to have a stronger regulating effect upon the same species than upon others, permit the coexistence of the species.

ACKNOWLEDGMENTS

Prof. G. E. Hutchinson and Dr. S. D. Ripley have played indispensable roles in the development of this work, providing advice, encouragement, and support. The author had valuable discussion with Dr. A. F. Skutch, James Bond, and Paul Slud concerning birds on their wintering grounds. Dr. L. R. Holdridge provided invaluable help in Costa Rica, acting as naturalist and guide. Sincere thanks also go to the following persons. Miss Helen T. Mac Arthur prepared the illustrations. Drs. R. A. Paynter and Dean Amadon gave information about or provided access to the collections under their supervision. Drs. C. L. Remington, W. R. Henson, and P. B. Dowden provided entomological information. Dr. J. W. Mac Arthur helped with the observations. Finally, the author wishes to thank his wife who helped with observations, prepared the manuscript, and provided encouragement.

The work was supported by grants from the Peabody Museum of Natural History of Yale University and from the Chapman Memorial Fund of the American Museum of Natural History.

REFERENCES

Amadon, D. 1950. The Hawaiian honeycreepers (Aves, Drepaniidae). Bull. Amer. Mus. Nat. Hist. **95**: 157-262.

Andrewartha, H. G. and L. C. Birch. 1954. The distribution and abundance of animals. Chicago: Univ. Chicago Press.

Banerjee, S. K. and K. R. Nair. 1940. Tables of confidence intervals for the median in samples from any continuous population. Sankya **4**: 551-558.

Bent, A. C. 1953. Life histories of the North American wood warblers. U. S. Nat. Mus. Bull. **203**.

Betts, M. 1955. The food of titmice in an oak woodland. Jour. Anim. Ecol. **24**: 282-323.

Bond, J. 1937. The Cape May warbler in Maine. Auk **54**: 306-308.

———. 1957. North American wood warblers in the West Indies. Audubon Mag. **59**: 20-23.

Bourne, W. R. P. 1957. The breeding birds of Bermuda. Ibis **99**: 94-105.

Breckenridge, W. J. 1956. Measurements of the habitat niche of the least flycatcher. Wilson Bull. **68**: 47-51.

Cheshire, W. P. 1954. Bird populations and potential predation on the spruce budworm. Canada Dept. Agric. Sci. Serv., Annual Tech. Report, Green River Project 1953, Sect. **14**.

Cruickshank, A. D. 1956. Aud. Field Notes **10**: 431-432. (and earlier censuses of the same plot).

———. 1956a. Nesting heights of some woodland warblers in Maine. Wilson Bull. **68**: 157.

Darwin, C. R. 1859. The origin of species by means of natural selection or the preservation of favoured races in the struggle for life. London: Murray.

Dixon, W. J. and F. J. Massey. 1951. Introduction to statistical analysis. New York: McGraw-Hill.

Eaton, S. W. 1953. Wood warblers wintering in Cuba. Wilson Bull. **65**: 169-174.

Forbush, E. H. 1929. The birds of Massachusetts and other New England states. Vol. **III**. Boston: Mass. Dept. Agric.

Gardner, L. L. 1925. The adaptive modifications and the taxonomic value of the tongue in birds. Proc. U. S. Nat. Mus. 67, art. **19**: 1-49.

Gause, G. F. 1934. The struggle for existence. Baltimore: Williams and Wilkins.

Greenbank, D. O. 1956. The role of climate and dispersal in the initiation of outbreaks of the spruce budworm in New Brunswick. Can. Jour. Zool. **34:** 453-476.

Grinnell, J. 1914. Barriers to distribution as regards birds and mammals. Amer. Nat. **48:** 249-254.

———. 1921. The principle of rapid peering in birds. Univ. Calif. Chron. **23:** 392-396.

———. 1922. The trend of avian populations in California. Science **56:** 671-676.

——— **and T. Storer.** 1924. Animal life in the Yosemite. Berkeley: Univ. Calif. Press.

Griscom, L. 1938. The birds of Lake Umbagog region of Maine. Compiled from the diaries and journals of William Brewster. Bull. Mus. Comp. Zool. **66:** 525-620.

Grosenbaugh, L. R. 1952. Plotless timber estimates—new, fast, easy. Jour. Forestry **50:** 33-37.

Haldane, J. B. S. 1955. Review of Lack (1954). Ibis **97:** 375-377.

Hausman, L. A. 1927. On the winter food of the tree swallow (*Iridoprocne bicolor*) & the myrtle warbler (*Dendroica coronata*). Amer. Nat. **61:** 379-382.

Hensley, M. M. and J. B. Cope. 1951. Further data on removal and repopulation of the breeding birds in a spruce-fir forest community. Auk **68:** 483-493.

Hinde, R. A. 1956. The biological significance of territories of birds. Ibis **98:** 340-369.

Hoel, P. G. 1954. Introduction to mathematical statistics. New York: Wiley.

Hutchinson, G. E. 1951. Copepodology for the ornithologist. Ecology **32:** 571-577.

Huxley, J. 1942. Evolution, the modern synthesis. New York: Harper.

Kendeigh, S. C. 1945. Community selection birds on the Helderberg Plateau of New York. Auk **62:** 418-436.

———. 1947. Bird population studies in the coniferous forest biome during a spruce budworm outbreak. Biol. Bull. **1**, Ont. Dept. Lands and For.

Kluijver, H. N. and N. Tinbergen. 1953. Regulation of density in titmice. Arch. Ned. Zool. **10:** 265-289.

Knight, O. W. 1908. The birds of Maine. Bangor.

Lack, D. 1947. Darwin's finches. Cambridge: Cambridge Univ. Press.

———. 1954. The natural regulation of animal numbers. Oxford: Oxford Univ. Press.

———. 1955. The mortality factors affecting adult numbers. In Cragg, J. B. and N. W. Pirie 1955. The numbers of man and animals. London: Oliver and Boyd.

MacKenzie, J. M. D. 1946. Some factors influencing woodland birds. Quart. Jour. For. **40:** 82-88.

Mayr, E. 1950. Speciation in birds. Proc. Xth Int. Ornith. Cong. Uppsala.

McAtee, W. L. 1926. The relation of birds to woodlots in New York State. Roosevelt Wildlife Bull. **4:** 7-157.

———. 1932. Effectiveness in nature of the so-called protective adaptations in the animal kingdom, chiefly as illustrated by the food habits of Nearctic birds. Smithsonian Misc. Coll. **85(7):** 1-201.

Mitchell, R. T. 1952. Consumption of spruce budworms by birds in a Maine spruce-fir forest. Jour. For. **50:** 387-389.

Palmer, R. S. 1949. Maine birds. Bull. Mus. Comp. Zool. **102:** 1-656.

Pettingill, O. S. 1951. A guide to bird finding east of the Mississippi. New York: Oxford Univ. Press.

Salomonsen, F. 1954. Evolution and bird migration. Acta **XI** Cong. Int. Orn. Basil.

Skutch, A. F. 1954. Life histories of Central American birds. Pacific Coast Avifauna No. **31.**

Smith, W. P. 1953. Aud. Field Notes **7:** 337 (and earlier censuses of the same plot).

Stewart, R. E. and J. W. Aldrich. 1951. Removal and repopulation of breeding birds in a spruce-fir forest community. Auk **68:** 471-482.

———. 1952. Ecological studies of breeding bird populations in northern Maine. Ecol. **33:** 226-238.

Street, P. B. 1956. Birds of the Pocono Mountains, Pennsylvania. Delaware Valley Ornith. Club. Philadelphia.

Swaine, J. M. and F. C. Craighead. 1924. Studies on the spruce budworm (*Cacoecia fumiferana Clem.*) Part I. Dom. of Canada Dept. Agric. Bull. **37:** 1-27.

Swed, F. S. and C. Eisenhart. 1943. Tables for testing randomness of grouping in a sequence of alternatives. Ann. Math. Stat. **14:** 66-87.

Volterra, V. 1926. Variazione e fluttuazione del numero d'individiu in specie animali conviventi. Mem. Accad. Lincei **2:** 31-113. (Translated in Chapman, R. N. 1931. Animal ecology. New York: McGraw-Hill.)

Wangersky, P. J. and W. J. Cunningham. 1956. On time lags in equations of growth. Proc. Nat. Acad. Sci. **42:** 699-702.

Williams, A. B. 1950. Aud. Field Notes **4:** 297-298 (and earlier censuses of the same plot).

Wilson, E. B. 1952. An introduction to scientific research. New York: McGraw-Hill.

EXPERIMENTAL STUDIES ON PREDATION: DISPERSION FACTORS AND PREDATOR-PREY OSCILLATIONS[1,2]

C. B. HUFFAKER[3]

INTRODUCTION

THIS PAPER is the second covering a series of experiments designed to shed light upon the fundamental nature of predator-prey interaction, in particular, and the interrelations of this coaction with other important parameters of population changes, in general. In the first of this series (Huffaker and Kennett, 1956),[4] a study was made of the predatory mites, *Typhlodromus cucumeris* Oudemans[5] and *Typhlodromus reticulatus* Oudemans, and their prey species, *Tarsonemus pallidus* Banks, the cyclamen mite which attacks strawberries. In that paper the authors discussed in a broad way the need for detailed studies of this kind and the implications of such results for theories of population dynamics, particularly the role of predation—which role has been minimized by a number of researchers (e.g., Uvarov, 1931; Errington, 1937, 1946; Leopold, 1954).

A significant result of the experiments of Huffaker and Kennett (1956) was the demonstration of two types of fluctuations in density. Where predators were excluded there was a regularized pattern of fluctuations of **decreasing** amplitude, a result of reciprocal density-dependent interaction of the phytophagous mite and its host plant. The other, sharply contrasting type of regularized fluctuation occurred as a primary result of predation on the phytophagous mite by the predatory form. The interacting reciprocal dependence of the prey and predator populations resulted in greatly reduced densities and amplitude of fluctuations, comparing this with the status when predators were absent.

In the present effort a considerable body of quantitative data is presented. Also, the outlines of an experimental method and design sufficiently flexible for use in studying some of the principles of population dynamics are

[1] Received for publication August 16, 1957.

[2] These results were obtained during a period of sabbatical leave in 1955. The generous assistance of C. E. Kennett and F. E. Skinner in the preparation of the illustrations is gratefully acknowledged.

[3] Entomologist in Biological Control in the Experiment Station, Berkeley.

[4] See "References" on page 383.

[5] H. Womersley and C. E. Kennett now consider that this predator is really *Typhlodromus bellinus* Womersley.

delineated. The specific results are discussed with respect to the much-debated question of whether the predator-prey relation is inherently self-annihilative, and the bearing on this of the type of dispersion and hazards of searching. Certain trends are exhibited; if these are further verified by later experiments they may be theoretically significant, but such possibilities will be covered only after the accumulation of additional data from this continuing series of studies.

The immediate objective in the present effort has been the establishment of an ecosystem in which a predatory and a prey species could continue living together so that the phenomena associated with their interactions could be studied in detail. Once conditions are established giving a measure of assurance against overexploitation, various other features could be introduced to study their relations to the periods and amplitudes of such oscillations in density as are demonstrated. This could include such factors as differences in temperature, humidity, or physical terrain, for example. Also, the effects could be studied of using two or more predatory species competing for the one prey species, or the simultaneous employment of two species of prey acceptable to the one predator. Many variations along these lines could be expected to furnish valuable information, and the present data represent only a beginning.

Some of the many questions that could ultimately be answered include:

1. Are such oscillations inherently of **increasing** amplitude?

2. Even if so, are there commonly present forces which act to cancel this tendency, and if so, what are these forces?

3. Is the predator-prey relation adequately described by the Gause theory of overexploitation and auto-annihilation except under conditions involving immigration from other ecosystems?

4. Does the presence of other significant species in addition to the two primary or original coactors introduce a stabilizing or disturbing effect?

5. What may be the effect of changes in the physical conditions upon the degree of stability or permanence of the predator-prey relation?

6. Can evidence be obtained supporting or refuting the concept that the prey, as well as the predators, benefits from the relation?

7. What is the order of influence on stability of population density of such parameters as shelter (from physical adversity of environment), food, disease, and natural enemies of other kinds?

There are no published accounts wherein the predator-prey relation has been followed under controlled conditions beyond a single wave or "oscillation" in density. Authorities differ as to whether this relation is inherently disoperative, leading inevitably to annihilation of either the predatory species alone or both the predator and its prey in the given universe or microcosm employed. In this controversy there is confusion as to what constitutes a **suitable** experimental microcosm. Published examples of such studies have been contradictory or inconclusive.

In the classic experiments of Gause (1934) and Gause *et al.* (1936), the predator and prey species survived together only under quite arbitrary conditions—either when a portion of the prey population was protected by a "privileged sanctuary" or when reintroductions were made at intervals. Gause concluded that such systems are self-annihilative, that predators characteristically overexploit their prey, and that in nature immigrants must repopulate the local environments where this has occurred. He argued against the theory that repeated waves or oscillations conforming to mathematical formulae have an inherent meaning in the absence of immigrations.

Nicholson (1933, 1954) advocates the contrary view, and he and Winsor (1934) criticized Gause's experiments on the grounds that the universes or microcosms he employed were too small to even approximate a **qualitative,** to say nothing of a **quantitative,** conformity to theory.

DeBach and Smith (1941) conducted a stimulating experiment with a special type of predator (an entomophagous "parasite") in which they tested the biological parameter of searching capacity against Nicholson's formula. The results conformed to theory very neatly. Ecologists consider the results as based upon too arbitrary assignments or omission of other biological parameters—such as length of a generation, fecundity, undercrowding phenomena at very low densities, et cetera. However, their work remains a strikingly successful pioneer endeavor in this field, and their method of isolating the variables other than **searching** was productive.

In the present study an effort was made to learn if an adequately large and complex laboratory environment could be set up in which the predator-prey relation would not be self-exterminating, and in which all the biological parameters are left to the free play of the interacting forces inherent in the experiment, once established. Consequently, the procedure was to introduce the prey species and the predator species only at the initiation of an experiment and to follow population trends afterward without any further introductions or manipulations. No assignments of biological parameters were made. Furthermore, no areas restrictive to the predators were furnished. Food "conditioning" is the only complicating variable and this disturbance was minimized by the methods used. However, as experiments were terminated because of the annihilative force of predation in the initial, limited universes employed, the conditions set up for subsequent experiments were made progressively more complex in nature and the areas larger.

EXPERIMENTAL DESIGN AND PROCEDURE

General Aspects

The six-spotted mite, *Eotetranychus sexmaculatus* (Riley), was selected as the prey species and the predatory mite *Typhlodromus occidentalis* Nesbitt as the predator. These species were selected because successful methods of rearing them in the insectary were already known, and because earlier observations had revealed this *Typhlodromus* as a voracious enemy of the six-spotted mite. It was known to develop in great numbers on oranges infested with the prey species, to destroy essentially the entire infestation, and then to die *en masse*. At this author's suggestion, Waters (1955) had studied the detailed biology of both species and had followed population trends on individual

Fig. 1. Orange wrapped with paper and edges sealed, ready for use with sample areas delineated. (Photograph by F. E. Skinner.)

oranges as a problem in predator-prey dynamics.[6] This work was valuable in the conduct of the present research.

Uniformity in certain characteristics was maintained throughout the course of these experiments. Temperature was maintained constant at 83°F. Relative humidity varied some but was not allowed to fall below 55 per cent. There were no means of dehumidifying the room, but automatic humidity controls assured against the damaging action of low humidity. The room was kept dark.

Uniformity in total areas of the universes was achieved by utilizing various combinations of oranges and rubber balls equivalent to them in size (see figs. 1, 2, 3, and 4, for examples). This made it possible to change either or both the total primary food substrate (orange surface) and the degree of dispersion of that substrate without altering the total area of surfaces in the universes or the general distribution of units of surface in the systems. The object was to make it possible to vary the surface of orange utilized and its

[6] The design of Waters' experiments, however, was not such as to answer some of the questions posed by this study. His universes were restricted and simple, with no possibility for return to oranges by individuals leaving them by "dropping off." His results were similar to those of Gause, but he drew several conclusions which are more generally applicable than some of Gause' generalizations.

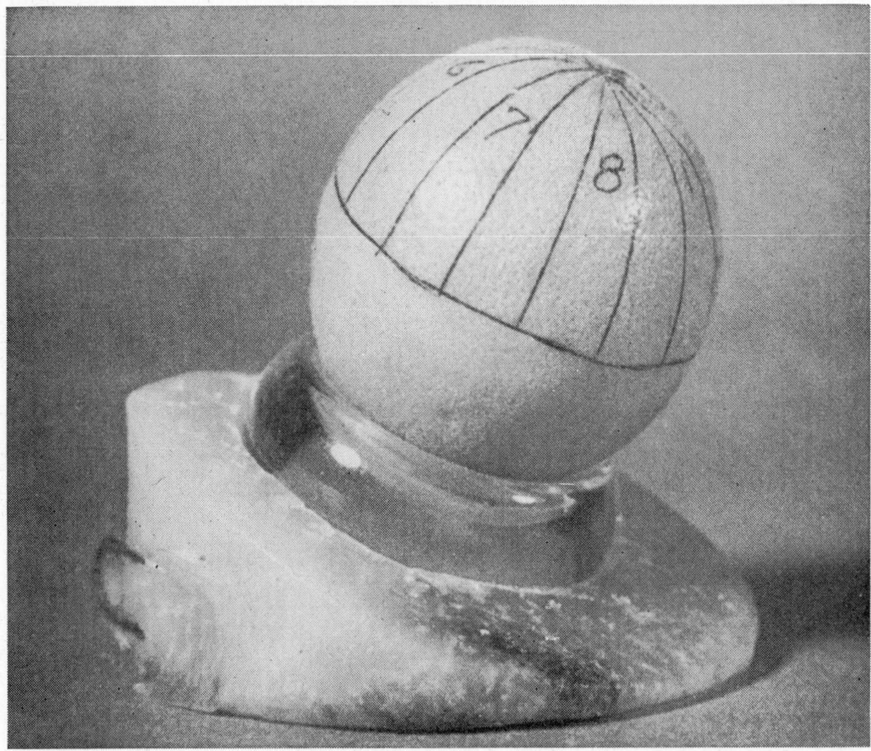

Fig. 2. Orange with lower half covered with paraffin and exposed upper half with sample areas delineated. Fuzzy surface is due to lint used. Paraffin base serves to bring all areas into focus under the microscope (see text). (Photograph by F. E. Skinner.)

Fig. 3. Four oranges, each with half-surfaces exposed (see fig. 2), grouped and joined with a wire loop, remainder of positions occupied by waxed, linted rubber balls, a 2-orange feeding area on a 4-orange dispersion, grouped. (Photograph by F. E. Skinner.)

distribution in order to complicate the search for food by both the prey and predator. Thus, a simple environment where all the food was concentrated to a maximum degree (fig. 3) could be compared with one in which the food was dispersed according to arbitrary degrees (fig. 4) throughout the system (the oranges being arranged or randomly dispersed among the rubber balls). Also, the quantity of food as well as the nature of the dispersion were varied by covering the oranges with paper to whatever degree desired, the paper being wrapped tightly, twisted and tied, and with circular holes then cut to expose the required areas of orange surface. The edges of the holes and the twisted ends were then sealed with paraffin to exclude the mites from gaining entrance to the covered surfaces. An example of an orange ready for use is shown in figure 1.

Fig. 4. Four oranges, each with half-surfaces exposed (see fig. 2), randomized among the 40 positions, remainder of positions occupied by waxed, linted rubber balls—a 2-orange feeding area on a 4-orange dispersion, widely dispersed. (Photograph by F. E. Skinner.)

Considerable difficulty was encountered in arriving at a proper means of limiting the feeding area on a given orange. The first method tried was to dip the naked oranges in hot paraffin, leaving the desired areas clean. Considerable time was lost during the operation of the first two series of experiments because the oranges which were almost completely coated with paraffin or, later, even those covered with polyethylene bags, rotted before results could be obtained. It was only subsequent to this difficulty that a good grade of typing paper was tried. The paper proved to be an excellent material but somewhat difficult to form to an adequately smooth, mite-excluding covering. This fault was corrected by very slightly dampening the paper before wrapping and by using paraffin as a sealing material.

A primary difficulty foreseen in this study was that of replenishing the food material as it is used or becomes conditioned. Under the conditions employed, oranges last from 60 to 90 days as suitable food for the prey species if not fed upon to the extent of conditioning. However, a heavy infestation can deplete an orange of suitable nourishment and thus condition it within three to five days. It is relatively impracticable to remove the food factor as a limiting feature. Also, localized food depletion by the prey species just as much as food depletion by the predator species is inherent to the natural scene. Yet, it was hoped that depletion of food could be evaluated and reduced to a minor position in limiting the populations. It was desirable to build into the design a schedule of removal of old oranges, whether or not conditioned, and their replacement by fresh ones. This would make possible a continuing system which would not automatically end if and when the original oranges became too old or conditioned. Also, by the use of careful notes on conditioning and by comparing universes where predators were introduced with universes which had none, conclusions could be drawn as to the relative importance of any interference occasioned by the conditioning of the oranges. The schedule consisted of removing 1/4 of the oranges (the oldest or obviously most unsuitable ones) at intervals of 11 days. This gave a complete change of oranges every 44 days—a period amply in advance of general unsuitableness because of age alone. One restriction was imposed. No **significant last** of a population in a subsection was removed—any such orange otherwise "due" being held another 11 days.

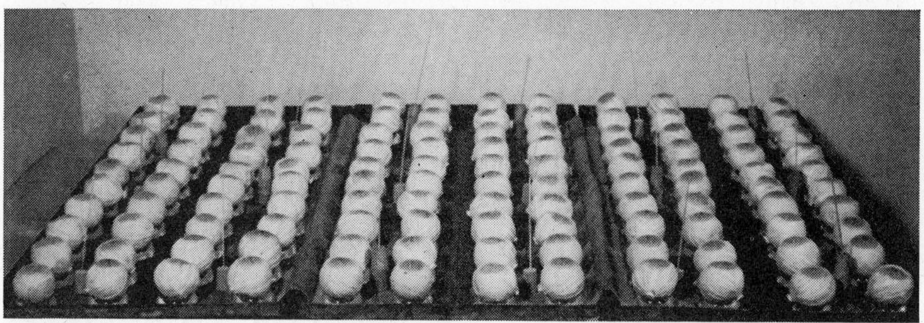

Fig. 5. 120 oranges, each with 1/20 orange-area exposed (method of fig. 1), occupying all positions in a 3-tray universe with partial-barriers of vaseline and wooden posts supplied—a 6-orange feeding area on a 120-orange dispersion with a complex maze of impediments (see text). Trays are broadly joined by use of paper bridges. (Photograph by F. E. Skinner.)

An estimate was made from general observations and the results of Waters (1955) that an orange area equivalent to that of two oranges, each 2½ inches in diameter, would be adequate, as a beginning, to study the predator-prey relation. With this premise, the smallest working basis for this design would utilize four oranges with each orange half-covered. This is because it was not desired to change more than 1/4 of the food surfaces at a given time; that is, one of the four oranges used. This made it impossible to go to the ultimate in simplicity of searching and greatest concentration of the orange surfaces by utilizing only two whole, uncovered oranges.

Each universe in the earlier experiments conformed to this pattern, but certain other changes were made later. Each universe consisted of a flat metal tray, 40 inches long and 16 inches wide, with a side wall 1 inch in height and with 40 Syracuse watch glasses on each of which rested either an orange or a rubber ball (see figs. 3, 4, and 5). The positions were arbitrarily arranged in rows to conform to the dimensions of the trays—10 oranges and/or balls along the long dimension and four along the short dimension. This gave a center to center distance of 4 inches. The upper rim of the bordering wall of each tray was kept coated with white petroleum jelly to prevent movement of mites into or out of the trays. The predators and prey were therefore free to move onto or leave oranges or rubber balls but were not permitted to leave or enter the universes.

Lint-covered oranges as used by Finney (1953) to culture the six-spotted mite were used in all the experiments. The lint gives an ideal physical environment for propagation of the species employed. It produces an orange surface similar to the covering of fine hairs and setae on the surfaces of many plant leaves. However, it also adds to the complexity of the searching problem for the predator and increases the maximal potentials in populations of both species. In addition, it was noted that populations on well-linted oranges were less subject to the adverse effects of low humidity.

Initially, experiments were arranged in duplicate; check units having the prey species alone were carried along with those having both the prey and predator species. However, as the experiments developed, certain universes automatically terminated, and new ones not synchronized chronologically or exactly comparable in other respects were substituted. With each new universe employed, some change designed to give a better chance for perpetuation of the predator and prey in the system was incorporated. These changes were based on deductive thought and trial and error processes. During this study, the author had the good fortune to have Dr. A. J. Nicholson of Australia, one of the world's leading theoreticians on population dynamics, examine the experiments, and he confirmed the view that these changes must largely be decided upon by trial and error processes. Concerning some points it was not known whether a given change would detract or add to the chances of perpetuation of the predator-prey relations—such is the reciprocal interdependence of some actions.

The exposed area of an orange was in the form of a circle which was stamped on the orange by use of a shell vial of the proper size and an inking pad. The space between the outer edge of this line was then covered with hot paraffin and joined with the edge of the paper surrounding the hole. Several layers of hot paraffin were laid down as a seal by use of a small camel's hair brush. The oranges were then placed in a refrigerator for about 1 hour to chill the surfaces. Upon removal to the laboratory, only two or three oranges at a time, condensation on the surfaces was sufficient for dampening the point of an indelible pencil as lines were drawn on the surfaces of the exposed circular areas. Diameter lines were drawn in this way, dividing the area into 16 or more sampling sections with each section numbered. This greatly facilitated the counting of the populations. The counting had to be done under a stereoscopic microscope.

When the populations reached very low levels, total populations were counted, but normally the populations were counted on only 1/4 or 1/8 of the total surfaces. The sample areas were taken in each case so as to be distributed evenly around the face of the "clock," but the first section to be counted was always taken at random.

Considering the universes employing oranges with all or one half their surfaces exposed, much difficulty was initially encountered in manipulating the oranges under the microscope so that the populations in the sample areas could be viewed fully, and without disturbance of the populations. However, the device shown in figure 2 solved this problem. It consists of a paraffin block cut so that one side at its highest point is 1 1/2 inches and is tapered to the other side which is only 1/8 inch high. An orange placed on the Syracuse watch glass, which sits loosely in a depression in the block, can then be turned by rotating the watch glass so that any desired sample area can be brought into focus without touching or awkwardly manipulating the orange.

Sampling Procedure

Sampling of partial areas and populations in the present study was necessary in order to reduce the time required in counting large populations. Hence, the populations in most cases were sampled. Statistical analyses of test examples furnished estimates of the loss in confidence occasioned by such sampling.

It was found that a population estimate based upon a subsample of a given size on an orange is more reproducible if composed of two or more noncontiguous areas evenly distributed among the position (see fig. 1). This method was used in all sampling.

TABLE 1

ANALYSIS OF VARIANCE FOR DATA OF APRIL 26 IN FIGURE 8.

Orange no.	1	2	3	4	5	6	7	8	9	10	11	12	13	14	15	16	17	18	19	20
Subsample																				
1	20	2	1	1	2	2	8	1	20	15	17	0	16	7	6	2	1	0	2	0
2	17	2	5	1	2	4	6	5	30	8	9	4	5	2	7	8	0	0	0	4
3	21	2	9	3	0	3	0	0	32	4	8	7	1	0	8	1	0	0	0	1
4	23	1	1	5	0	2	4	3	24	2	15	5	2	4	7	1	0	0	1	1
Sums	81	7	16	10	4	11	18	9	106	29	49	16	24	13	28	12	1	0	3	6

Source V.	d.f.	S.S.	M.S.
Total	79	4,160	
Between oranges	19	3,679	194*
Within oranges	60	481	8

Standard error general mean, $S\bar{x}_g = 0.81$, or 14.6% of $\bar{x}_g$.

Standard error between oranges, $S\bar{x}_o = 6.9$, or 31.2% of $\bar{x}_o$.

Using this method of assignment of the positions of the subsamples on an orange, examples of data were analyzed to establish whether the within-orange variance which is associated with subsampling is significantly greater than the variance between the oranges. The data of Table 1 for April 26 illustrate the nature of the variance, and show that the within-orange variance, which is associated with the subsamples, is very small, and that if greater accuracy were required, it could best be achieved by counting populations on more oranges rather than by altering the technique of subsampling on a given orange.

It was therefore decided that the samples include every orange, but the subsamples on each orange would be varied with the approximate densities of the populations encountered, the usual proportion being ½ or ¼ the total exposed area on each orange.

Early in the study in deciding upon the technique of sampling, the **entire** population of the prey species was counted on a representative group of 44 orange units, with each unit exposing $\frac{1}{20}$ of an orange area. This population was thus finite and known. The data used were for July 5 from the experiment illustrated in figure 18. The mean, x, for the 44 items was 6.95 mites per exposed area, with a standard error of $\pm$ 1.09, which is 15.7 per cent of the mean. This standard error reflects the variance inherent to the particular type of conglomerate distribution exhibited by such populations.

In order to determine if the subsamples could be used to estimate the total populations, half-area counts were first used. Series of six half-area random lots of the component items were drawn from the aforementioned total population on the 44 representative oranges. The means, standard errors, and the coefficient of variation were then compared with the values based upon the total known population. These statistical parameters were little changed: the standard errors being $\pm$ 0.52, $\pm$ 0.68, $\pm$ 0.65, $\pm$ 0.63, $\pm$ 0.56, and $\pm$ 0.64, respectively, as compared with a half-value of $\pm$ 0.55 for the total population; the coefficient of variation varying from 16.2 per cent to 19.3 per cent compared with 15.7 per cent (the coefficient of variation of the whole population); and the means, as estimates of the mean of the total population, averaging only 4.7 per cent higher or lower than the corresponding half-value for the total population—the range being from 3.3 to 7.8.

A test was also made to determine if a further reduction in the counting (to ¼ the total area) would give adequate estimates of the population when large universes or high populations were encountered. Both the predator and prey populations on August 1 (see fig. 18) were analyzed for this purpose.

It should be noted that some basic change had occurred between July 5 and August 1 contributing to greater skewness of distribution. This is revealed by an increase in the coefficient of variation from 15.7 per cent for the whole population count of July 5 (analysis just discussed) to 22.3 per cent for the large sample count on August 1. The six subsamples of reduced size taken on August 1 closely approximated the large sample in coefficient of variation, these being 23.3 per cent, 23.9 per cent, 23.3 per cent, 22.8 per cent, 23.3 per cent, and 23.5 per cent, respectively.

There are two probable reasons for this change in the nature of the variation. In the former instance, the predators had not yet been introduced while they were significantly active on August 1. The predator-prey relation characteristically contributes to skewness, colonial, or conglomerate distribution. Also, the prey were introduced into the universe in equal numbers on all oranges at the initiation of the experiment, and some time is necessary for the typical conglomerate distribution to become manifested, even disregarding predation. Therefore, the larger, although uniform coefficient of variation of the samples on August 1 are not the result of inadequate sampling technique but express the nature of the distribution of the population.

Comparing the prey populations of the ¼-area samples with the composite "total" or ½-area sample on August 1, the standard errors were little changed: these being ± 2.43, ± 2.63, ± 2.70, ± 2.67, ± 2.60, and ± 2.48, respectively, for the six ¼-area samplings, as compared with a half-value of ± 2.39 for the ½-area sample; the coefficient of variation, previously listed, varied only from 22.8 per cent to 23.9 per cent, compared with 22.3 per cent for the sample of double size; and the means, as estimates of the mean of the population present on twice the area, averaging only 4.7 per cent higher or lower than the corresponding half-value for the larger sample—the range being from 1.6 to 9.2.

Predator populations were more variable than were the prey populations. The standard error for total counts of the large (½ area) sample was ± 0.254, with a half-value of ± 0.127, while the values for the counts made on six ¼-area samples were ± 0.117, ± 0.150, ± 0.155, ± 0.167, ± 0.153, and ± 0.151. The coefficient of variation also varied more than the corresponding values for the prey population, these being 24.6 per cent, 34.6 per cent, 32.6 per cent, 29.0 per cent, 32.8 per cent, and 27.2 per cent, compared with 26.7 per cent for the sample of double size. The same was true for the means, these values, as estimates of the mean of the population on the larger area, averaging 5.7 per cent higher or lower, but having a range from 0.0 to 12.1.

When such ranges of error relating to the various observed points in the illustrations are considered, comparing positions of high and low densities, it is obvious that there is adequate accuracy in the estimates to establish the validity of the major trends or patterns of population change exhibited with respect to the predators and their prey in the various experiments. Yet, obviously, some of the minor, inconsistent changes following no general trend in time may be the result of inadequacy of sampling, and hence have a random character independent of predation.

RESULTS

A group of eight universes was started on February 4 and February 10. These were duplicates of an earlier group—which, as previously stated, had to be discarded because the oranges were rotting—except that the covering used on the oranges was part polyethelene material and part paraffin, rather than paraffin alone. This group also had to be discarded except for certain universes which utilized four oranges each, and these were half-covered with paraffin. Oranges only half-covered with paraffin proved satisfactory, and those units were retained.

A basic idea in this study has been the comparison of results when the plant food (oranges) is readily accessible (massed in one location in the universes) with other examples having the food widely dispersed, with the problems of dispersal and searching thus made more difficult for both the predators and the prey. The control universes which reveal the approximate levels of density of the prey species in the **absence** of predation, thus limited by the availability of food, were followed under several conditions of dispersion of the food material. These are considered representative of densities permitted by the respective levels of availability of food; and the degree to which the prey fail to reach these densities under the pressure of predation in the other universes is a measure of the effect of that predation.

The specific designs of experiments which differ from the general methods and procedures discussed previously will be covered, along with the results obtained, under each type of universe employed.

I. Densities of Prey and Fluctuations in the Absence of Predation

The following three universes were used as a measure of the population dynamics of the prey species in the absence of predators.

A. Predators Absent, Simplest Universe, Four Large Areas of Food, Grouped at Adjacent, Joined Positions. In this universe a 2-orange feeding area on a 4-orange dispersion was employed, and the unit was started February 10 and ended July 1 (see figs. 3 and 6). The initial colony was established by placing 20 female six-spotted mites, *E. sexmaculatus* (the prey species), on one of the four oranges. Movement to the other oranges was delayed until the period between March 4 and March 8 at which time the orange originally colonized was beginning to become conditioned and migrants had started moving. Thus, on a feeding area as large as a half orange, overpopulation may be delayed for about three weeks. This is significant with respect to attempts to establish self-sustained existence of both the predator and its prey in a universe. If the prey do not move readily or at least are not moving from some arenas rather readily most of the time, the predators only have to locate a colony arena and stay with it until it is overexploited, resulting in its own extinction and possibly that of its prey as well. On a given orange, this predator commonly overexploits such a colony in much less than the three week period required for conditioning pressure under these conditions (see figs. 9, 10, and 11). This question will be discussed further in relation to the data of Subsections F, G, H, and I of Section II, and it led to the arrangements used in those universes.

Regarding densities, the approximate mean population reached in this universe (fig. 6) was 9,400 *E. sexmaculatus* (all stages), or 4,700 per orange-area. Two major peaks above that level, once population growth had progressed that far, and two subsequent, resultant depressions below it occurred. These indicate a trend of a somewhat "oscillatory" nature due to occurrence of waves of maximal or excessive utilization of the food, followed by inadequate food to support the high levels. This trend may be only a carry-over result of the arbitrary unnaturally high abundance of entirely "unconditioned" or unutilized food at the initiation of the experiment, in interaction with the pattern of orange replacement. This example was not continued long enough to learn if the degree of such fluctuations would continue undiminished in amplitude or whether an inherent oscillation associated with factors of dispersal and population density under related conditions is a real feature of well-established, long-term system—i.e., ones which have reached internal balance, or relative calm.

These results do establish that a relatively high mean population is characteristic of this experimental arrangement, contrasted to that which results when predators are present. Perhaps a sizeable part of the large fluctuations may be the result of variations in the nutritional qualities of the

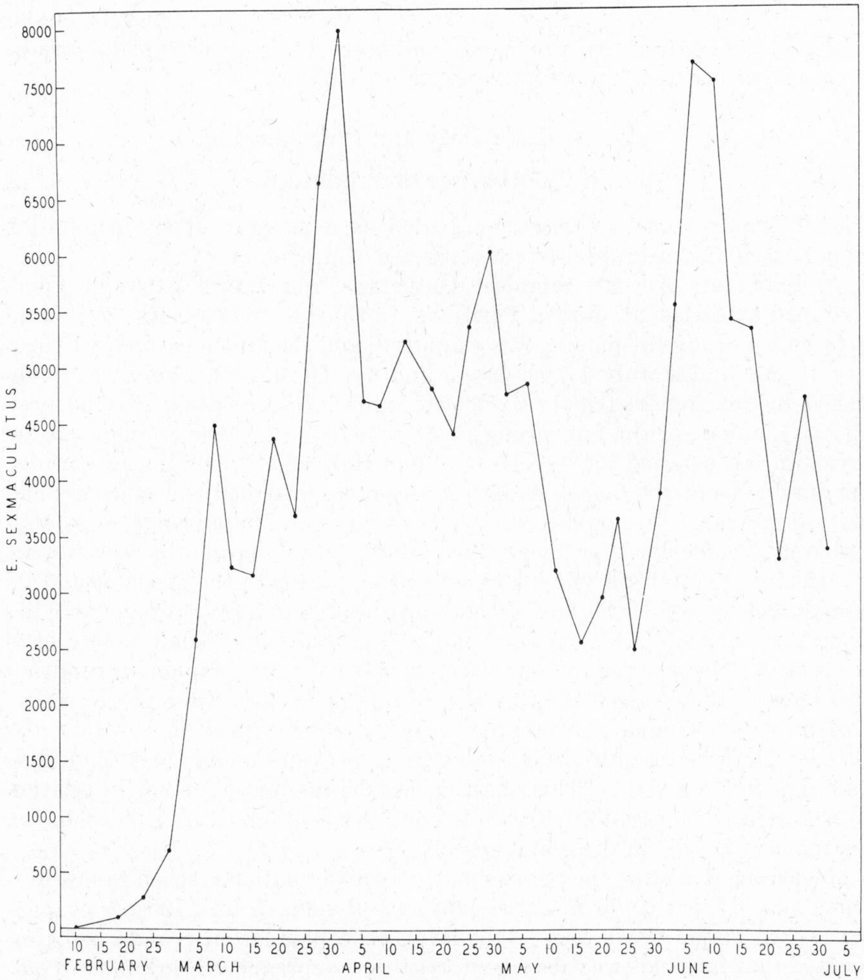

Fig. 6. Densities per orange-area of *Eotetranychus sexmaculatus* in the absence of predators in the simplest universe used, with four large areas of food (orange surface) grouped at adjacent, joined positions—a 2-orange feeding area on a 4-orange dispersion (see fig. 3 and text, Subsection A, Section I of "Results").

oranges supplied during the course of the experiment. It is known that oranges do vary in nutritional value for this mite. Beginning with March 30, at which time the population had first attained maximal utilization of the food, the oranges afterward removed in the replacement scheme were invariably fully utilized or conditioned. This full utilization is probably the most important reason why the mean level of this population was higher than that in the next two universes discussed. In fact, it was characteristic that the populations on these oranges reached conditioning levels well in advance of the dates for removal of the respective oranges, and such conditioning pressure, sometimes from two oranges at once, accomplished very prompt natural

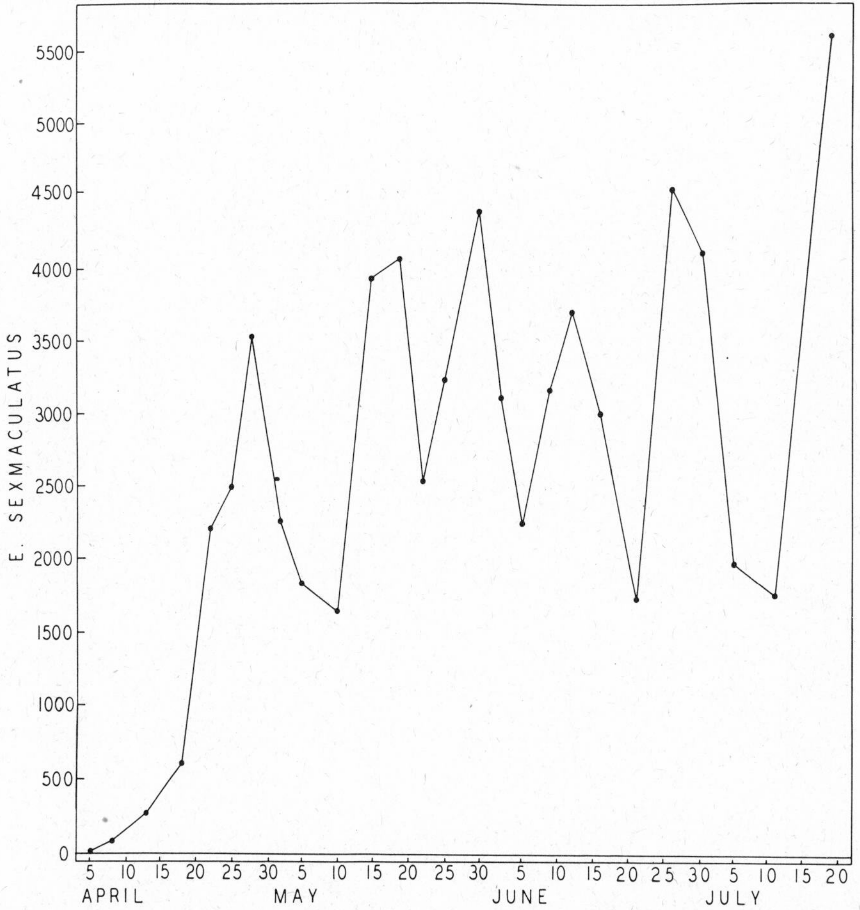

Fig. 7. Densities per orange-area of *Eotetranychus sexmaculatus* in the absence of predators, with four large areas of food (orange surface) widely dispersed among 36 foodless positions—a 2-orange feeding area on a 4-orange dispersion (see fig. 4 and text, Subsection B, Section I of "Results").

colonization of each new orange added, and thus little loss of time in utilization of the food was occasioned. Also, even after such prompt conditioning, the oranges continued to support for some time a much reduced but sizeable population of mites, and these factors support the position that in this universe the more complete utilization accounted for the higher mean level of density, comparing this universe with those of Subsections B, figure 7, and C, figure 8, of this section.

B. Predators Absent, Four Large Areas of Food Widely Dispersed. In this universe, as in the last, a 2-orange feeding area on a 4-orange dispersion was employed (in this case, not grouped), and the unit was started on April 5 and ended July 18 (see figs. 4 and 7).

The mean level of density of *E. sexmaculatus* subsequent to the initial period prior to May 20 was 7,000, or 3,500 per orange-area. It is seen, there-

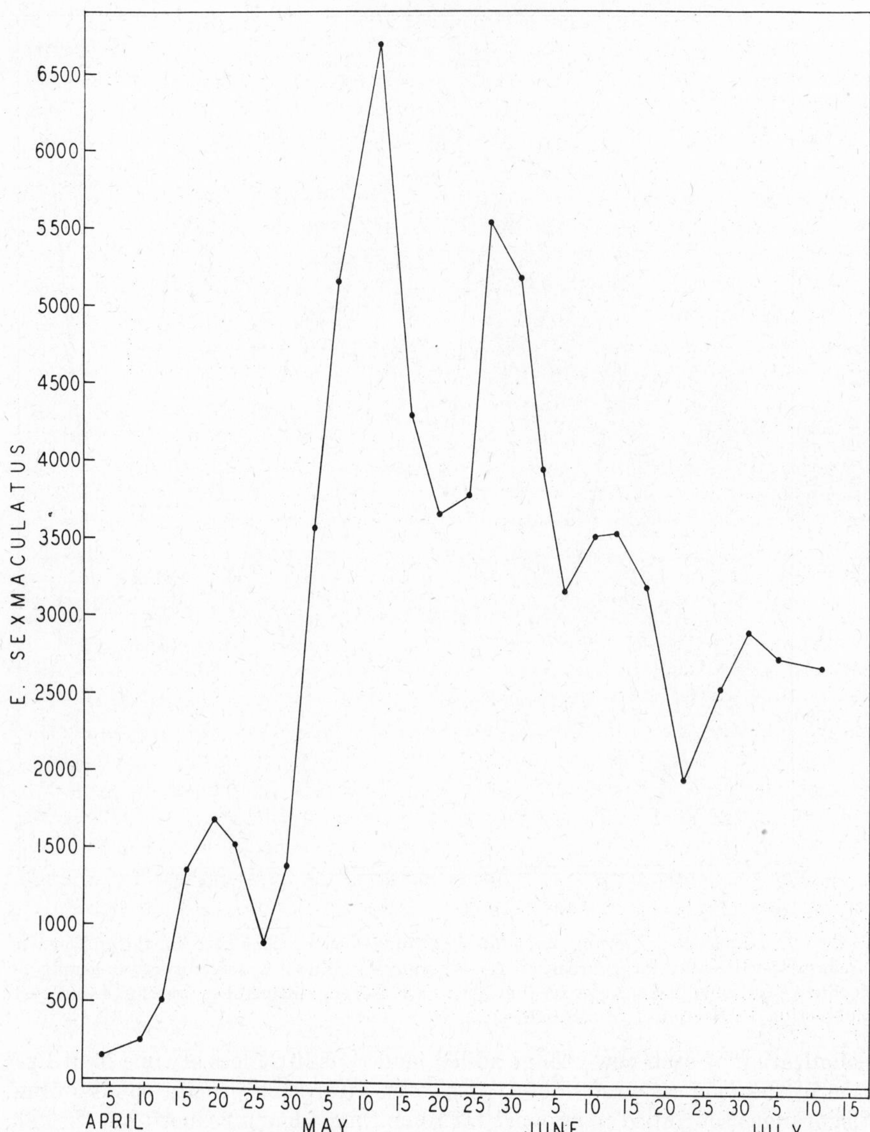

Fig. 8. Densities per orange-area of *Eotetranychus sexmaculatus* in the absence of predators with 20 small areas of food alternating with 20 foodless positions occupied by rubber balls—a 2-orange feeding area on a 20-orange dispersion (no photograph of this exact arrangement, but see text, Subsection C, Section I of "Results").

fore, that although the same quantity of food was supplied, the utilization was somewhat lower due to the difficulty the mites had in quickly locating the new orange units and the resulting loss in population in doing so, with reduced utilization during the time the oranges were in the universe.

There was also a different pattern of fluctuation in numbers, the changes being somewhat more regular in occurrence, and less marked maxima exhibited, than was so when the four oranges were placed adjacent and joined at one arena in the universe. The interaction between the difficulty of dispersal and the supply of food appears to have had a slightly stabilizing effect, compared with the condition when the supply of food alone was the primary feature and problems of dispersal minimal in effects. Unquestionably, the known variation in the quality of the oranges used is a source of error—but doubtfully sufficient to nullify this indication.

Tracing this population, 20 female mites were placed on a single orange and the population growth occurred almost entirely on the single originally stocked orange until just prior to April 28 at which time conditioning of that orange had forced migrants to search for food. By May 2 they had located the other three oranges, but not in sufficient numbers to forestall the decline in the general population resulting from conditioning of the orange originally stocked. The second ascent followed an expected course and was also short-circuited by conditioning on one of the first naturally colonized oranges on which the population first got well under way, at a time before the numbers which had located the other two oranges had increased enough to offset the decline. Subsequent events were similar; the distances between positions with food, and the difficulty the mites had in locating them were such that usually only one orange was highly productive at a time and occasionally an orange came due for removal prior to full utilization. However, none was removed which harbored a major portion of the total population. This would account for the mean density being somewhat lower than that which was experienced in the universe of Subsection A, figure 6, of this section, in which relatively full utilization was experienced.

Unusually high levels of density were the result of a partial chance occurrence of simultaneous productivity on two or more of the four oranges, but the resultant steep ascents such as those occurring during the last half of June and again between July 12 and July 18 are certain to be followed swiftly by corresponding declines in density.

C. Predators Absent, 20 Small Areas of Food Alternating with 20 Positions with No Food. In this universe, also, a 2-orange feeding area was employed, but this was segmented into 20 parts of $1/10$ orange-area each, with one part on each of 20 oranges. The 20 oranges were placed in alternate positions with 20 rubber balls. The universe was started on March 31 and ended on July 11, but the first count was made on April 4 (see fig. 8).

It should be noted that although the food material was segmented into 20 parts and dispersed over 20 oranges (equalizing to a much greater degree the variation in orange quality) and 20 positions in the universe, each orange was only one position distant from another and the positions having no food (the rubber balls) were much fewer in number. Consequently, although the food was widely dispersed it was readily accessible and sources of migrants were close at hand to any new orange added. In this respect the unit more nearly resembled those universes in which all the food was massed at one arena in the universe and on adjacent oranges.

The mean level of density of mites subsequent to the initiation period prior to May 20 was 6,600, or 3,300 per orange-area. This is slightly lower than the results of the previously discussed universe. It is likely that the differences in the actual levels of the means in these last two instances do not have real meaning, but the patterns of change in density are probably meaningful of an inherent relation to the types of dispersion employed. Yet, if the initial extreme high in density, occurring during the middle of May, is **included**, the mean level would be approximately 3,800 per orange-area—still somewhat below the mean level of the universe in which the oranges were grouped and joined (fig. 6), but slightly higher than that exhibited in the universe just discussed.

Tracing the history of this population, it was initiated by placing 10 female *E. sexmaculatus* on each of two of the 20 oranges. The first count on April 4 showed a mean population of 152 per orange-area, and these were still located only on the two colonized, or stocked, oranges. Not until April 19, at which time the population on these two oranges was first noted as causing conditioning and under competitive pressure, had migrants generally moved to other oranges; only one other orange had a few mites prior to that time. That date also marked the decline of the population, and this decline was due to the conditioning on the two oranges stocked originally, before the other 18 oranges had been located and population growth on them gotten under way. In this universe nearly all the oranges were found at this same initial period of migrants and the subsequent very steep population increase was the result of simultaneous utilization of the unused oranges in the entire universe. The second depression in the middle of May was due to rather general conditioning of many of those oranges, and the next increase was made possible by the replacement of utilized oranges by new ones according to the predetermined schedule.

There was in this case a strong indication that the period of initiation and establishment of a balance between density and the schedule of supplying food is prolonged much beyond a period of 45 days. The large amplitude of fluctuations in the early stages of the experiment, considered in relation to the successive **steady decrease** in this amplitude, and in view of the much reduced probable source of error associated with variations in orange quality, makes it likely that a position around 5,500, or 2,750 mites per orange-area, is nearer to a true equilibrium, and that the wide fluctuations and high densities which persisted during the early course of the experiment were adjustments prior to establishment of a semblance of such balance.

In contrast to this, the data illustrated in figure 7 probably represent a meaningful difference in patterns of population change. In that case the large fluctuations did **not** diminish with time. In the universe illustrated in figure 7, a position with food is found with great difficulty, but each such position has a supply five-fold in quantity. In the present example, figure 8, there are five times as many positions with food, but each has only $\frac{1}{5}$ the quantity. The positions with food are more readily located but each is depleted more rapidly. Additional replicates would need to be run and continued over a longer period of time in order to answer the questions raised.

II. Population Changes under Predator and Prey Interactions

A. Predators Present, Simplest Universe, Four Large Areas of Food, Grouped at Adjacent Joined Positions. In this universe a 2-orange feeding area on a 4-orange dispersion was employed. The unit was started February 4 by stocking with 20 female six-spotted mites. It ended April 5 (fig. 9). The

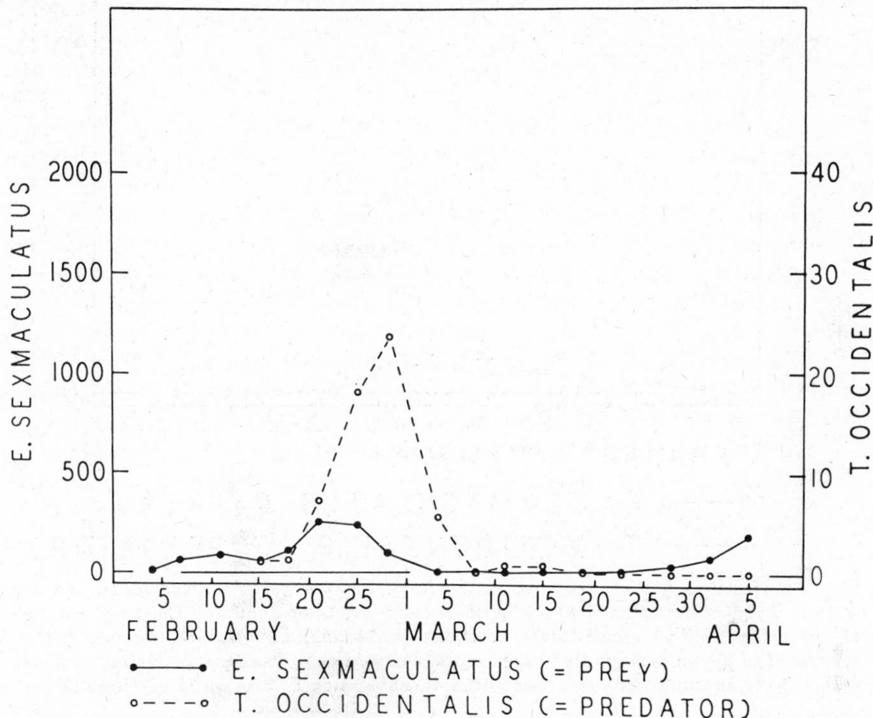

Fig. 9. Densities per orange-area of the prey, *Eotetranychus sexmaculatus,* and the predator, *Typhlodromus occidentalis,* with 4 large areas of food for the prey (orange surface) grouped at adjacent, joined positions—a 2-orange feeding area on a 4-orange dispersion (see fig. 3 and text, Subsection A, Section II of "Results").

arrangement was the same as the control universe of Subjection A of Section I (see also figs. 3 and 6) except that in this universe the predatory species was present. Two female predators were introduced 11 days after the introduction of the six-spotted mites. Both predators were placed on a single orange. This scheme was followed with all the universes except as otherwise stated.

The stocked orange spoiled between February 7 and February 11, and, consequently, the prey then declined in numbers and only increased after moving to the adjacent oranges. The prey then increased to a level of 500,

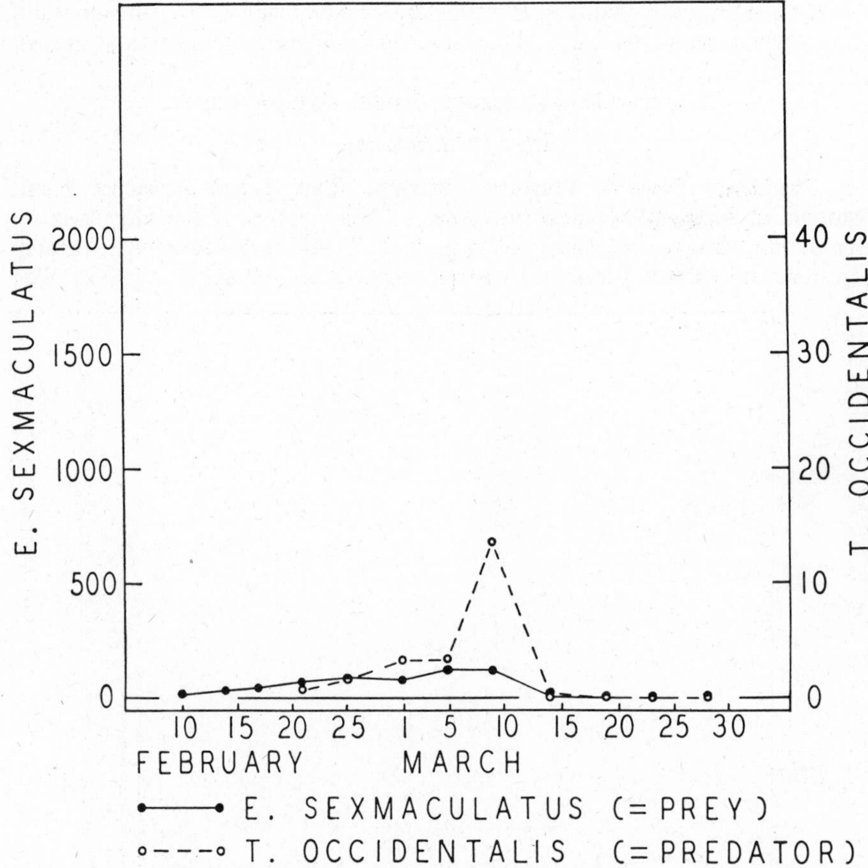

Fig. 10. Densities per orange-area of the prey, *Eotetranychus sexmaculatus,* and the predator, *Typhlodromus occidentalis,* with 8 large areas of food for the prey (orange surface) grouped at adjacent, joined positions—a 4-orange feeding area on an 8-orange dispersion (no photograph of this exact arrangement, but it was similar to that of figure 3 except that 8 oranges were used; see also text, Subsection B, Section II of "Results").

or 250 per orange-area, at which time it was preyed upon so severely that it was reduced to a nil density within 10 days and all the predators subsequently starved. The consequent characteristic, very gradual increase in the numbers of the prey was then prolonged for about 15 days before there was attained a state of vigorous population growth (see "Discussion").

B. Predators Present, Eight Large Areas of Food, Grouped at Adjacent Joined Positions. In this universe a 4-orange feeding area on an 8-orange dispersion was employed, and the unit was started February 10 and ended March 28 (fig. 10). The eight oranges were grouped in one end of the tray and joined with wire loops. In this case, because of the larger quantity of food supplied, 40 female six-spotted mites, or prey, were colonized initially, 20 on each of two of the eight oranges. Two female predators were added 11 days later.

The notes taken during the early days of this universe reveal that the female six-spotted mites used for colonizing were old and not from the usual stock colony of vigorous young females. These females died quickly without producing the usual quota of eggs after colonizing. Hence, the population could not increase at the usual rate until the first daughters became fecund. By the time that occurred and the normal population increase would other-

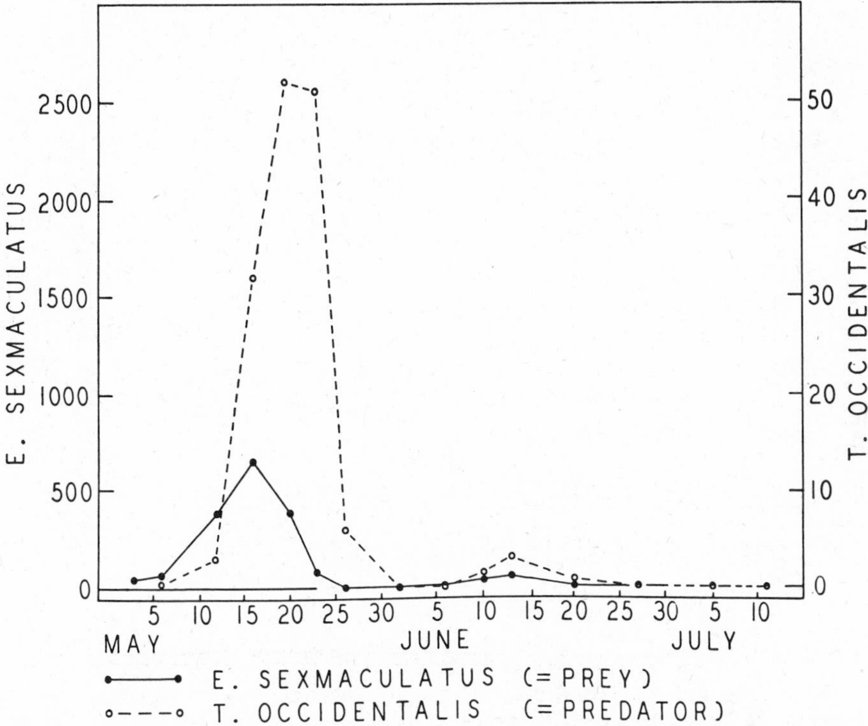

Fig. 11. Densities per orange-area of the prey, *Eotetranychus sexmaculatus,* and the predator, *Typhlodromus occidentalis,* with 6 large areas of food for the prey (orange surface) grouped at adjacent joined positions—a 6-orange feeding area on a 6-orange dispersion (no photograph of this exact arrangement, but it was similar to that of figure 3 except that 6 whole oranges were used; see text, Subsection C, Section II of "Results").

wise have ensued, the predators had become sufficiently abundant that the increase never occurred at all, even though migrants had moved to and populated at least six of the eight oranges. Hence, the population reached a maximal level of only 451 mites, or 113 per orange-area.

In this universe the predators overexploited the prey by March 14 to the extent that not only did they annihilate themselves but they also annihilated the prey species, even though the latter had dispersed successfully throughout the universe.

C. Predators Present, Six Whole Oranges as Food, Grouped at Adjacent Joined Positions. In this universe a 6-orange feeding area on a 6-orange dispersion was employed. The unit was started with 20 female six-spotted mites on April 26 and ended July 11 (fig. 11). The prey were introduced on two oranges, the two female predators on only one of them.

The prey temporarily thus escaped severe predator action on one of the oranges and a few migrants moved onto some of the other oranges, but this was not until about May 15, and before these were able to effect an appreciable general population growth, the predators reached all the infested oranges. The peak population reached was 3,900 mites, or 650 per orange-area. After May 18 to 20, the prey suffered the characteristic crash effect. Contrary to what happened in most similar universes, there was limited temporary survival of the prey **and** the predator species. The prey increased very slightly from June 5 to June 13, and this was followed by a corresponding increase in the predators, after which time the predators quickly annihilated their prey and thus themselves.

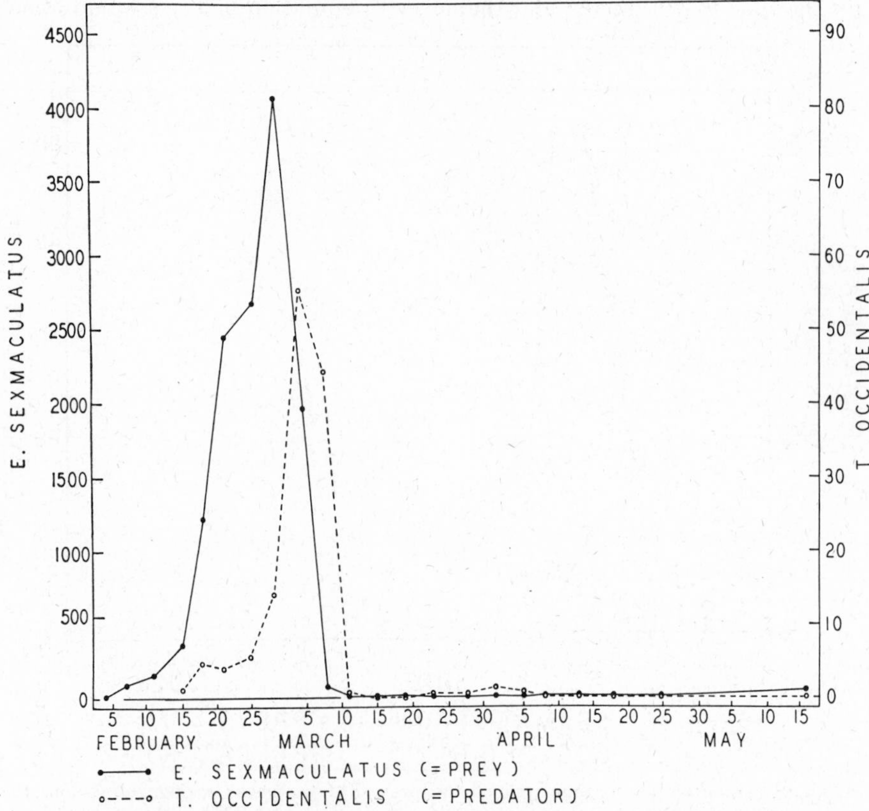

Fig. 12. Densities per orange-area of the prey, *Eotetranychus sexmaculatus,* and the predator, *Typhlodromus occidentalis,* with 4 large areas of food for the prey (orange surface) widely dispersed among 36 foodless positions—a 2-orange feeding area on a 4-orange dispersion (see fig. 4 and text, Subsection D, Section II of "Results").

D. Predators Present, Four Large Areas of Food Widely Dispersed. In this universe a 2-orange feeding area on a 4-orange dispersion was used (see figs. 4 and 12). The oranges were placed at randomized positions among rubber balls as shown in figure 4. Twenty female six-spotted mites were colonized on one orange on February 4, and two female predators were put on the same orange on February 11. The universe was ended May 17.

The wide dispersal of the food among the 40 positions presented an obstacle to movement of both the prey and the predators. In fact, neither species reached the unstocked oranges until March 28 when both did and, thus, densities on the other oranges were never substantial. The colonized orange was

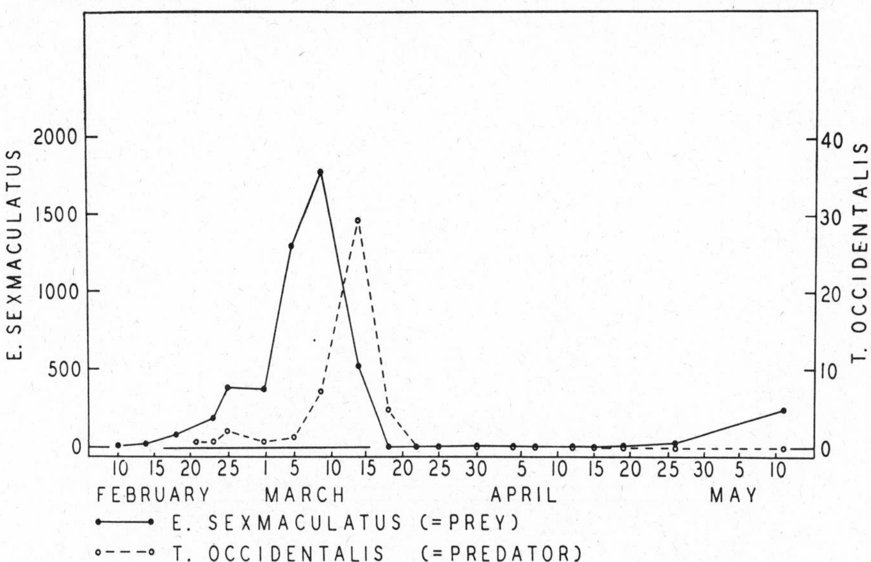

Fig. 13. Densities per orange-area of the prey, *Eotetranychus sexmaculatus*, and the predator, *Typhlodromus occidentalis*, with 8 large areas of food for the prey (orange surface) widely dispersed among 32 foodless positions—a 4-orange feeding area on an 8-orange dispersion (no photograph of this arrangement, but it was similar to that of figure 4 except that 8 oranges were used; see also text, Subsection E, Section II of "Results").

apparently phenomenal in nutritional quality for on it the prey reproduced at a very high rate, so much so that the predators did not quickly overtake it even though the latter were present on that orange from the eleventh day. The population of predators did not increase rapidly at first, although at the low density at that time it is probable that the numbers missed in the counting may have been enough to explain a part or most of this retarded increase in the midst of an abundance of prey.

At any rate, the prey population reached the high level of 8,113, or 4,056 per orange-area. This level could not be maintained on the single orange longer than a few days even in the absence of predation; thus, both conditioning of that orange and intense predation jointly accounted for the very abrupt crash which followed. Nearly all the predators then starved but a very few survived and prevented any resurgence of the prey until after April 8 at which time the last predator died and the prey began a very gradual increase in numbers (see "Discussion").

E. Predators Present, Eight Large Areas of Food Widely Dispersed. In

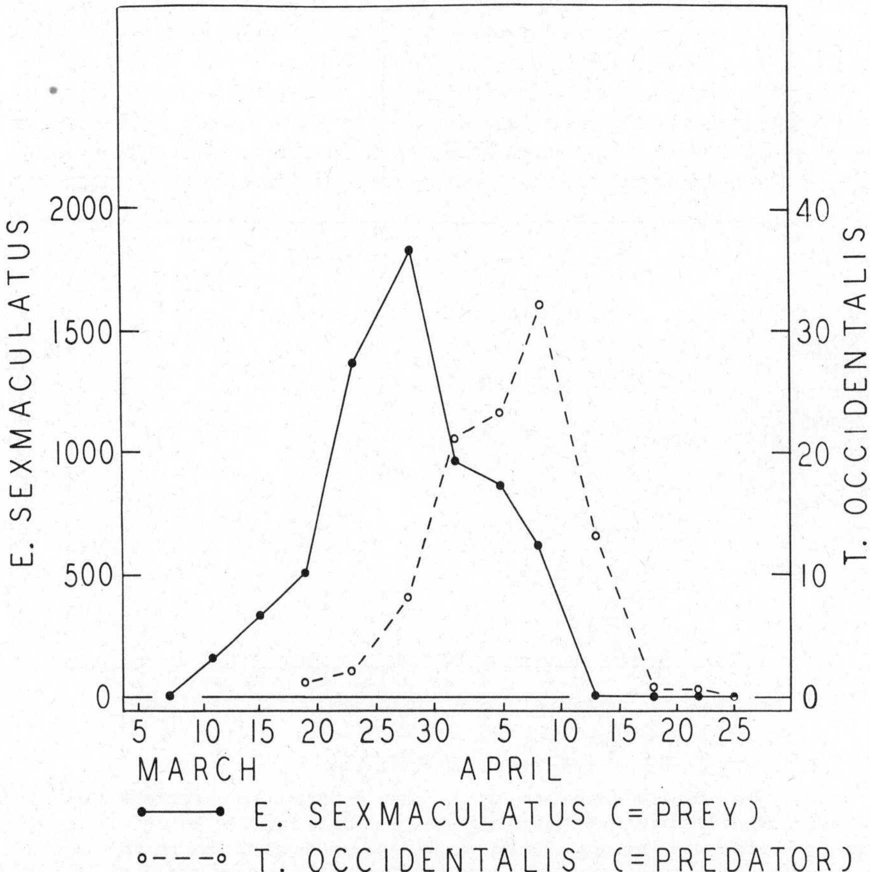

Fig. 14. Densities per orange-area of the prey, *Eotetranychus sexmaculatus*, and the predator, *Typhlodromus occidentalis*, with 20 small areas of food for the prey (orange surface) alternating with 20 foodless positions—a 2-orange feeding area on a 20-orange dispersion (no photograph of this exact arrangement, but see text, Subsection F, Section II of "Results").

this universe a 4-orange feeding area on an 8-orange dispersion was utilized, the remainder of the 40 positions being occupied by rubber balls. The unit was started February 10 and ended May 11 (fig. 13). Twenty female six-spotted mites were colonized on each of two of the eight oranges, whereas the two female predators were introduced 11 days later on one of the oranges colonized with the prey species.

There was a logical delay of about 14 days between the ascent in the prey population and the ascent in the predator population. Thus, the prey could increase unabated on the oranges which did not receive predators until such time as the latter moved onto them. The dispersed condition of the oranges made more likely such a lag in general predator action. In the examples of the universes otherwise comparable except that the food was grouped in one area and joined (figs. 9, 10, and 11), the ascents in predator densities fol-

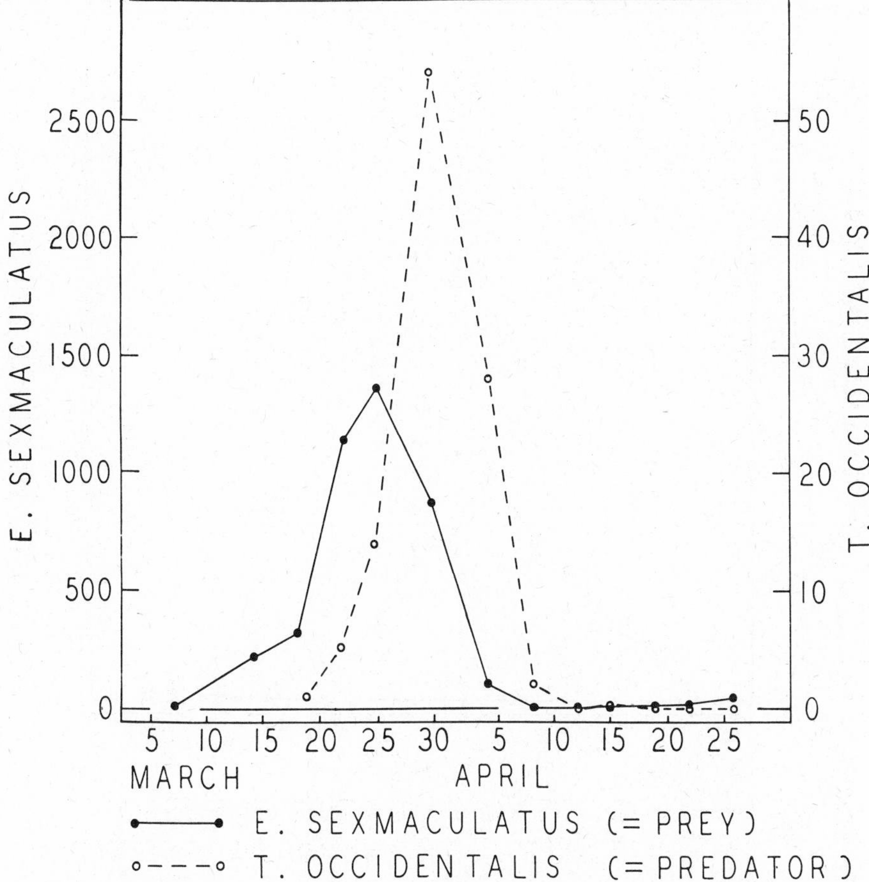

Fig. 15. Densities per orange-area of the prey, *Eotetranychus sexmaculatus*, and the predator, *Typhlodromus occidentalis*, with 20 small areas of food for the prey (orange surface) alternating with 20 foodless positions—a 2-orange feeding area on a 20-orange dispersion (no photograph of this exact arrangement, but see text, Subsection F, Section II of "Results").

lowed the respective ascents in prey densities within intervals of two or three days. Also, in those universes the prey never reached such high levels.

The lag period in this universe was sufficient for the general prey population to reach a level of 7,046, or 1,761 per orange-area before the predators moved through the universe and reduced the prey to a very low level, after which all the predators starved. The very gradual subsequent increase in the numbers of the prey up to May 25 is obvious in figure 13. After that date the undercrowding effects from the intense predator action had been overcome and a *substantial* increase followed.

F. Predators Present, 20 Small Areas of Food Alternating with 20 Foodless Positions. Two universes of this arrangement were used. In each, a 2-orange feeding area on a 20-orange dispersion was used and both were started on March 7. One was ended on April 25, the other on April 26 (figs.

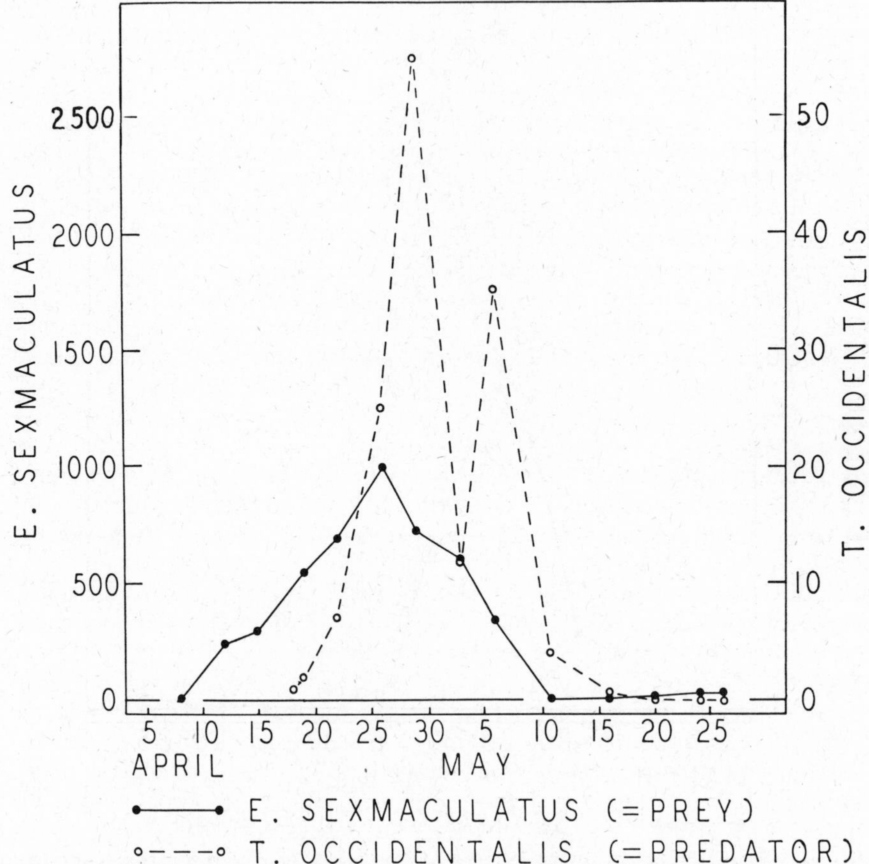

Fig. 16. Densities per orange-area of the prey, *Eotetranychus sexmaculatus*, and the predator, *Typhlodromus occidentalis*, with 40 small areas of food for the prey (orange surface) occupying all 40 positions—a 2-orange feeding area on a 40-orange dispersion, but with units of food thus adjacent (no photograph of this exact arrangement, but it was similar to ⅓ of the universe shown in figure 5 except that the wooden posts were not used and the maze of vaseline partial-barriers was much less complex; see also text, Subsection G, Section II of "Results").

14 and 15). In each universe, 10 female six-spotted mites were introduced onto each of two of the oranges, and in each, two female predators were introduced onto one of the two oranges 11 days later.

In these universes the feeding area employed on a given orange was reduced to a $\frac{1}{10}$-orange area. Large areas support the prey species for long periods of time. Dispersal pressure, or overpopulation—which is now known to cause practically all movement from orange to orange—is delayed. It was felt that by decreasing the feeding surface at each orange position—thus having more positions—the prey would be kept on the move from more individual sources so that following a localized crash from predation, there would occur sooner a subsequent population pressure which would cause more rapid dispersal and resultant repopulation on a broader spatial basis in the universe. This seemed to offer a better possibility for achieving perpetuation of the predators and prey than would wider dispersion of the smaller number of larger areas of food.

With one of the examples, the period of lag in the increase in predators was just as long, and, with the other, it was three to four days shorter than it was for the units just previously discussed. However, the prey populations did not reach levels quite so high. The higher level, however, occurred in the universe where there was the longer period of lag in the predator response to prey increase (see fig. 14). In this universe the predators exterminated the prey by April 18 and then died themselves. In the other example (see fig. 15), the prey was almost, but not entirely, exterminated by April 8. The predators quickly starved after that date and subsequently the prey gradually increased in numbers. Thus, even when 20 positions of food were used, the prey was exterminated in one instance although it survived in the other (see "Discussion").

G. Predators Present, 40 Small Areas of Food Occupying All Positions. In this universe a 2-orange area was again utilized, but the feeding area on each orange was further reduced to $\frac{1}{20}$-orange area; thus, all 40 positions were occupied by oranges (a 40-orange dispersion)—i.e., no rubber balls were used. The unit was started April 8 and ended May 26 (fig. 16). Ten female six-spotted mites were colonized on each of two of the oranges and 10 days later two female predators were colonized on one of them.

The tray used was also divided into three areas, mostly, but not entirely, separated by vaseline barriers as an impediment but not an exclusion to movement. The barrier pattern was not as complicated as that used in the later experiments such as those shown in figure 19. It was felt that the presence of the barriers would introduce greater difficulty for the predators in contacting all general positions of prey at a time, and the smaller areas of food would insure quicker movement of the prey and repopulation of depopulated areas by migrants from areas missed at the time of greatest predator abundance and pressure.

Subsequent to the expected initial increase, there was a sharp decline in the predators between April 29 and May 3 to a level below that which could be supported by the prey population in the total universe at the time. There was then a second sharp increase in the predators as they moved into one of the areas where they had not previously made contact with the prey. The second decline in predators and prey was general throughout the universe and the predators then starved since the prey reached a level which would not support a single predator. The prey population then began a gradual increase in numbers.

In this universe it became obvious that the history of events could not be properly illustrated by use of a simple line graph plotting densities, and this became increasingly true when still greater complexity was introduced. The counts made on the individual oranges revealed, unquestionably, that the sharp drop in predator abundance between April 29 and May 3, and the immediately subsequent sharp increase in numbers, were reliable reflections of the changes in the total populations in the universe. Only a pictorial record

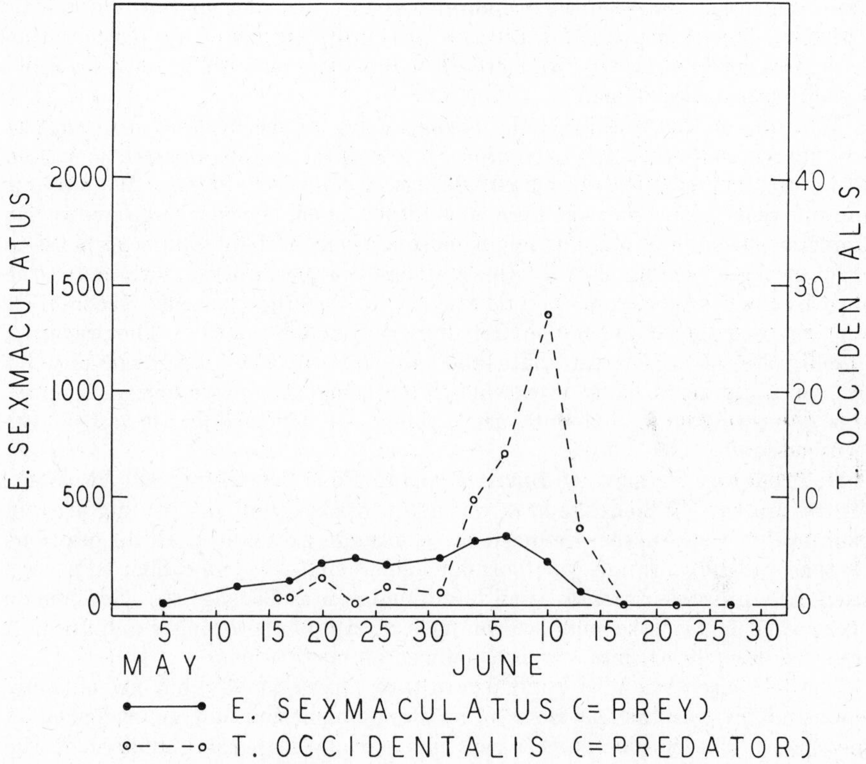

Fig. 17. Densities per orange-area of the prey, *Eotetranychus sexmaculatus,* and the predator, *Typhlodromus occidentalis,* with 120 small areas of food for the prey (orange surface) occupying all 120 positions in a 3-tray universe—a 6-orange feeding area on a 120-orange dispersion, with a simple maze of vaseline partial-barriers utilized (no wooden posts), but with the stocking done in a very restricted manner (see fig. 5 and text, Subsection H, Section II of "Results").

of the densities of the predators and the prey in the specific geographic areas in which the predators were active, and in which they were not active, could be expected accurately to portray the situation. Otherwise, the data reveal a sharp decline in predators, followed by a rapid increase, and then followed again by a rapid decline—all taking place synchronously with a rather steady general decline in density of the prey, if the data for the whole universe are plotted as a single unit as in figure 16.

Such events are contrary to the known fact of specific dependence of this predator upon this prey in these universes and, as well, contrary to the fact of the predator's rapid response to changes in the numbers of its prey by corresponding changes in its own numbers if it contacts its prey. Such a pictorial record was constructed for the data of the most important of these experiments (see fig. 18), but the time required to do this for each universe would be excessive. In any event, this does not appear to be necessary when simple universes are used (see "Discussion").

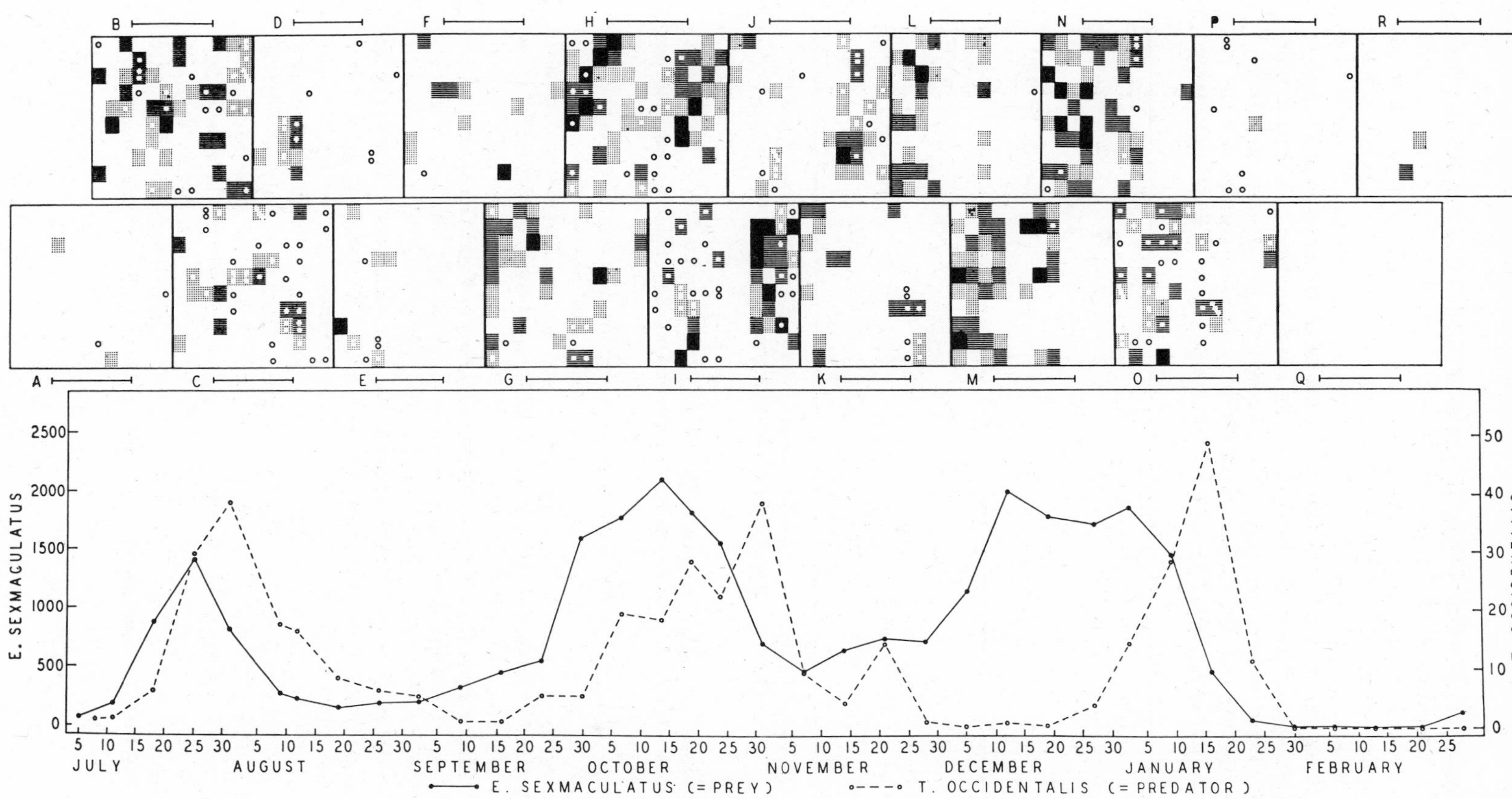

Fig. 18. Three oscillations in density of a predator-prey relation in which the predatory mite, *Typhlodromus occidentalis,* preyed upon the orange feeding six-spotted mite, *Eotetranychus sexmaculatus.*

The graphic record below shows the sequence of densities per orange-area, while the pictorial record, charts A to R, above, shows both *densities* and *positions* within the universe. The horizontal line by each letter "A," "B," et cetera, shows the period on the time scale represented by each chart. A photograph of the arrangement of this universe is shown in figure 5 and a sketch of the complex maze of vaseline partial-barriers in figure 19—a 6-orange feeding area on a 120-orange dispersion (see text, Subsection I, Section II of "Results").

H. Predators Present, 120 Small Areas of Food Occupying All 120 Positions, a 6-Orange Area. In this universe the area of orange exposed at a position was the same as that used in the universe just discussed and the food occupied all positions (no rubber balls were used), but the need for an increase in the total potentials and complexity had become obvious. Hence, in this unit, the food potential and the total areas required to be covered in searching were trebled, i.e., a 6-orange area was used on a 120-orange dispersion. The universe consisted of three of the trays (previously used singly) joined together (see fig. 5). An arrangement of vaseline partial-barriers was again used (see fig. 19). The universe was started with 10 female six-spotted

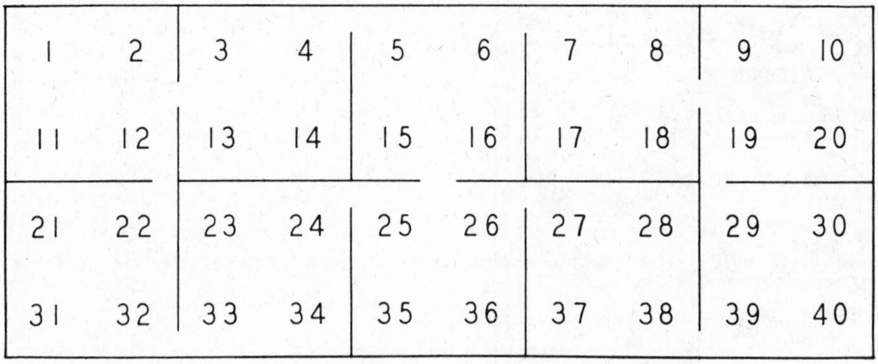

1 2 3 4 5 6 7 8 9 10
11 12 13 14 15 16 17 18 19 20
21 22 23 24 25 26 27 28 29 30
31 32 33 34 35 36 37 38 39 40

Fig. 19. Diagram of a tray used in the complex 3-tray universes (see figs. 17 and 18) with the positions of vaseline barriers shown by black lines.

mites, placed on each of two oranges in one of the trays on May 5. Two female predators were added on one of these oranges on May 16. The universe was ended June 27 (fig. 17).

In this universe the predator action was again delayed. However, movement of the prey from the one tray in which the initial colonies of both species were introduced never occurred, and it thus became obvious that with the use of such universes a wider arbitrary spread of the initial stock should be employed. Otherwise, the data of this universe added nothing new.

I. Predator-Prey Oscillations, 120 Small Areas of Food Occupying all 120 Positions, a 6-orange Area. This universe was basically like that of the last discussed but greater complexity and a different scheme of introducing the initial colonizing stock were employed. The universe was a three-tray arrangement, and a 6-orange feeding area on a 120-orange dispersion was again used. The partial barriers of vaseline were also used (see fig. 19). Contrary to previous procedure, 120 female six-spotted mites were introduced on June 30 (the graph of fig. 18 shows the first count date, July 5). That is, one mite was placed on each of the 120 oranges. In this universe also, the predators were added only five days later so as to permit them to become effective prior to general conditioning of the stocked oranges by the prey. Also contrary to the previous procedure, 27 female predators were introduced, and these were distributed, one on each of 27 oranges, these being representative of all major sections of the universe. This scheme assured that the populations would not become annihilated prior to dispersal to all parts of the universe—such as happened in the unit previously discussed. This experiment was ended March 27, although because of engraving difficulties, the data were plotted only to February 28 (see fig. 18).

In addition, small wooden posts were placed in upright positions in each of the major sections of the universe. This was to give the prey species a maximal opportunity to disperse over the vaseline barriers, thus utilizing its adaptive ability to drop by silken strands and be carried by air currents to new locations. An electric fan was used to create a mild air movement in the room. Although the predators have superior dispersal ability within a **limited** environment where movement by wind is not involved, they do not utilize this method of movement. On the other hand, by virtue of such adaptations the prey species has very superior abilities to disperse over greater distances to entirely new areas and environments. Therefore, a restricted environment or universe of the kind used in these experiments utilizes the superior dispersal power of the predator within local areas without giving chance for expression of the equally important superior dispersal power of the prey across greater distances and obstacles. The wooden posts were introduced in an effort to partially correct this condition in these experiments. They did not prove entirely satisfactory, and a more elaborate arrangement to accomplish this purpose should be employed.

Although they were joined into a single universe, the three trays may be looked upon as adjacent microenvironments, and so may the smaller subdivisions within the trays. By this scheme the changes in various areas or the geographic waves in distribution (see charts A to R of fig. 18), as well as the general density changes in the whole universe were followed. It should be noted that the horizontal dimensions of these charts were reduced (relative to the vertical dimensions) because of difficulties in reproduction on a single page. The horizontal dimension of each universe was 50 inches, the dimension shown vertically was 40 inches.

It is obvious in the charts of figure 18 that the divisions between trays, although not covered with a barrier, were an impediment to movement of somewhat greater effect than that caused by the vaseline barriers used **within** each tray.

The charts, A to R of figure 18 represent a compromise with the ideal of showing the exact locations in the universe and the densities of the entire population **on each** date of sampling. In order to have the charts on the same page and running synchronously with the linear graphs of density on the same time scale, the data for each pair of sampling dates were combined. The horizontal lines by each letter "A," "B," "C," et cetera indicate the corresponding time period of the two dates of counting. Note that the chart for the first period, "A," is below, the second, above, the third, below, the fourth, above, et cetera. The classes of density used for the predators and for the prey were limited in number.

In some instances a few prey were present but not enough to be shown. In some instances of predators being shown in areas where no prey are shown, that is a true condition; in others, it may mean only that although the prey were present, there were too few to justify shading. In either instance, such rarity of the prey means that the predators there would be doomed shortly to starvation, and the charts reveal this fact. Note also that the predators are shown in such "white" areas by white circles (ringed), whereas within the shaded areas indicating prey densities, they are shown by white circles also, but no bordering rings are used.

Considering the trays individually, or any sections of the trays individually, the predators either moved away or died in every case just as was true in Gause's experiments with protozoa and with cheese mites, or has been so in all the universes previously discussed herein. However, by utilizing the large and more complex environment so as to make less likely the predators' contact with the prey at all positions at once, or essentially so, it was possible to produce three waves or oscillations in density of predators and prey. That these waves represent a direct and reciprocal predator-prey dependence is obvious.

The maximal density of prey during the first oscillation was 8,550, or 1,425 per orange-area. The predator population responded quickly to the increase in abundance of the prey since the two species occupied the same arenas by virtue of the manual distribution in stocking of the oranges initially (see "Discussion").

The second peak density of prey occurred about October 15 and was somewhat higher than the first at 12,624, or 2,104 per orange-area. The higher level was an automatic effect of the greater lag in response by the predator population during the initial period of this oscillation—i.e., from September 10 to September 30 or somewhat beyond. This lag resulted from the predator's lack of contact with the main masses of the prey which were present in two of the three trays (left third and right third—see charts F and G, fig. 18), although they were in substantial contact with the prey of the center tray (lower center area of chart G) and slightly so with the much larger population in the left tray, or section. Thus the prey were able to sustain a marked increase in density in two of the three trays, as is shown by the progress seen from chart F to chart H and as seen in the graph for this period. More general contact with the prey was eventually achieved but the pattern of achievement reveals the reason for the rather erratic changes in density of the prey * during the process (from October 7 to October 31). On October 7 the predators had reached a moderate density in the universe of 19 per orange-area, but most of these were located in the lower section of the middle tray (chart G), the aftereffect of which is shown in chart H in the elimination of most of the prey in that area and the numbers of predators still present in that area but without food. This chart also shows that their general movement had been partly onto oranges where their prey was abundant and partly onto ones where they found little or no food. As shown in this chart, also, the predators had made substantial contact with the main mass of prey in the left tray but still had not done so in the right tray in which the prey were now rapidly increasing in numbers. It was not until later (chart I) that the right tray also was reached and general population decline of both predators

*The word "prey" should read "predator."

and prey ensued. Thus, localized discontinuity in contact accounts for the zig-zag pattern of increase in the density of the predators during the period involved. A smoothed curve of densities of the predators would correspond to the usual pattern of a predator-prey relation.

During the third major increase in the population of the prey, the maximal density reached was 11,956, or 1,993 per orange-area. In this instance, the prey had escaped substantial predation for a long period. Using chart K of figure 18 to represent the end of the second oscillatory wave, it is seen that the predators survived only in the lower right area of the universe where only a minor portion of the prey was present. With the near annihilation of this localized center of population by the predators, the latter then starved as is shown in the subsequent chart L, although one female predator had wandered off into an area where there was no food but from which position it later moved to the left and located the edge of the main mass of prey (chart M). During this time (charts K to M), the prey increased greatly in the absence of predators in the large area it inhabited. Considering the universes having predators, conditioning of the oranges for the first time became a dominant depressive feature for the prey population.

Shortage of food was the principal reason why the population leveled off at a high density of approximately 1,800 mites per orange-area between December 12 and January 2. Except for the fact that the main masses of the population encountered a shortage of food at that time because of the predators' loss of contact with it (charts L, M, and N of fig. 18), the numbers almost certainly would have increased to a position approximating at least 2,500 per orange-area. It is probable that such an increase would have contributed to a compensating, slightly earlier rise in the predator population and, consequently, a slightly earlier decline in the prey population. The resultant crash recorded just subsequent to January 2 was largely an effect of predation, although, as stated, the level from which it was initiated would have been higher (and the resultant aftereffect correspondingly more drastic) except for the ameliorating effect of the shortage of food for the prey just prior to that time. During this time and just subsequently, the approximate proportion of conditioned oranges among those which had reached the age for replacement was 38 per cent (see also "Discussion").

Also, during the peak period of the second oscillation there was a substantial but not principal contribution toward leveling off of the prey population at the approximate position of 1,700 mites per orange-area. In this instance, the proportion of conditioned oranges among those removed from the universe was 25 per cent, but the period of this influence was of shorter duration, and the predators earlier achieved more significant contact with the main masses of the prey, thus preventing a greater degree of food conditioning by the prey. In this instance, it is doubtful whether the prey would have increased to a significantly higher level even if the food had not become limiting to this degree. Thus, 75 per cent of the oranges remained unused to a damaging degree for the 56 days they were present in the universe, and predator action was the principal reason for this.

During the initial oscillatory wave, shortage of food did not enter as a contributive factor. Only six of the 120 oranges removed from the universe were conditioned, i.e., 5 per cent, 95 per cent remaining unconditioned for the 56 days (in this experiment only) each was present in the universe.

The data of this universe with relation to certain points will be covered further under the section on "Discussion."

DISCUSSION

The Experimental Data

Discussed in this section are certain topics pertaining to the data of the various universes (figs. 1 to 18), collectively, and, as well, the significance of these results as exemplifying the role of dispersion in the predator-prey relation.

Since the universe illustrated in figure 18 approaches in result one of the main objectives of this study, those data will be compared with the results in various of the other universes. The arbitrary imposition of wide distribution of both interacting species throughout all sections of the universe in the initial stocking of this universe had several effects which bear a relation to the subsequent events in this universe and to those occurring in other universes otherwise similar: 1) Both species found favorable quantities of food readily at hand for population growth, for during the initial period neither the predator nor the prey faced impediments. 2) The increase in density of the predator in response to increase in density of its prey was immediate. 3) There was very little conditioning of the oranges by the prey during this early phase, for the predators increased their action swiftly and precluded this. 4) The changes in general density of both species during this phase represent rather smooth curvilinear regressions, for the changes in density were relatively simultaneous throughout the universe, with few localized departures from the general pattern (the data thus support the contention that the actual error of sampling is small—see subsection on "Sampling Procedures"). Some of these interrelated points require clarification.

Since in this first oscillation it was not necessary that the predators overcome substantial impediments (with consequent lag effects and losses in numbers) in locating sources of prey, this oscillation is perhaps typical of one where dispersion of food and habitat and the hazards associated with finding them are minimal. In general, the simple universes previously used where the food was massed in one area gave similar results.

On the other hand, the lag effect of predator action exhibited in most of the complex universes discussed earlier, where the colonizing stock of predators was introduced at only a single or very restricted number of positions, is typical of the **second** and **third** oscillatory waves in density as shown for this universe (see fig. 18). Furthermore, the gradual, progressive change in the nature of the distributions (from one oscillation to another) in this universe was such that introductions of the predators into more than a limited number of arenas or introductions of the prey into all sections or arenas of universes would appear to create a condition of distribution not at all natural to such interactions of predators and prey. In this still-too-restricted universe, the predators survived the two critical, post-crash periods only at a single arena and in extremely small numbers, perhaps only a single female in each instance, certainly so in the second. During the third critical, post-crash phase, all the predators perished. Thus, the time required for the interacting populations to adjust to patterns of spatial and quantitative distribution more characteristic of a predator-prey relation which has come closer to **internal** balance may be the principal reason why the lag effect was accumulative from oscillation to oscillation.

Regarding the results of the universes illustrated in figures 14 and 15, the significant fact is that the exact course which may be taken locally at such very low levels of density is a product of chance events, the course of which could be best expressed as a probability of occurrence under various stipulated conditions. In the one instance, the prey were annihilated by the predators, whereas in the other identical universe the predators starved before all the prey were dead, and the prey population then gradually recovered.

Thus, generally, as to whether the participants survive the critical phase and thus make possible the second oscillation is locally a matter of chance, but as the universe considered is increased in complexity and total potentials, the probability that the participants **will** survive is increased.

In this connection it is obvious that the prey must survive the exploitation by the predator as a prerequisite to any possibility of the predator's survival. Thus, the first object is to devise an ecosystem in which there is a near certainty that the prey will survive. In the first universes employed, this condition was not even approached, but the larger, more complex universe employed (see fig. 18) comes closer to this requirement (but, considering the position of the predator, is still far from adequate).

Obviously, for given conditions, the probability that three or four successive oscillations will occur is progressively more remote and is the **product** of the separate probabilities of survival of both participants through **each** component critical phase. This would be true even disregarding the view of Nicholson (1933, 1954) that the amplitude of such oscillations will increase with time. If his view is correct and its tenets **not** modified by damping features, the probability of such a relation continuing for a successively longer number of oscillations would be correspondingly even more reduced. Yet, this cannot be interpreted as contrary to the principle that as density of the prey decreases, the pressure of predator action on it will also decrease.

In this connection, Huffaker and Kennett (1956), as previously stated, demonstrated that biotic interaction between a phytophagous form and its plant host, (with examples which feed in a way as to cause **reaction** by the plant in a manner as to alter the food potential produced subsequently) may be such that the oscillations in the absence of predation may be of **decreasing** amplitude, due to progressive weakening of the plants. Franz (in press) also showed that such interaction may predetermine in a rather subtle way the potentials of subsequent populations of plant feeding forms and, correspondingly, the natural enemies which attack them. Such mechanisms tend to reduce the amplitude of predator-prey oscillations as interactions occur between predator actions and nutritional limitations in time and place.

Shortage of food was also discussed in Subsection I of Section II in relation to damping of the amplitude in a predator-prey universe. It should be noted also that in the universe illustrated in figure 12, there was substantial shortage of food for the prey in local arenas, such was the interaction of problems of dispersal (in this universe where the oranges were widely dispersed) and predator action (see also Subsection D of Section II). While 1/4 of the orange supply was fully utilized at its replacement, the predators prevented the utilization of the other 3/4 of the food.

Thus, it is obvious that even though action of a predator may be **locally** insignificant at a given time and compensatory in nature (only a substitute for food conditioning which would surely limit the density **there** anyway), the predation may be **far more significant** throughout the larger sphere which would be reached by migrants from the nutritionally overpopulated area. That is, such migrants could proceed to overpopulate the new areas as well but for the predators which preclude the possibility in an example such as this.

This type of control by predation, associated or not with shortage of food for the prey in local arenas, is generally illustrated by the data of this study. The degree of lag in appearance or introduction of the predators into the ecosystem or local arenas is the critical feature of how much of the plant food may be depleted prior to effective curtailment of the plant feeding form. Significantly, in the presence of an effective predator, overpopulation by the plant feeding form in one arena is to a marked degree an assurance against such overpopulation in other arenas. Thus, the common contention by biological control specialists that the farmer should be willing to accept some crop injury is theoretically sound and has been practically demonstrated many times.

In the universes of Subsections A, B, and C of Section II (illustrations of figures 9, 10, and 11), the food of the prey was readily accessible, joined and grouped (a minimum of dispersion). In those universes the predators readily found their prey, responded more quickly to changes in density of the prey and were able quickly to destroy them. This condition appears to offer greater likelihood that **both** the predators and the prey will be annihilated, although in one of the three examples the prey escaped that end.

The occurrence of an almost imperceptible second wave or increase in the universe in which six whole oranges were used (see fig. 11) does not justify the conclusion that simple increase in the area or quantity of food used necessarily greatly increases the chances of creating a self-perpetuating predator-prey system. It is logical to assume that increased complexity is a more important element of the prerequisites than increased area or quantity of food for the prey. Such complexity creates greater relative refuge or protection against the prey's being overexploited, and also reduces its effective reproduction, but it is significant that refuges **restrictive** to the predators such as envisaged by Gause (1934) and Gause, *et al.* (1936) are not implied as essential.

Comparatively, increase of a prey population recovering from the effects of extreme predation is much less rapid than that which results when an original colony is started with an equally low number of colonizing individuals. This has been a characteristic feature in these experiments. Examples of this may be seen in figures 9, 12, 15, 16, and 18 by comparing the steepness of the curves, at the initiation of the universes, with the obviously very gradual increases which resulted from the small numbers which escaped the predators at the end of the crashes in the populations and subsequent to starvation of all the predators.

The reason seems to lie with certain undercrowding phenomena and with the fact that very few females escape the predators, and these are often unmated. Unless copulation occurs later they produce only male offspring. If the female survives long enough and remains in the area, promoting likelihood of contact, she may then copulate with one of her own sons or perhaps another male, and female progeny would result. Two or more generations may be required for the population to attain a favorable proportion of fertilized females and, thus, vigorous population growth, even when predators are no longer present.

Another partial explanation is the observed fact that the females which survive are more commonly found on partially or heavily conditioned oranges. On these oranges the presence of a much greater quantity of webbing, cast skins, and bodies of dead mites affords a relative sheltering effect and thus reduces the probability of the predators' destroying the last survivors. These heavily conditioned oranges are very poor sources of food for population increase; hence, a slow recovery results from the survivors.

CONCLUSIONS

The aforestated considerations suggest that the most satisfactory universe employed (see fig. 18) is still far too restricted, and that, for a perpetuating system, sufficient potentialities must be incorporated to assure several or many such arenas of "last survivors" of predators. This system would leave little probability that all such "last survivors" will simultaneously starve and none find new arenas inhabited by the prey. Thus, there is envisaged in such a system many intergrading, larger, nearly self-sustaining subuniverses or ecosystems, each one as adequate or more adequate than the one illustrated in figure 18.

A major difficulty in demonstrating the existence of reciprocal predator-prey oscillations in nature is associated with the patchy or wavelike occurrence of the predation in time and place, particularly true with examples which are wingless such as the mites and which may have limited extensive dispersal power over distances or from tree to tree, for example. In such studies an inherent oscillatory relation would be confused if the sample area taken to reveal the dynamics of a population unit is too large and, obviously, if it is too small.

Nearly any field entomologist who has studied the action of natural enemies of insect pests has noted that the pattern of action is often patchy in occurrence, proceeding in irregular waves from one or more centers. It is obvious that in one local arena the predator-prey relation may be in one phase of an oscillation while in an adjacent arena it may be in a diametrically opposed phase. Therefore, any combining of two such populations into one would not give a reliable picture of the inherent oscillatory nature of the relation.

Thus, in selecting an environmental area it must be large enough to permit the continued existence of both the predator and its prey, yet not so large that the populations in its several sections may proceed asynchronously, due to too limited interchange of the biotic participants.

It is thus more philosophical than factual to discuss whether or not the predator-prey relation is "inherently" disoperative or self-exterminative in arbitrarily restricted environments. To use an extreme example, the end result would be certain if a small universe or enclosure were employed in which only one pair of mountain lions was confined with only one pair of mule deer. Although in the case of this predatory mite and its prey, an orange is a far more nearly adequate base for a suitable ecosystem, yet, on a single orange the predator has invariably overexploited its prey and become exterminated as a local population. With many examples, the prey has been exterminated also, but with others the prey has been able to recover after the starvation of all the predators. Obviously, if the area is sufficiently small and arbitrarily simple, the biological parameters which have been present during the long evolutionary origins of the relations involving the participants are absent, and capture is so simple that the coaction is disoperative. It is necessary that a system be adequate to assure a high probability that some prey will be missed and that somewhere reasonably accessible, but not too readily so, there are local populations of prey which are thriving and sending emigrants to repopulate the depopulated areas. Also, this predator cannot survive on very low populations (although it requires many fewer prey than does the beetle, *Stethorus* spp., which feeds on the same prey—see also Kuenen, 1945), but must contact a fair density of prey at least at small micro-arenas in order to reproduce and survive.

That self-sustaining predator-prey coactions cannot be maintained without "migration" is self-evident. In this type of study the distinction between migration and any movement at all becomes rather ephemeral. The author disagrees that these migrations must be from beyond the limits of a reasonably adequate system. They may be a result of normal movements within the system—if the system is adequate to give expression to the inherent balance in the biological relations of the predator, its prey, and their coinhabited environment. In an unpublished study, the author and C. E. Kennett have demonstrated that a single strawberry plant is an adequate universe during its life span to sustain a predator-prey coaction. No smaller universe utilizing strawberries is conceivable since a single leaf or flower is not a self-perpetuating living unit.

The speed of local-arena extermination by a predator does not define the period of an oscillation. In fact, it appears to bear little relation to that period. Local extermination of the prey on an orange exposing only $\frac{1}{20}$ orange area has often occurred within three days of the entry of a female predator in that area. Even if the density of the prey population is high, with several hundreds on such an area, they are often exterminated within a period of five or six days. If the environment considered is increased to a single half-orange unit, the time required for self-extermination has been, on the average, longer. In most of the more complicated environments, and involving at least a 2-orange area, the time required to produce the drastic decline in population sufficiently general to jeopardize the predator's existence or cause its extermination has been greatly extended—20 to 40 days for a complicated arrangement involving a single-tray universe and a 2-orange feeding area widely dispersed. The same interval was increased to 30 to 60 days for the most complicated system employing a 6-orange feeding area dispersed over 120 oranges and including a maze-effect of vaseline partial-barriers.

It seems, therefore, that the complexity of the dispersal and searching relationships, combined with the period of time required for the prey species to recover in local arenas from the effects of severe predation and accomplish general repopulation, is more important in determining the period of oscillation than is the intensity of predation once contact is made with local arenas of prey. The rapid recovery of the prey is essential to maintain the predator unless there are arenas of high population which are missed.

It is thought that the existence of barriers increases the chances that the prey species will survive at a level conducive to its rapid recovery. However, it is recognized that the barriers may act as a double-edge sword and defeat the purpose of their use. They do increase the incompleteness of contact and cause marked delay in predator increase. This delay also subsequently causes a greater predator population, which then tends to offset the purpose of the barriers during the crash period. Only further experimentation would really prove whether the barrier feature of this experiment has been a deterrent or an aid to continuance of the coaction. Theoretically, the greater violence of oscillation caused by the barriers would be disoperative in nature, but, on the other hand, they do create the partial asynchrony in geographic position and promote earlier population recovery of the prey species. These features are essential to survival of the predator. They may be more than enough to offset the disoperative pressure created by the higher populations achieved at the crests of population densities. Perhaps, also, the partial ameliorating effect from conditioning of the food in local arenas tends to cancel the greater amplitude otherwise occasioned by the use of the barriers.

The complexity of the environment being searched by both predators and prey lends to the relations a marked inconstancy of hazards from micro-area to micro-area. The idea of a constant area of discovery for the predator or of a constancy in dispersal effectiveness for the prey is difficult to visualize in this environment or in nature. There is not only inconstancy, but nothing resembling a progressive gradation in the hazards. The area of discovery, or that area effectively covered and in which all prey are destroyed by a predator of this species, would vary with its hunger, the density of the prey population independently of hunger of the predator (due to the greater webbing, the added cast skins, debris, et cetera present), the complexity of the general environment with respect to the variability of physical barriers or restrictions of all kinds, and the degree of synchrony in responses, preferences, and tolerances between predator and the prey to such conditions as gravity, light, temperature, moisture, the physical surfaces, air movements, et cetera. The idea of a constant area of discovery has theoretical meaning, particularly where simple, uniform areas are involved to which both predators and prey are rigidly restricted and no chance afforded them to express the broad or narrow ranges of asynchrony in behavior and ecology.

The author feels that the balance or stability observed in nature is characteristic of the total environments in which the evolution of a relation occurred, and forms related to one another in a manner notable for the lack of stability in the community would tend to be replaced by others whose relations are more stable and, thus, the assets of the environment more efficiently utilized. The same effect would be achieved if they were forced by better adjusted competitors to occupy progressively less significant niches within which adequate stability does prevail. It cannot be overstressed that what happens with one predator-prey relation, in one ecosystem, or under a given environmental complex, as to seasons or period of years, for instance, does not necessarily apply to others.

While these data indicate that, other things being equal, simplified monocultures of crops are likely to have greater problems with insect pests than are diversified plantings, it is, nevertheless, known that a single species of introduced natural enemy has in many cases throughout the world permanently solved the most severe problems relating to such pests of monocultures. In this connection, it is interesting to note that Taylor (1955) expressed the opinion that because of the variety and mosaic of small plantings in Britain, the complex of forces for solid natural control are more favorable than in regions where extensive acreages of monocultures are the rule—the reasons for which he considered are yet unknown.

SUMMARY

An experimental study of the role of dispersion in the predator-prey relation was made, using the predatory mite, *Typhlodromus occidentalis,* and the phytophagous mite, *Eotetranychus sexmaculatus,* as the prey. Earlier experimental work by G. F. Gause and associates had led to some acceptance among ecologists of the view that the predator-prey relation is inherently self-annihilative and that continuation of this relation or coaction is dependent upon either: 1) immigrations into the depopulated areas from without, or 2) the existence of definite refuges restrictive to the predators.

In this study, a wide variety of different arrangements in dispersion of plant food (and microhabitat) was tested experimentally. In all the simple universes employed the conclusions of Gause with respect to the predator, but not to the prey, seemed to apply. The unacceptability of that view was demonstrated by the use of a larger, much more complex universe utilizing wide dispersion and incorporating also partial barriers, thus increasing still further the relative dispersion while still not incorporating restrictive refuges. By this method, predator-prey coaction was maintained for three successive oscillations. It is thus quite probable that a controlled, experimental ecosystem can be established in which the predator-prey coaction would not be inherently self-annihilative. It is believed also that various damping mechanisms would come into play which would serve to ameliorate the theoretically sound concept that oscillations arising from this coaction are inherently of increasing severity in amplitude.

The whole controversy becomes rather more philosophical than factual, considering that the earlier view incorporated the purely relative concept of immigration of new stock from without, and any distinction between immigration or emigration and any movement at all on the part of the participants can hardly be upheld. The suggestion seems more appropriate that artificial universes are inadequate if they do not give possibility of expression of the major parameters intrinsic to the specific predator-prey coaction in the natural habitat, and that conclusions drawn from such data as to principles have limited value. The success we have in sustaining such a coaction under experimental conditions is probably a measure of the degree to which we have duplicated the inherent essentials.

In this study, arbitrary selection of different degrees of dispersion and segmentation of the units of food for the prey was accomplished without altering the total surfaces to be searched, and, when desired, without altering the total amounts of food used. This was done by covering oranges to various degrees, leaving known exposed portions, and dispersing them as desired among waxed rubber balls of the same size. The technique offers possibilities of elaborate and varied studies along these lines. For example, further modifications could make it possible to study the predator-prey relation with greater assurance against overexploitation, and, thus, various other features, such as the introduction of a competing predatory species or a competing prey species, could be introduced in order to study their relations to the periods and amplitudes of the oscillations. By elaboration along these lines it should be possible to establish empirically whether employment of quite diversified agricultures may offer prospects of relief from insect pests—in comparison with extensive cultivations of single crops.

REFERENCES

DEBACH, P., and H. S. SMITH

1941. Are population oscillations inherent in the host-parasite relations? Ecology 22: 363–69.

ERRINGTON, P.

1937. What is the meaning of predation? Smithsn. Inst. Ann. Rpt. 1936:243–52.

1946. Predation and vertebrate populations. Quart. Rev. Biol. 21:144–77.

FINNEY, G. L.

1953. A technique for mass-culture of the six-spotted mite. Jour. Econ. Ent. 46:712–13.

FRANZ, J.

In Press. The effectiveness of predators and food as factors limiting gradations of *Adelges* (*Dreyfusia*) *piceae* (Ratz.) in Europe. Tenth Inter. Cong. Ent., 1956.

GAUSE, G. F.

1934. The struggle for existence. (163 pp.) Williams & Wilkins, Baltimore. Md.

GAUSE, G. F., N. P. SMARAGDOVA, and A. A. WITT

1936. Further studies of interaction between predators and prey. Jour. Anim. Ecol. 5:1–18.

HUFFAKER, C. B., and C. E. KENNETT

1956. Experimental studies on predation: Predation and cyclamen-mite populations on strawberries in California. Hilgardia 26(4):191–222.

KUENEN, D. J.

1945. On the ecological significance of *Metatetranychus ulmi* C. L. Koch (Acari, Tetranychidae). Tijdschr. v. Ent. 88:303–12.

LEOPOLD, A. S.

1954. The predator in wildlife management. Sierra Club Bul. 39:34–38.

NICHOLSON, A. J.

1933. The balance of animal populations. Jour. Anim. Ecol. 2, Supp.:132–78.

1954. An outline of the dynamics of animal populations. Austral. Jour. Zool. 2:9–65.

TAYLOR, T. H. C.

1955. Biological control of insect pests. Ann. Appl. Biol. 42:190–96.

UVAROV, B. P.

1931. Insects and climate. Ent. Soc. London, Trans. 78:1–247.

WATERS, N. D.

1955. Biological and ecological studies of *Typhlodromus* mites as predators of the six-spotted mite. (Unpublished Ph.D. dissertation, University of California, Berkeley.)

WINSOR, C. P.

1934. Mathematical analysis of growth of mixed populations. Cold Spring Harbor Symposia on Quant. Biol. 2:181–89.

PART IV

COMMUNITY METABOLISM: ENERGETICS AND PRODUCTIVITY

THE TROPHIC-DYNAMIC ASPECT OF ECOLOGY

Raymond L. Lindeman

Osborn Zoological Laboratory, Yale University

Recent progress in the study of aquatic food-cycle relationships invites a reappraisal of certain ecological tenets. Quantitative productivity data provide a basis for enunciating certain trophic principles, which, when applied to a series of successional stages, shed new light on the dynamics of ecological succession.

"Community" Concepts

A chronological review of the major viewpoints guiding synecological thought indicates the following stages: (1) the static species-distributional viewpoint; (2) the dynamic species-distributional viewpoint, with emphasis on successional phenomena; and (3) the trophic-dynamic viewpoint. From either species-distributional viewpoint, a lake, for example, might be considered by a botanist as containing several distinct plant aggregations, such as marginal emergent, floating-leafed, submerged, benthic, or phytoplankton communities, some of which might even be considered as "climax" (cf. Tutin, '41). The associated animals would be "biotic factors" of the plant environment, tending to limit or modify the development of the aquatic plant communities. To a strict zoologist, on the other hand, a lake would seem to contain animal communities roughly coincident with the plant communities, although the "associated vegetation" would be considered merely as a part of the environment[1] of the animal community. A more "bio-ecological" species-distributional approach would recognize both the plants and animals as co-constituents of restricted "biotic" communities, such as "plankton communities," "benthic communities," etc., in which members of the living community "co-act" with each other and "react" with the non-living environment (Clements and Shelford, '39; Carpenter, '39, '40; T. Park, '41). Coactions and reactions are considered by bio-ecologists to be the dynamic effectors of succession.

The trophic-dynamic viewpoint, as adopted in this paper, emphasizes the relationship of trophic or "energy-availing" relationships within the community-unit to the process of succession. From this viewpoint, which is closely allied to Vernadsky's "biogeochemical" approach (cf. Hutchinson and Wollack, '40) and to the "oekologische Sicht" of Friederichs ('30), a lake is considered as a primary ecological unit in its own right, since all the lesser "communities" mentioned above are dependent upon other components of the lacustrine food cycle (cf. figure 1) for their very existence. Upon further consideration of the trophic cycle, the discrimination between living organisms as parts of the "biotic community" and dead organisms and inorganic nutritives as parts of the "environment" seems arbitrary and unnatural. The difficulty of drawing clear-cut lines between the living *community* and the non-living *environment* is illustrated by the difficulty of determining the status of a slowly dying pondweed covered with periphytes, some of which are also continually dying. As indicated in figure 1, much of the non-living nascent ooze is rapidly reincorporated through "dis-

[1] The term *habitat* is used by certain ecologists (Clements and Shelford, '39; Haskell, '40; T. Park, '41) as a synonym for *environment* in the usual sense and as here used, although Park points out that most biologists understand "habitat" to mean "simply the place or niche that an animal or plant occupies in nature" in a species-distributional sense. On the other hand, Haskell, and apparently also Park, use "environment" as synonymous with the *cosmos*. It is to be hoped that ecologists will shortly be able to reach some sort of agreement on the meanings of these basic terms.

Reproduced with permission from Ecology, 23: 399-418, 1942. Published in cooperation with The Ecological Society of America by The Brooklyn Botanic Garden, Brooklyn, New York.

solved nutrients" back into the living "biotic community." This constant organic-inorganic cycle of nutritive substance is so completely integrated that to consider even such a unit as a lake primarily as a biotic community appears to force a "biological" emphasis upon a more basic functional organization.

This concept was perhaps first expressed by Thienemann ('18), as a result of his extensive limnological studies on the lakes of North Germany. Allee ('34) expressed a similar view, stating: "The picture than finally emerges . . . is of a sort of superorganismic unity not alone between the plants and animals to form biotic communities, but also between the biota and the environment." Such a concept is inherent in the term *ecosystem*, proposed by Tansley ('35) for the fundamental ecological unit.[2] Rejecting the terms "complex organism" and "biotic community," Tansley writes, "But the more fundamental conception is, as it seems to me, the whole *system* (in the sense of physics), including not only the organism-complex, but also the whole complex of physical factors forming what we call the environment of the biome. . . . It is the systems so formed which, from the point of view of the ecologist, are the basic units of nature on the face of the earth. . . . These *ecosystems*, as we may call them, are of the most various kinds and sizes. They form one category of the multitudinous physical systems of the universe, which range from the universe as a whole down to the atom." Tansley goes on to discuss the ecosystem as a category of rank equal to the "biome" (Clements, '16), but points out that the term can also be used in a general sense, as is the word "community." The *ecosystem* may be formally defined as the system composed of physical-chemical-biological processes active within a space-time unit of any magnitude, i.e., the biotic community *plus* its abiotic environment. The concept of the ecosystem is believed by the writer to be of fundamental importance in interpreting the data of dynamic ecology.

Trophic Dynamics

Qualitative food-cycle relationships

Although certain aspects of food relations have been known for centuries, many processes within ecosystems are still very incompletely understood. The basic process in trophic dynamics is the transfer of energy from one part of the ecosystem to another. All function, and indeed all life, within an ecosystem depends upon the utilization of an external source of energy, solar radiation. A portion of this incident energy is transformed by the process of photosynthesis into the structure of living organisms. In the language of community economics introduced by Thienemann ('26), autotrophic plants are *producer* organisms, employing the energy obtained by photosynthesis to synthesize complex organic substances from simple inorganic substances. Although plants again release a portion of this potential energy in catabolic processes, a great surplus of organic substance is accumulated. Animals and heterotrophic plants, as *consumer* organisms, feed upon this surplus of potential energy, oxidizing a considerable portion of the consumed substance to release kinetic energy for metabolism, but transforming the remainder into the complex chemical substances of their own bodies. Following death, every organism is a potential source of energy for saprophagous organisms (feeding directly on dead tissues), which again may act as energy sources for successive categories of consumers. Heterotrophic bacteria and fungi, representing the most important saprophagous consumption of energy, may be conveniently differentiated from animal consumers as special-

[2] The ecological system composed of the "biocoenosis + biotop" has been termed the *holocoen* by Friederichs ('30) and the *biosystem* by Thienemann ('39).

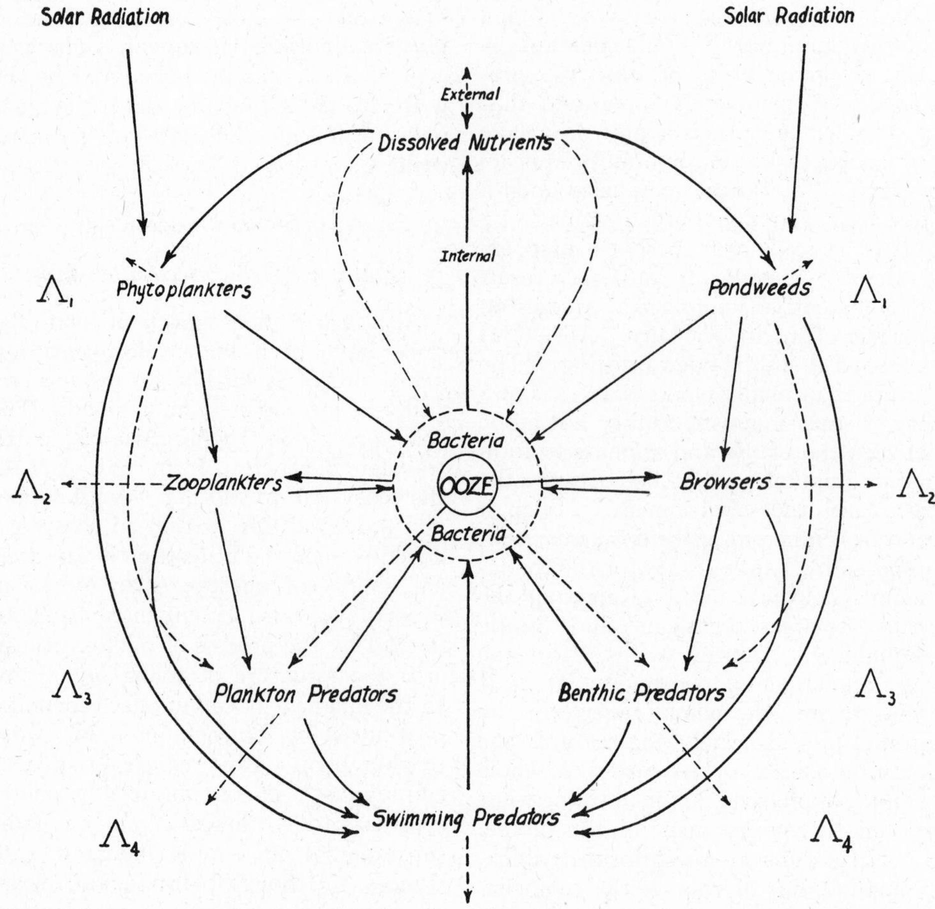

FIG. 1. Generalized lacustrine food-cycle relationships (after Lindeman, '41b).

ized *decomposers*[3] of organic substance. Waksman ('41) has suggested that certain of these bacteria be further differentiated as *transformers* of organic and inorganic compounds. The combined action of animal consumers and bacterial decomposers tends to dissipate the potential energy of organic substances, again transforming them to the inorganic state. From this inorganic state the autotrophic plants may utilize the dissolved nutrients once more in resynthesizing complex organic substance, thus completing the food cycle.

The careful study of food cycles reveals an intricate pattern of trophic predilections and substitutions underlain by certain basic dependencies; food-cycle diagrams, such as figure 1, attempt to portray these underlying relationships. In general, predators are less specialized in food habits than are their prey. The ecological importance of this statement seems to have been first recognized by Elton ('27), who discussed its effect on the survival of prey species when predators are numerous and its effect in enabling predators to survive when their

[3] Thienemann ('26) proposed the term *reducers* for the heterotrophic bacteria and fungi, but this term suggests that decomposition is produced solely by chemical reduction rather than oxidation, which is certainly not the case. The term *decomposers* is suggested as being more appropriate.

usual prey are only periodically abundant. This ability on the part of predators, which tends to make the higher trophic levels of a food cycle less discrete than the lower, increases the difficulties of analyzing the energy relationships in this portion of the food cycle, and may also tend to "shorten the food-chain."

Fundamental food-cycle variations in different ecosystems may be observed by comparing lacustrine and terrestrial cycles. Although dissolved nutrients in the lake water and in the ooze correspond directly with those in the soil, the autotrophic producers differ considerably in form. Lacustrine producers include macrophytic pondweeds, in which massive supporting tissues are at a minimum, and microphytic phytoplankters, which in larger lakes definitely dominate the production of organic substance. Terrestrial producers are predominantly multicellular plants containing much cellulose and lignin in various types of supporting tissues. Terrestrial herbivores, belonging to a great number of specialized food groups, act as *primary consumers* (sensu Jacot, '40) of organic substance; these groups correspond to the "browsers" of aquatic ecosystems. Terrestrial predators may be classified as more remote (secondary, tertiary, quaternary, etc.) consumers, according to whether they prey upon herbivores or upon other predators; these correspond roughly to the benthic predators and swimming predators, respectively, of a lake. Bacterial and fungal decomposers in terrestrial systems are concentrated in the humus layer of the soil; in lakes, where the "soil" is overlain by water, decomposition takes place both in the water, as organic particles slowly settle, and in the benthic "soil." Nutrient salts are thus freed to be reutilized by the autotrophic plants of both ecosystems.

The striking absence of terrestrial "life-forms" analogous to plankters[4] (cf. figure 1) indicates that the terrestrial food cycle is essentially "mono-cyclic" with macrophytic producers, while the lacustrine cycle, with two "life-forms" of producers, may be considered as "bi-cyclic." The marine cycle, in which plankters are the only producers of any consequence, may be considered as "mono-cyclic" with microphytic producers. The relative absence of massive supporting tissues in plankters and the very rapid completion of their life cycle exert a great influence on the differential productivities of terrestrial and aquatic systems. The general convexity of terrestrial systems as contrasted with the concavity of aquatic substrata results in striking trophic and successional differences, which will be discussed in a later section.

Productivity

Definitions.—The quantitative aspects of trophic ecology have been commonly expressed in terms of the productivity of the food groups concerned. Productivity has been rather broadly defined as the general rate of production (Riley, '40, and others), a term which may be applied to any or every food group in a given ecosystem. The problem of productivity as related to biotic dynamics has been critically analyzed by G. E. Hutchinson ('42) in his recent book on limnological principles. The two following paragraphs are quoted from Hutchinson's chapter on "The Dynamics of Lake Biota":

> The dynamics of lake biota is here treated as primarily a problem of energy transfer . . . the biotic utilization of solar energy entering the lake surface. Some of this energy is transformed by photosynthesis into the structure of phytoplankton organisms, representing an energy content which may be expressed as Λ_1 (first level). Some of the phytoplankters will be eaten by

[4] Francé ('13) developed the concept of the *edaphon*, in which the soil microbiota was represented as the terrestrial equivalent of aquatic plankton. This concept appears to have a number of adherents in this country. The author feels that this analogy is misleading, as the edaphon, which has almost no producers, represents only a dependent side-chain of the terrestrial cycle, and is much more comparable to the lacustrine microbenthos than to the plankton.

zooplankters (energy content Λ_2), which again will be eaten by plankton predators (energy content Λ_3). The various successive levels (i.e., stages[5]) of the food cycle are thus seen to have successively different energy contents (Λ_1, Λ_2, Λ_3, etc.).

Considering any food-cycle level Λ_n, energy is entering the level and is leaving it. The rate of change of the energy content Λ_n therefore may be divided into a positive and a negative part:

$$\frac{d\Lambda_n}{dt} = \lambda_n + \lambda_n',$$

where λ_n is by definition positive and represents the rate of contribution of energy from Λ_{n-1} (the previous level) to Λ_n, while λ_n' is negative and represents the sum of the rate of energy dissipated from Λ_n and the rate of energy content handed on to the following level Λ_{n+1}. The more interesting quantity is λ_n which is defined as the true *productivity* of level Λ_n. In practice, it is necessary to use mean rates over finite periods of time as approximations to the mean rates λ_0, λ_1, λ_2. . . .

In the following pages we shall consider the quantitative relationships of the following productivities: λ_0 (rate of incident solar radiation), λ_1 (rate of photosynthetic production), λ_2 (rate of primary or herbivorous consumption), λ_3 (rate of secondary consumption or primary predation), and λ_4 (rate of tertiary consumption). The total amount of organic structure formed per year for any level Λ_n, which is commonly expressed as the annual "yield," actually represents a value uncorrected for dissipation of energy by (1) respiration, (2) predation, and (3) post-mortem decomposition. Let us now consider the quantitative aspects of these losses.

Respiratory corrections.—The amount of energy lost from food levels by catabolic processes (respiration) varies considerably for the different stages in the life histories of individuals, for different levels in the food cycle and for different seasonal temperatures. In terms of annual production, however, individual deviates cancel out and respiratory differences between food groups may be observed.

[5] The term *stage*, in some respects preferable to the term *level*, cannot be used in this trophic sense because of its long-established usage as a successional term (cf. p. 23).

Numerous estimates of average respiration for photosynthetic producers may be obtained from the literature. For terrestrial plants, estimates range from 15 per cent (Pütter, re Spoehr, '26) to 43 per cent (Lundegårdh, '24) under various types of natural conditions. For aquatic producers, Hicks ('34) reported a coefficient of about 15 per cent for Lemna under certain conditions. Wimpenny ('41) has indicated that the respiratory coefficient of marine producers in polar regions (diatoms) is probably much less than that of the more "animal-like" producers (peridinians and coccolithophorids) of warmer seas, and that temperature may be an important factor in determining respiratory coefficients in general. Juday ('40), after conducting numerous experiments with Manning and others on the respiration of phytoplankters in Trout Lake, Wisconsin, concluded that under average conditions these producers respire about ⅓ of the organic matter which they synthesize. This latter value, 33 per cent, is probably the best available respiratory coefficient for lacustrine producers.

Information on the respiration of aquatic primary consumers is obtained from an illuminating study by Ivlev ('39a) on the energy relationships of *Tubifex*. By means of ingenious techniques, he determined calorific values for assimilation and growth in eleven series of experiments. Using the averages of his calorific values, we can make the following simple calculations: *assimilation* (16.77 cal.) − *growth* (10.33 cal.) = *respiration* (6.44 cal.), so that respiration in terms of growth $= \frac{6.44}{10.33} = 62.30$ per cent. As a check on the growth stage of these worms, we find that $\frac{\text{growth}}{\text{assimilation}} = 61.7$ per cent, a value in good agreement with the classical conclusions of Needham ('31, III, p. 1655) with respect to embryos: the efficiency of all developing embryos is numerically similar, between 60 and 70 per cent, and independent of temperature within the range of biological tolerance. We may therefore conclude that the worms were growing at nearly maximal efficiency, so that the above respiratory coefficient is nearly minimal. In the absence of further data, we shall tentatively accept 62 per cent as the best available respiratory coefficient for aquatic herbivores.

The respiratory coefficient for aquatic predators can be approximated from data of another important study by Ivlev ('39b), on the energy transformations in predatory yearling carp. Treating his calorific values as in the preceding paragraph, we find that *ingestion* (1829 cal.) − *defecation* (454 cal.) = *assimilation* (1375 cal.), and *assimilation* − *growth* (573 cal.) = *respiration* (802 cal.), so that respiration in terms of growth $= \frac{802}{573} = 140$ per cent, a much higher coefficient than that found for the primary consumer, *Tubifex*. A rough check on this coefficient was obtained by calorific analysis of data on the growth of yearling green sunfishes (*Lepomis cyanellus*) published by W. G. Moore ('41), which indicate a respiratory coefficient of 120 per cent with respect to growth, suggesting that these fishes were growing more efficiently than those studied by Ivlev. Since Moore's fishes were fed on a highly concentrated food (liver), this greater growth efficiency is not surprising. If the maximum growth efficiency would occur when $\frac{\text{growth}}{\text{assimilation}}$ = 60–70 per cent (AEE of Needham, '31), the AEE of Moore's data (about 50 per cent) indicates that the minimum respiratory coefficient with respect to growth might be as low as 100 per cent for certain fishes. Food-conversion data from Thompson ('41) indicate a minimum respiratory coefficient of less than 150 per cent for young black bass (*Huro salmoides*) at 70° F., the exact percentage depending upon how much of the ingested food (minnows) was assimilated. Krogh ('41) showed that predatory fishes have a higher rate of respiration than the more sluggish herbivorous species; the respiratory rate of *Esox* under resting conditions at 20° C. was $3\frac{1}{2}$ times that of *Cyprinus*. The form of piscian growth curves (cf. Hile, '41) suggests that the respiratory coefficient is much higher for fishes towards the end of their normal life-span. Since the value obtained from Ivlev (above) is based on more extensive data than those of Moore, we shall tentatively accept 140 per cent as an average respiratory coefficient for aquatic predators.

Considering that predators are usually more active than their herbivorous prey, which are in turn more active than the plants upon which they feed, it is not surprising to find that respiration with respect to growth in producers (33 per cent), in primary consumers (62 per cent) and in secondary consumers (>100 per cent) increases progressively. These differences probably reflect a trophic principle of wide application: the percentage loss of energy due to respiration is progressively greater for higher levels in the food cycle.

Predation corrections.—In considering the predation losses from each level, it is most convenient to begin with the highest level, Λ_n. In a mechanically perfect food cycle composed of organically discrete levels, this loss by predation obviously would be zero. Since no natural food cycle is so mechanically constituted, some "cannibalism" within such an arbitrary level can be expected, so that the actual value for predation loss from Λ_n probably will be somewhat above zero. The predation loss from level Λ_{n-1} will represent the total amount of assimilable energy passed on into the higher level (i.e., the true productivity, λ_n), plus a quantity representing the average content of substance killed but not assimilated by the predator, as will be discussed in the following section. The predation loss from level Λ_{n-2} will likewise represent the total amount of assimilable energy passed on to the next level (i.e., λ_{n-1}), plus a similar factor for unassimilated material, as illustrated by the data of tables II and III. The various categories of parasites are somewhat comparable to those of predators, but the details of their energy relationships have not yet been clarified, and cannot be included in this preliminary account.

Decomposition corrections. — In conformity with the principle of Le Chatelier, the energy of no food level can be completely extracted by the organisms which feed upon it. In addition to the energy represented by organisms which survive to be included in the "annual yield," much energy is contained in "killed" tissues which the predators are unable to digest and assimilate. Average coefficients of indigestible tissues, based largely of the calorific equivalents of the "crude fiber" fractions in the chemical analyses of Birge and Juday ('22), are as follows:

Nannoplankters	ca. 5%
Algal mesoplankters	5–35%
Mature pondweeds	ca. 20%
Primary consumers	ca. 10%
Secondary consumers	ca. 8%
Predatory fishes	ca. 5%

Corrections for terrestrial producers would certainly be much higher. Although the data are insufficient to warrant a generalization, these values suggest increasing digestibility of the higher food levels, particularly for the benthic components of aquatic cycles.

The loss of energy due to premature death from non-predatory causes usually must be neglected, since such losses are exceedingly difficult to evaluate and under normal conditions probably represent relatively small components of the annual production. However, considering that these losses may assume considerable proportions at any time, the above "decomposition coefficients" must be regarded as correspondingly minimal.

Following non-predated death, every organism is a potential source of energy for myriads of bacterial and fungal saprophages, whose metabolic products provide simple inorganic and organic solutes reavailable to photosynthetic producers. These saprophages may also serve as energy sources for successive levels of consumers, often considerably supplementing the normal diet of herbivores (ZoBell and Feltham, '38). Jacot ('40) considered saprophage-feeding or coprophagous animals as "low" primary consumers, but the writer believes that in the present state of our knowledge a quantitative subdivision of primary consumers is unwarranted.

Application.—The value of these theoretical energy relationships can be illustrated by analyzing data of the three ecosystems for which relatively comprehensive productivity values have been published (table I). The summary account of Brujewicz ('39) on "the dynamics of living matter in the Caspian Sea" leaves much to be desired, as bottom animals are not differentiated into their relative food levels, and the basis for determining the annual production of phytoplankters (which on theoretical grounds appears to be much too low) is not clearly explained. Furthermore, his values are stated in terms of thousands of tons of dry weight for the Caspian Sea as a whole, and must be roughly transformed to calories per square centimeter of surface area. The data for Lake Mendota, Wisconsin, are

TABLE I. *Productivities of food-groups in three aquatic ecosystems, as g-cal/cm²/year, uncorrected for losses due to respiration, predation and decomposition. Data from Brujewicz ('39), Juday ('40) and Lindeman ('41b).*

	Caspian Sea	Lake Mendota	Cedar Bog Lake
Phytoplankters: Λ_1	59.5	299	25.8
Phytobenthos: Λ_1	0.3	22	44.6
Zooplankters: Λ_2	20.0	22	6.1
Benthic browsers: Λ_2	} 20.6	1.8*	0.8
Benthic predators: Λ_3		} 0.9*	0.2
Plankton predators: Λ_3			0.8
"Forage" fishes: $\Lambda_3(+\Lambda_2?)$	0.6	?	0.3
Carp: $\Lambda_3(+\Lambda_2?)$	0.0	0.2	0.0
"Game" fishes: $\Lambda_4(+\Lambda_3?)$	0.6	0.1	0.0
Seals: Λ_5	0.01	0.0	0.0

* Roughly assuming that ⅔ of the bottom fauna is herbivorous (cf. Juday, '22).

taken directly from a general summary (Juday, '40) of the many productivity studies made on that eutrophic lake. The data for Cedar Bog Lake, Minnesota, are taken from the author's four-year analysis (Lindeman, '41b) of its food-cycle dynamics. The calorific values in table I, representing annual production of organic matter, are uncorrected for energy losses.

TABLE II. *Productivity values for the Cedar Bog Lake food cycle, in g-cal/cm²/year, as corrected by using the coefficients derived in the preceding sections.*

Trophic level	Uncorrected productivity	Respiration	Predation	Decomposition	Corrected productivity
Producers: Λ_1	70.4±10.14	23.4	14.8	2.8	111.3
Primary consumers: Λ_2	7.0±1.07	4.4	3.1	0.3	14.8
Secondary consumers: Λ_3	1.3±0.43*	1.8	0.0	0.0	3.1

* This value includes the productivity of the small cyprinoid fishes found in the lake.

Correcting for the energy losses due to respiration, predation and decomposition, as discussed in the preceding sections, casts a very different light on the relative productivities of food levels. The calculation of corrections for the Cedar Bog Lake values for producers, primary consumers and secondary consumers are given in table II. The application of similar corrections to the energy values for the food levels of the Lake Mendota food cycle given by Juday ('40), as shown in table III, indicates that Lake Mendota is much more productive of producers and primary consumers than is Cedar Bog Lake, while the production of secondary consumers is of the same order of magnitude in the two lakes.

In calculating total productivity for Lake Mendota, Juday ('40) used a blanket correction of 500 per cent of the annual production of all consumer levels for "metabolism," which presumably includes both respiration and predation. Thompson ('41) found that the "carry-

TABLE III. *Productivity values for the Lake Mendota food cycle, in g-cal/cm²/year, as corrected by using coefficients derived in the preceding sections, and as given by Juday ('40).*

Trophic Level	Uncorrected productivity	Respiration	Predation	Decomposition	Corrected productivity	Juday's corrected productivity
Producers: Λ_1.	321*	107	42	10	480	428
Primary consumers: Λ_2.	24	15	2.3	0.3	41.6	144
Secondary consumers: Λ_3.	1†	1	0.3	0.0	2.3	6
Tertiary consumers: Λ_4.	0.12	0.2	0.0	0.0	0.3	0.7

* Hutchinson ('42) gives evidence that this value is probably too high and may actually be as low as 250.

† Apparently such organisms as small "forage" fishes are not included in any part of Juday's balance sheet. The inclusion of these forms might be expected to increase considerably the productivity of secondary consumption.

ing-capacity" of lakes containing mostly carp and other "coarse" fishes (primarily Λ_3), was about 500 per cent that of lakes containing mostly "game" fishes (primarily Λ_4), and concluded that "this difference must be about one complete link in the food chain, since it usually requires about five pounds of food to produce one pound of fish." While such high "metabolic losses" may hold for tertiary and quaternary predators under certain field conditions, the physiological experiments previously cited indicate much lower respiratory coefficients. Even when predation and decomposition corrections are included, the resultant productivity values are less than half those obtained by using Juday's coefficient. Since we have shown that the necessary corrections vary progressively with the different food levels, it seems probable that Juday's "coefficient of metabolism" is much too high for primary and secondary consumers.

Biological efficiency

The quantitative relationships of any food-cycle level may be expressed in terms of its efficiency with respect to lower levels. Quoting Hutchinson's ('42) definition, "the efficiency of the productivity of any level (Λ_n) relative to the productivity of any previous level (Λ_m) is defined as $\frac{\lambda_n}{\lambda_m} 100$. If the rate of solar energy entering the ecosystem is denoted as λ_0, the efficiencies of all levels may be referred back to this quantity λ_0." In general, however, the most interesting efficiencies are those referred to the previous level's productivity (λ_{n-1}), or those expressed as $\frac{\lambda_n}{\lambda_{n-1}} 100$. These latter may be termed the *progressive efficiencies* of the various food-cycle levels, indicating for each level the degree of utilization of its potential food supply or energy source. All efficiencies discussed in the following pages are progressive efficiencies, expressed in terms of relative productivities $\left(\frac{\lambda_n}{\lambda_{n-1}} 100\right)$. It is important to remember that efficiency and productivity are not synonymous. Productivity is a rate (i.e., in the units here used, cal/cm²/year), while efficiency, being a ratio, is a dimensionless number. The points of reference for any efficiency value should always be clearly stated.

The progressive efficiencies $\left(\frac{\lambda_n}{\lambda_{n-1}} 100\right)$ for the trophic levels of Cedar Bog Lake and Lake Mendota, as obtained from the productivities derived in tables II and III, are presented in table IV. In view of the uncertainties concerning some of the Lake Mendota productivities, no definite conclusions can be drawn from their relative efficiencies. The Cedar Bog Lake ratios, however, indicate that the progressive efficiencies increase from about 0.10 per cent for production, to 13.3 per cent for primary consumption, and to 22.3 per cent for secondary consumption. An uncorrected efficiency of tertiary consumption of 37.5 per cent ± 3.0 per cent (for the weight ratios of "carnivorous" to "forage" fishes in Alabama ponds) is indicated in data published by Swingle and Smith ('40). These progressively increasing efficiencies may well represent a fundamental trophic principle, namely, that the consumers at progressively higher levels in the food cycle are progressively more efficient in the use of their food supply.

At first sight, this generalization of increasing efficiency in higher consumer groups would appear to contradict the previous generalization that the loss of energy due to respiration is progressively greater for higher levels in the food cycle. These can be reconciled by remembering that increased activity of predators considerably increases the chances of encountering suitable prey. The ultimate effect of such antagonistic principles would present a picture of a predator completely wearing itself out in the process of completely exterminating its prey, a very improbable situation. However, Elton ('27) pointed out that food-cycles rarely have more than five trophic levels. Among the several factors involved, increasing respiration of successive levels of predators contrasted with their successively increasing efficiency of predation appears to be important in restricting the number of trophic levels in a food cycle.

The effect of increasing temperature is alleged by Wimpenny ('41) to cause a decreasing consumer/producer ratio, presumably because he believes that the "acceleration of vital velocities" of consumers at increasing temperatures is more rapid than that of producers. He

TABLE IV. *Productivities and progressive efficiencies in the Cedar Bog Lake and Lake Mendota food cycles, as g-cal/cm²/year*

	Cedar Bog Lake		Lake Mendota	
	Productivity	Efficiency	Productivity	Efficiency
Radiation	≤118,872		118,872	
Producers: Λ_1	111.3	0.10%	480*	0.40%
Primary consumers: Λ_2	14.8	13.3%	41.6	8.7%
Secondary consumers: Λ_3	3.1	22.3%	2.3†	5.5%
Tertiary consumers: Λ_4	—	—	0.3	13.0%

* Probably too high; see footnote of table III.
† Probably too low; see footnote of table III.

cites as evidence Lohmann's ('12) data for relative *numbers* (not biomass) of Protophyta, Protozoa and Metazoa in the centrifuge plankton of "cool" seas (741:73:1) as contrasted with tropical areas (458:24:1). Since Wimpenny himself emphasizes that many metazoan plankters are larger in size toward the poles, these data do not furnish convincing proof of the allegation. The data given in table IV, since Cedar Bog Lake has a much higher mean annual water temperature than Lake Mendota, appear to contradict Wimpenny's generalization that consumer/producer ratios fall as the temperature increases.

The Eltonian pyramid

The general relationships of higher food-cycle levels to one another and to community structure were greatly clarified following recognition (Elton, '27) of the importance of size and of numbers in the animals of an ecosystem. Beginning with primary consumers of various sizes, there are as a rule a number of food-chains radiating outwards in which the probability is that predators will become successively larger, while parasites and hyper-parasites will be progressively smaller than their hosts. Since small primary consumers can increase faster than larger secondary consumers and are so able to support the latter, the animals at the base of a food-chain are relatively abundant while those toward the end are progressively fewer in number. The resulting arrangement of sizes and numbers of animals, termed the pyramid of Numbers by Elton, is now commonly known as the Eltonian Pyramid. Williams ('41), reporting on the "floor fauna" of the Panama rain forest, has recently published an interesting example of such a pyramid, which is reproduced in figure 2.

The Eltonian Pyramid may also be expressed in terms of biomass. The weight of all predators must always be much lower than that of all food animals, and the total weight of the latter much lower than the plant production (Bodenheimer, '38). To the human ecologist, it is noteworthy that the population density of the essentially vegetarian Chinese, for example, is much greater than that of the more carnivorous English.

The principle of the Eltonian Pyramid has been redefined in terms of productivity by Hutchinson (unpublished) in the following formalized terms: the rate of production cannot be less and will almost certainly be greater than the rate of primary consumption, which in turn cannot be less and will almost certainly be greater than the rate of secondary consumption, which in turn . . . , etc. The energy-relationships of this principle may be epitomized by means

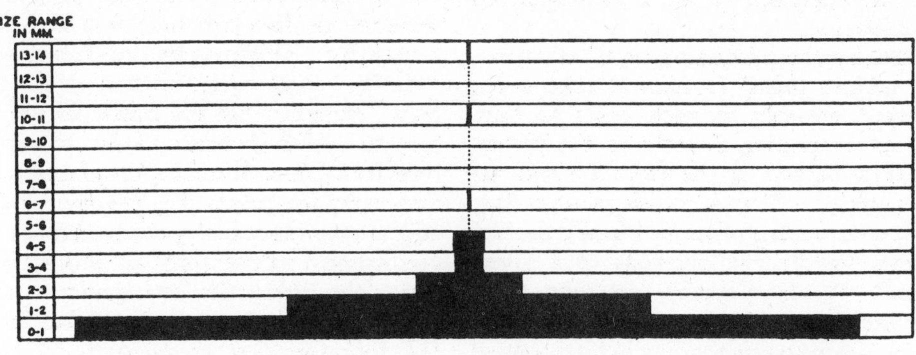

FIG. 2. Eltonian pyramid of numbers, for floor-fauna invertebrates of the Panama rain forest (from Williams, '41).

of the productivity symbol λ, as follows:

$$\lambda_0 > \lambda_1 > \lambda_2 \ldots > \lambda_n.$$

This rather obvious generalization is confirmed by the data of all ecosystems analyzed to date.

Trophic-Dynamics in Succession

Dynamic processes within an ecosystem, over a period of time, tend to produce certain obvious changes in its species-composition, soil characteristics and productivity. Change, according to Cooper ('26), is the essential criterion of succession. From the trophic-dynamic viewpoint, succession is the process of development in an ecosystem, brought about primarily by the effects of the organisms on the environment and upon each other, towards a relatively stable condition of equilibrium.

It is well known that in the initial phases of hydrarch succession (oligotrophy → eutrophy) productivity increases rapidly; it is equally apparent that the colonization of a bare terrestrial area represents a similar acceleration in productivity. In the later phases of succession, productivity increases much more slowly. As Hutchinson and Wollack ('40) pointed out, these generalized changes in the rate of production may be expressed as a sigmoid curve showing a rough resemblance to the growth curve of an organism or of a homogeneous population.

Such smooth logistic growth, of course, is seldom found in natural succession, except possibly in such cases as bare areas developing directly to the climax vegetation type in the wake of a retreating glacier. Most successional seres consist of a number of *stages* ("recognizable, clearly-marked subdivisions of a given sere"—W. S. Cooper), so that their productivity growth-curves will contain undulations corresponding in distinctness to the distinctness of the stages. The presence of stages in a successional sere apparently represents the persistent influence of some combination of limiting factors, which, until they are overcome by species-substitution, etc., tend to decrease the acceleration of productivity and maintain it at a more constant rate. This tendency towards *stage-equilibrium* of productivity will be discussed in the following pages.

Productivity in hydrarch succession

The descriptive dynamics of hydrarch succession is well known. Due to the essentially concave nature of the substratum, lake succession is internally complicated by a rather considerable influx of nutritive substances from the drainage basin surrounding the lake. The basins of lakes are gradually filled with sediments, largely organogenic, upon which a series of vascular plant stages successively replace one another until a more or less stable (climax) stage is attained. We are concerned here, however, primarily with the productivity aspects of the successional process.

Eutrophication. — Thienemann ('26) presented a comprehensive theoretical discussion of the relation between lake succession and productivity, as follows: In oligotrophy, the pioneer phase, productivity is rather low, limited by the amount of dissolved nutrients in the lake water. Oxygen is abundant at all times, almost all of the synthesized organic matter is available for animal food; bacteria release dissolved nutrients from the remainder. Oligotrophy thus has a very "thrifty" food cycle, with a relatively high "efficiency" of the consumer populations. With increasing influx of nutritives from the surrounding drainage basin and increasing primary productivity (λ_1), oligotrophy is gradually changed through mesotrophy to eutrophy, in which condition the production of organic matter (λ_1) exceeds that which can be oxidized (λ_1') by respiration, predation and bacterial decomposition. The oxygen supply of the hypolimnion becomes depleted, with disastrous effects on the oligotrophconditioned bottom fauna. Organisms especially adapted to endure temporary anaerobiosis replace the oligotrophic species, accompanied by anaerobic bacteria which during the stagnation period cause reduction rather than oxidation of the organic detritus. As a result of this process, semi-reduced organic ooze, or *gyttja*, accumulates on the bottom. As oxygen supply thus becomes a limiting factor of productivity, relative efficiency of the consumer groups in utilizing the synthesized organic substance becomes correspondingly lower.

The validity of Thienemann's interpretation, particularly regarding the trophic mechanisms, has recently been challenged by Hutchinson ('41, '42), who states that three distinct factors are involved: (1) the edaphic factor, representing the potential nutrient supply (primarily phosphorus) in the surrounding drainage basin; (2) the age of the lake at any stage, indicating the degree of utilization of the nutrient supply; and (3) the morphometric character at any stage, dependent on both the original morphometry of the lake basin and the age of the lake, and presumably influencing the oxygen concentration in the hypolimnion. He holds that true eutrophication takes place only in regions well supplied with nutrients, lakes in other regions developing into "ideotrophic types." The influx of phosphorus is probably very great in the earliest phases, much greater than the supply of nitrogen, as indicated by very low N/P ratios in the earliest sediments (Hutchinson and Wollack, '40). A large portion of this phosphorus is believed to be insoluble, as a component of such mineral particles as apatite, etc., although certainly some of it is soluble. The supply of available nitrogen increases somewhat more slowly, being largely dependent upon the fixation of nitrogen by microorganisms either in the lake or in the surrounding soils. The photosynthetic productivity (λ_1) of lakes thus increases rather rapidly in the early phases, its quantitative value for lakes with comparable edaphic nutrient supplies being dependent on the morphometry (mean depth). Since deep lakes have a greater depth range for plankton photosynthesis, abundant oxygen and more chance for decomposition of the plankton detritus before reaching the bottom, such deep lakes may be potentially as productive as shallower lakes, in terms of unit surface area. Factors tending to lessen the comparative productivity of deep lakes are (1) lower temperature for the lake as a whole, and (2) greater dilution of nutrients in terms of volume of the illuminated "trophogenic zone" of the lake. During eutrophication in a deep lake, the phosphorus content of the sediment falls and nitrogen rises, until a N/P ratio of about 40/1 is established. "The decomposition of organic matter presumably is always liberating some of this phosphorus and nitrogen. Within limits, the more organic matter present the easier will be such regeneration. It is probable that benthic animals and anion exchange play a part in such processes" (Hutchinson, '42). The progressive filling of the lake basin with sediments makes the lake shallower, so that the oxygen supply of the hypolimnion is increasingly, and finally completely, exhausted during summer stagnation. Oxidation of the sediments is less complete, but sufficient phosphorus is believed to be regenerated from the ooze surface so that productivity in terms of surface area remains relatively constant. The nascent ooze acts as a trophic buffer, in the chemical sense, tending to maintain the productivity of a lake in stage-equilibrium (*typological equilibrium* of Hutchinson) during the eutrophic stage of its succession.

The concept of eutrophic stage-equilibrium seems to be partially confused (cf. Thienemann, '26; Hutchinson and Wollack, '40) with the theoretically ideal condition of complete *trophic equilibrium*, which may be roughly defined as the dynamic state of continuous, complete utilization and regeneration of chemical nutrients in an ecosystem, without loss or gain from the outside, under a periodically constant energy source—such as might be found in a perfectly balanced aquarium or terrarium. Natural ecosystems may tend to approach a state of trophic equilibrium under certain conditions, but it is doubtful if any are sufficiently autochthonous to attain, or maintain, true trophic equilibrium for any length of time. The biosphere as a whole, however, as Vernadsky ('29, '39) so vigorously asserts, may exhibit a high degree of true trophic equilibrium.

The existence of prolonged eutrophic stage-equilibrium was first suggested as a result of a study on the sediments of Grosser Plöner See in Germany (Groschopf, '36). Its significance was recognized by Hutchinson and Wollack ('40), who based their critical discussion on chemical analyses (ibid.) and pollen analyses (Deevey, '39) of the sediments of Linsley Pond, Connecticut. They reported a gradual transition from oligotrophy to eutrophy (first attained in the oak-hemlock pollen period), in which stage the lake has remained for a very long time, perhaps more than 4000 years. They report indications of a comparable eutrophic stage-equilibrium in the sediments of nearby Upper Linsley Pond (Hutchinson and Wollack, unpublished). Similar attainment of stage-equilibrium is indicated in a preliminary report on the sediments of Lake Windermere in England (Jenkin, Mortimer and Pennington, '41). Every stage of a sere is believed to possess a similar stage-equilibrium of variable duration, although terrestrial stages have not yet been defined in terms of productivity.

The trophic aspects of eutrophication cannot be determined easily from the sediments. In general, however, the ratio of organic matter to the silt washed into the lake from the margins affords an approximation of the photosynthetic productivity. This undecomposed organic matter, representing the amount of energy which is lost from the food cycle, is derived largely from level Λ_1, as plant structures in general are decomposed less easily than animal structures. The quantity of energy passed on into consumer levels can only be surmised from undecomposed fragments of organisms which are believed to occupy those levels. Several types of animal "microfossils" occur rather consistently in lake sediments, such as the carapaces and post-abdomens of certain cladocerans, chironomid head-capsules, fragments of the phantom-midge larva *Chaoborus*, snail shells, polyzoan statoblasts, sponge spicules and rhizopod shells. Deevey ('42), after making comprehensive microfossil and chemical analyses of the sediments of Linsley Pond, suggested that the abundant half-carapaces of the planktonic browser *Bosmina* afford "a reasonable estimate of the quantity of zooplankton produced" and that "the total organic matter of the sediment is a reasonable estimate of the organic matter produced by phytoplankton and littoral vegetation." He found a striking similarity in the shape of the curves representing *Bosmina* content and total organic matter plotted against depth, which, when plotted logarithmically against each other, showed a linear relationship expressed by an empirical power equation. Citing Hutchinson and Wollack ('40) to the effect that the developmental curve for organic matter was analogous to that for the development of an organism, he pressed the analogy further by suggesting that the increase of zooplankton (*Bosmina*) with reference to the increase of organic matter (λ_1) fitted the formula $y = bx^k$ for allometric growth (Huxley, '32), "where y = *Bosmina*, x = total organic matter, b = a constant giving the value of y when $x = 1$, and k = the 'allometry constant,' or the slope of the line when a double log plot is made." If we represent the organic matter produced as λ_1 and further assume that *Bosmina* represents the primary consumers (λ_2), neglecting benthic browsers, the formula becomes $\lambda_2 = b\lambda_1^k$. Whether this formula would express the relationship found in other levels of the food cycle, the development of other stages, or other ecosystems, remains to be demonstrated.[6] Stratigraphic analyses in Cedar Bog Lake (Lindeman and Lindeman, unpublished) suggest a roughly similar increase of both organic matter and *Bosmina* carapaces in the earliest sediments. In the modern senescent lake, however, double logarithmic plottings of the calorific values for λ_1 against λ_2, and λ_2 against λ_3, for the four years studied, show no semblance of linear relationship, i.e., do not fit any power equation. If Deevey is correct in his interpretation of the Linsley Pond microfossils, allometric growth would appear to characterize the phases of pre-equilibrium succession as the term "growth" indeed implies.

The relative duration of eutrophic stage-equilibrium is not yet completely understood. As exemplified by Linsley Pond, the relation of stage-equilibrium to succession is intimately concerned with the trophic processes of (1) external influx and efflux (partly controlled by climate), (2) photosynthetic productivity, (3) sedimentation (partly by physiographic silting) and (4) regeneration of nutritives from the sediments. These processes apparently maintain a relatively constant ratio to each other during the extended equilibrium period. Yet the food cycle is not in true trophic equilibrium, and continues to fill the lake with organic sediments. *Succession* is continuing, at a rate corresponding to the rate of sediment accumulation. In the words of Hutchinson and Wollack ('40), "this means that during the equilibrium period the lake, through the internal activities of its biocoenosis, is continually approaching a condition when it ceases to be a lake."

Senescence.—As a result of long-continued sedimentation, eutrophic lakes attain senescence, first manifested in bays and wind-protected areas. Senescence is usually characterized by such pond-like conditions as (1) tremendous increase in shallow littoral area populated with pondweeds and (2) increased marginal invasion of terrestrial stages. Cedar Bog Lake, which the author has studied for several years, is in late senescence, rapidly changing to the terrestrial stages of its succession. On casual inspection, the massed verdure of pondweeds and epiphytes, together with sporadic algal blooms, appears to indicate great photosynthetic productivity. As pointed out by Wesenberg-Lund ('12), littoral areas of lakes are virtual hothouses, absorbing more radiant energy per unit volume than deeper areas. At the present time the entire aquatic area of Cedar Bog Lake is essentially littoral in nature, and its productivity per cubic meter of water is probably greater than at any time in its history. However, since radiant energy (λ_0) enters a lake only from the surface, productivity must be defined in terms of surface area. In these terms, the present photosynthetic productivity pales into insignificance when compared with less advanced lakes in similar edaphic regions; for instance, λ_1 is less than $\frac{1}{3}$ that of Lake Mendota, Wisconsin (cf. table IV). These facts attest the essential accuracy of Welch's ('35) generalization that productivity declines greatly during senescence. An interesting principle demonstrated in Cedar Bog Lake (Lindeman, '41b) is that during late lake senescence general productivity (λ_n) is increasingly influenced by climatic factors, acting through

[6] It should be mentioned in this connection that Meschkat ('37) found that the relationship of population density of tubificids to organic matter in the bottom of a polluted "Buhnenfeld" could be expressed by the formula $y = a^x$, where y represents the population density, x is the "determining environmental factor," and a is a constant. He pointed out that for such an expression to hold the population density must be maximal. Hentschel ('36), on less secure grounds, suggested applying a similar expression to the relationship between populations of marine plankton and the "controlling factor" of their environment.

water level changes, drainage, duration of winter ice, snow cover, etc., to affect the presence and abundance of practically all food groups in the lake.

Terrestrial stages.—As an aquatic ecosystem passes into terrestrial phases, fluctuations in atmospheric factors increasingly affect its productivity. As succession proceeds, both the species-composition and the productivity of an ecosystem increasingly reflect the effects of the regional climate. Qualitatively, these climatic effects are known for soil morphology (Joffe, '36), autotrophic vegetation (Clements, '16), fauna (Clements and Shelford, '39) and soil microbiota (Braun-Blanquet, '32), in fact for every important component of the food cycle. Quantitatively, these effects have been so little studied that generalizations are most hazardous. It seems probable, however, that productivity tends to increase until the system approaches maturity. Clements and Shelford ('39, p. 116) assert that both plant and animal productivity is generally greatest in the subclimax, except possibly in the case of grasslands. Terrestrial ecosystems are primarily convex topographically and thus subject to a certain nutrient loss by erosion, which may or may not be made up by increased availability of such nutrients as can be extracted from the "C" soil horizon.

Successional productivity curves.—In recapitulating the probable photosynthetic productivity relationships in hydrarch succession, we shall venture to diagram (figure 3) a hypothetical hydrosere, developing from a moderately deep lake in a fertile cold temperate region under relatively constant climatic conditions. The initial period of oligotrophy is believed to be relatively short (Hutchinson and Wollack, '40; Lindeman '41a), with productivity rapidly increasing until eutrophic stage-equilibrium is attained. The duration of high eutrophic productivity depends upon the mean depth of the basin and upon the rate of sedimentation, and productivity fluctuates about a high eutrophic mean until the lake becomes too shallow for maximum growth of phytoplankton or regeneration of nutrients from the ooze. As the lake becomes shallower and more senescent, productivity is increasingly influenced by climatic fluctuations and

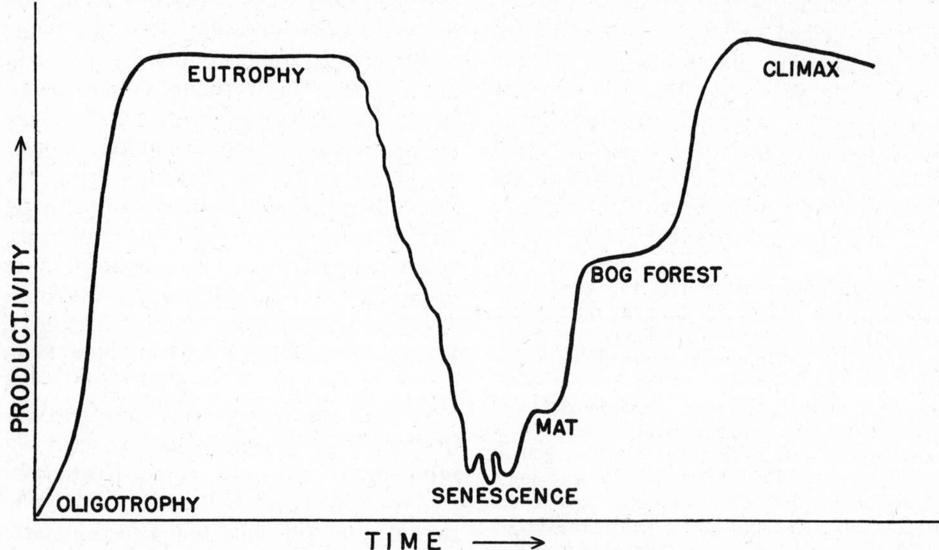

FIG. 3. Hypothetical productivity growth-curve of a hydrosere, developing from a deep lake to climax in a fertile, cold-temperate region.

gradually declines to a minimum as the lake is completely filled with sediments.

The terrestrial aspects of hydrarch succession in cold temperate regions usually follow sharply defined, distinctive stages. In lake basins which are poorly drained, the first stage consists of a mat, often partly floating, made up primarily of sedges and grasses or (in more coastal regions) such heaths as *Chamaedaphne* and *Kalmia* with certain species of sphagnum moss (cf. Rigg, '40). The mat stage is usually followed by a bog forest stage, in which the dominant species is *Larix laricina*, *Picea mariana* or *Thuja occidentalis*. The bog forest stage may be relatively permanent ("edaphic" climax) or succeeded to a greater or lesser degree by the regional climax vegetation. The stage-productivities indicated in figure 3 represent only crude relative estimates, as practically no quantitative data are available.

Efficiency relationships in succession

The successional changes of photosynthetic efficiency in natural areas (with respect to solar radiation, i.e., $\left.\frac{\lambda_1}{\lambda_0} 100\right)$ have not been intensively studied. In lake succession, photosynthetic efficiency would be expected to follow the same course deduced for productivity, rising to a more or less constant value during eutrophic stage-equilibrium, and declining during senescence, as suggested by a photosynthetic efficiency of at least 0.27 per cent for eutrophic Lake Mendota (Juday, '40) and of 0.10 per cent for senescent Cedar Bog Lake. For the terrestrial hydrosere, efficiency would likewise follow a curve similar to that postulated for productivity.

Rough estimates of photosynthetic efficiency for various climatic regions of the earth have been summarized from the literature by Hutchinson (unpublished). These estimates, corrected for respiration, do not appear to be very reliable because of imperfections in the original observations, but are probably of the correct order of magnitude. The mean photosynthetic efficiency for the sea is given as 0.31 per cent (after Riley, '41). The mean photosynthetic efficiency for terrestrial areas of the earth is given as 0.09 per cent $\pm$ 0.02 per cent (after Noddack, '37), for forests as 0.16 per cent, for cultivated lands as 0.13 per cent, for steppes as 0.05 per cent, and for deserts as 0.004 per cent. The mean photosynthetic efficiency for the earth as a whole is given as 0.25 per cent. Hutchinson has suggested (cf. Hutchinson and Lindeman, '41) that numerical efficiency values may provide "the most fundamental possible classification of biological formations and of their developmental stages."

Almost nothing is known concerning the efficiencies of consumer groups in succession. The general chronological increase in numbers of *Bosmina* carapaces with respect to organic matter and of *Chaoborus* fragments with respect to *Bosmina* carapaces in the sediments of Linsley Pond (Deevey, '42) suggests progressively increasing efficiencies of zooplankters and plankton predators. On the other hand, Hutchinson ('42) concludes from a comparison of the P : Z (phytoplankton : zooplankton) biomass ratios of several oligotrophic alpine lakes, ca 1 : 2 (Ruttner, '37), as compared with the ratios for Linsley Pond, 1 : 0.22 (Riley, '40) and three eutrophic Bavarian lakes, 1 : 0.25 (Heinrich, '34), that "as the phytoplankton crop is increased the zooplankton by no means keeps pace with the increase." Data compiled by Deevey ('41) for lakes in both mesotrophic (Connecticut) and eutrophic regions (southern Wisconsin), indicate that the deeper or morphometrically "younger" lakes have a lower ratio of bottom fauna to the standing crop of plankton (10–15 per cent) than the shallower lakes which have attained eutrophic equilibrium (22–27 per cent). The ratios for senescent Cedar Bog Lake, while not directly comparable because of its essentially littoral nature, are even higher. These meager data suggest that the efficiencies of consumer groups may increase throughout the aquatic phases of succession.

For terrestrial stages, no consumer efficiency data are available. A suggestive series of species-frequencies in mesarch succession was published by Vera Smith-Davidson ('32), which indicated greatly increasing numbers of arthropods in successive stages approaching the regional climax. Since the photosynthetic productivity of the stages probably also increased, it is impossible to determine progressive efficiency relationships. The problems of biological efficiencies present a practically virgin field, which appears to offer abundant rewards for studies guided by a trophic-dynamic viewpoint.

In conclusion, it should be emphasized that the trophic-dynamic principles indicated in the following summary cannot be expected to hold for every single case, in accord with the known facts of biological variability. *à priori*, however, these principles appear to be valid for the vast majority of cases, and may be expected to possess a statistically significant probability of validity for any case selected at random. Since the available data summarized in this paper are far too meager to establish such generalizations on a statistical basis, it is highly important that further studies be initiated to test the validity of these and other trophic-dynamic principles.

Summary

1. Analyses of food-cycle relationships indicate that a biotic community cannot be clearly differentiated from its abiotic environment; the *ecosystem* is hence regarded as the more fundamental ecological unit.

2. The organisms within an ecosystem may be grouped into a series of more or less discrete trophic levels (Λ_1, Λ_2, Λ_3, . . . Λ_n) as producers, primary consumers, secondary consumers, etc., each successively dependent upon the preceding level as a source of energy, with the producers (Λ_1) directly dependent upon the rate of incident solar radiation (productivity λ_0) as a source of energy.

3. The more remote an organism is from the initial source of energy (solar radiation), the less probable that it will be dependent solely upon the preceding trophic level as a source of energy.

4. The progressive energy relationships of the food levels of an "Eltonian Pyramid" may be epitomized in terms of the productivity symbol λ, as follows:

$$\lambda_0 > \lambda_1 > \lambda_2 \ldots > \lambda_n.$$

5. The percentage loss of energy due to respiration is progressively greater for higher levels in the food cycle. Respiration with respect to growth is about 33 per cent for producers, 62 per cent for primary consumers, and more than 100 per cent for secondary consumers.

6. The consumers at progressively higher levels in the food cycle appear to be progressively more efficient in the use of their food supply. This generalization can be reconciled with the preceding one by remembering that increased activity of predators considerably increases the chances of encountering suitable prey.

7. Productivity and efficiency increase during the early phases of successional development. In lake succession, productivity and photosynthetic efficiency increase from oligotrophy to a prolonged eutrophic stage-equilibrium and decline with lake senescence, rising again in the terrestrial stages of hydrarch succession.

8. The progressive efficiencies of consumer levels, on the basis of very meager data, apparently tend to increase throughout the aquatic phases of succession.

Acknowledgments

The author is deeply indebted to Professor G. E. Hutchinson of Yale University, who has stimulated many of the trophic concepts developed here, generously placed at the author's disposal several unpublished manuscripts, given valuable counsel, and aided the final development of this paper in every way possible. Many of the concepts embodied in the successional sections of this paper were developed independently by Professor Hutchinson at Yale and by the author as a graduate student at the University of Minnesota. Subsequent to an exchange of notes, a joint preliminary abstract was published (Hutchinson and Lindeman, '41). The author wishes to express gratitude to the mentors and friends at the University of Minnesota who encouraged and helpfully criticized the initial development of these concepts, particularly Drs. W. S. Cooper, Samuel Eddy, A. C. Hodson, D. B. Lawrence and J. B. Moyle, as well as other members of the local Ecological Discussion Group. The author is also indebted to Drs. J. R. Carpenter, E. S. Deevey, H. J. Lutz, A. E. Parr, G. A. Riley and V. E. Shelford, as well as the persons mentioned above, for critical reading of preliminary manuscripts. Grateful acknowledgment is made to the Graduate School, Yale University, for the award of a Sterling Fellowship in Biology during 1941–1942.

Literature Cited

Allee, W. C. 1934. Concerning the organization of marine coastal communities. Ecol. Monogr., **4**: 541–554.

Birge, E. A., and C. Juday. 1922. The inland lakes of Wisconsin. The plankton. Part I. Its quantity and chemical composition. Bull. Wisconsin Geol. Nat. Hist. Surv., **64**: 1–222.

Bodenheimer, F. S. 1938. Problems of Animal Ecology. London. Oxford University Press.

Braun-Blanquet, J. 1932. Plant Sociology. N. Y. McGraw-Hill Co.

Brujewicz, S. W. 1939. Distribution and dynamics of living matter in the Caspian Sea. Compt. Rend. Acad. Sci. URSS, **25**: 138–141.

Carpenter, J. R. 1939. The biome. Amer. Midl. Nat., **21**: 75–91.

——. 1940. The grassland biome. Ecol. Monogr., **10**: 617–687.

Clements, F. E. 1916. Plant Succession. Carnegie Inst. Washington Publ., No. 242.

—— and V. E. Shelford. 1939. Bio-Ecology. N. Y. John Wiley & Co.

Cooper, W. S. 1926. The fundamentals of vegetational change. Ecology, **7**: 391–413.

Cowles, H. C. 1899. The ecological relations of the vegetation of the sand dunes of Lake Michigan. Bot. Gaz., **27**: 95–391.

Davidson, V. S. 1932. The effect of seasonal variability upon animal species in a deciduous forest succession. Ecol. Monogr., **2**: 305–334.

Deevey, E. S. 1939. Studies on Connecticut lake sediments: I. A postglacial climatic chronology for southern New England. Amer. Jour. Sci., **237**: 691–724.

——. 1941. Limnological studies in Connecticut: VI. The quantity and composition of the bottom fauna. Ecol. Monogr., **11**: 413–455.

——. 1942. Studies on Connecticut lake sediments: III. The biostratonomy of Linsley Pond. Amer. Jour. Sci., **240**: 233–264, 313–338.

Elton, C. 1927. Animal Ecology. N. Y. Macmillan Co.

Francé, R. H. 1913. Das Edaphon, Untersuchungen zur Oekologie der bodenbewohnenden Mikroorganismen. Deutsch. Mikrolog. Gesellsch., Arbeit. aus d. Biol. Inst., No. 2. Munich.

Friederichs, K. 1930. Die Grundfragen und Gesetzmässigkeiten der land- und forstwirtschaftlichen Zoologie. 2 vols. Berlin. Verschlag. Paul Parey.

Groschopf, P. 1936. Die postglaziale Entwicklung des Grosser Plöner Sees in Ostholstein auf Grund pollenanalytischer Sedimentuntersuchungen. Arch. Hydrobiol., **30**: 1–84.

Heinrich, K. 1934. Atmung und Assimilation im freien Wasser. Internat. Rev. ges. Hydrobiol. u. Hydrogr., **30**: 387–410.

Hentschel, E. 1933–1936. Allgemeine Biologie des Südatlantischen Ozeans. Wiss. Ergebn. Deutsch. Atlant. Exped. a. d. Forschungs- u. Vermessungsschiff "Meteor" 1925–1927. Bd. **XI.**

Hicks, P. A. 1934. Interaction of factors in the growth of *Lemna:* V. Some preliminary observations upon the interaction of temperature and light on the growth of *Lemna.* Ann. Bot., **48**: 515–523.

Hile, R. 1941. Age and growth of the rock bass *Ambloplites rupestris* (Rafinesque) in Nebish Lake, Wisconsin. Trans. Wisconsin Acad. Sci., Arts, Lett., **33**: 189–337.

Hutchinson, G. E. 1941. Limnological studies in Connecticut: IV. Mechanism of intermediary metabolism in stratified lakes. Ecol. Monogr., **11**: 21–60.

——. 1942. Recent Advances in Limnology (*in manuscript*).

—— and R. L. Lindeman. 1941. Biological efficiency in succession (Abstract). Bull. Ecol. Soc. Amer., **22**: 44.

—— and Anne Wollack. 1940. Studies on Connecticut lake sediments: II. Chemical analyses of a core from Linsley Pond, North Branford. Amer. Jour. Sci., **238**: 493–517.

Huxley, J. S. 1932. Problems of Relative Growth. N. Y. Dial Press.

Ivlev, V. S. 1939a. Transformation of energy by aquatic animals. Internat. Rev. ges. Hydrobiol. u. Hydrogr., **38**: 449–458.

——. 1939b. Balance of energy in carps. Zool. Zhurn. Moscow, **18**: 303–316.

Jacot, A. P. 1940. The fauna of the soil. Quart. Rev. Biol., **15**: 28–58.

Jenkin, B. M., C. H. Mortimer, and W. Pennington. 1941. The study of lake deposits. Nature, **147**: 496–500.

Joffe, J. S. 1936. Pedology. New Brunswick, New Jersey. Rutgers Univ. Press.

Juday, C. 1922. Quantitative studies of the bottom fauna in the deeper waters of Lake Mendota. Trans. Wisconsin Acad. Sci., Arts, Lett., **20**: 461–493.

——. 1940. The annual energy budget of an inland lake. Ecology, **21**: 438–450.

Krogh, A. 1941. The Comparative Physiology of Respiratory Mechanisms. Philadelphia. Univ. Pennsylvania Press.

Lindeman, R. L. 1941a. The developmental history of Cedar Creek Bog, Minnesota. Amer. Midl. Nat., **25**: 101–112.

——. 1941b. Seasonal food-cycle dynamics in a senescent lake. Amer. Midl. Nat., **26**: 636–673.

Lohmann, H. 1912. Untersuchungen über das Pflanzen- und Tierleben der Hochsee, zugleich ein Bericht über die biologischen Arbeiten auf der Fahrt der "Deutschland" von Bremerhaven nach Buenos Aires. Veröffentl. d. Inst. f. Meereskunde, N.F., A. Geogr.-naturwissen. Reihe, Heft 1, 92 pp.

Lundegårdh, H. 1924. Kreislauf der Kohlensäure in der Natur. Jena. G. Fischer.

Meschkat, A. 1937. Abwasserbiologische Untersuchungen in einem Buhnenfeld unterhalb Hamburgs. Arch. Hydrobiol., **31**: 399–432.

Moore, W. G. 1941. Studies on the feeding habits of fishes. Ecology, **22**: 91–95.

Needham, J. 1931. Chemical Embryology. 3 vols. N. Y. Cambridge University Press.

Noddack, W. 1937. Der Kohlenstoff im Haushalt der Natur. Zeitschr. angew. Chemie, **50**: 505–510.

Park, Thomas. 1941. The laboratory population as a test of a comprehensive ecological system. Quart. Rev. Biol., **16**: 274–293, 440–461.

Rigg, G. B. 1940. Comparisons of the development of some Sphagnum bogs of the Atlantic coast, the interior, and the Pacific coast. Amer. Jour. Bot., **27**: 1–14.

Riley, G. A. 1940. Limnological studies in Connecticut. III. The plankton of Linsley Pond. Ecol. Monogr., **10**: 279–306.

——. 1941. Plankton studies. III. Long Island Sound. Bull. Bingham Oceanogr. Coll. **7** (3): 1–93.

Ruttner, F. 1937. Limnologische Studien an einigen Seen der Ostalpen. Arch. Hydrobiol., **32**: 167–319.

Smith-Davidson, Vera. 1932. The effect of seasonal variability upon animal species in a deciduous forest succession. Ecol. Monogr., **2**: 305–334.

Spoehr, H. A. 1926. Photosynthesis. N. Y. Chemical Catalogue Co.

Swingle, H. S., and E. V. Smith. 1940. Experiments on the stocking of fish ponds. Trans. North Amer. Wildlife Conf., **5**: 267–276.

Tansley, A. G. 1935. The use and abuse of vegetational concepts and terms. Ecology, **16**: 284–307.

Thienemann, A. 1918. Lebensgemeinschaft und Lebensraum. Naturw. Wochenschrift, N.F., **17**: 282–290, 297–303.

——. 1926. Der Nahrungskreislauf im Wasser. Verh. deutsch. Zool. Ges., **31**: 29–79. (or) Zool. Anz. Suppl., **2**: 29–79.

——. 1939. Grundzüge einen allgemeinen Oekologie. Arch. Hydrobiol., **35**: 267–285.

Thompson, D. H. 1941. The fish production of inland lakes and streams. Symposium on Hydrobiology, pp. 206–217. Madison. Univ. Wisconsin Press.

Tutin, T. G. 1941. The hydrosere and current concepts of the climax. Jour. Ecol. **29**: 268–279.

Vernadsky, V. I. 1929. La biosphere. Paris. Librairie Felix Alcan.

——. 1939. On some fundamental problems of biogeochemistry. Trav. Lab. Biogeochem. Acad. Sci. URSS, **5**: 5–17.

Waksman, S. A. 1941. Aquatic bacteria in relation to the cycle of organic matter in lakes. Symposium on Hydrobiology, pp. 86–105. Madison. Univ. Wisconsin Press.

Welch, P. S. 1935. Limnology. N. Y. McGraw-Hill Co.

Wesenberg-Lund, C. 1912. Über einige eigentümliche Temperaturverhaltnisse in der Litoralregion. . . . Internat. Rev. ges. Hydrobiol. u. Hydrogr., **5**: 287–316.

Williams, E. C. 1941. An ecological study of the floor fauna of the Panama rain forest. Bull. Chicago Acad. Sci., **6**: 63–124.

Wimpenny, R. S. 1941. Organic polarity: some ecological and physiological aspects. Quart. Rev. Biol., **16**: 389–425.

ZoBell, C. E., and C. B. Feltham. 1938. Bacteria as food for certain marine invertebrates. Jour. Marine Research, **1**: 312–327.

Addendum

While this, his sixth completed paper, was in the press, Raymond Lindeman died after a long illness on 29 June, 1942, in his twenty-seventh year. While his loss is grievous to all who knew him, it is more fitting here to dwell on the achievements of his brief working life. The present paper represents a synthesis of Lindeman's work on the modern ecology and past history of a small senescent lake in Minnesota. In studying this locality he came to realize, as others before him had done, that the most profitable method of analysis lay in reduction of all the interrelated biological events to energetic terms. The attempt to do this led him far beyond the immediate problem in hand, and in stating his conclusions he felt that he was providing a program for further studies. Knowing that one man's life at best is too short for intensive studies of more than a few localities, and before the manuscript was completed, that he might never return again to the field, he wanted others to think in the same terms as he had found so stimulating, and for them to collect material that would confirm, extend, or correct his theoretical conclusions. The present contribution does far more than this, as here for the first time, we have the interrelated dynamics of a biocoenosis presented in a form that is amenable to a productive abstract analysis. The question, for instance, arises, "What determines the length of a food chain?"; the answer given is admittedly imperfect, but it is far more important to have seen that there is a real problem of this kind to be solved. That the final statement of the structure of a biocoenosis consists of pairs of numbers, one an integer determining the level, one a fraction determining the efficiency, may even give some hint of an undiscovered type of mathematical treatment of biological communities. Though Lindeman's work on the ecology and history of Cedar Bog Lake is of more than local interest, and will, it is hoped, appear of even greater significance when the notes made in the last few months of his life can be coordinated and published, it is to the present paper that we must turn as the major contribution of one of the most creative and generous minds yet to devote itself to ecological science.

G. Evelyn Hutchinson.
Yale University.

METABOLISM AND BIOENERGETICS

OLIVER P. PEARSON

Dr. Pearson, who completed this work at the Biological Laboratories at Harvard, is now with the Museum of Vertebrate Zoology, University of California, Berkeley.

THE most fundamental physiological property of all plants and animals, the rate at which they are living, is reflected quantitatively in their metabolic rates. Metabolism is a complex, inscrutable process—but its rate is easily measured. Heretofore, such measurements have been used chiefly by physiologists as tools for studying the functioning of organisms; I shall endeavor to show that they can also be used by ecologists and philosophers in understanding the energy balance of the earth, and that a person could even, through measurements of metabolic rates (and here I exaggerate only slightly), relate every beat of a mouse's heart to the entropy of the cosmos.

Consider the mouse represented in Figure 1. He takes in food, water, minerals, oxygen, nitrogen, and many other essential, helpful, or useless materials, but almost everything is returned to the environment, as shown in the segment of Figure 1 marked "Borrowed and Returned." Some substances, like the nitrogen of tidal air, are borrowed for only a moment; an indigestible seed might be borrowed for several hours, and a milligram of calcium for a fleeting lifetime, but all are returned to the environment to play a part in the lives of other animals or plants. The only permanent loss to the environment is the energy dissipated in the form of heat, represented in the third segment of Figure 1. The mouse has taken a bit of solar energy (captured and made edible by plants) and released it. Perhaps we should say the animal has squandered it, because the energy has been degraded to such an extent that it is beyond recall by the plant and animal kingdoms. It is this energy degradation that is measured as the metabolic rate.

As long ago as 1886, Boltzmann (quoted by Tizard, 1932) remarked that the struggle for existence is a struggle for free energy available for work. Therefore, to know the metabolism of an animal for a day is to know how successful it has been in the struggle for existence, how successfully it has deprived some rival of energy, how much of its organic heritage it has reduced to impotent isothermality.

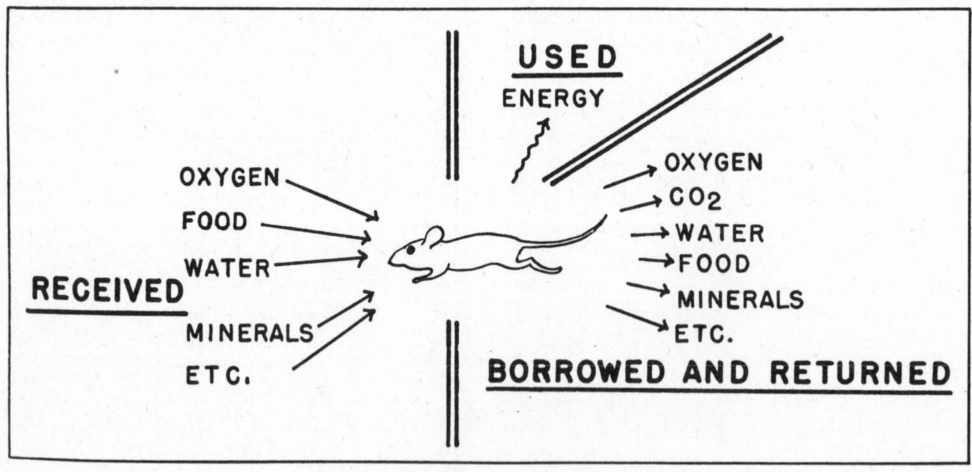

FIG. 1. INTAKE AND OUTPUT OF A MOUSE

Reproduced with permission from The Scientific Monthly, LXVI: 131-134, 1948. Published by The American Association for the Advancement of Science, Washington, D. C.

Since Mother Nature's ability to keep her cupboard supplied is limited by the earth's meager quota of sunshine, since many animals and plants are making use of the cupboard quite freely, if not recklessly, and since I am somewhat fearful that this pilferage may become so rampant as to make it difficult for my friends and me to satisfy our needs, I have decided to expose some of the culprits.

The rate of living of many citizens has been measured and recorded in the papers. Consequently, I can calculate the extent of their thievery from the public energy supply and can state definitely that big, boisterous Smith, because of his flagrant metabolism, is Public Enemy No. 1, whereas little, mild Miss Jones is only a Lesser Public Enemy. But I can go further. I can group all the Smiths and Joneses together (for not one of them has a clear record) into a genus, *Homo,* and compare their thieving, their dissipation of this limited supply of energy, with that of a host of smaller public enemies—the mice, for example, or the earthworms.

Table 1 might be considered a rogues' gallery of the records of most of the common small mammals living in forests in eastern Pennsylvania. The animals are listed in order of their metabolic (or catabolic) importance. The metabolic values are taken from Pearson (1947) and are not basal rates, but are average daily rates taken over 24-hour periods at a temperature of about 25° C., with the animals free to move about and express their normal nocturnal-diurnal rhythms. The figures for population per acre are estimates based on personal trapping experience in the northeastern United States and on many recently published population studies.

TABLE 1

THE ENERGY DISSIPATION OF SMALL MAMMALS ON AN ACRE OF FOREST IN PENNSYLVANIA IN SUMMERTIME

	Ave. wt. (gm.)	No. per acre	Gm. per acre	METABOLIC RATE	
				Kg. Cal./ kg./day	Kg. Cal./ acre/day
Short-tailed shrew (*Blarina brevicauda*)	18.0	4.0	72.0	600	43.2
Deer mouse (*Peromyscus leucopus*)	20.0	5.0	100.0	416	41.6
Red-backed mouse (*Clethrionomys gapperi*)	22.0	0.5	11.0	414	4.5
Woodland jumping mouse (*Napaeozapus insignis*)	24.0	0.5	12.0	360	4.3
Flying squirrel (*Glaucomys volans*)	70.0	0.1	7.0	231	1.6
Long-tailed shrew (*Sorex cinereus*)	3.5	0.2	0.7	1,800	1.3
Total		10.3	202.7		96.5

It will be seen that short-tailed shrews and deer mice are metabolically the most important species. Deer mice are more abundant than shrews in the forest, but since they have a lower metabolic rate they are no more important. The long-tailed shrews, despite their astonishingly fast rate of metabolism, have little effect on the total energy exchange of the area because they are so small and so few. The total impact of all these small mammals from the Pennsylvania acre considered in Table 1, all 203 grams of them, is reflected in a metabolic rate of 96 kg. Cal. per acre per day.

This metabolism may be compared with that of other kinds of animals living in Pennsylvania (Table 2). Deer, for example, which are unusually abundant in the state, dissipate the energy in vegetation at a rate of 70 kg. Cal./acre/day—about three-quarters as fast as all the small mammals listed. This calculation is based on the following assumptions: 1,100,000 deer in the state (Biological Surveys Inventory, 1943), average weight of 100 pounds, and an average daily metabolic rate of 40 kg. Cal./kg./day (twice the basal metabolism of goats).

To introduce man into Table 2, I have used the density of Indians rather than that of modern man because Indians lived in closer harmony and more exact balance with their environment than does man today. In the year 1600 there was about 0.00054 Indian per acre in New England, New York, Pennsylvania, and New Jersey (calculated from data given by Mooney, 1928). At a daily metabolic rate of 2,500 kg. Cal. per person, their total metabolism would have amounted to only 1.4 kg. Cal./acre/day—about the same as that of the smallest mammal of the region, the long-tailed shrew. Modern man, however, is living in Pennsylvania at a density of 0.3 persons per acre, which results in a metabolism of 750 kg. Cal./acre/day—nearly seven times greater than that of all the small mammals listed in Table 1, and 535 times greater than that of the Indians. Even when we consider a less-urbanized state, such as New Hampshire, with a present population density of 0.09 per acre, the energy dissipated by man is about 225 kg. Cal./acre/day, which is nearly double that of all the smaller mammals put together.

Actually, man is an even more expensive item in the energy budget than these figures indicate, for he has been able to supplement his own metabolism by putting fire to work. I shall not attempt to calculate exactly how much of this energy is totally wasted and how much is "saved" by charging batteries, heating houses to lower man's metabolism, etc., but let us suppose that each person finds it necessary to burn one ton of carbon each year, and that all the resulting energy "goes up the chimney." All this supplementary oxidation would drain 1,765 kg. Cal./acre/day from New Hampshire and 5,980 from Pennsylvania. With this outside help, man's impact on the environment, his bioenergetic importance, becomes much greater than that of any other mammalian species—probably greater than that of all other mammals combined. For many years he has been drawing on the earth's capital to support this high living; most of the other animals live frugally within the earth's income.

Having found that modern man is the greatest energy squanderer among the mammals, let us see if he has any rivals among other groups. We are faced at once with a shortage of population and metabolism data, but we can make some rough estimates. Using the method described by Eaton and Chandler (1942), I have estimated that there were 125,000 earthworms (25,400 gm.) to an acre of hardwood forest at Swarthmore, Pennsylvania, on June 10, 1947. At 19° C. these would use oxygen at a rate of 0.07 cc./gm./hr. (Loewy, 1926), or 1,778 cc./acre

TABLE 2

Disposition of the Energy Falling on an Acre in Pennsylvania in Summertime*

	No. per acre	Gm. per acre	Metabolism (Kg. Cal./acre/day)	
Used by man (Indians)	0.00054	25	1.4	
Used by deer	0.04	1,700	70.0	
Used by small mammals	10.3	203	96.5	
Used by earthworms	125,000.0	25,400	205.0	
Used by microorganisms	3×10^{18} (?)	3×10^{6} (?)	2,700.0	
Total used by above animals			3,072.9	3,073
Energy still available to other organisms				12,927

* Rate of incident radiation, 25,000,000 kg. Cal./day; rate of capture by plants (net productivity), 16,000.

/hr. At an equivalence of 4.8 kg. Cal. per liter of oxygen, this would be 205 kg. Cal. /acre/day. The worms on this acre, therefore, would be about twice as important metabolically as the mice and shrews, but less important than "barehanded" modern man in Pennsylvania.

If we go to the bottom of the size scale and consider the microorganisms in the soil (mostly bacteria), we find that on an acre such as the one postulated in Table 2 they are the most important of the groups listed. Metabolically, they are more than ten times as important as the earthworms. (I have used Russell's figures [1937, p. 459] for the energy dissipation of microorganisms on unfertilized land.)

We must now compare the rate at which these organisms are depleting the supply in Nature's cupboard with the rate at which it is being stocked—that is, the rate at which plants are capturing and storing our quota of energy. The energy serving to warm the earth and atmosphere is not being considered here, for although an unknown amount of it is "conserved" by lowering the metabolism of birds and mammals, at the same time it increases the metabolism of the cold-blooded animals. During Indian times in Pennsylvania, plants captured about 16,000 kg. Cal./acre/day of the 25,000,000 kg. Cal. that bathed each acre daily. I have assumed that all the land was forested and had an annual net productivity of 200 tons of organic carbon per square kilometer (Noddack, 1937). In Table 2 this income is compared with the expenditures of the few groups of animals that I have mentioned. It may be seen that these animals dissipate 3,073 of the 16,000 calories made available each day, leaving some 12,000 available for the birds, bees, toadstools, and a host of others, or for storage. This storage is temporary, however. More energy is captured each day during the summer than is used, resulting in the storage of some, but almost all seems to be used up over the winter. Geologists support this belief that there is little energy being stored in forests today, and Russell (1937) states that the soil microorganisms live right up to their income in the matter of nutrients and energy supply.

In the preceding pages I have only outlined an approach that should yield interesting results when it is applied to different kinds of terrain at different seasons with *all* the animals and plants carefully accounted for. I have not undertaken this task, for, finding unexpectedly that my friends and I with our cars and furnaces and washing machines are by far the greatest of the public enemies, I have had a twinge of conscience, a resurgence of altruism, and am preparing to retire to a life of studied inactivity and heat conservation under the whispering leaves of the nearest palm tree.

REFERENCES

Eaton, T. H., Jr., and Chandler, R. F., Jr. The Fauna of Forest-humus Layers in New York. *Cornell Univ. Agric. Exp. Station Memoir 247,* 1942, 1–26.

Loewy. Sauerstoff-Verbrauch von Kaltblütern. *Tabulae Biologicae,* 1926, **3,** 503.

Mooney, J. The Aboriginal Population of America North of Mexico. *Smiths. Misc. Coll.,* 1928, **80,** 1–40.

Noddack, W. Der Kohlenstoff im Haushalt der Natur. *Zeit. ang. Chem.,* 1937, **50,** 505–10.

Pearson, O. P. The Rate of Metabolism of Some Small Mammals. *Ecology,* 1947, **28,** 127–45.

Russell, E. J. *Soil Conditions and Plant Growth.* (7th ed.) New York: Longmans, Green, 1937. Pp. i–viii, 1–655.

Tizard, H. T. Thermochemistry. *Encyclopaedia Britannica.* (14th ed.) 1932, **22,** 83–91.

THE DAILY ENERGY REQUIREMENTS OF A WILD ANNA HUMMINGBIRD

By OLIVER P. PEARSON

The daily energy requirements of wild, unfettered birds are difficult to estimate because the metabolic costs of flying, hopping, scratching and other common activities are not known, and were they known, it would still be almost impossible to divide a bird's day neatly into periods spent at the different energy levels. Hummingbirds, however, spend almost their entire active day at only two metabolic levels, hovering and perching, and their rate of metabolism during these activities is known. Therefore, to calculate the energy expenditure of a wild hummingbird, one has only to watch a hummingbird all day and record with a stopwatch how much time is spent in the air and how much is spent perching. I shall report below two such attempts to watch a male Anna Hummingbird (*Calypte anna*) on September 3 and September 8, 1953, in the botanical gardens of the University of California at Berkeley.

METABOLIC GROUNDWORK

Before calculating the energy balance of this bird for the day, it is necessary to estimate his rate of metabolism while hovering and while perching. On the basis of previous work (Pearson, Condor, 52, 1950:145), I shall assume that Anna Hummingbirds while hovering consume oxygen at the rate of 68 cc per gram of body weight per hour. In the absence of evidence to the contrary, the energy cost of linear flight will be assumed to be the same as for hovering. Should this assumption prove to be unsound, only a slight error will have been introduced because only a small fraction of the airborn time is spent in linear flight.

For calculating the metabolism of hummingbirds perching at the temperatures encountered in the wild, two 24-hour recordings of oxygen consumption of captive Anna Hummingbirds are available (fig. 1), one at 24°C. and one at 12°. The 24° run has been reported earlier (Pearson, *op. cit.*). These records were obtained in a modification of the apparatus described by Morrison (Jour. Biol. Chem., 169, 1947:667). The bird was confined under a belljar whose inside dimensions were six inches in diameter and four inches high, a space too small to permit flight. Containers of soda lime and calcium chloride served to absorb the water vapor and carbon dioxide produced by the bird, and a generous supply of food was provided. The belljar with the bird inside was submerged in a water bath of appropriate temperature and was connected to a floating spirometer that supplied oxygen at atmospheric pressure. The chamber was illuminated by natural daylight. The bird was weighed at the beginning and end of each 24-hour run and his weight at any time during the run was estimated by interpolation. Results are given in cubic centimeters of oxygen consumed per gram of body weight per hour. The volume of oxygen has been corrected for water vapor and temperature and therefore corresponds to dry gas at 0°C. For conversion to Calories, I have assumed each liter of oxygen consumed to be equivalent to 4.8 Calories, a value appropriate to the respiratory quotient of actively digesting small birds (Kendeigh, Jour. Exp. Zool., 96, 1944:1).

From the data on which figure 1 is based, I calculate that the daytime perching

Reproduced with permission from The Condor, 56: 317-322, 1954. Published by the Cooper Ornithological Society, Berkeley, California.

metabolism (including activities such as preening) at 24° is 16.3 cc/gm/hr and at 12° is 21.0 cc/gm/hr. The mean hourly daytime temperature in the shade on the observed hummingbird's territory on September 3 was 17.3°, and on September 8, 18.1° (fig. 2). The resting metabolism at these temperatures was calculated by linear interpolation between 16.3 and 21.0 cc./gm/hr. Body weight was estimated at 4.0 grams.

Finally, before calculating the total energy expenditure of this wild hummingbird for a 24-hour period, one must assign a metabolic rate for overnight. It has been shown

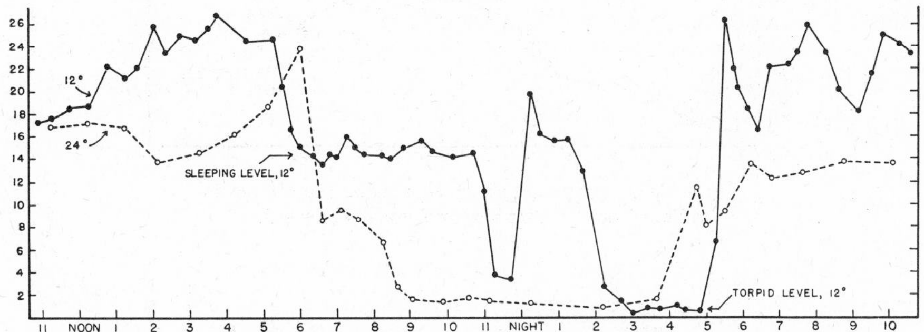

Fig. 1. The 24-hour metabolism of two male Anna Hummingbirds, one at 12°C. and one at 24°. The bird at 12° reached a sleeping level of 14.5 cc/gm/hr at about 6 p.m. and continued at this level until it dropped abruptly into torpor at 11 p.m. However, before reaching the minimal level, its metabolism reversed and the bird, for no apparent reason, emerged from torpor only to drop a short time later to a level of only 0.76 cc/gm/hr. During the 24° as well as the 12° run the birds emerged from torpor spontaneously before daybreak. The torpid level at 12° is somewhat lower than at 24°, but close comparison cannot be made because the accuracy of the apparatus is not great at such low levels of oxygen consumption.

that Anna Hummingbirds frequently pass the night in a condition of torpor at an extremely low metabolic level (Pearson, *op. cit.*, and fig. 1), but on the other hand an incubating female observed by Howell and Dawson (Condor, 56, 1954:93) did not become torpid. It is probable, furthermore, that many hummingbirds in the wild spend part of the night torpid and part merely sleeping, as did the bird whose metabolism was measured at 12° (fig. 1). Therefore, I have made two sets of calculations, one assuming that the night was spent entirely at the sleeping level at an environmental temperature of 12°, and one assuming that the night started as in the 12° run illustrated in figure 1, but that metabolism dropped to the 0.76 cc/gm/hr torpor level at 8 p.m. and remained there until the pre-dawn rise at 5 a.m.

RESULTS

Early in September, when the observations were made, male Anna Hummingbirds vigorously defend a small feeding territory. The territory of the male under observation was only 50 feet in diameter. He rarely left this territory except to chase other hummingbirds, and he drove off every hummingbird that he saw on his territory, regardless of its sex. At dusk, however, he flew off more than 300 feet to his night roosting place.

Figure 3 reveals that he was especially active in the mornings and in the evenings and relatively inactive during the early afternoon. He was flying only 10 per cent of the time early in the afternoons but as much as 30 per cent of one hour just before dark. During his active day, which was 12 hours and 52 minutes long on both days, he averaged 18.7 per cent of the time flying on September 3 and 17.9 per cent on September 8. The longest perching period was between 1:05 and 1:35 p.m. on September 3, although during a brief observation period on September 1 I noted that he remained perched for as long as 34 minutes between 1:27 and 2:01 p.m.

Using the metabolism data given earlier, one can calculate the daily energy values presented in table 1 and illustrated in figure 4. Assuming torpidity at night, the energy exchange of this bird for 24 hours of normal life in the wild was 7.55 Calories (average of two days), and assuming sleep at night, 10.32 Calories. This is, of course, a consider-

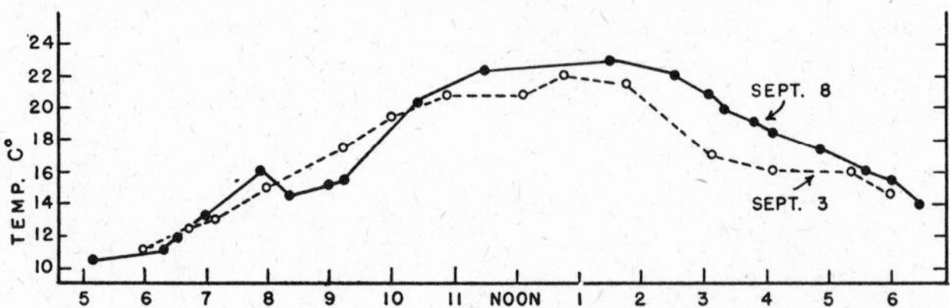

Fig. 2. Shade temperatures on September 3 and 8 on the territory of the hummingbird under observation.

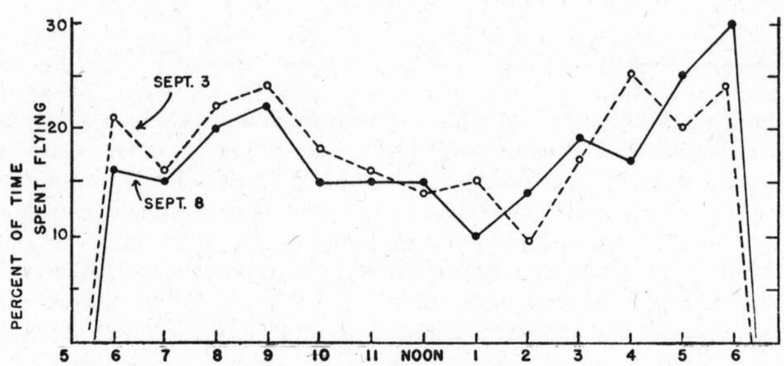

Fig. 3. Per cent of each hour spent airborne. Same male Anna Hummingbird on two days.

ably higher metabolic rate than that of the birds confined in the metabolism apparatus, which totalled 4.88 Calories at 24° and 6.77 Calories at 12°. Agreement is good, however, with the results of some feeding experiments reported by van Riper (Nature Mag., 54, 1953:135). He found that a 4.3-gram Broad-tailed Hummingbird (*Selasphorus platycercus*) removed 7.31 Calories of sugar solution from a feeder each day.

The male Anna Hummingbird's day (fig. 4) can be divided into three major metabolic levels that are at the same time crude categories of activity: daytime perching, flying, and night roosting. If the bird spends the night at the sleeping level, rather than in torpor, then one-third of his 24-hour *energy* budget is spent in each of these three activities, although his *time* is spent in an entirely different ratio.

The category "flying" can be subdivided successfully into the following activities: 1. Nectar flights. By far the largest part of his flying time and flying energy could be assigned to this category. 2. Insect-catching flights. These consisted of forays of only a few seconds, similar to the insect-catching flights of flycatchers. The prey was usually gnats. 3. Territory defense. Usually chases in which an intruding hummingbird was pursued, but occasionally flights to the edge of the territory to forestall trespass by a nearby hummingbird. 4. Perch changes. Short flights to a nearby perch for no obvious reason. 5. Disturbances. Short flights of a few yards to avoid workmen and visitors in the botanical gardens. 6. Unclassified flying. The bird was out of sight during 1.5 to 2.0 per cent of each day. After each disappearance an estimate was made of the prob-

Table 1

Time and Energy Values for Two Days of Activity of a Male Anna Hummingbird

	Basic data		Per cent of daytime activity		Per cent of 24 hours		
	Time	Energy	Time	Energy	Time	Energy assuming torpidity	Energy assuming sleep
Daytime activity	12 hr. 52 min. (12.52–12:52)	6.88 Cal. (6.95–6.80)	100	100	53.7 (53.7–53.7)	91.2 (91.3–91.1)	66.6 (66.8–66.4)
Perching	10 hr. 32 min. (10:28–10:36)	3.81 (3.82–3.80)	81.8 (81.4–82.2)	55.5 (55.0–55.9)	43.8 (43.6–44.1)	50.5 (50.1–50.9)	36.8 (36.7–37.0)
Flying	2 hr. 21 min. (2:24–2:18)	3.07 (3.13–3.00)	18.2 (18.7–17.9)	44.6 (45.1–44.2)	9.8 (10.0–9.6)	40.7 (41.2–40.2)	29.7 (30.1–29.3)
120 (120–119) nectar-feeding flights	1 hr. 53 min. (1:58–1:49)	2.46 (2.55–2.37)	14.6 (15.2–14.1)	35.7 (36.7–34.8)	7.85 (8.15–7.55	32.5 (33.4–31.7)	23.8 (24.5–23.1)
Chasing 78 (108–62) insects	4.45 min. (5.50–3.40)	.094 (0.110–.077)	0.54 (0.65–0.44)	1.34 (1.58–1.10)	0.30 (0.35–0.24)	1.22 (1.44–1.00)	0.90 (1.06–0.75)
50 (47–53) territory defenses	13.76 min. (10.00–17.52)	0.305 (.230–.379)	1.8 (1.3–2.3)	4.48 (3.34–5.61)	0.96 (.70–1.22)	4.08 (3.05–5.11)	2.96 (2.22–3.70)
60 (70–50) perch changes	2.75 min. (3.37–2.13)	.058 (.072–.043)	0.36 (.44–.28)	0.85 (1.04–0.66)	0.19 (.23–.15)	0.78 (.95–.60)	0.55 (.69–.42)
39 (64–14) dis-turbances	0.65 min. (1.07–.23)	.014 (.024–.005)	.08 (.14–.03)	0.20 (.32–.09)	.04 (.07–.01)	0.18 (.29–.08)	0.14 (.23–.05)
Unclassified flying	6.87 min. (7.50–6.25)	0.148 (.163–.134)	0.89 (.97–.81)	2.17 (2.35–2.00)	0.45 (.47–.43)	1.97 (2.14–1.81)	1.44 (1.57–1.31)
Night roosting (torpid)	11 hr. 8 min. (11:08–11:08)	0.672			46.5 (46.5–46.5)	8.91 (8.83–9.00)	
Night roosting (asleep)	11 hr. 8 min. (11:08–11:08)	3.446			46.5 (46.5–46.5)		33.3 (33.1–33.6)

able time spent flying, the estimate depending upon what the bird was doing when it disappeared and how soon it returned. All such estimates of flying time were then added to make up the "Unclassified Flying" category. Figure 4 and table 1 divide the bird's day into these activities. In table 1 the average figure for the two days is given as well as, in parentheses, the separate value for September 3 followed by that for September 8. The values for the two days agree surprisingly well.

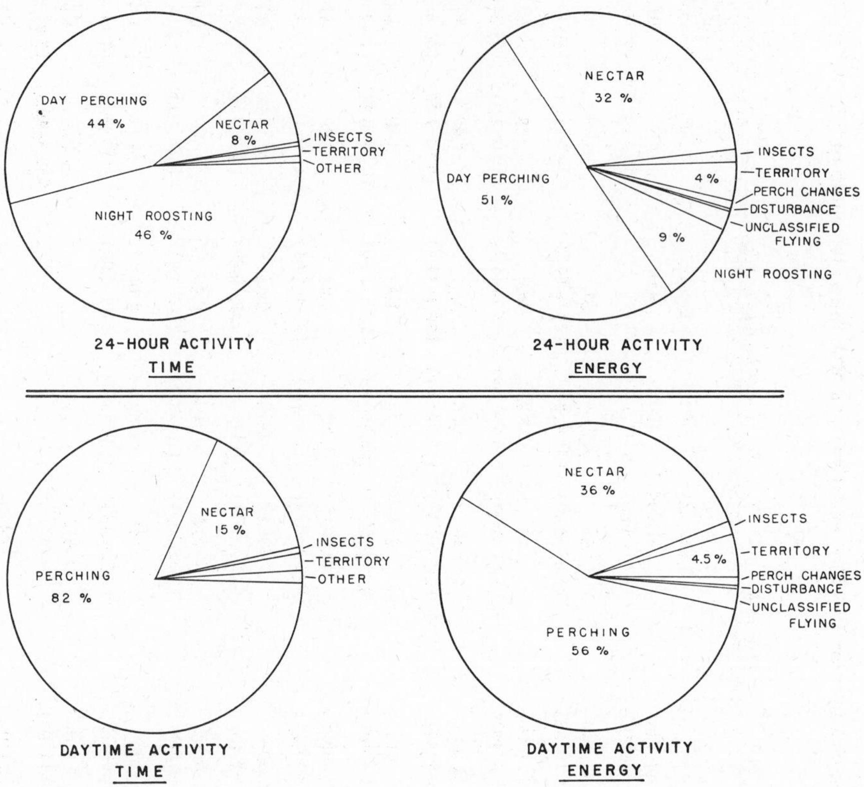

Fig. 4. Upper. Expenditure of time and energy by a hummingbird for 24 hours; average of September 3 and 8. The energy diagram was constructed assuming that the bird became torpid at night.

Lower. Expenditure of time and energy during the 12-hour, 52-minute active day. Same observations as above but the night period at unknown metabolic level has been omitted.

The hummingbird under observation did approximately 90 per cent of his nectar feeding from the blossoms of a single large bush of *Fuchsia macrostemma*. On a few occasions when his attention was directed elsewhere another bird managed to feed for a short period on these blossoms. If we assume that this pilfering just balances the nourishment that the resident bird obtained feeding on insects and on other flowers, then it becomes possible to say that the 7.6 (assuming torpidity at night) to 10.3 Calories (assuming no torpidity) required every day by this bird could be supplied by nectar from the 1022 blossoms available on this bush.

The value of defended territory to an individual bird or to a species is difficult to measure and to put into quantitative terms, yet the concept of territories is basic in the study of bird behavior and avian ecology. It is probably safe to assume that the true value of territorial defense to an individual or species is greater than the cost, otherwise the habit would have been eliminated through centuries of evolution. If, then, one can calculate how much energy a bird spends defending its territory, one has a minimal estimate of the value received by the bird as a result of its expenditure. In figure 4 and table 1 can be seen the cost of territorial defense to this hummingbird. The cost is expressed in Calories, an international currency that lends itself to comparison of the territorial defense costs of the same individual on different days, at different seasons, or even of comparing the defense costs of widely different species. The male Anna Hummingbird watched on September 3 and 8 devoted 1.8 per cent of his 12-hour 52-minute active day to an average of 50 flights in defense of his territory. This amounts to 0.305 Calories, 4.48 per cent of his daytime energy expeniture, or 4.08 per cent of his 24-hour metabolic needs (assuming torpidity at night). In more tangible units this represents the energy derived from 42 blossoms of *Fuchsia macrostemma* (4.08 per cent of 1022). This is the expense of active defense of his territory. Probably a small fraction should be added for the cost of territorial singing. Perching of the bird in conspicuous places where he can be seen by birds on neighboring territories can also, like singing, be considered a kind of territorial advertisement, but unless such perches require more energy to reach than do alternate perches no allowance need be made for this territorial display because it does not necessitate increased metabolism.

It will be seen from figures 3 and 4 that only about one-fifth of the daytime is spent on the wing. Of the remaining four-fifths, a small fraction is necessary for preening to keep the plumage in serviceable condition and probably a small fraction is required for rest, but the remainder of the perching time is available for more strenuous activity should occasion demand. At some seasons the territory must be considerably larger to allow gathering of sufficient food, and at such seasons more time and energy would be spent feeding and less perching. During the early spring considerable energy must be expended in the spectacular diving display, thereby necessitating more feeding. Each hour of flight not only subtracts that much time from the perching time, but necessitates approximately 15 minutes more of flying to replace the *additional* food consumed during the hour of flight. Accordingly figure 4 may be expected to have a quite different appearance if plotted for other seasons of the year. It is my impression that early September, despite vigorous territorial defense, is a time of abundant food, small territories, and relative inactivity. It is a season of leisure for the Anna Hummingbird.

SUMMARY

A male Anna Hummingbird watched on September 3 and 8 flew on the average 18.7 per cent of the time. His energy exchange for 24 hours of normal life in the wild was calculated to be 7.55 Calories (assuming torpidity at night) or 10.32 Calories (assuming sleep at night). During his 12-hour 52-minute active day, most of his energy expenditure was distributed as follows: perching, 3.81 Calories (56 per cent); nectar flights, 2.46 (36 per cent); insect-catching flights, .09 (1.3 per cent); and defense of territory, .30 (4.5 per cent). The nectar secretion of about 1022 *Fuchsia* blossoms can supply this daily need.

Museum of Vertebrate Zoology, Berkeley, California, August 13, 1954.

ECOLOGICAL ENERGY RELATIONSHIPS AT THE POPULATION LEVEL*

L. B. SLOBODKIN

Department of Zoology, University of Michigan, Ann Arbor, Michigan

I will be concerned with the ecologically significant energy relationships of single species populations. The theoretical analysis and data deal primarily with laboratory populations of *Daphnia pulex*, but I believe that the conclusions have significance for nature as will be indicated in the discussion.

The number and kind of organisms found in nature is variable from year to year and even from day to day. Despite this variability, it can be said that a sufficiently detailed and temporally extensive examination of any one species, or even of an isolated population of a species, will show that the number of organisms and volume of protoplasm represented by that species or population remain approximately constant. Some populations may vary in size in a cyclic way, either annually or possibly with some other period; others may vary in a random way, but in any case there is some definite mean population size, if data over a period of the order of ten times the mean generation time is considered.

Mean population size does not represent an equilibrium value in the sense that the position of a pendulum bob at rest represents an equilibrium, but rather represents a steady state. The steady state can be characterized by the fact that it requires energy for its maintenance. Just as the steady state temperature gradients in a metal bar heated at one end would disappear in the absence of an energy source, so the steady state properties of the ecological world would vanish in the absence of the radiant energy of sunlight.

It is possible to conceive of a series of metal bars in contact at their ends, with the terminal bar converting radiant energy into heat and this heat then being transmitted by conduction through the whole series of bars. Again a steady state temperature gradient would characterize each bar. Similarly in nature radiant energy is converted into potential energy by the green plants and this potential energy is transmitted through a chain of organisms. There will be various steady state values characterizing this chain of organisms. We will be concerned with some of the values that are more or less immediately recognizable as functions of energy, in particular the potential energy, contained in the various single species populations, that is, the standing crops, and with the ratios between the various steady state rates of energy transfer in the system, that is, the efficiencies (Lindeman, 1942).

*Presented at "Interactions in Nature: A Symposium on Modern Ecology" at the meeting of the American Society of Naturalists, cosponsored by the Ecological Society of America and the American Society of Limnology and Oceanography, Chicago, Illinois, December 27–28, 1959.

I have confined myself to steady state values since a short period of very high ecological efficiency or standing crop maintenance has very little applicability to long term values that are likely to occur in nature. Non-steady state efficiencies or standing crops must eventually receive intensive study, but I feel that more immediate progress will be made by considering them as minor perturbations of the steady state values for the moment.

Examining the analogy between metal bars, electric wires, flowing water and other inanimate models on one hand and an ecological community on the other, it is seen that the analogy breaks down almost immediately. In a heat transmission system or in an electric wiring diagram the continued physical existence of the energy transmitting elements is not contingent on the maintenance of energy flow. In a biological system, if energy flow ceases there is almost immediate dissolution of the system's components.

The process of energy flow in ecological systems does not lend itself to discussion in terms of gradients or flow diagrams, except on the most rudimentary level. Flow diagrams are primarily suitable to discussion of heat or radiant energy transport in which physical contact or simply suitable geometric distribution of the physical elements will permit energy flow to occur. In ecological interactions the energy involved is in the form of potential energy, which in general can not be transmitted between parts of a system without displacement or distortion of the physical elements. That is, energy flows from a plant population to an animal population only when a concrete plant or piece of plant is physically removed into the body of some particular animal. It only remains for the ecologist, if he is to concern himself with energy at all, to develop his theories and concepts on a biological basis rather than by assuming the direct applicability of the laws developed for the simple systems of physics and electronics.

Even such elementary concepts as efficiency and energy, and such universal generalizations as the second law of thermodynamics have very peculiar properties on the level of the ecological community.

I will therefore discuss the concepts of efficiency, energy and entropy as they apply to ecology. Ecological efficiency will then be shown to have at least three distinct, operationally defined meanings. These three different concepts of efficiency will be evaluated from the data on *Daphnia pulex.* I will then suggest that certain kinds of efficiency are actually constant for most populations in nature. I will finish with some speculations on the relation between energetics and the future development of a complete theory of community ecology.

AN ELEMENTARY CLARIFICATION OF EFFICIENCY, ENTROPY AND ENERGY IN ECOLOGICAL SYSTEMS

The superficial simplicity of the concept of ecological efficiency requires careful analysis.

The efficiency of an energy machine is easy to define. A machine, in general, is designed and constructed to do a particular kind of work or to produce a particular form of energy. The ratio of the output to the input (both in energy units) is the efficiency of the machine. The output of a moving locomotive is in energy used to overcome the forces that tend to stop the train; the input is in the potential energy of coal or oil burned in the process. The output of a light bulb is in visible radiation; the input in electrical energy and the ratio of the two is the efficiency. But notice that it is possible to read by the light of a coal locomotive's fire box or to warm oneself at a cloth-draped light bulb. These do not seem particularly clever ways to read or to keep warm, but they are conceivable. From the standpoint of a moronic bookworm the efficiency of a locomotive might be measured as the ratio of visible radiant energy from the fire box to potential energy consumption. For most locomotives this efficiency is lower than our initial calculations of the efficiency of the locomotive. Our chilled illiterate in front of the draped light bulb might measure efficiency as total radiant energy output over total electrical energy input and this ratio would be higher than our original estimate of the efficiency of the bulb. I conclude from this that the magnitude of an efficiency need have nothing to do with the importance of the process to which the efficiency ratio refers, even in the case of a machine.

An organism must do many things that require energy. Movement of its internal parts, movement of itself in its environment, producing new protoplasm to compensate for attrition of its own body, adding new protoplasm to its own body and producing offspring are all energy utilizing processes involving single organisms. On the level of the individual we will be concerned with the efficiency of the last two of these only.

This limitation of our concern is due to a peculiar property of ecological interactions. In order to maintain an ecological community of several kinds of animals and plants at a steady state, the new protoplasm made by any population of organisms of any one species, above and beyond replacement requirements, must be consumed during the process of maintaining the steady state of one or more of the other species present. The new protoplasm produced by any population is in one sense a sum of the new growth occurring in all the individuals of that population. I will therefore consider only new protoplasm to be an ecologically useful kind of potential energy and will largely ignore other possible uses of energy on the individual level.

It is impossible to refer to *the efficiency* of a population. The term must, at all times, be qualified. We can speak only of the efficiency of producing energy in some form which we arbitrarily consider useful (the output) from some other form which we arbitrarily define as useless (the input).

The concept of energy is used rather loosely in ecological literature, and recently the concepts of entropy, negative entropy and information have been used equally loosely. We have statements in print that organisms live on order or that communities consume negative entropy, eat information, etc. It therefore seems appropriate to present a statement of the role of energy in ecology.

Radiant energy is absorbed by green plants and part of this is converted to potential energy by the process of photosynthesis. The slow conversion of this potential energy to kinetic energy permits ecological communities to survive.

Particular compounds in the plant will be converted into other compounds in the herbivore. To the extent that individual reversible chemical reactions are being considered the various terms in the equation

(1) $$\Delta H = \Delta F + T \Delta S$$

may be evaluated and the change in entropy per mole computed. An appropriate summation of the entropy contributions of all the reactions that occur in the process of incorporating plant material into the herbivore might be considered the entropy production of the herbivore, were it not that:

1. All of the reactions tend to interact with each other.
2. Phase differences and structural restrictions of complicated kinds occur in both plants and animals and the reactions producing these phase differences are, in general, not reversible in any practical sense, at least in the aggregate.

In other words, it is very difficult by simply supplying energy to get an organism to undigest a meal and thereby measure the ΔF associated with the digestion process. The entropy associated with the process of food assimilation is therefore not conveniently measurable.

It is possible to consider the state of all materials entering an organism and the state of the material leaving the organism, duplicate the degradation process in a reversible way and make the appropriate entropy calculation. To my knowledge this has never been explicitly done for all of the ingested and waste products of any particular organism. It is clear, in principle, that it could be done and if it were done we would find an increase in entropy associated with this passage through the organism as illustrated:

$$\Delta H \longrightarrow \boxed{\text{organism}} \longrightarrow \Delta F + T \Delta S + Q'$$

(2) $$\Delta H = \Delta F + Q' + T \Delta S$$

This requires explication. ΔH can be defined as calories ingested per unit time and ΔF in this context is the calories egested which are still of use to organisms as a supply of energy. $T \Delta S + Q'$ are the caloric equivalent of the heat produced in the utilization of the energy ΔH.

$T \Delta S$ is the heat that would be produced in the various transformations occurring in the organism on the assumption that all reactions were reversible, independent, and of infinitely slow occurrence. None of these conditions is met.

Q' is the heat produced from friction within the organism and from work done by the organism on its environment. In principle, Q' can be evaluated experimentally, but the problem is technically difficult; and except for very simple systems is not likely to be done. It is possible, in an ecological steady state, to write the equation:

Caloric equivalent of the potential energy ingested = caloric equivalent of the potential energy removed from the population by egestion, predation, mortality, etc., plus the heat produced by the population.

It may be legitimate to equate this heat to entropy, but it is not clear what proportion of the potential energy ingested actually shows up as entropy. Estimates of anywhere from two to 50 per cent might be offered.

The notion of entropy content of a living organism is extremely complex. Normal thermodynamic theories apply to an equilibrium state, which is equivalent in one sense to death. The theory of thermodynamics of steady states (Denbigh, 1951) is not yet capable of handling elaborate multiphasic systems. The Onsager equations which permit some development of steady state thermodynamics depend on the rigorous definition of fluxes and on their associated forces.

Any energy gradient of an appropriate sort can be considered a generalized force. This is particularly evident in the relation between a temperature gradient and heat flow. The interesting ecological energy flow is in the form of potential energy. Potential energy can have a gradient, as in the glucose gradient in a single cell. Ecologically, however, the gradient is a rather coarse histogram, of standing crop vs. trophic level. The precise procedure for the interpretation of this histogram as a generalized force seems unclear.

The fluxes can, therefore, be stated but the forces can only be dealt with on an almost metaphorical level in ecology. While metaphor leads to certain sorts of insight it does not have predictive power.

A further complication in the application of thermodynamics to steady state systems has been considered by Foster, Rappoport and Trucco (1957) who find that Prigogine's theorem, which states that steady state systems tend to a condition of minimum entropy production, is not applicable to certain types of feedback systems. It is now generally conceded that individual organisms, populations of organisms, and natural communities must be treated as complex feedback systems and it is quite likely that Prigogine's theorem does not apply to ecological systems, or at least its validity can not simply be assumed.

Potential energy (ΔH) can be approximately measured by direct combustion of dried tissue. A certain amount of entropy ought to be subtracted from the combustion calories but this is not practical for reasons indicated above. Some free energy is lost prior to combustion in the drying process but this has not yet been evaluated.

When I speak of the energy content of an organism I will be referring to the calories released by burning that organism under normal atmospheric conditions and measured as heat. This is equal to the difference in potential energy per gram between dried protoplasm and the various oxidation products of that protoplasm and includes both the free energy and the entropy.

When I refer to a flow of energy through a population I will be considering only the steady state in which the rate of energy accumulation is zero.

THEORY OF ECOLOGICAL EFFICIENCIES AND THEIR INTERACTIONS

A population of organisms is characterized by new animals being born, by animals dying or being consumed (by other animals or by man). I will be concerned with the potential energy content of the animals removed from the population by predators or man as a useful energy output and will consider the food consumed by the population as the energy input. That is, when I speak of ecological efficiency, I am assuming the viewpoint of a predator.

In one sense, the removal of an animal by a predator can be considered a divergence of energy from the other possible roles it might play in the population. In particular, the greater the rate at which yield is removed from the population the smaller the standing crop that the population is capable of maintaining. The yield to the predator divided by the difference between the energy used in maintaining a population in the absence of predation and that used in maintaining the same population under predation will be called the population efficiency.

The ratio of the potential energy in an individual organism to the potential energy utilized in its birth and growth will be called growth efficiency, or individual growth efficiency.

The interrelation between these three concepts of efficiency is discussed below.

The gross inflow will be in units of calories per time per volume and will be designated I_F. This will be the amount of food made available to the population from some outside source. In nature food is available to an animal population as a result of the activities of some other population or populations of plants, animals or both. In the laboratory I_F is the potential energy in the food made available to the population by the experimenter. The population does not necessarily consume all of this food. In nature part of it may pass through the ecological space of a particular population without being altered at all. In the laboratory the experimenter may periodically remove excess food.

We must therefore distinguish between I_F, the food available, and I, the energy input or ingested food. $I_F \geq I$ is always trivially valid.

I is the potential energy ingested per day per population and therefore is slightly different in concept from I_F, unless the volume considered only contains one population. In experimental situations discussed here this difference is not significant.

Population size is effectively constant at a steady state in the absence of cropping, fishing and predation. In a typical experimental study of efficiency the population is cropped and censused at regular intervals so that a plot of population size as a function of time would be saw-toothed. For our present discussion we will consider the population size as the size at the base of the saw teeth. This is equivalent to assuming that no energy must be expended in maintaining those animals which are destined to be cropped at the next census. This assumption is not dangerous so long as the ratio $\left(\frac{\text{yield/census interval}}{\text{population size}}\right)$ is small. (See Armstrong, 1960.)

Let P′ be the caloric content of the standing crop of a population subjected to some arbitrary predation process and let P be the caloric content of the appropriate control population in the absence of predation. P and P′

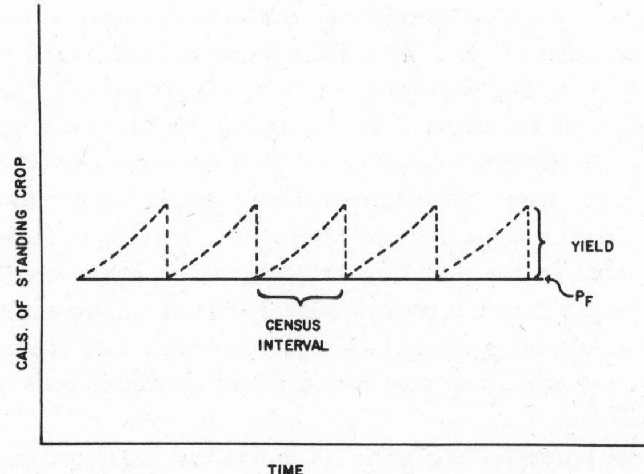

FIGURE 1. The term standing crop (P_F) is used as indicated in this diagram, ignoring the maintenance cost of the animals destined to constitute yield. A more precise but less convenient measure of standing crop would be the dotted line.

have the dimensions of calories and represent the potential energy maintained in the living protoplasm of the population. Occasionally we will use the letters P and P′ as names for populations.

In order to maintain living protoplasm, energy must be expended. The greater this energy expenditure per calorie of standing crop per time the smaller will be the value of P that can be maintained by a given energy income per day (I).

In general, increase of I will imply increase of P. The precise relation between P and I is not obvious *a priori* since the maintenance cost per calorie of standing crop may be a complicated function of the interactions between individual organisms in the population.

In the most general case, since there is a unique age distribution and total number of organisms corresponding to any steady state caloric content we can write

$$I = Pc + P^2c' + P^3c'' \ldots . \tag{3}$$

where c is the proportion of the total cost in (calories/calorie day) of maintaining one calorie of standing crop which is assignable to first order interactions in the population, c′ the proportion assignable to second order interactions, etc.

It has been experimentally demonstrated in Daphnia that only first order interactions are significant over a wide range of population densities (Slobodkin, 1954) so that for the present discussion (3) reduces to

$$I = Pc. \tag{3'}$$

When a population is subjected to predation it either becomes extinct or it comes to a new steady state caloric content P′. If the population can survive steady predation potential energy now leaves the population at some steady state rate as yield to the predator. The ratio of yield (Y) in calories per day to I is the ecological efficiency.

The age and size of the individuals that make up the yield is determined by the interaction between the predator's method and intensity of capturing the yield animals and the population dynamics of the prey and predator.

Assuming that I is not altered by predation, we can take account of the change in maintenance cost associated with predation by writing

$$(4) \qquad I = P'(c + \Delta c) + (P')^2(c' + \Delta c') + \ldots.$$

and in the case of Daphnia populations

$$(4') \qquad I = P'c + P'\Delta c \; .$$

Assume the prey to consist only of animals of age i, taken by the predator at the rate Y_i calories/day. Then

$$(5) \qquad P'\Delta c = \frac{Y_i}{E_{pi}}$$

where E_{pi} is the efficiency, in one sense, of this predation process. An efficiency of this type will be referred to as a population efficiency. Since

$$(5') \qquad E_{pi} = \frac{Y_i}{P'\Delta c}$$

population efficiency can be interpreted as the ratio of yield of a particular kind to the increase of maintenance cost associated with the production of that yield. It will vary with the kind of organism taken as yield. It is independent of the intensity of predation so long as the linearity implicit in equation (4′) holds.

The precise value of E_{pi} depends on growth and survival and their interaction with age in an intimate way which will be indicated below.

In order to clarify the meaning of E_{pi} we must examine an individual organism more closely. At the time an individual organism begins to take nourishment, say age j, it already represents the end product of a series of metabolic processes, all of which have involved the degradation of potential energy. As it grows to some arbitrary age, say i, it will consume more potential energy and may have increased its caloric content. In any case the total potential energy that must be used to replace an animal of age $i > j$ will be greater than that required to replace an animal of age j.

If we designate the total energetic cost of replacing an animal age i as $\frac{S_i}{E_i}$, in which S_i is the caloric content of the animal age i, then E_i is the growth efficiency of this animal. The caloric content (S_i) is usually proportional to the size of the animal. E_i can be evaluated as the inverse of the total calories consumed in the production of one calorie of protoplasm at age i and is the "individual growth efficiency" of an animal aged i. It varies with the age and feeding rate of the animal concerned and with the energy expended by the parents of that individual in producing it.

The concept of growth efficiency has suffered in the past from failure to specify precisely the time interval over which the growth of the animal is to be considered. Here we have taken this as the entire life span over which an energetic cost can be meaningfully associated with the individual, following the suggestion of Armstrong (1960).

The relation between E_i and E_{pi} can be clarified as follows.

Let N_o and N'_o be the number of newborn animals produced per day in populations P and P′ respectively, and let l_x and l'_x be the per cent survival to age x in the two populations respectively. Define q_x as

$$q_x = \frac{l_x - l_{x+1}}{l_x}$$

and correspondingly define q'_x.

Also let

$$d_x = q_x\, l_x \text{ and similarly for } d'_x \tag{6}$$

and

$$D_x = d_x N_o \text{ and similarly for } D'_x. \tag{7}$$

The deaths per day in population P is $\sum_o^\infty D_x$ and in population P′, $\sum_o^\infty D'_x$. The primary characteristic of a steady state population is that births and deaths are equal and there is no change in mean total biomass with time.

The caloric cost per day of replacing the dying individuals and maintaining biomass constancy is $\sum \frac{D_x S_x}{E_x}$ in population P and assuming that caloric content as a function of age and growth efficiency are both dependent on predation $\sum \frac{D'_x S'_x}{E'_x}$ in population P′.

In other words

$$I = \sum_o^\infty \frac{D_x S_x}{E_x} = Pc \tag{8}$$

$$= \sum_o^\infty \frac{D'_x S'_x}{E'_x} = P'(c + \Delta c)$$

whence

$$c = \frac{1}{P} \sum_o^\infty \frac{D_x S_x}{E_x} \tag{9}$$

and

$$\Delta c = \frac{1}{P'}\left(\sum_o^\infty \frac{D'_x S'_x}{E'_x}\right) - \frac{1}{P}\left(\sum_o^\infty \frac{D_x S_x}{E_x}\right) \tag{10}$$

and substituting (10) in (5′) we define the population efficiency of animals age i as

$$E_{pi} = \frac{Y_i}{\left(\sum_{o}^{\infty} \frac{D'_x S'_x}{E'_x}\right) - \frac{P'}{P}\left(\sum_{o}^{\infty} \frac{D_x S_x}{E_x}\right)} \tag{11}$$

or if food ingestion is constant under predation simply:

$$E_{pi} = \frac{Y_i}{I\left(1 - \frac{P'}{P}\right)} \tag{11'}$$

From equation (11) it can be seen that population efficiency varies inversely with the depletion of standing crop population size associated with the removal of the yield. Decrease in life expectancy with predation also lowers population efficiency. A predator would be acting with maximum prudence if he removed yield from his prey in such a way as to maximize population efficiency.

We will return to this concept after we have considered ecological efficiency. The commonest usage of the term efficiency in ecological literature is the ratio of the energy per unit time taken from some population (the prey) as yield by some other population (the predator) to the energy per unit time ingested by the prey population. I am deliberately ignoring the often made distinction between ingestion and assimilation, since the meaning of ingestion seems fairly clear while it is an almost arbitrary matter to decide when, or what portion of, a particular mouthful of food is assimilated.

Food chain efficiency (a term borrowed from LaMont Cole) is similar to ecological efficiency except that the denominator is the food available (I_F) rather than the food ingested (I).

Ecological efficiency (E) is therefore defined by $\frac{Y}{I}$. Since population efficiency is defined for any constant predation method, if I is not changed by predation

$$E = E_p \left(1 - \frac{P'}{P}\right), \tag{12}$$

from which it is clear that for any predation method

$$E \leq E_p . \tag{13}$$

The relation $E = E_p$ will hold only for a scavenger or for a predator which replaces some other source of mortality. If there is any selective advantage in maintaining a large standing crop, a predator population will tend to maximize yield from its prey. This is equivalent to maximizing food chain efficiency $\left(\frac{Y}{I_F}\right)$. As predation becomes more intense, the food consuming capacity and standing crop of the prey population will decrease. The decrease of prey standing crop associated with a given yield can be minimized by the predator if he chooses his yield in such a way as to maximize population efficiency. This can generally be accomplished by taking yield animals which are about to die in any case, so that their replacement cost would have to be paid even in the absence of the predator.

APPLICATION OF THE THEORY

First order evaluations of the various concepts of efficiency have been made in laboratory populations of *Daphnia pulex* by Richman (1958), Armstrong (1960) and Slobodkin (1959). All three workers have depended on the caloric determinations of *D. pulex* and *Chlamydomonas reinhardi* made by Richman.

Richman (1958) analyzed the growth and feeding of *Daphnia pulex*.

Slobodkin provided an initial theoretical analysis of laboratory predation experiments (1959) and that analysis has been considerably amplified and modified in the present paper.

Armstrong has reconsidered certain of the theoretical assumptions of both Richman and Slobodkin and has amplified their calculations, in addition to providing new data on growth and predation.

All three workers dealt with a system consisting of *Daphnia pulex* and *Chlamydomonas reinhardi* in which the Daphnia were maintained in conditioned tap water and the algae were grown on sterile agar. Algae was fed to the Daphnia by washing it off the agar, measuring its optical density with a photometer and adding an aliquot of suspension to the Daphnia. Any of the three above cited papers will provide more detailed information on culture techniques.

Richman collected 50 mg. dry samples of Chlamydomonas. These were combined with 250 mg. of benzoic acid and burned in a semi-micro calorimeter bomb. Twelve determinations gave a mean of 5289 cal./gm. on a dry weight basis or 5506 on an ash-free dry weight basis. These figures are very close to those for other Chlorophyceae. The mean of 17 analysis of five species reported by Ketchum and Redfield (1949) is 5340 cal./gm. dry weight and 6154 cal./gm. ash-free dry weight. The caloric content of one Chlamydomonas cell is given by Richman as 1.308×10^{-6} cal.

He sorted *Daphnia pulex* into three size categories. Dried samples of 10–25 mg. were combined with c. 275 mg. of benzoic acid and burned. Mean caloric contents per gram were 4059 ± 203, 4124 ± 229 and 5075 ± 235 respectively for animals of mean length 0.7, 1.3 and 1.8 mm.

Trama found from 5295 to 5975 cal./gm. in the may fly *Stenonema pulchellum* (Trama, 1957). Golley (undated mimeographed sheets) reports cal./gm. determinations for a variety of animals. The extremes are 1780 for the mud crab *Panopius herbsti* and 6273 for *Mus musculus*. Presumably the cal./gm. ash-free dry weight would be somewhat higher since all his reported values for whole Malacostraca seem low, indicating possible inclusion of the mineralized exoskeletons in the samples.

There is sufficiently close agreement between Richman's analyses and the various values reported by Golley and Ketchum and Redfield, to indicate that neither *Daphnia pulex* nor Chlamydomonas are at all extraordinary

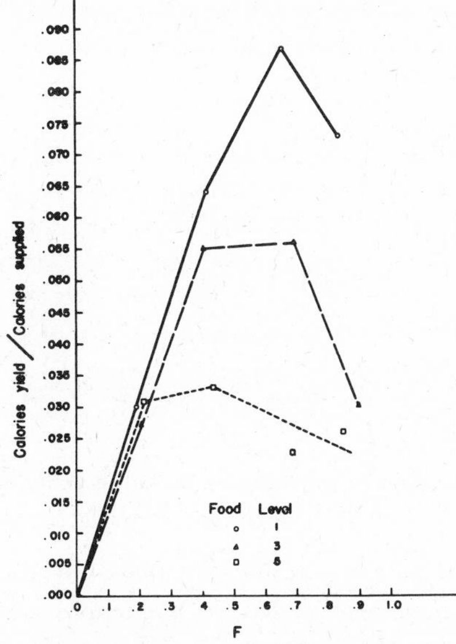

FIGURE 2 a. Food chain efficiency on the ordinate vs. F on the abscissa for populations in which adult animals were preferentially removed as yield.

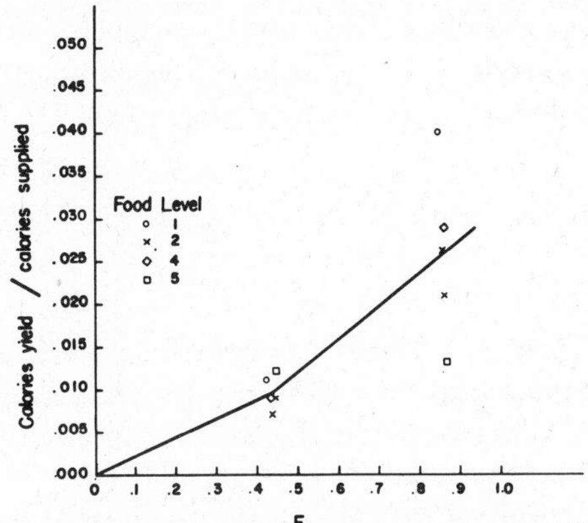

FIGURE 2 b. Identical with 2 a except that young animals were preferentially removed as yield.

in caloric content. This point is of some importance since I will later make the claim that ecological efficiencies are quite likely as similar as caloric contents.

Using Richman's caloric content data Slobodkin (1959) assumed three conversion constants which were used to translate numerical census and yield data, derived from 22 laboratory populations, into terms of calories. In addition, the number of Chlamydomonas cells provided for these populations was estimated and translated into calories by using Richman's value for calories per algal cell. This provides a direct estimate of I_F.

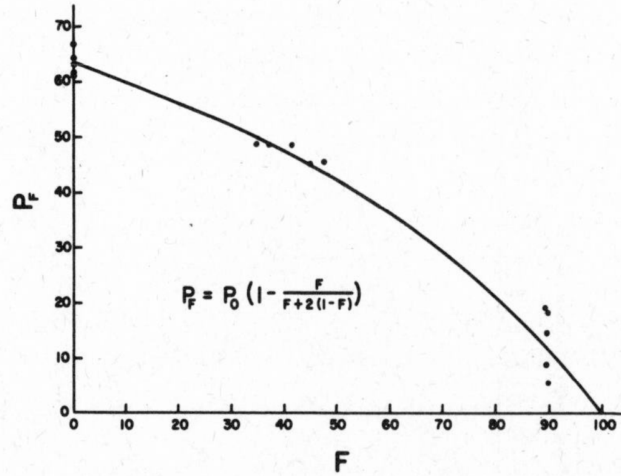

FIGURE 3. P_F, for populations in which young animals were preferentially removed, vs. F.

From I_F and the calories of yield the food chain efficiency could be evaluated directly for each population. This is presented as a function of the intensity of the predation process (figure 2). This measure of fishing intensity is defined elsewhere (Slobodkin, 1957, 1959) and for present purposes we need simply indicate that it is a fishing rate set as a per cent of the births occurring in the population.

Daphnia population standing crops are linearly proportional to their food consumption in the absence of predation (Slobodkin, 1954). There is a simple relation between F and standing crop when all food is consumed, namely

$$\frac{P_F}{P_O} = \left(1 - \frac{F}{2 - F}\right) \tag{14}$$

(Slobodkin, 1957) figure 3. These two relations were assumed generally valid for Daphnia populations and were used to estimate the proportion of the food provided (I_F) that was actually eaten. From this, values of I, the food ingested, could be computed for each population.

Armstrong (1960) computed food ingestion for some of the populations discussed by Slobodkin (1959) on the basis of filtration rate estimates. Comparative values are shown in table 1 and are seen to be of the same order of

TABLE 1

Population	Armstrong (1960)	Slobodkin (1959)	
		I	I′
1.25 A	8.1	8.3	8.6
1.50 A	8.1	7.1	7.9
1.75 A	8.1	8.1	7.7
1.90 A	7.7	6.2	4.9
1.50 Y	8.1	8.1	9.0
1.90 Y	8.0	7.3	9.5

magnitude, but in general somewhat lower estimates of I are derived by the method of Slobodkin than by the more direct method of Armstrong.

Having estimates of I/four days, standing crop calories and also yield/four days of small animals, large animals and eggs, for 22 experimental populations, an equation of the form

$$I = P'c + \sum \frac{Y_i}{E_{pi}} \tag{15}$$

was set up for each population. The subscript i can take the values A for large animals, S for small animals and E for eggs.

This system of 22 equations was then reduced to a set of four equations:

$$\begin{aligned}
\sum_{1}^{22} P'I &= (c)\sum (P')^2 + \frac{\sum P'Y_A}{E_{pA}} + \frac{\sum P'Y_Y}{E_{pY}} + \frac{\sum P'Y_E}{E_{pE}} \\
\sum Y_A I &= (c)\sum Y_A P' + \frac{\sum Y_A^2}{E_{pA}} + \frac{\sum Y_A Y_Y}{E_{pY}} + \frac{\sum Y_A Y_E}{E_{pE}} \\
\sum Y_Y I &= (c)\sum Y_Y P' + \frac{\sum Y_Y Y_A}{E_{pA}} + \frac{\sum Y_Y^2}{E_{pA}} + \frac{\sum Y_Y Y_E}{E_{pE}} \\
\sum Y_E I &= (c)\sum Y_E P' + \frac{\sum Y_E Y_A}{E_{pA}} + \frac{\sum Y_E Y_Y}{E_{pY}} + \frac{\sum Y_E^2}{E_{pE}}
\end{aligned} \tag{16}$$

This set of equations was then solved for c, and the three E_{pi}.

$$c = 1.68 \text{ cal./cal. day}, \; E_{pA} = .48, \; E_{pY} = .036, \; E_{pE} = .062.$$

We have implicitly assumed that the increments in standing crop maintenance cost associated with the various kinds of yield are additive. This assumption probably does not hold at high rates of yield production but precise analysis of the interaction has not yet been made. The E_{pi} are dimensionless, while c has the dimensions $\frac{\text{cal.}}{\text{cal.} \times \text{days}}$

The values E_{pi} found from equation (16) are the population efficiencies that would presumably be associated with predation that took only one category of organism as yield. The calculated value of c successfully predicted the mean standing crop of five control populations which did not enter directly into the analysis of equation (15). (Observed 4.8, calculated 4.7). The control populations were used in computing I for each population by means of the relation shown in figure 3.

There also exists a population efficiency for any distribution of the age and size of yield organisms at a steady state in a particular population.

From our previous assumptions and equations (11) and (14) this can be determined for each population, as

$$E_p = \frac{\frac{2Y}{F} - Y}{I}. \tag{17}$$

The only explicit free variables in this equation are Y and F, since I has already been adjusted in value by the use of (14). In addition, the age and

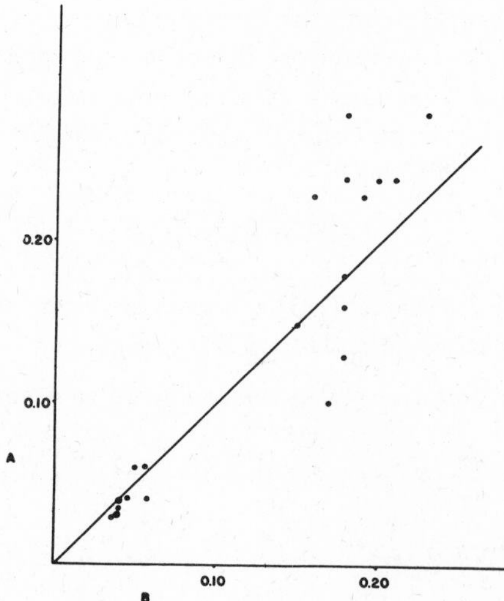

FIGURE 4. The ordinate (A) is given by $E_p = \frac{\frac{2Y}{F} - Y}{I}$. The abscissa (B) is $E_p = \sum \frac{Y_i/\sum Y_i}{E_{pi}}$. The line assumes A = B.

size distribution of the yield are free to vary from population to population, thereby permitting the estimation of E_p from the composition of the yield and the E_{pi} as

$$\frac{1}{E_p} = \sum \frac{Y_i/\sum Y_i}{E_{pi}} \tag{18}$$

The relation between population efficiency estimated from (17) and from the relative composition of the yield (18) is shown in figure 4.

The I' values listed in table 1 are the result of substituting c and the E_{pi} from the solution of equation (16) back into equation (15) for each population and solving for the input. The fact that the individual values I' tend to diverge from Armstrong's estimates more than do the values of I must be attributed to non-linear effects. Ecological efficiency, expressed as $\frac{Y}{I'}$ is presented in figure 5 as a maximum estimate of ecological efficiency. The maximum estimate obtained is 12.5 per cent and it seems clear that ecological efficiency would not exceed 14 per cent under any conceivable experimental circumstances.

Values for ecological efficiency of animals in the field, summarized by Patten (1959) include a value of 75 per cent from Teal (1957) which seems almost impossible, a rather high value of 21 per cent (Lindeman, 1942) and eight other non-zero values ranging from 5.5 per cent to 13.3 per cent. There is no significant relation between trophic level and efficiency in these eight values. Top trophic levels have zero ecological efficiency by definition.

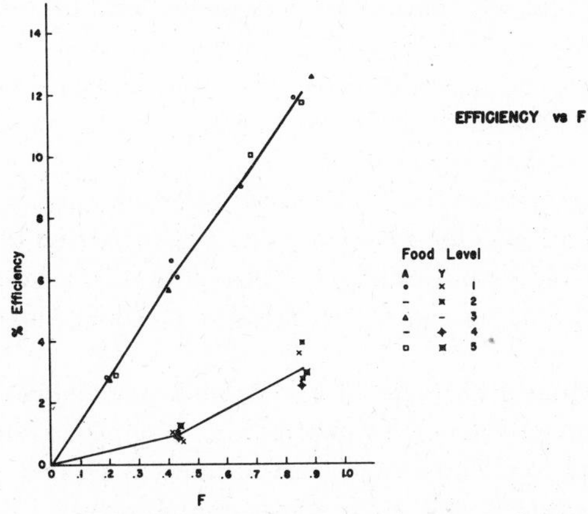

FIGURE 5. A maximum estimate of ecological efficiency in the Daphnia populations. Ordinate: Y/I′; abscissa: F.

The Daphnia experimental maximum is therefore in good accord with other data. It seems likely on general grounds that any population in nature will be producing yield at close to its maximum steady state efficiency.

Combining life table data with growth data Armstrong could compute a table of E_i for the age categories "eggs," "young," "small," "large" and "adult." The process of solution was remarkably ingenious but would involve excessive digression to present here. These efficiencies are presented diagrammatically in figure 6, with the omission of the data for eggs.

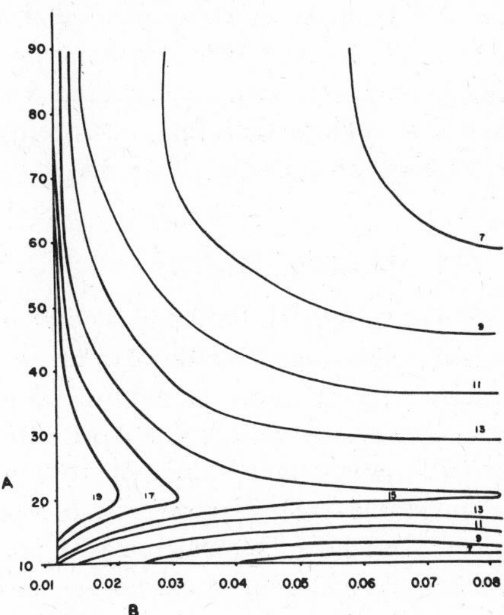

FIGURE 6. Individual growth efficiency × 100 of *Daphnia pulex* as a function of Chlamydomonas concentration in thousands of cells per ml. (ordinate) and the caloric content of the animals (abscissa). (Using data from Armstrong, 1960).

In excessively low concentrations of algae, growth efficiency is low, since the effort involved in feeding is not compensated adequately by the food acquired. As algal concentrations increase, individual efficiencies increase and then decrease as the rate of ingestion of food exceeds the capacity of the gut to digest the food.

Individual growth efficiencies in Daphnia are somewhat higher in maximum value than ecological efficiencies. They are dependent on the food consumption and growth of individual animals as a function of time and on the energetic cost of producing an egg. (See Armstrong, 1960; Slobodkin, 1959, Appendix B.)

The rather startling difference in age dependence between population efficiency and growth efficiency is explicable in terms of the distribution of life expectancy and food consumption as a function of age. Frank, Boll and Kelly (1957) and Pratt (1943) have shown that Daphnia life expectancy decreases as a function of age, after the first week of life. Various workers (Richman, 1958; Ryther, 1954) have shown the rate of filtration to be considerably greater for an adult Daphnia than for a small Daphnia. Removal of an adult Daphnia will therefore be expected to make relatively little difference in the mean life expectancy of the animals in the population, not only because the adult animals' probability of survival in the absence of predation is not particularly high but also because its removal results in a food increase for the survivors which tends to lengthen their life expectancy. This, in effect, decreases the denominator of equation (11). At the same time the large size of an adult tends to increase the numerator. The older and bigger an animal gets, the greater this effect. To remove animals that are growing slowly, have lived most of their time and have a low reproductive value (see Fisher, 1958) is the epitome of prudent predation and therefore has a high population efficiency. The consumption of old sows will do little to deplete a pig population, while consuming suckling pig in equal quantity will be disastrous, despite the high growth efficiency of the piglet and the low growth efficiency of the sow. This may be verified at any meat market.

CONCLUSIONS

Three types of efficiency have been defined. These are:

1. Ecological efficiency, the steady state ratio of yield to food ingested. This is of primary interest in analysis of natural community interactions. There is some reason to believe that ecological efficiency, at least in aquatic environments, will always have values of from five to 15 per cent.

2. Population efficiency, the steady state ratio of yield to the alteration in population maintenance produced by the removal process. The precise value of population efficiency will depend on the age distribution of the animals removed and the population and growth dynamics of the population in question. It may have values greater than one, under some circumstances. In Daphnia it varies from four per cent for the removal of young animals to

48 per cent for old animals. It is of primary interest in establishing criteria for the removal of yield, by relating efficiency to standing crop size.

3. Growth efficiency, the ratio of the calories in an individual organism to the calories expended in the course of its development. This is dependent on a variety of physiological responses of the organism to its immediate environment and has no direct relation to community dynamics. In Daphnia the extreme values found by Armstrong (1960) are 37 per cent for eggs at 20,000 algal cells per ml. and six per cent for adults at algal concentrations of 70,000 cells per ml.

The Daphnia values for all three types of efficiency may be considered typical, at least until more data are available for other species, since the ecological efficiencies determined from Daphnia seem of the same order as those determined from various natural situations.

SPECULATION

A single laboratory population requires approximately two to five hours of work per week for a year, not counting data reduction time or effort. A significant number of populations must be run in any one experiment.

Field studies are even more time consuming and expensive. The laboratory suffers from a lack of reality and the field from a lack of repeatability. At those points where concepts are comparable, the Daphnia laboratory studies agree with various field studies, enhancing my faith in the applicability of the laboratory and the reliability of the field.

As the phenomena that cry for explanation by the physiologist and biochemist are the simple observational facts of animal life, so the phenomena that must be predictable from any ecological theory are the facts of natural history and species abundance distributions. So far we are a long way from explaining these facts. The hope is raised by the present study that just as the metabolism of all organisms turned out to be essentially the same, so the economy of all populations may turn out to be roughly the same. The only way to tell is to repeat these rather painful studies on as many organisms as possible in the laboratory, if possible with considerable increase in precision. I expect to find that ecological efficiency will have approximately the same maximum throughout the animal kingdom, that growth efficiency will vary as a function of age to the same degree as growth rate and that population efficiency as a function of age will vary somewhat more widely, just as population growth curves are more variable than individual growth curves.

In further field studies, it is more difficult to make clear predictions of the pattern that future data will show. I can, however, make a guess. Sampling errors and errors in the conversion of animals to energy units and errors due to failure to have steady state data will all diminish.

In my own laboratory, Richman and I are getting equipment in operating order which will permit us to measure the calories released on combustion of tissue samples weighing as little as four mg. Golley, in Georgia, is now collecting data on larger animals. In a few years it should be possible to convert biomass data from field studies directly into energetic units, not only for large animal studies but for studies of terrestrial and aquatic microfauna. I expect that the use of direct conversion constants for each species will considerably increase the precision of field studies of energetics.

Concurrently, the laboratory predation studies are now being repeated on two species of Hydra and on Chlorohydra. I hope that this will test the applicability of the efficiency values determined for Daphnia to carnivorous animals.

The apparent differences between the estimates of food chain efficiency of corresponding trophic levels in different communities will also tend to vanish. I would guess that herbivores in general will have an efficiency of from ten to 13 per cent. Higher trophic levels may quite likely have slightly lower efficiencies. The presently accepted order of magnitude for food chain efficiencies of from c. six to c. 15 per cent is almost certainly correct.

In the absence of yield removal, the corpses in a laboratory Daphnia population represent five per cent of the energy input. Even on high trophic levels, in which predation in the normal sense is not occurring, an efficiency of conversion to decomposer of the same order as the other efficiencies in the system might be expected.

Assuming that we do find constancy of the food chain efficiencies in a steady state community, what type of theoretical structure can be built with this information? By itself, it tells us relatively little that would not have been predictable from elementary thermodynamics or elementary biochemistry. In combination with other ecological information it may provide a set of restrictions that will severely limit the range of possible ecological speculation.

The basic theoretical problem of community ecology is to construct a model or metamodel (Slobodkin, 1958) based on a simple set of assumptions that will generate not only the steady state conditions of the biosphere at a particular instant but the responses of these steady states to various climatic and geologic perturbations. These responses will constitute a theoretical reconstruction of evolution and almost incidentally will be a guide to exploitation of the natural world by man.

It seems possible that the following ecological generalizations are valid.

1. Food chain efficiencies can only have a narrow range of values.

2. Species abundance distribution patterns can only take the form of distributions generated from the theory of interspecific competition (Hairston, 1959; MacArthur, 1957).

3. Pairs of competing species must have a certain minimum of ecological difference if they are to coexist in a steady state (Hutchinson, 1959).

If we now demand that all models of the ecological world that make any pretense to reality must meet all of these conditions simultaneously we will be saved from unbridled speculations and misleading metaphors.

To the degree that these and other generalizations hold we may eventually be able to turn to the mathematician or even to his idiot cousin, the IBM machine, and ask him, or it, to build us all the theoretical models which will meet our restrictions and still maintain steady states and evolve properly under perturbation. At that time, community and population ecology will enter the company of the exact sciences.

In the interim we must increase the precision of those measurements which we know must be made and test the range of applicability of those generalizations which now seem valid.

SUMMARY

The energetic relation between different trophic levels and populations in a community involves primarily potential energy transfer in complex feedback systems, making the applicability of existing steady state thermodynamic theory questionable, since the requirements for direct evaluation of entropy are not met by ecological systems. The only form of energy considered here was potential energy.

The efficiency of a population does not have a unique meaning. Three different concepts of efficiency were defined and evaluated for *Daphnia pulex.* Two of these, the ecological efficiency and population efficiency, refer to the population level. The growth efficiency refers to individual organisms.

Ecological efficiency is a function of the rate of removal of yield and of the kind of yield animals removed. Population efficiency is a function of the kind of animals removed as yield and the interaction between these animals and the population. Growth efficiency does not depend on the removal of yield at all. It is a function of individual food consumption, growth rate and the energetic cost of reproduction.

These three are interrelated. In general, for a particular system of predation ecological efficiency is proportional to population efficiency. Population efficiency is related to the individual growth efficiency through the effect of the removal of animals on the maintenance cost per calorie of standing crop, which in turn is a function of growth efficiency.

The maximum ecological efficiencies found in the Daphnia experiments are of the same order as ecological efficiencies found in nature, implying that ecological efficiency is effectively constant. Presumably the observed value of c. ten per cent has selective significance.

In speculating on the future development of community ecology, I suggested that certain generalizations now available, including the approximate constancy of ecological efficiency, restrict the development of possible theories. When a sufficient number of these generalizations have been stated and tested a comprehensive predictive general theory of community ecology will appear, if only by the elimination of all conceivable theories whose predictions do not conform to the generalizations.

ACKNOWLEDGMENTS

The studies reported here were initially supported by The Rockefeller Foundation and The Phoenix Memorial Project of the University of Michigan.

For the past three years they have been supported by the National Science Foundation.

I am grateful to the staff and graduate students that have participated in the community ecology seminar at the University of Michigan for their discussion of this work. Drs. Armstrong and Richman have been particularly helpful. Dr. Peter Ovenburg has criticized the mathematical presentation. Profs. G. E. Hutchinson, Anatol Rappoport and Karl Guthe have been liberal with their knowledge and encouragement.

LITERATURE CITED

Armstrong, J. T., 1960, Ph.D. dissertation, Department of Zoology. University of Michigan, Ann Arbor, Mich.

Cole, L. C., 1959, Personal communication.

Denbigh, K. G., 1951, The thermodynamics of the steady state. 103 pp. Methuen & Co., London, England.

Fisher, R. A., 1958, The genetical theory of natural selection. pp. 27–30. Dover Publications, Inc., New York, N. Y.

Foster, C., A. Rappoport and E. Trucco, 1957, Some unsolved problems in the theory of non-isolated systems. General Systems 3: 9–29.

Frank, P. W., C. D. Boll and R. W. Kelly, 1957, Vital statistics of laboratory cultures of *Daphnia pulex* DeGeer as related to density. Physiol. Zool. 30: 287–305.

Golley, F. B., 1959, Table of caloric equivalents. Mimeographed, 7 pp. Available from the author. Department of Zoology, University of Georgia, Athens, Ga.

Hairston, N. G., 1959, Species abundance and community organization. Ecology 40: 404–416.

Hutchinson, G. E., 1959, Homage to Santa Rosalia or why there are so many kinds of animals. Amer. Nat. 93: 145–159.

Ketchum, B. H., and A. C. Redfield, 1949, Some physical and chemical characteristics of algae grown in mass culture. J. Cell. and Comp. Physiol. 33: 281–300.

Lindeman, R. L., 1942, The trophic-dynamic aspect of ecology. Ecology 23: 399–418.

MacArthur, R. H., 1957, On the relative abundance of bird species. Proc. Nat. Acad. Sci. U.S. 43: 293–295.

Patten, B. C., 1959, An introduction to the cybernetics of the ecosystem: the trophic-dynamic aspect. Ecology 40: 221–231.

Pratt, D. M., 1943, Analysis of population development in Daphnia at different temperatures. Biol. Bull. 85: 116–140.

Richman, S., 1958, The transformation of energy by *Daphnia pulex*. Ecol. Monogr. 28: 273–291.

Ryther, J. H., 1954, Inhibitory effects of phytoplankton upon the feeding of *Daphnia magna* with reference to growth, reproduction, and survival. Ecology 35: 522–533.

Slobodkin, L. B., 1954, Population dynamics in *Daphnia obtusa* Kurz. Ecol. Monogr. 24: 69–88.

1957, A laboratory study of the effect of removal of newborn animals from a population. Proc. Nat. Acad. Sci. U. S. 43: 780–782.

1958, Meta-models in theoretical ecology. Ecology 39: 550–551.
1959, Energetics in *Daphnia pulex* populations. Ecology 40: 232–243.
Teal, J. M., 1957, Community metabolism in a temperate cold spring. Ecol. Monogr. 27: 283–302.
Trama, F. B., 1957, The transformation of energy by an aquatic herbivore, *Stenonema pulchellum* (Ephemeroptera). Ph.D. dissertation, Department of Zoology, University of Michigan, Ann Arbor, Mich.

GLOSSARY OF SYMBOLS

Symbol	Units	Meaning
c	calories/(calories × days)	Maintenance cost of one calorie of standing crop for one unit of time
Δc	calories/(calories × days)	Increment in maintenance cost per calorie of standing crop attributable to the removal of yield.
d_x	animals/animals	The fraction of animals born at time 0 that die during the age interval x.
D_x	animals/days	The number of animals that die during the age interval x.
E	$\frac{\text{calories/time}}{\text{calories/time}}$	Yield calories divided by input calories. Ecological efficiency.
E_i	$\frac{\text{calories}}{\text{calories}}$	Potential energy in an individual of age i, divided by the potential energy needed to replace that individual. Growth efficiency.
E_p	$\frac{\text{calories/time}}{\text{calories/time}}$	Yield calories divided by the difference in maintenance cost between the population producing the yield and a corresponding control population. Population efficiency.
E_{pi}	$\frac{\text{calories/time}}{\text{calories/time}}$	Population efficiency for the situation in which the yield consists exclusively of animals age i.
i and j	days	Age categories.
l_x	animals/animals	The fraction of animals born at time 0 that survive to time x.
N_o	animals/days	Number of newborn animals produced in a population during one time interval.
P	calories	Steady state standing crop caloric content of a population.
q_x	animals/animals	The proportion of animals that survive up to an age interval that die during that interval.

GLOSSARY OF SYMBOLS (*continued*)

Symbol	Units	Meaning
S_x	calories	The calories of potential energy contained in an animal of age x.
$\sum$		Summation sign.
x	days	An age category. (Occasionally used as a size category.)
Y	calories/time	Total steady state yield removed from a population per unit time.
Y_i	calories/time	Steady state yield of animals age i removed from a population per unit time.

Note: Except for c' and $\Delta c'$, in equations (3) and (4), a symbol with a prime (that is, P' or S'_x) refers to a property of a population subject to predation, but is otherwise understood to have the same meaning as the corresponding symbol without the prime (that is, P or S_x).

In the discussion of entropy the symbols all have their conventional meanings.

Symbol	Meaning
ΔF	Change in free energy
ΔH	Change in enthalpy
Q'	Non-entropic heat.
ΔS	Change in entropy.
T	Absolute temperature

Primary Production in Flowing Waters[1]

HOWARD T. ODUM

Department of Zoology, Duke University, Durham, N. C.

ABSTRACT

Respiration, photosynthetic production, and diffusion interact to produce the daily curve of oxygen change in a segment of flowing water. Conversely, the observed curves of oxygen in streams can be used to calculate the component rates of production, respiration, and diffusion. New production values obtained with these analyses of oxygen curves from various sources, as well as a few previously existing estimates of primary production, indicate a generally higher rate of production in flowing waters than in other types of aquatic environments.

The ratio of total primary production to total community respiration is used to classify communities quantitatively according to their predominantly heterotrophic or autotrophic characteristics. Longitudinal succession within a stream tends to modify the ratio towards unity from higher values for autotrophic and from lower values for heterotrophic communities. The behavior of this ratio is described for the annual cycle in a stream, for the sequence of pollution recovery, and for diverse types of communities.

INTRODUCTION

To the casual eye the biota of flowing waters is rich. Coral reefs, river rapids, tidal channels, and the lush plant beds of calcareous streams seem to be full of life. In the polluted Illinois River, almost unbelievable concentrations of bottom organisms have been found. How are such communities supported? What is the magnitude of primary production in comparison to other communities? How does the dominating current-flow relate to other energy-flows through the communities?

A large literature exists on the limnology of streams and the biology of flowing sea waters, but apparently studies on community function have rarely been oriented to obtain information on primary production (exceptions: Nusbaum and Miller 1952, Sargent and Austin 1949, 1954; Odum and Odum 1955, Purdy as quoted by Phelps 1944). This is very peculiar because the continual mixing makes *in situ* measurements of production very simple in flowing water. The task here, therefore, is to re-evaluate some of the extensive information on flowing waters in terms of productivity and community respiration especially by using diurnal gas curves and the upstream-downstream method of measuring community metabolism. A summary will then be made of the production and respiration of flowing communities relative to succession, velocity of current, and the classification of communities.

THEORETICAL CONSIDERATION OF DAILY PROCESSES OF OXYGEN METABOLISM IN FLOWING WATERS

Consider a stretch of flowing water delimited by two stations, one upstream from the other. During the usual daily cycle four main processes affect the oxygen and carbon-dioxide concentrations of water flowing between the stations. Although the discussion here is presented in terms of oxygen, it should be understood that carbon dioxide behaves similarly but with reversed sign.

(1) There is a release of oxygen into the water as a result of photosynthetic primary production during the day by both benthic plants and phytoplankton.

(2) There is an uptake of oxygen from the water as a result of the respiration of benthic

[1] Presented as part of a symposium, Primary Production in Waters, September 6, 1955, at the American Society of Limnology and Oceanography meeting, East Lansing, Michigan. Studies summarized here were aided by the Biology Branch, Office of Naval Research and the University of Florida. Appreciation is expressed to Dr. Jacob Verduin and Dr. John Ryther for criticism of the manuscript.

organisms, planktonic organisms, and sometimes chemical oxidation.

(3) There is an exchange of oxygen with the air in a direction depending on the saturation gradient.

(4) There may be an influx of oxygen with accrual of ground water and surface drainage along the stretch. In most of the examples discussed here, accrual is assumed to be negligible relative to the other influences.

These processes between stations may be quantitatively summarized on an area basis (i.e., g/m²/hr) as follows:

$$Q = P - R + D_{\text{in}} + A \qquad (1)$$

Q	P	R	D_{in}	A
Rate of change of dissolved oxygen per area	Rate of gross primary production per area	Rate of respiration per area	Rate of oxygen uptake by diffusion per area	Rate of drainage accrual

Note that capital letters have been used for these quantities that are defined on an area basis.

By dividing through by the depth in meters (z), the relationships are expressed in concentration-units (i.e., g/m³/hr). Small letters have been used for these quantities which are defined on a volume basis.

$$q = p - r + d_{\text{in}} + a = \frac{Q}{z} \qquad (2)$$

The usual diurnal (24 hours) course of change for the component processes is given in Figure 1 for a hypothetical flowing system without accrual, which is both oversaturated and undersaturated with oxygen relative to the atmosphere and which has a balance of production and respiration. The photosynthesis-curve has the same shape as the incident light with a morning and afternoon symmetry as shown in Figure 1 for a clear day unmodified by cloud patterns.

If the plankton and biochemical oxygen-demand in the inflowing water remains fairly constant as assumed for the case in Figure 1, then respiration remains relatively constant. Whether plant respiration is depressed during photosynthesis or not is still an unsettled question since evidence is conflicting (Rabinowitch 1951, Whittingham 1955). In strongly polluted waters with very low oxygen concentrations there may be a diurnal increase in respiratory oxidation during the day due to the formation of photosynthetic oxygen, where at night there is no oxygen. Respiration was found to be dependent upon oxygen tension below 1 ppm for sewage by Pomeroy (1938) and for marine waters by ZoBell (1940). Jackson and McFadden (1954) found an increase in community respiration during the day in lake waters. Until more is known about these and other diurnal effects, it may

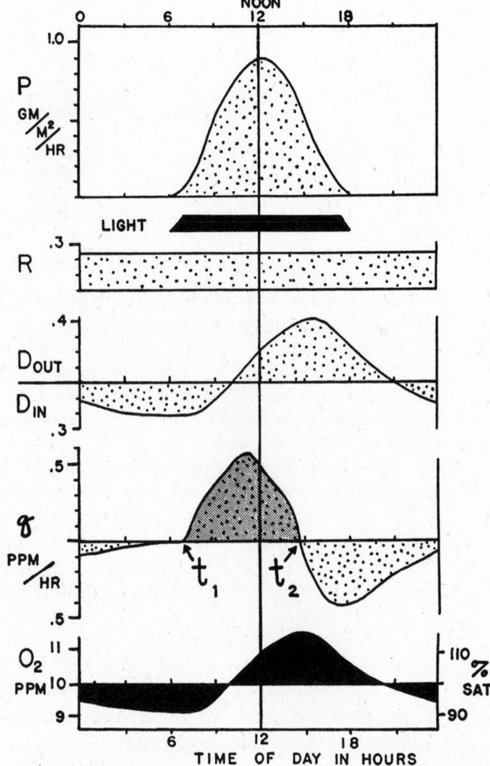

Fig. 1. Component processes in the oxygen metabolism of a section of a hypothetical stream during the course of a cloudless day. Production (P), respiration (R), and diffusion (D) are given on an areal basis. The combined effect of these rate processes for a stream 1 meter deep is given in ppm/hr (q). In the lowermost curve are given the actual oxygen values that would result in a stream with a long homogeneous community. The diffusion curve is linearly proportional to the oxygen concentration curve. The shaded area delimited by t_1 and t_2 is used in Equation (5) to obtain an approximate production estimate uncorrected for diffusion.

be simplest here to continue to assume constant community respiration day and night. This assumption will not apply to flows a short distance below pollution outfall, where the volume of pollution discharge itself is frequently in diurnal cycle so as to cause minimum conditions of oxygen during the day (Schmassmann 1951, Calvert 1932, Mohlman *et al.* 1931).

Ordinarily the accrual of water is small and without daily variation. This is the case in Figure 1 where zero accrual is assumed.

Two recent reviews (Haney 1954, Ammon 1954) summarized knowledge on gaseous transfer into water. The rate of diffusion depends on the degree of saturation of the inflowing water.

$$D = KS = zkS \qquad (3)$$

where D is the diffusion rate per area, S is the saturation deficit between water and air, z the depth, K the gas transfer coefficient defined on an area basis (i.e., $g/m^2/hr$ for 0% saturation) and k the gas transfer coefficient defined on a volume basis (i.e., $g/m^3/hr$ for 0% saturation). The diffusion-curve sketched in Figure 1 was drawn for the case where the inflowing water had a similar history to the water preceding it because of similar conditions upstream. In this case an accumulation of oxygen develops in the water as production exceeds respiration during the morning so that diffusion into the water is replaced by diffusion out as the water becomes supersaturated. During the course of the day the other factors affecting diffusion rate such as depth, velocity, and bottom character tend to remain constant for the section of flow. Stream flows with large temperature ranges and changes in stratification-tendency may be exceptions.

When each of the component rates (P, R, D) given on an area basis are summed as in Equation (1), the total rate of change of oxygen is found for the zone between the two stations on an area basis. If this sum (Q) is divided by the mean depth (z) the rate of change of oxygen concentration is obtained (q), as in Figure 1 for a 1-meter deep flow.

From this rate-of-change curve of oxygen one may construct the curve of oxygen concentration by adding successive hours of change to the oxygen concentration at each hour. Thus, beginning with simple assumptions a diurnal oxygen curve for a stream was constructed (Fig. 1) to illustrate some of the known workings of stream communities. The oxygen curve obtained is typical of the curves observed by authors whose work was examined (see Table 2, also Cerny 1948, Wiken 1936). A morning maximum in the rate-of-change curve and an afternoon maximum in the oxygen-concentration curve are typical. Maximum rate of oxygen decrease occurs after sunset. Minimum oxygen concentration and minimum rates of change occur in the predawn hours. In the next paragraphs the procedure of reversing this analysis is described so that primary production may be estimated from observed oxygen curves.

MEASUREMENT OF METABOLISM IN STREAMS

Measurement of gross primary production

The light-dark bottle method for measuring gross primary production of the community (defined as the sum of the net plant production and community respiration during the daytime) is seldom applicable in flowing waters because much of the community is benthic and heterogeneous rather than planktonic. Furthermore, any measurement made without the normal turbulent flow may be questioned on grounds that production is a function of current flow. The upstream-downstream measurement of oxygen, carbon-dioxide, and other properties is apparently the chief method available for the study of metabolism of flowing water communities.

If the area under the upstream-downstream rate-of-change graph (q in Fig. 1) above a horizontal line drawn through the predawn point is measured, a first approximation to daily, gross primary production is obtained in concentration units (ppm/day). By this procedure one subtracts the accrual, respiration, and diffusion of the predawn hours from the rest of the curve as though these predawn values were representative of the entire day. Where the change in oxygen concentration during 24 hours is small, so that diffusion is not markedly different between day and night, this approximation will give production values close to but always less than the actual production values. Therefore, the area under a rate-of-change curve of oxygen q (Fig. 1) expressed in ppm/day multiplied by the mean depth between stations (z in m) gives the gross production per area in g/m²/day (P).

The following is an alternative calculation where the oxygen change is expressed as the difference between stations rather than as the change per hour. The area under a curve of oxygen change between two stations (Δc) expressed in ppm-hours, multiplied by the discharge in m³/hr (F) and divided by the area between stations in m² (X) also gives the gross primary production per day (P).

These conversions may be summarized as follows:

$$P_{\text{day}} = z \int_{t_1}^{t_2} (q - q_1)\, dt = \frac{F}{X} \int_{t_1}^{t_2} (\Delta c - \Delta c_1)\, dt \tag{4}$$

where t_1 is sunrise and t_2 is the time in the evening when q or Δc returns to its value at sunrise q_1 or Δc_1 respectively.

Or as measured in practice:

$$P_{\text{day}} = (z)(\text{area under diurnal } q \text{ curve}) = \frac{F}{X} (\text{area under diurnal } \Delta c \text{ curve}) \tag{5}$$

These areas are hatched in Figures 1, 2, and 3.

The first of the calculation methods is used in the dye spot example for the marine turtle grass (Table 2) and in the analysis of single-station oxygen curves from the literature. The second of the calculation procedures is used in the Silver Springs example.

These simple methods without diffusion-corrections were used by Sargent and Austin (1949, 1954) in coral reef work at Rongelap where deviations from saturation were small relative to the total production.

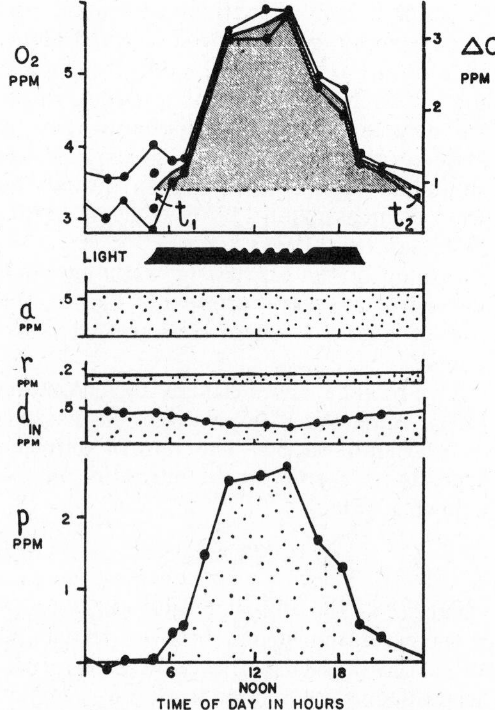

Fig. 2. Component processes in ppm in the daily oxygen metabolism in the upper ¾-mile zone of Silver Springs, Florida, March 23–24, 1954. In the upper graph duplicate oxygen analyses ¾ mile downstream from the outflow boil are expressed in ppm on the left ordinate. The ordinate on the right indicates the oxygen change (Δc) relative to the constant boil value of 2.50 ppm. The accrual (a) due to addition of more oxygenated water from side springs, respiration (r) as estimated with black belljars, and the diffusion in (d) as estimated from the gas transfer coefficient and the saturation deficit are given next. In the lower curve the production in ppm is computed by separating accrual, respiration, and diffusion from the observed oxygen change in the ¾-mile zone. The area under the lower curve expressed in ppm-hrs may be converted into daily production as indicated in Equation (5). The shaded area in the upper curve delimited by t_1 and t_2 is used in Equation (5) to obtain an approximate estimate of production uncorrected for diffusion.

It should be noted that the magnitude of diurnal change in ppm oxygen concentration gives no indication of the metabolic rates per area unless depth and velocity or discharge and area between stations are known. Small oxygen changes in deep or rapid streams may indicate larger production values than do larger oxygen changes of oxygen in shallow streams.

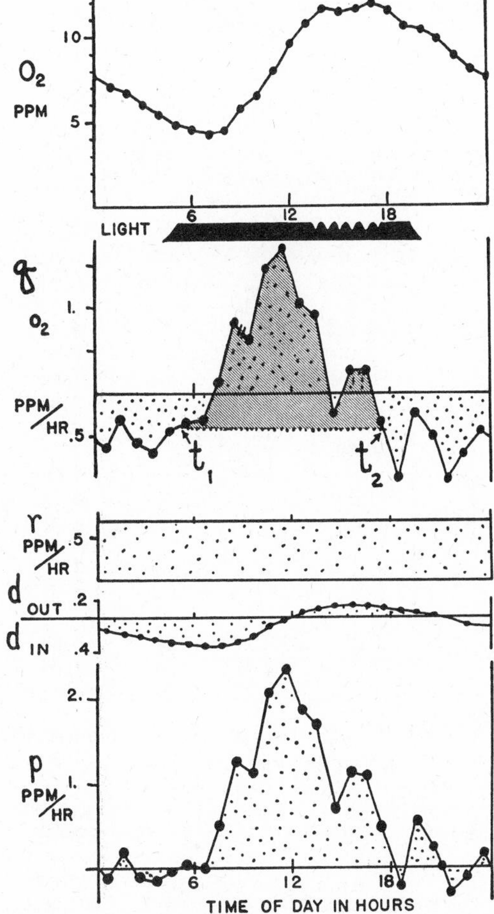

FIG. 3. Component processes in ppm/hr in the daily oxygen metabolism of the River Lark, England, calculated by the single-curve method from data given by Butcher, Pentelow, and Woodley (1930). In the upper curve is given the observed diurnal (24-hr) oxygen curve. From this is calculated the rate of change per hour in ppm/hr (q). Respiration (r), diffusion (d), and production (p) on a ppm-basis are calculated as indicated in the text on the assumption that the stream is homogeneous. The shaded area delimited by t_1 and t_2 is used in Equation (5) to determine the approximate production uncorrected for diffusion.

As considered so far these calculations of gross primary production do not consider diurnal variations in respiration, accrual, and diffusion. Since diffusion ordinarily is the main process which fluctuates diurnally, the success and reliability of the upstream-downstream method is dependent upon the accuracy of corrections for diurnal diffusion-change.

Measurement of diffusion

Especially where differences in rate of diffusion between night and day are large, such as in the diagrammatic example in Figure 1, it is necessary to estimate the change in diffusion due to the daily change in saturation deficit. If a coefficient of gas-transfer (K) is available or can be obtained for the stream section in question, it may be used to apply a correction for each hour of the day as in Figures 2 and 3 according to the saturation deficit for each hour.

In Table 1 are given various estimates of K for oxygen transfer in flux units. Values for still water with mostly molecular diffusion are about 0.03 g/m²/hr/0.2 atm. Values for bubbles and droplets as in waterfalls are as high as 34 g/m²/hr/0.2 atm. The values for flowing waters are in between, depending upon the rate at which the surface film is dispersed downward due to turbulent mixing.

The following procedures can be used to measure the gas transfer coefficient in flowing waters:

(a) The gas transfer coefficient may be obtained from two measurements of oxygen content of the water, one after sunset and one just before sunrise.

According to the relationships in equations (2) and (3) before sunrise:

$$q_m = \frac{KS_m}{z} - r \tag{6}$$

where S_m is the predawn saturation deficit and q_m is the rate change of oxygen concentration in the morning. After sunset:

$$q_e = \frac{KS_e}{z} - r \tag{7}$$

where S_e is the evening saturation deficit and q_e is the rate of change of oxygen concentration in the evening.

Subtracting these expressions leads to:

$$K = \frac{z(q_m - q_e)}{S_m - S_e} \tag{8}$$

The gas transfer coefficient can be readily obtained from diurnal oxygen curves by

TABLE 1. *Coefficients of gas transfer for oxygen*

Water type, Source of data	Velocity m/sec	Depth m	Temp. °C	K g/m²/hr at 0% saturation
Still water				
(Hutchinson, Becker, quoted by Haney, 1954)	0.0	—	20–25	.034
(Adenay, quoted by Kehr 1938)	0.0	—	—	0.03–0.08
Moving water				
Stirred water (quoted by Haney 1954)	—	—	25	0.09–0.74
Shallow circulating trough (Streeter, Wright, and Kehr 1936)	0.01	0.1	0–10	0.037
	0.01	0.1	10–20	0.043
	0.01	0.1	20–30	0.047
	0.013	0.1	12	0.12
	0.070	0.1	17	0.52
	0.119	0.1	14	1.12
	0.20	0.1	13	3.8
Sewage in circulating trough (Kehr 1938)	0.05	0.45	25–26	0.38
	0.15	0.45	25–26	1.5
Stream and ponds (Imhoff and Mahr 1932)	—	—	—	0.08
New York Harbor (Gould 1921)	tidal	—	—	0.23
Tank with a wave machine (Borst, quoted by Phelps 1944)	—	1.8	— —	0.31
Sea Surface (Redfield 1948)				
Summer	—	—	12–20	1.1
Winter	—	—	3–7	5.2
Silver River, Florida, July 21, 1955 (Odum)				
Subtraction-of-respiration method	0.21	2.77	23	0.92
Dye-measured-turnover method	0.21	2.77	23	1.00
Green Cove Springs, Florida (Odum) From carbon-dioxide by respiratory-quotient method	0.3	0.23	24	0.55
Small rivers, diurnal oxygen curve analyses in Table 2	—	0.5–3.	—	0.6–4.3
Ohio River below Cincinnati (Velz 1939)	0.05–0.09	4.8	15–25	1.5–5.0
Bubbles and drops (K given per area of drop or bubble)				
Air bubble (Krogh, quoted by Redfield 1948)	—	—	37	13.1
Air bubbles (Ippen, Adenay, Spuler, and Schwab, quoted by Haney 1954)	—	—	20–25	2.8–28.
Water drops (Whitman, quoted by Haney 1954)	—	—	24	22–34.

substitution of measured values in Equation (8).

The rapid production of gases in some cases produces local extreme supersaturations so that bubbles break to the surface without going into solution even in undersaturated waters. Measurements by trapping bubbles in funnel devices showed about 1.5% of the production or 0.3 g/m²/day loss during the daylight hours in Silver Springs. The effect is more important in shallower streams. Even though the rate is partly a function of the saturation deficit, it ceases as an oxygen-loss mechanism at night. Thus, diffusion coefficients determined at night may fail to include this effect. In shallow supersaturated waters this loss leads to underestimation.

(b) If some estimate of the time required for vertical mixing and dispersion of the surface film is available, the coefficient of diffusion may be computed on theoretical grounds (Phelps 1944, after Black and Phelps 1911). In Silver Springs fluorescein dye was observed from under water with a face mask. The yellow surface film was readily observed to become dispersed vertically in about 1 minute. The calculated gas transfer constant was similar to the inferred value from balance sheet calculations (Table 1).

(c) If a respiration value has been obtained for a stream and if accural is negligible, the diffusion rate for a known saturation deficit may be obtained by subtracting the respiration from the upstream-downstream change at night. For example, belljar measurements were used to obtain an estimate of respiration in Silver Springs. The diffusion was then calculated (Table 1).

(d) If the diffusion rate is found for one gas (i.e. CO_2) the diffusion rate for another gas may be related as their molecular diffusion coefficients. When transfer coefficients are expressed in g/m^2/hr/atmosphere saturation-deficit, similar values are found for both gases.

(e) If river slope, velocity, and depth are known, some idea of K may be obtained by using empirical equations based on observations on the Ohio River (Phelps 1944, Streeter and Phelps 1925).

(f) In a section of a river without accrual the difference between gross primary production and respiration, expressed in organic matter, is the organic matter synthesized in this section. P-R is readily measured by upstream-downstream organic matter measurements. Substitution in Equation (1) permits the calculation of the diffusion. This method assumes that sedimentation is balanced by erosion, as in the middle sections of many rivers.

(g) Lacking other means a value may be selected from Table 1 for similar conditions of depth and turbulence.

Measurement of community respiration

Where community respiration is to be measured, the following procedures are available:

(a) Black belljars over typical bottom-substrates and black bottles in the water may be combined to obtain respiration rates. In many streams the black bottle respiration-rate differs from the stream respiration due to differences in bacteria, turbulence, oxygen conditions, and benthic communities. Similar difficulties arise with attempts to anticipate the natural black bottle measurements with BOD tests of pollution effluents.

(b) During darkness, the diffusion may be subtracted from the observed rate of change to obtain the respiration in ppm. The ppm/hr respiration multiplied by the depth in meters gives the respiration per area per time in g/m^2/hr. If during darkness there is a time of saturation with respect to the atmosphere, such as occurs after sunset in Figure 1, the upstream-downstream change is equal to the respiration providing the accrual is negligible.

(c) If one gas (i.e. CO_2) is nearly at saturation, and its respiration component can thus be obtained at night, the respiration of the other gas (i.e. O_2) may be obtained assuming a respiratory quotient characteristic of the stream or arbitrarily 0.8 as an approximation.

The methods suggested here for measurement of diffusion, respiration, and photosynthesis are demonstrated in subsequent paragraphs with three examples representing three important, frequently occurring cases.

An example of production measurement in constant inflow situations

Silver Springs, Florida, is an example of chemostatically regulated inflow. Since there is no diurnal change in the upstream station (the boil outflow), the downstream concentration curve is readily converted into an upstream-downstream rate of change curve by subtracting the upstream value from each downstream value and dividing by the time of flow to the downstream station. In Figure 2 is shown the oxygen concentration curve, upstream-downstream change curve, and component respiration, accrual, and production curves based on detailed work presented elsewhere (Odum 1954). The accrual is large and the zone is always undersaturated. Respiration was measured by belljar measurements of the benthic communities, and diffusion estimated as indicated in Table 1. Possible errors in this method were cited previously.

Other flows with fairly constant inflow without much diurnal oxygen variation are found downstream from large waterfalls, in ground water flows, and downstream from surf. The Rongelap and Eniwetok coral reef studies include measurements under situations of relatively constant inflow (Sargent and Austin 1949, 1954; Odum and Odum 1955).

Production measurements by the difference between upstream and downstream diurnal curves

For the usual complex case where no simplifying assumptions may be made about the inflowing water, complete curves should be taken at two stations. Upstream-downstream changes were used in the coral reef studies of Sargent and Austin (1949, 1954) and Odum and Odum (1955). The upstream and downstream curves in Schmassmann (1951) are examples of data to which this analysis might be applied if information on depth and flow rate were available. The upstream curve can be subtracted from the downstream curve after shifting the upstream curve to the left by a time period corresponding to the time required for the flow to pass from the first to the second station. Unfortunately, most of the diurnal oxygen and carbon-dioxide curves in the literature are from single stations.

An example of production measurement by single curve analysis

Where a curve for only one station is available, but an assumption of stream homogeneity above the zone of measurement is reasonable, the curve for rate of change may be obtained from a single diurnal oxygen graph. With this procedure one assumes that the incoming water had had the same diurnal history as the water just preceding. In other words the whole stream is experiencing a simultaneous rise and fall of oxygen. In a stream where this assumption applies perfectly, a second station would reveal a curve identical with that of the first station. The assumption is consistent with the theoretical case of a circular stream and a homogeneous community. Most of the data discussed in this paper are based on curve-analysis of single curves.

In Figure 3 the oxygen curve, rate-of-change curve, and resulting component curves of respiration and diffusion are shown for the River Lark based on data given by Butcher, Pentelow, and Woodley (1930). It should be emphasized that this single-curve procedure is no substitute for a double-curve analysis, but is useful in obtaining orders of magnitude. A partial curve analysis was used by Jackson and McFadden (1954) for measuring production in a lake.

Spot method

A very simple method used by the author and J. Yount for obtaining upstream-downstream changes in flowing water is outlined as follows: A spot of fluorescein dye is placed in the water and followed for about 15 minutes. Measurements are taken in water adjacent to the marker spot before and after the period. Then the observers return upstream to the starting point before making the second measurement. In this way a diurnal rate of change curve is obtained which is then analyzed to obtain diffusion, respiration, and production as described above. This method was used for a bed of marine turtle grass (*Thalassia*) in 3 ft of water along the causeway at Long Key, Florida (Table 2). This is probably the simplest of all the methods described here.

PRODUCTION AND COMMUNITY STRUCTURE OF STREAM COMMUNITIES

Magnitudes of primary production in streams

Using the methods described in preceding sections, data from the literature have been used to obtain the estimates in Table 2. For comparison recall that eutrophic lakes have a gross primary production of organic matter of the order of magnitude of 1 (0.5–5) g/m^2/day (Gessner 1949) during seasons of maximum growth; oceanic waters have gross production magnitudes of 0.17–1.6 g/m^2/day (Riley 1953); terrestrial agriculture under the best circumstances achieves sustained net production of 10–20 g/m^2/day (Kalle 1948); and mass *Chlorella*-cultures under strong light and bubbling carbon-dioxide yield a net production of 2–19 g/m^2/day (Wassink, Kok, and Oorschot 1953). If the ratio of photosynthesis to respiration is about 2.0 this indicates a maximum gross primary production of *Chlorella* of 28 g/m^2/day. It is immediately observed that the estimates in Table 2 for production in flowing waters are very high. It may be suggested that streams are among the most productive biological environments, a conclusion that has been suspected for a long time on the basis of estimates of standing crop.

Comparison among the streams indicates that the highest primary production rates are in the recovery zones of streams polluted with organic wastes. Thus the pollution not only increases the biota due to an additional organic nutritive source, but subse-

TABLE 2. *Productivity and classification of flowing water communities on the basis of oxygen metabolism data*

Stream, Date, Source	*P* Gross production g/m²/day	*R* Community respiration g/m²/day	*P/R*	*K* Gas transfer coefficient g/m²/hr at 0% saturation
Autotrophic communities ($P/R > 1$)				
Windward coral reef, Eniwetok, July, 1954 (Odum and Odum 1955)	24	24	1	—
Silver Springs, Florida (Odum) respiration from bell jars				
Winter, 1952, 1953	8	2.8	2.9	—
March 23–24, 1954	35	5	7.0	0.92
Birs, Switzerland (Schmassman 1951)[1] April 11–12, 1946	50	18	2.8	3.3
White River, Indiana; zone of recovery from pollution (Denham 1938)[1] July 23–24, 1933	57	18	3.2	1.6
Kljasma, Russia (Brujewica 1931)[1] July 21, 1929	2.4	1.9	1.3	0.6
10 Florida Springs (Odum) July, August, 1955	0.6–59.	—	>1	—
Turtle Grass, Long Key, Florida (Odum and Yount) August 14, 1955	34.	24.	1.4	2.6
Heterotrophic communities ($P/R < 1$)				
Itchen River, England; unpolluted (Butcher, *et al.* 1930)[1], Figure 4				
April–October	5.5–14.0	5.8–18.6	0.6–1.1	0.9–2.8
November–March	0.4–7.1	4.2–20.2	0.1–0.5	1.5–4.3
River Lark, England; polluted (Butcher *et al.* 1930)[1]				
November 17–18, 1927	0.53	53	0.01	—
May 18–19, 1927	39.	35	1.1	2.3
White River Indiana, near pollution outfall (Denham 1938)[1] July 21, 1934	0.24	29	0.008	1.22
Potomac Estuary; balance sheet calculation by Purdy, 1917 (quoted by Phelps 1944), eelgrass; polluted	11.0	16.8	0.66	3.7
San Diego Bay, black bottle method; production estimates of Nusbaum and Miller (1952)	2.8	4.4	0.65	1–2.

[1] Diurnal oxygen curves from the paper cited were used as described in the text to obtain production, respiration, and gas transfer estimates.

quently increases the autotrophic based growth rates.

High production is not limited, however, to polluted waters. Three flows with the lowest organic matter contents of all waters (0.1–1 ppm)—the Pacific coral reef environment, the Caribbean turtle grass and the large artesian calcareous springs in Florida—possess very high productivities (Table 2).

The seasonal course of gross production and community respiration has been calculated for the unpolluted River Itchen from data given by Butcher, Pentelow, and Woodley (1930) and summarized in Figure 4. Each point was obtained with a curve analysis like that in Figure 3. An approximation was introduced in the calculations by the use of the average depth 0.6 m rather than the river stages on the particular days, which were not readily available. The production curve shows a seasonal trend correlated with the course of sunlight. That the light is the main cause of this pattern seems likely. A similar curve was found in the constant temperature of Silver Springs (Odum 1954). Verduin (1956) found that naturally adjusted plankton populations had a primary production independent of temperature. The constancy of respiration in Figure 4 is supported by Butcher, Pentelow, and Woodley's (1930) account of fairly constant benthic plant populations during the year in the River Itchen. That similar values of the gas transfer coefficients were obtained (Table 1) in spite of the depth approximation used, gives one some confidence in the single-curve analysis procedure used. The seasonal shift in K values for a given stream may not be more than 2- or 3-fold.

Although the downstream longitudinal

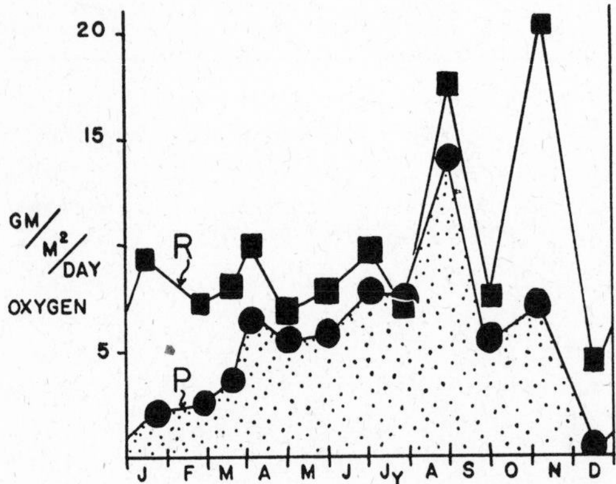

Fig. 4. Seasonal course of production (P) and community respiration (R) for the Itchen River, England, estimated with the single-station method from data given by Butcher, Pentelow, and Woodley (1930). Production per day in ppm was converted to an areal basis using an approximate depth of 0.6 meters. The stream was unpolluted, calcareous, and contained large plant populations.

succession of species, physical conditions, and rates of waste decomposition are now well-known and fairly similar throughout the world where studied, almost no effort has been made to estimate the primary production rates in the recovery sequence below sewage pollution discharges. Using some oxygen curves of Calvert (1932, 1933) and Denham (1938) for the White River in Indiana, the single-curve procedure has been used to obtain the longitudinal distribution of primary production and respiration over the 160 miles below the Indianapolis waste outfall. As shown in the pattern in Figure 5, respiratory metabolism far exceeds production in the first 20 miles as the sewage decomposes. Production, however, rises rapidly so that primary production far exceeds the decomposition processes in the early recovery zone. Here the organic matter is being made faster than it is being used. The rise in respiration that seems to occur below this point may be a result of the increased organic matter and increased populations of respiratory organisms. This is in keeping with the idea that the respiratory metabolism of a polluted stream is proportional to the organic matter content at a rate determined by the deoxygenation constant (Streeter 1935, Velz 1939, Phelps 1944). The second peak of respiratory metabolism 100 miles downstream is accompanied by aerobic daytime conditions although the diurnal varition is large. A supersaturated oxygen condition during the day and an anaerobic condition at night is a property of such waters. For example, Schmassmann (1951) used the range of oxygen concentration to classify such streams. Low oxygen and high organic matter are therefore not always correlated. Far downstream there is a gradual decline of both production and respiration. The pattern of maximum primary production in the early recovery zone fits the observed maxima of algal populations in this zone as observed,

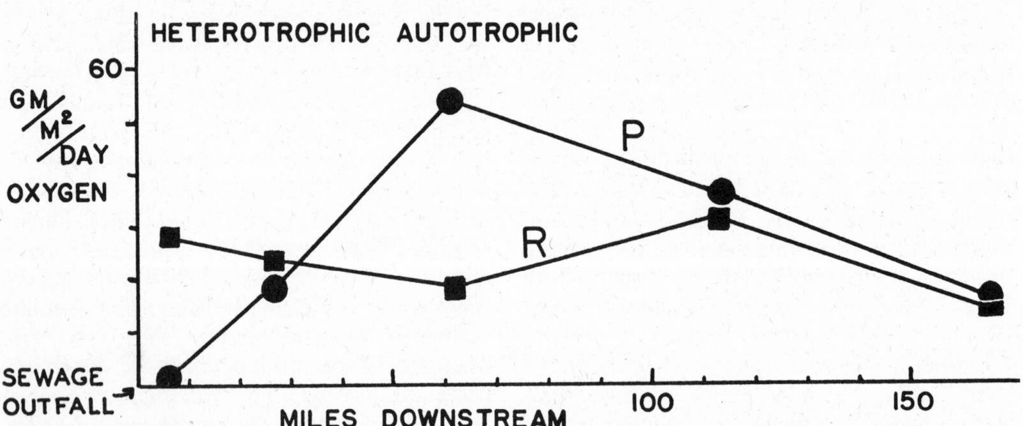

Fig. 5. The downstream sequence of production (P) and community respiration (R) estimated with the single-station method from data given by Denham (1938) below a sewage pollution outfall in the White River, Indiana, July 21–27, 1934.

for example, in the River Trent by Butcher (quoted by Macan and Worthington 1947).

Enormous values of primary production are also found in recovery zones of other polluted streams as shown in Table 2 and including the River Lark, England, and Birs, Switzerland. It may be found eventually that the most productive communities in existence are those in polluted streams.

Efficiency and current velocity

The estimates of high production in Table 2 for flows of many kinds suggest some consistent difference between the production in running waters and the production in other environments. One is tempted to conclude that the efficiencies of primary production in streams are higher than those of most other environments.

Although many streams maintain higher nutrient concentrations than still waters, this cannot be the entire reason for the high production. The high production-measurements in extremely low nutrient waters at Eniwetok and at Rongelap indicate that nutrient concentration can be overcome where current velocities are large and the organisms are adapted. Ruttner in 1926 (Ruttner 1953) showed that a flow of current past a community accelerates those metabolic processes that are limited by slow rates of diffusion. The current renews the depleted requirements for life and removes accumulating by-products of metabolism. Many organisms adapted to such currents cannot survive outside of the currents. The importance of this phenomenon has been recognized in some small invertebrate animals in their current demand and the high metabolic rates in comparison to similar lake species. Munk and Riley (1952) have made computations as to the effect of falling plankton of various shapes in stimulating their own metabolism by moving relative to the water.

Organic matter, productivity, and succession

In flowing systems there are three time sequences in the adjustment of communities to the physical environment. One is the sequence at one place in the stream, the temporal (short term) succession. The second is the action of a community upstream in determining subsequent events downstream by affecting the contents of the water passing downstream (the longitudinal succession). The third is the long-time geological succession by which erosion transforms "V"-shaped valley headwaters into flood-plain physiography. Long-time geological processes will not be considered further here. Considerable opinion and evidence exists that temporal succession rapidly leads to an aquatic climax (Butcher, 1945, 1949; Shelford and Eddy 1929), which is maintained until the properties of the water-flow change. Similarly, detailed studies have shown sequences of longitudinal succession such as the pollution-recovery sequence already considered, the cooling sequence downstream from hot springs (Seurat 1922, quoted by Hesse, Allee, and Schmidt 1951), or the diversification sequence downstream from cold springs (Sloan 1956). Although data are scarce, some basic considerations of the production processes may help to relate production to successional sequences.

In Figure 6 is given an energy flow diagram for a community composed of the 5 trophic levels: primary producing plants, herbivores, decomposers, carnivores, and top carnivores. The diagram is drawn so as to separate the photosynthetic part of the community from all the respiratory parts of the community including the plant respiration. Following the first law of thermodynamics the rates of influx of both light and organic matter energy sources are equal to the energy outflux of heat and organic matter. According to the second law of thermodynamics, any process that takes place spontaneously involves a heat loss (dispersal) as an entropy tax. From this diagram it should be clear that when subsequently gross production, net production and respiration are used, community values are intended rather than physiological values.

In many stream communities, there is a large influx of imported organic matter. The word export is appropriate for the organic matter that leaves an active community either by being sent downstream or sedimented below the active metabolic level

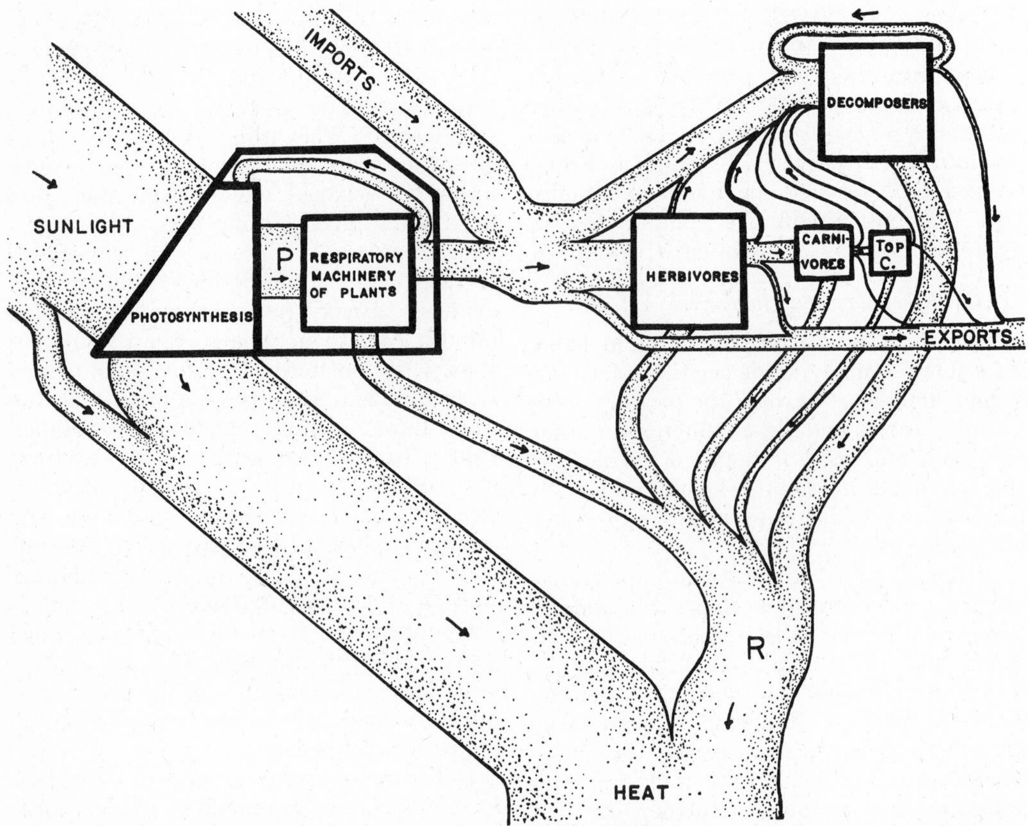

FIG. 6. A generalized diagram of energy flow for steady-state natural communities. P is the gross primary production; R is the total community respiration; the 5 trophic levels are indicated by boxes. Imports and exports are included as dominant flows which may equal the flow of primary production in some streams. The flow from the top of those boxes representing consumer trophic levels indicates unassimilated materials. The laws of thermodynamics are illustrated since inflows balance outflows and every process is accompanied by dispersion of heat energy as entropy tax.

(into a condition of low oxidation potential) of the community. Thus for the whole flowing community:

$$I_m + P = E_x + R \tag{9}$$

where I_m is the import rate, E_x the export rate, P the production rate, and R the community respiration rate. The quantity of consumers that can be supported is dependent both on the primary production and the import.

There seems to be inherent in these arrangements a self-regulating mechanism that tends to direct longitudinal succession but not succession *in situ*. If as cited above for polluted streams, the respiration is a function of the concentration of organic matter in the water and on the bottom, while the primary production is a function of light and nutrients, there is possible an organic matter concentration in the water at which production will balance respiration. For concentrations of organic matter below this there will be too little available free energy in organic matter to build large populations of organisms. In these cases production will exceed respiration and there will be a net storage or export of organic matter. On the other hand when respiration exceeds production there will be a net loss or import of organic matter. The types of standing crop characteristic of these regions may show dramatic differences. Silver Springs, Florida, is an example of a community that has

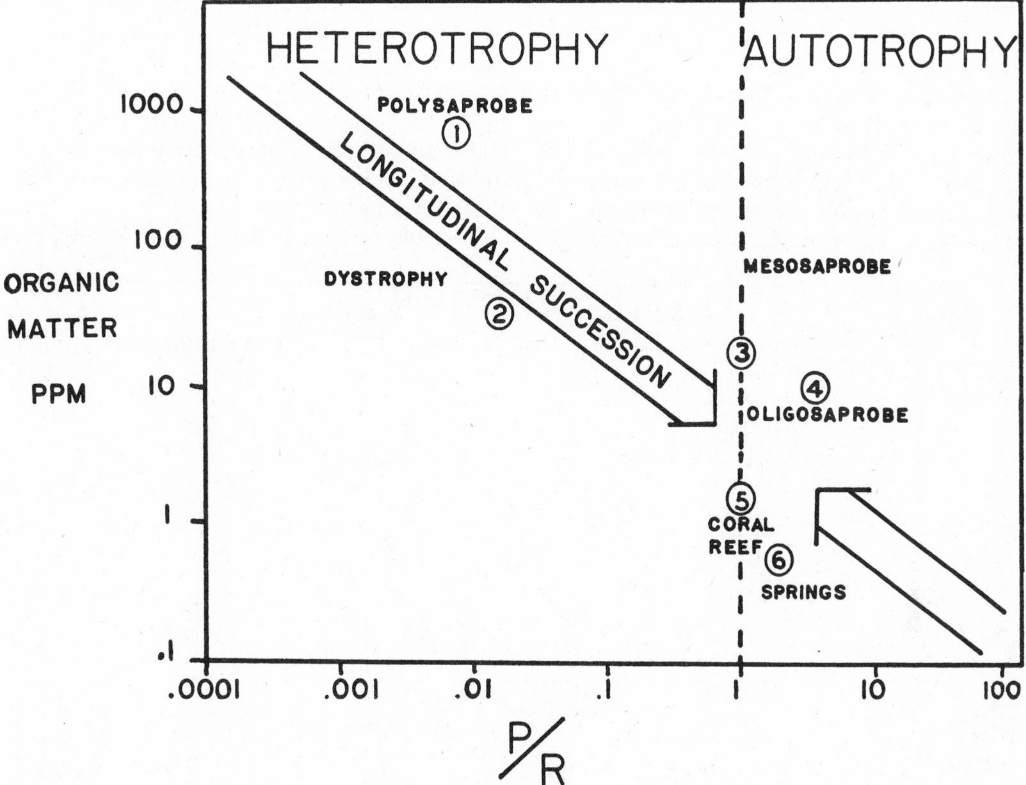

FIG. 7. The relationship of longitudinal succession, total organic matter in waters, and the relative dominance of autotrophic and heterotrophic metabolism as indicated by the *P/R* ratio. The arrows indicate the trend of concentration of organic matter in waters, depending on the *P/R* ratio of the communities over which the water flows. Several specific communities are plotted: (1) White River pollution outfall (see Fig. 5); (2) an approximate point for a dystrophic stream based on the observation that the oxygen tension remains below saturation (3.5 ppm) both day and night (Santa Fe River, Fla., Oct. 31, 1953); (3) recovery zone of the Illinois River at Averyville, Aug. 24, 1927, from single station calculation of diurnal oxygen curve given by Mohlman *et al.* (1931); (4) Birs, Switzerland (Table 2); (5) coral reefs from Sargent and Austin (1948, 1954), and Rongelap and Eniwetok from Odum and Odum (1955); (6) Silver Springs, Fla., annual means.

an excess of production over respiration so that the organic matter is exported and the particulate organic content of the water increases downstream. Thus longitudinal succession beginning with either high or low organic content will trend towards an intermediate organic matter content as a steady state downstream condition. Within the length of most streams there is not time for much succession. Many streams with large and continual allochthonous organic matter imports from land drainage will be in an arrested longitudinal succession. These concepts can be made operational if the ratio of production to respiration can be related to the concentration of organic matter in the water (expressed in mg/l). For natural summer light intensities the organic matter content corresponding to a *P/R* of 1 is of the order of magnitude of 1–15 ppm. Purdy (1935) found photosynthesis exceeded respiration in mixed algal and bacterial cultures containing 10 ppm dextrose and peptone. Many harmonic and unpolluted lakes and oceans tend to be maintained in this range (Thunmark 1937, Birge and Juday 1926). According to this thinking, deviations much below or above this range cannot occur without addition and removal of organic matter by other agencies, as in ground water filtration or in allochthonous organic matter drainages. These trends are summarized in Figure 7.

Temporal succession in one place in flowing systems is unable to modify its own water environment, since its products are whisked away to cause downstream succession. Thus successional phenomena in streams are much more a function of the influx than in terrestrial or still water communities. It seems likely that there are a great many possible climaxes depending on the hydrographic climate provided by the inflowing water. A rational basis for classifying these climaxes in terms of production and respiration processes is provided by the P/R ratio.

The tendency for the P/R values to ap-

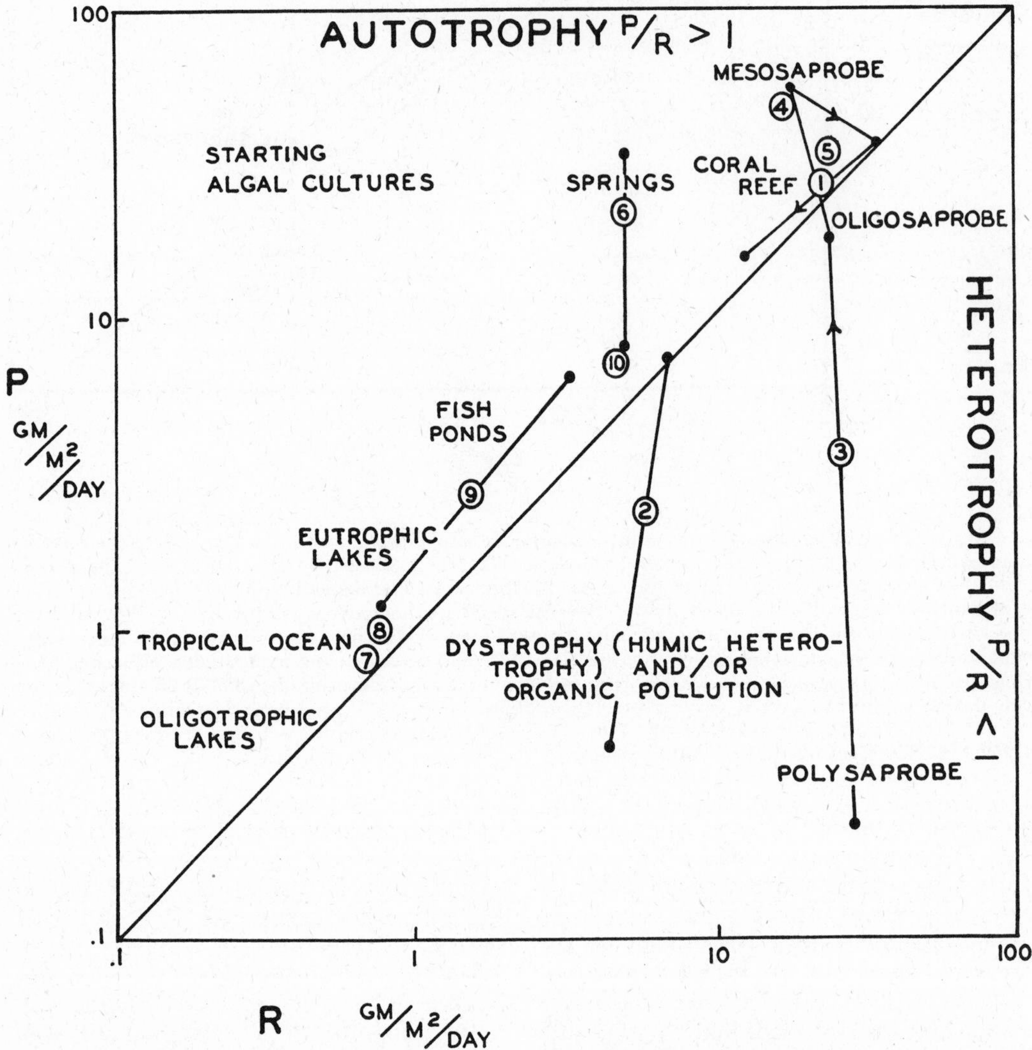

FIG. 8. A diagram for the functional classification of communities according to the total metabolism and relative dominance of autotrophic and heterotrophic metabolism. Specific examples are indicated as follows: (1) Coral reefs (Table 2); (2) Itchen River, England (Fig. 4 and Table 2); (3) recovery sequence on the White River, Indiana (see Figure 5); (4) Birs, Switzerland (see Table 2); (5) Turtle grass (see Table 2); (6) Silver Springs (see Table 2); (7) Tropical ocean (after Riley 1953); (8) Linsley Pond, Conn. (Riley 1940); (9) Little John Pond, Wisconsin (Juday, Blair, and Wilda 1943); (10) fish ponds (from Winberg, 1937, as quoted by Juday *et al.* 1943). Ryther (1954) described the behavior of the P/R ratio in algal cultures.

proach some moderate value is consistent with the qualitative description of rocky stream biota, which is dominated by algae in the headwaters and by consumer animals in the downstream sections. Pennak (1943) described a dominance of phytoplankton over zooplankton in the headwaters of a mountain stream. An amusing example was provided by Nikolsky (1937), who showed that fishes in the headwaters of the Amudaria River had gut lengths 235% of body length, decreasing to but only 170% of body length in the delta. The long guts are presumably a correlation of the plant-eating habits of the fish in the headwaters.

The P/R *diagram*

As described in the foregoing paragraphs the *P*/R ratio enables one to make a logical classification of communities into autotrophic and heterotrophic types. In Figure 8, *P* and *R* are used as coordinates of a diagram thus providing a useful graph for quantitative comparison of communities. The flowing water communities discussed in this paper are plotted along with some representative values from other environments. The diagram shows how some streams may be fertile in having high total respiratory metabolism and yet possess little primary productivity. It may be desirable to distinguish heterotrophic and autotrophic types of fertility with such terms as hetero-eutrophic, hetero-oligotrophic, auto-eutrophic, and auto-oligotrophic. The diagram suggests a quantitative definition of dystrophy as a term applicable to communities with humic-colored water and a *P/R* less than 1.

REFERENCES

Ammon, F. v. 1954. Die mathematische Erfassung der natürlichen Selbstreinigung und der Abwasserbelastung in Fliessgewässern. In Biologie und Chemie des ungestauten und gestauten Stromes. Münchner Beiträge zur Abwasser, Fisherei- und Flussbiologie, Band 2. R. Oldenbourg, München.

Birge, E. A., and C. Juday. 1926. The organic content of lake water. Proc. Nat. Acad. Sci., Wash., **12:** 515–519.

Brujewica, S. W. 1931. Tägliche Schwankungen der hydrochemischen Faktoren im Flusswasser. Proc. Int. Assoc. Limnol., **5:** 442–457.

Butcher, R. W. 1945. Studies on the ecology of rivers. VI. The algal growth in certain highly calcareous streams. J. Ecol., **33:** 268–283.

———. 1949. Problems of distribution of sessile algae in running water. Proc. Int. Assoc. Limnol., **10:** 98–103.

Butcher, Roger W., F. T. K. Pentelow, and J. W. A. Woodley. 1930. Variations in composition of river waters. Int. Rev. Hydrobiol., **24:** 47–80.

Calvert, C. K. 1932. The hourly variation of Indianapolis sewage. Sewage Wks. J., **4:** 815–820.

———. 1933. Effects of sunlight on dissolved oxygen in White River. Sewage Wks. J., **5:** 685–694.

Cerny, Adulf von. 1948. Zur Dynamik von Seichtgewässern. Schweiz. Zeit. Hydrol., **10:** 36–52.

Denham, Stacey C. 1938. A limnological investigation of the West Fork and common branch of White River. Invest. Indiana Lakes and Streams, **1**(5): 17–72.

Gessner, F. 1949. Der Chlorophyllgehalt im See und seine photosynthetische Valenz als Geophysikalisches Problem. Schweiz. Zeit. Hydrol., **11:** 378–410.

Gould, Richard H. 1921. The area of water surface as a controlling factor in the condition of polluted harbor waters. Proc. Amer. Soc. Civ. Engrs., **47**(10): 603–616.

Haney, Paul D. 1954. Theoretical principles of aeration. J. Amer. Wat. Wks. Ass., **46:** 355–376.

Hesse, R., W. C. Allee, and K. P. Schmidt. 1951. Ecological Animal Geography. New York, John Wiley. 715 pp.

Imhoff, K., and G. Mahr. 1932. Required degree of treatment of sewage prior to its disposal by dilution. Sewage Wks. J., **4:** 892–898.

Jackson, D. F., and J. McFadden. 1954. Phytoplankton photosynthesis in Sanctuary Lake, Pymatuning Reservoir. Ecology, **35:** 1–4.

Juday, C., J. M. Blair, and E. F. Wilda. 1943. The photosynthetic activities of the aquatic plants of Little John Lake, Vilas County, Wisconsin. Amer. Midl. Nat., **30:** 426–446.

Kalle, K. von. 1948. Zur Frage der Produktionsleistung des Meeres. Dtsch. hydrogr. Zeit., **1:** 1–17.

Kehr, R. W. 1938. Measures of natural oxidation in polluted streams. IV. Effect of sewage on atmospheric reaeration rates under stream flow conditions. Sewage Wks. J., **10:** 228–240.

Macan, T. T., and E. B. Worthington. 1951. Life in lakes and rivers. Collins, London. 272 pp.

Mohlman, F. W., T. L. Herrick, and H. Gladys Swope. 1931. Technique of stream pollution investigations. Industr. Engr. Chem., **23:** 209–213.

MUNK, W. H., AND G. RILEY. 1952. Absorption of nutrients by aquatic plants. J. Mar. Res., **9**: 215–240.

NIKOLSKY, G. 1937. On the distribution of fishes according to the nature of their food in the rivers flowing from the mountains of middle Asia. Proc. Int. Assoc. Limnol., **8**: 169–176.

NUSBAUM, I., AND H. E. MILLER. 1952. The oxygen resources of San Diego Bay. Sewage Industr. Wastes, **24**: 1512–1527.

ODUM, H. T. 1952, 1953, 1954. Productivity in Florida Springs. 1st, 2nd and 3rd progress reports to ONR. Unpublished report.

ODUM, H. T., AND E. P. ODUM. 1955. Trophic structure and productivity of a windward coral reef community on Eniwetok Atoll. Ecol. Monogr., **25**: 291–320.

PENNAK, R. W. 1943. Limnological variables in a Colorado mountain stream. Amer. Midl. Nat., **29**: 186–199.

PHELPS, E. B. 1944. Stream sanitation. John Wiley and Sons, N. Y. 276 pp.

POMEROY, R. 1938. Influence of oxygen concentration on biochemical oxygen demand. Sewage Wks. J., **10**: 465–472.

PURDY, W. C. 1935. Results of algal activity, some familiar some obscure. J. Amer. Water Wks. Ass., **27**: 1120–1133.

RABINOWITCH, E. I. 1951. Photosynthesis, Volume II, Part 1. Interscience, N. Y. pp. 603–1208.

REDFIELD, A. C. 1948. The exchange of oxygen across the sea surface. J. Mar. Res., **7**: 347–361.

RILEY, G. A. 1940. Limnological studies in Connecticut. III. The plankton of Linsley Pond. Ecol. Monogr., **10**: 280–306.

———. 1953. Letter to the editor. J. Cons. int. Explor. Mer., **19**: 85–89.

RUTTNER, F. 1953. Fundamentals of Limnology. Translated by D. G. Frey and F. E. J. Fry. Univ. of Toronto Press. 242 pp.

RYTHER, JOHN H. 1954. The ratio of photosynthesis to respiration in marine plankton algae and its effect upon the measurement of productivity. Deep Sea Res., **2**: 134–139.

SARGENT, MARSTON C., AND T. S. AUSTIN. 1949. Organic productivity of an atoll. Trans. Amer. Geophys. Un., **30**: 245–249.

———. 1954. Biologic economy of coral reefs. Bikini and nearby atolls, Part 2. Oceanography (biologic). U. S. Geol. Surv. Prof. Paper 260-E: 293–300.

SCHMASSMANN, HANSJORG VON. 1951. Untersuchungen über den Stoffhaushalt fliessender Gewässer. Schweiz. Zeit. Hydrol., **13**: 300–335.

SHELFORD, V. E., AND S. EDDY. 1929. Methods for the study of stream communities. Ecology, **10**: 282–391.

SLOAN, W. C. 1956. The distribution of aquatic insects in two Florida springs. Ecology, **37**: 81–98.

STREETER, H. W. 1935. Industrial wastes measures of natural oxidation in polluted streams. I. The oxygen demand factor. Sewage Wks. J., **7**: 251–279.

STREETER, H. W., AND E. B. PHELPS. 1925. Studies of the pollution and natural purification of the Ohio River. Publ. Hlth. Bull., Wash., No. 146, 75 pp.

STREETER, H. W., C. T. WRIGHT, AND R. W. KEHR. 1936. Measures of natural oxidation in polluted streams. III. An experimental study of atmospheric reaeration under stream flow conditions. Sewage Wks. J., **8**: 282–316.

THUNMARK, SVEN. 1937. Über die regionale Limnologie von Südschweden. Sveriges Geolog. Undersok., ser C, No. 410. P. A. Norstedt & Sons, Stockholm.

VELZ, C. J. 1939. Deoxygenation and reoxygenation. Proc. Amer. Soc. Civ. Engrs., **65**: 677–680.

VERDUIN, J. 1956. Energy fixation and utilization by natural communities in Western Lake Erie. Ecology, **37**: 40–50.

WASSINK, E. C., B. KOK, AND J. L. P. OORSCHOT. 1953. The efficiency of light conversion in Chlorella cultures as compared with higher plants, pp. 55–62. In: BURLEW, J. S. Algal culture from laboratory to pilot plant. Publ. Carnegie Inst. 357 pp.

WHITTINGHAM, C. P. 1955. Energy transformation in photosynthesis and the relation of photosynthesis to respiration. Biol. Rev., **30**: 40–64.

WIKEN, T. 1936. Über biogene und abiogene Sauerstoffvariation im Oberflächenwasser. Svensk bot. Tidskr., **30**: 165–192.

ZOBELL, C. E. 1940. The effect of oxygen tension on the rate of oxidation of organic matter in the sea. J. Mar. Res., **3**: 211–223.

Potential Productivity of the Sea

Organic production by marine plankton algae is comparable to agricultural yields on land.

John H. Ryther

Under ideal conditions for photosynthesis and growth, what is the maximum potential rate of production of organic matter in the sea? Is this potential ever realized, or even approached? How does the sea compare with the land in this respect? These questions may be approached empirically with some measure of success but, aside from the time and effort required by this method, one can never be certain how close to the optimum a given environment may be and, hence, to what extent the biotic potential is realized.

However, we do know with some degree of certainty the maximum photosynthetic efficiency of plants under carefully controlled laboratory conditions; and there is a considerable literature concerning the effects of various environmental conditions on photosynthesis, respiration, and growth, particularly with respect to the unicellular algae. From such information it should be possible to estimate photosynthetic efficiencies and, for given amounts of solar radiation, organic production under natural conditions. This indirect and theoretical approach cannot be expected to provide exact values, but it does furnish a supplement to the empirically derived data which may help substantiate our concepts both of the environmental physiology of the plankton algae and the level of organic production in the sea.

An attempt has been made to use this joint approach for the marine environment in the following discussion. The only variable considered is light, and the assumption is made that virtually all of the light which enters the water (and remains) is absorbed by plants. Such situations are closely approximated in plankton blooms, dense stands of benthic algae, eelgrass, and other plants. For the rest, it is assumed that temperature, nutrients, and other factors are optimal, or at least as favorable as occur under ideal culture conditions. Given these conditions, I have attempted to calculate the organic yields which might be expected within the range of solar radiation incident to most of the earth. These data are then compared with maximal and mean observed values in the marine environment and elsewhere, and an attempt is made to explain discrepancies.

The calculations which appear below are based, for the most part, upon experimentally derived relationships between unicellular algae and the envi-

The author is on the staff of the Woods Hole Oceanographic Institution, Woods Hole, Mass. This article is based on a paper presented by the author at the AAAS meeting in Washington, D.C., December 1958.

ronment, and are therefore applicable only to this group. This must be kept in mind when, later in the discussion, comparisons are drawn between the theoretical yields and observed values of production by larger aquatic and terrestrial plants.

The values for the efficiency of photosynthesis under natural conditions are based on the utilization of the visible portion of the solar spectrum only (400 to 700 mμ), or roughly half of the total incident radiation. In converting these efficiencies to organic yields, it is assumed that the heat of combustion of the dry plant material is 5.5 kcal per gram, which closely approximates values for unicellular algae reported by Krogh and Berg (*1*), Ketchum and Redfield (*2*), Kok (*3*), Aach (*4*), Wassink *et al.* (*5*), and others.

Reflection and Backscattering

Of the sunlight which strikes the surface of the ocean, a certain fraction is reflected from its surface and never enters the water. The remainder penetrates to depths which depend upon the concentration of absorbing and scattering particles or dissolved colored substances. While scattering may be as important as absorption in the vertical attenuation of the light, it makes little difference as far as the biological utilization of the radiation is concerned, since the scattered light is eventually absorbed, with the exception of a small fraction which is backscattered up out of the water. The combined reflected and backscattered light is lost to the aquatic system; the rest remains in the water, where, under the ideal conditions postulated, it is absorbed entirely by plants.

The fraction of the incident radiation which is reflected and backscattered has been studied by Powell and Clarke (*6*), Utterback and Jorgenson (*7*), and Hulburt (*8*). The two factors have been treated separately, but they may be considered together here. Their combined effect is rather small, ranging from about 3 to 6 percent, depending somewhat upon who made the measurements and the conditions under which the measurements were made. The highest values were observed when the sky was overcast. Sea states, ranging from flat calm to whitecap conditions, made surprisingly little difference. Reflection and backscattering were also found by Hulburt to be independent of the sun's angle, despite the fact that reflection increases greatly with the angle (from the zenith) of the incident light, particularly at angles above 60°. The explanation for this apparent contradiction lies in the fact that as the sun approaches the horizon, indirect sky light becomes increasingly important, and it eventually exceeds the intensities of the sun itself.

Hulburt's data also indicate that backscattering is not greatly influenced by the amount of particulate matter in the water, since his values in the clear Gulf Stream did not differ appreciably from those made in the turbid waters of Chesapeake Bay.

For the calculations which are made here, it is considered that an average of 5 percent of the incident radiation is lost through the combined effects of reflection and backscattering.

Photosynthesis and the Visible Spectrum

We first consider the efficiency of photosynthesis in sunlight at levels below the saturation intensity. Within this range, photosynthesis is directly proportional to the light intensity (or very nearly so), and the efficiency is therefore constant.

Despite the vast numbers of studies of quantum yield (that is, photosynthetic efficiency) in the literature, few data are available for the entire visible spectrum. Figure 1*A* shows two such series of measurements, one with the green alga *Chlorella* (Emerson and Lewis, *9*), the other with the diatom *Navicula minima* (Tanada, *10*). The ordinate is expressed as quantum requirement (the number of quanta required to reduce 1 mole of CO_2) rather than a reciprocal, quantum yield (moles of CO_2 reduced per quantum) as shown originally by the authors. Although the two organisms have strikingly different pigment complements, the curves are surprisingly similar, with minimal requirements in the red and yellow parts of the spectrum, maximal in the blue-green. *Navicula* appears to be somewhat more efficient than *Chlorella,* but the differences may not be significant.

Figure 1*B* illustrates the fact that the energy per quantum between 400 and 700 mμ decreases from a maximum of 71 kcal per mole quanta of blue light to 41 cal per mole quanta of red light. The heat of combustion of one reduced mole of CO_2 (reduced to CH_2O) is 112 kcal. A quantum requirement of 10 therefore represents an efficiency of $112/(41 \times 10) = 27.3$ percent in red light and $112/(71 \times 10) = 15.7$ percent in blue light. Figure 1*C* shows the efficiencies of *Chlorella* and *Navicula* throughout the visible solar spectrum.

The spectral distribution of daylight varies with solar altitude and with the water vapor, carbon dioxide, and dust content of the atmosphere. Figure 2 shows the spectral distribution of daylight under average atmospheric conditions and with an air mass of 2 (solar angle = 30° from zenith) as given by Moon (*11*).

If the curves in Fig. 1*C* are averaged and the mean efficiency for the entire visible spectrum is calculated, weighing the mean for the average spectral distribution of sunlight as given in Fig. 2, this value turns out to be 18.4 percent. Taking into consideration a 5-percent reflection and backscattering loss, the efficiency of photosynthetic utilization of visible sunlight *below saturation intensity* incident to the water surface is 17.5 percent.

In extremely turbid waters and in those containing organic stains (the "yellow substance" described by Kalle, *12*), blue and green light may be selectively absorbed, resulting in somewhat higher efficiencies in the utilization of the light penetrating to greater depths. On the other hand, in normal, clear oceanic water the red light is selectively absorbed by the water and blue-green light penetrates to the greatest depths, where it is used still less effectively than the average incident daylight considered above. These modifications are not considered in this article, since we are dealing with an idealized situation in which all of the light entering the water is absorbed by plants.

Intensity Effect

Above the saturation point, photosynthesis does not increase in proportion to light intensity, but remains constant or, at high intensities, is actually depressed, owing to photooxidation or other inhibitory processes.

Figure 3*A* shows a curve of photosynthesis by marine plankton algae as a function of light intensity, from Ryther (*13*). This is a mean curve of experiments with cultures of 14 species of organisms, preconditioned to a variety of different light regimes. Photosynthesis was measured by C^{14} uptake under solar radiation during the 4-hour period (10 A.M. to 2 P.M.) when the intensity is nearly constant and maximum. Graded intensities were obtained with neutral density filters. Almost identical curves were obtained by Steemann Nielsen and Jensen (*14*) for natural plankton populations.

Photosynthetic efficiencies remain constant, or nearly so, up to the saturation point, but then decline sharply at higher intensities. This decrease is illustrated by the difference between the actual photosynthesis curve in Fig. 3*A* and the dotted line, which is an extrapolation of the linear portion of the solid curve and represents photosynthesis if the efficiency remained constant. Figure 3*B* shows relative efficiencies as a function of light intensity, obtained from the ratio between the solid and dotted lines in Fig. 3*A*.

Using the data in Fig. 3*A,* Ryther (*13*) has calculated relative photosynthesis throughout the day and at various depths within the euphotic (illuminated) zone of the ocean for days with different values for total incident radiation. Several curves were thereby produced showing values for total daily photosynthesis at several depths within

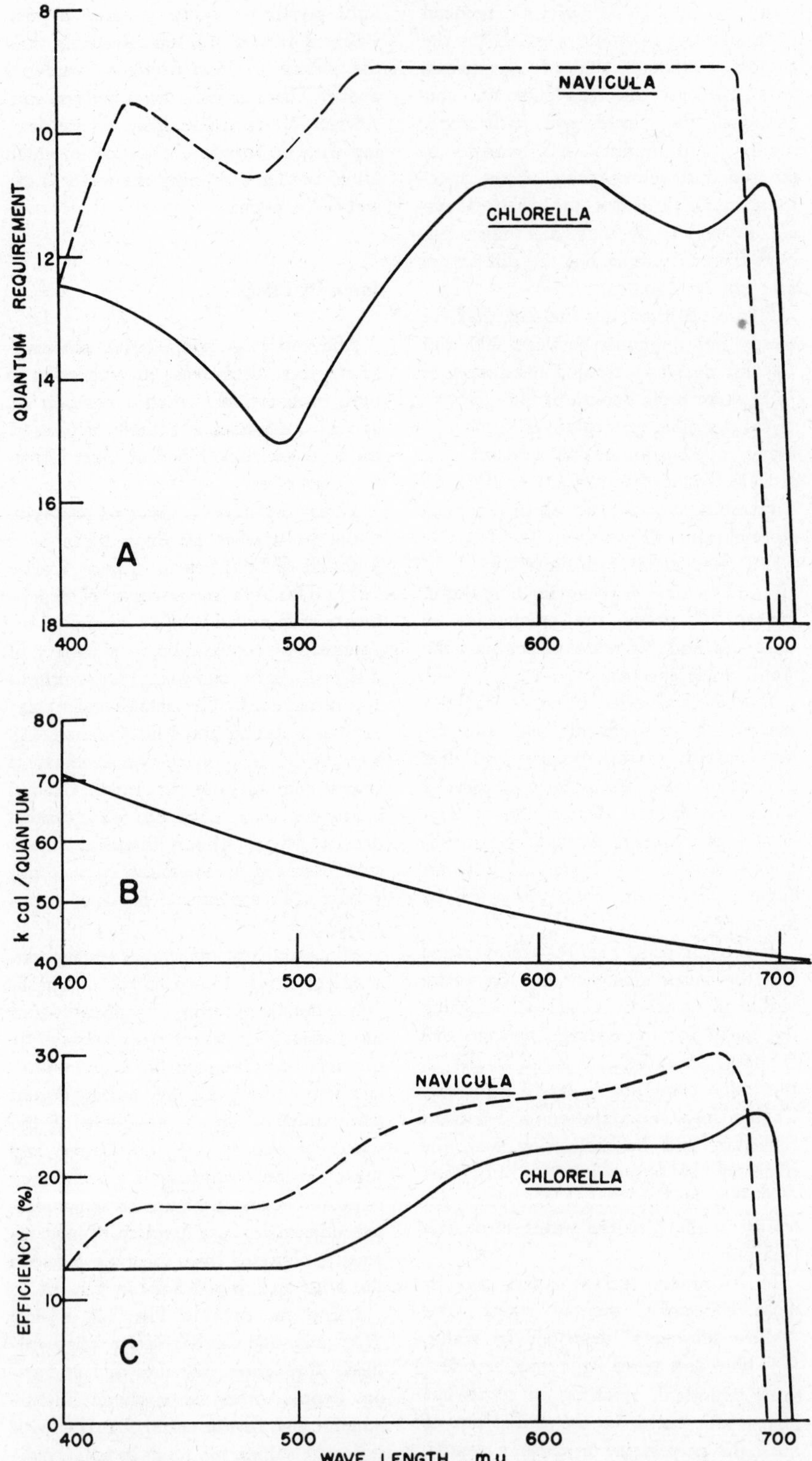

Fig. 1. (*A*) Quantum requirement of photosynthesis as a function of wavelength of light for *Chlorella* [after Emerson and Lewis, *9*] and for *Navicula* [after Tanada, *10*]. (*B*) Energy per mole quantum of light as a function of wavelength. (*C*) Efficiency of photosynthesis as a function of wavelength, calculated from (*A*) and (*B*).

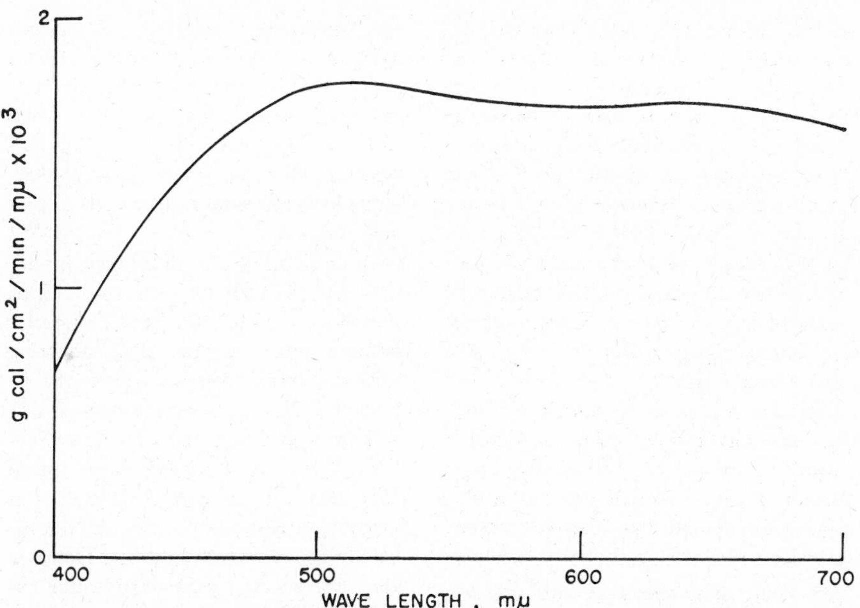

Fig. 2. The spectral distribution of daylight under average atmospheric conditions with air mass equal to 2. [After Moon, *11*]

the euphotic zone relative to the hourly rate of photosynthesis at light saturation.

On extremely dull days, when the intensity never reaches the saturation region, photosynthesis is directly proportional to light intensity at all depths, and the curve of photosynthesis with depth shows an exponential decrease from the surface, as does that of light. On bright, sunny days, intensities at the surface exceed saturation and normally produce inhibition (which occurs at ⅓ or less the intensity of full sunlight). On such days, photosynthesis at the surface is less than that at intermediate depths. In all cases, photosynthesis at depths where the surface light is reduced to 10 percent or less is directly proportional to intensity, and in this region it decreases exponentially, following the light curve.

By extrapolating the lower, exponential portion of the photosynthesis curve to the surface, one may create a hypothetical curve of photosynthesis if the latter maintained the same efficiency at all depths. The ratio of the actual photosynthesis curve to this hypothetical exponential curve will then show the reduction in efficiency caused by light intensities above saturation in the upper waters. This has been done in Fig. 4 for a series of photosynthesis curves on days of varying incident radiation. Since photosynthesis at the various depths is a function of light intensity and not of depth per se, the units on the ordinate of Fig. 4 are natural logarithms of I_0/I and thus represent the depths to which given fractions of the incident radiation penetrate. The curve for the day with lowest radiation (20 gcal/cm² day) is exponential all the way to the surface, indicating that on such a day there is no reduction in photosynthetic efficiency from the effects of light intensity. On days of progressively higher light intensity, the photosynthesis curve departs more and more from the exponential curve illustrating the increasing reduction in efficiency.

If it is assumed that the maximum efficiency (with no intensity effect) is 17.5 percent, as calculated in the previous section, Fig. 5 shows the cumulative intensity effect with efficiencies plotted as a function of total daily incident radiation. The points were obtained from Fig. 4 from the ratio of the actual photosynthesis curves for each value of radiation to the exponential curve of maximum (17.5 percent efficiency. It may be seen that efficiencies decrease from 17.5 percent at low intensities to 6.5 percent on a day when 600 g cal/cm² reaches the earth's surface. It is noteworthy that the efficiency curve does not decrease in a regular way with increasing intensities, but that the rate of decrease becomes less at higher intensities. This is due to the fact that higher values of daily radiation are caused not only by higher intensities of sunlight but to an even greater extent by longer days including more hours of low intensity light.

We are now ready to calculate photosynthesis for different values of incident radiation from the efficiency curve shown in Fig. 5. This is done by multiplying the efficiency by one-half the appropriate values of radiation (that portion of the solar spectrum available for photosynthesis). This gives the amount of energy fixed in photosynthesis. Dividing this by 5.5 (the heat of combustion of a gram of average plant material, as discussed in the first section) we obtain a value which represents grams of organic matter produced per day beneath a square meter of water surface, provided that all the light entering this 1-meter-square column of water is effectively absorbed by plants. These values, shown as the upper broken line in Fig. 5, are equivalent to "real photosynthesis" or "gross production." They are hypothetical in the sense that they cannot be observed as a yield, since the plants must draw upon this organic matter to satisfy their own metabolic requirements. We must therefore subtract an amount of organic matter equivalent to the plants' respiration in order to calculate the amount of material available for harvest, the so-called "net production."

Respiratory Loss

Under conditions of active growth, photosynthesis at light saturation is some 10 to 20 times as great as dark respiration (see Ryther, *15*). Higher values have been reported, but it seems doubtful that they could represent steady-state conditions in natural populations. If we take a ratio of 15:1 as average for $P:R$ (photosynthesis: respiration) at optimal light, it is obvious that over a 24-hour period, half of which is dark, and within an entire plant community, of which many of the plants are in suboptimal light at all times, respiration must account for a much greater fraction of photosynthesis.

In calculating the ratio $P:R$ in natural communities, the oversimplified assumption will be made that respiration remains constant and independent of light and photosynthesis. While the literature pertaining to this subject is contradictory and in a state of great confusion (see, for example, Rabinowitch, *16*), there is mounting evidence that respiration and photosynthesis are not wholly independent processes. However, since there is no good quantitative formulation of a relationship between them which may be incorporated into our calculations, it must be neglected here.

As mentioned above, the data from Fig. 3*A* together with light intensity values for a group of days with varying total incident radiation have been used to calculate photosynthesis as a function of radiation. (See Ryther, *13*, for a full description of these calculations). The values given by this treatment represent photosynthesis per day beneath a square meter of surface relative to the value for photosynthesis per cubic meter per hour at light saturation. For example, a value of 100 would mean that daily photosynthesis beneath a 1-meter-square water column is 100 times as great as photosynthesis within a 1-cubic-meter aliquot of that water column for 1 hour at optimal light intensity (assuming that the plant population is evenly distributed within this water column).

Since respiration is 1/15 photosynthesis at light saturation and is also stipulated to be constant with respect to light, depth, and time of day, we may calculate total daily respiration in the same relative units as photosynthesis. The curves of photosynthesis and respiration as functions of radiation are shown in Fig. 6. They cross at 100 g cal/cm² × day, which may be considered the daily compensation level for an entire plant community. The value $(R/P) \times 100$ is the percentage of respiratory

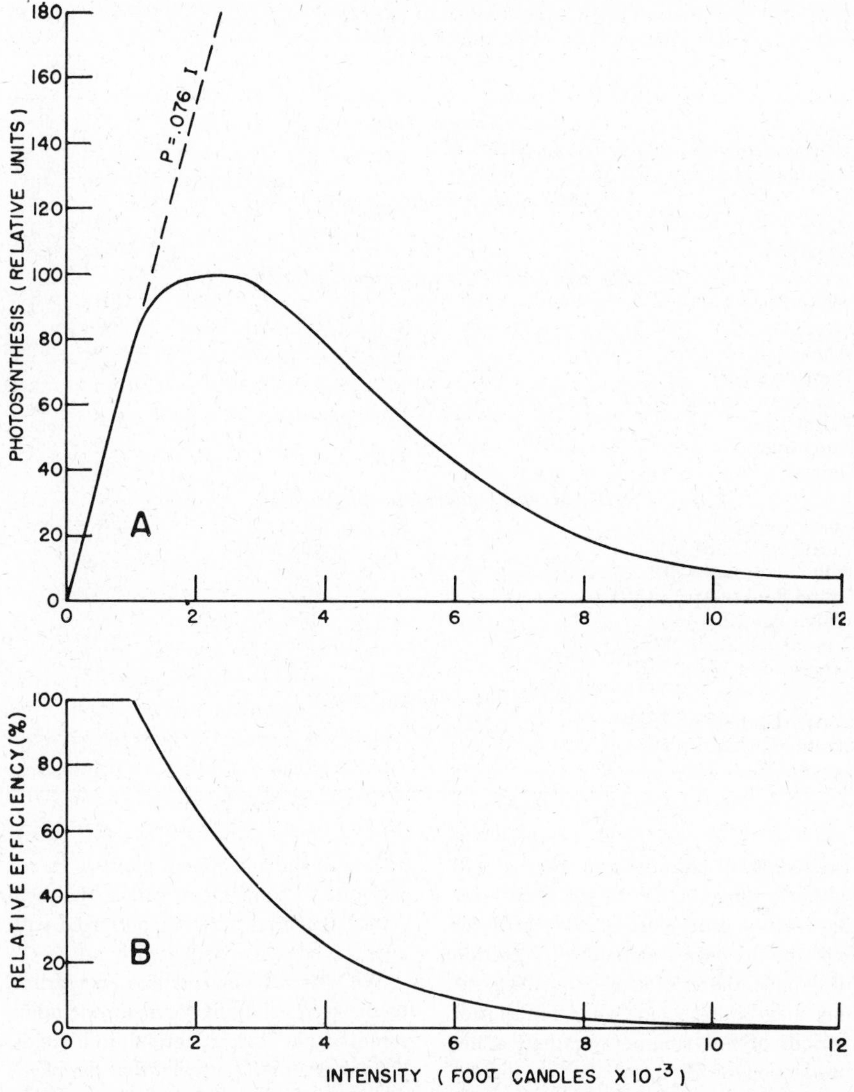

Fig. 3. (*A*) Photosynthesis of marine phytoplankton as a function of light intensity [after Ryther, *13*]. Broken line is the extrapolation of the linear portion of the solid line representing hypothetical sustained maximum photosynthetic efficiency. (*B*) Efficiency of photosynthesis as a function of light intensity, calculated from *A*.

loss and is shown as the lower broken line in Fig. 6. It ranges from 100 percent at radiation values of 100 g cal/cm^2 day or less to 28 percent on extremely bright, long days.

Net Production

Returning to Fig. 5, gross production may be reduced by the respiratory loss (Fig. 6), giving the curve of net production, which begins at 100 g cal/cm^2 day and reaches a value of 25 g/m^2 day under radiation of 600 g cal/m^2 day (the lower broken line in Fig. 5).

Although the annual range of daily incident radiation is extremely wide, even for a given latitude, this short-term variability is probably not very significant in affecting the general level of organic production of a given area. If one examines the tables compiled by Kimball (*17*) showing mean monthly radiation for different latitudes, it appears that over 80 percent of the data

Table 1. Gross and net organic production of various natural and cultivated systems in grams dry weight produced per square meter per day.

System	Gross	Net
A. Theoretical potential		
Average radiation (200 to 400 g cal/cm² day)	23–32	8–19
Maximum radiation (750 g cal/cm² day)	38	27
B. Mass outdoor Chlorella *culture* (*26*)		
Mean		12.4
Maximum		28.0
C. Land (*maximum for entire growing seasons*) (*18*)		
Sugar cane		18.4
Rice		9.1
Wheat		4.6
Spartina marsh		9.0
Pine forest (best growing years)		6.0
Tall prairie		3.0
Short prairie		0.5
Desert		0.2
D. Marine (*maxima for single days*)		
Coral reef (*27*)	24	(9.6)
Turtle grass flat (*28*)	20.5	(11.3)
Polluted estuary (*29*)	11.0	(8.0)
Grand Banks (Apr.) (*30*)	10.8	(6.5)
Walvis Bay (*23*)	7.6	
Continental Shelf (May) (*19*)	6.1	(3.7)
Sargasso Sea (Apr.) (*31*)	4.0	(2.8)
E. Marine (*annual average*)		
Long Island Sound (*32*)	2.1	0.9
Continental Shelf (*19*)	0.74	(0.40)
Sargasso Sea (*31*)	0.88	0.40

(including all latitudes and seasons) fall within a range of 200 to 400 g cal/cm² day. Thus, over most of the earth for most of the year a potential production of organic matter of some 10 to 20 g/m² day may be expected, while for shorter periods of fine summer weather, a net production of 25 g/m² day or slightly more may occur.

Comparison of Theoretical and Observed Production Rates

We may now compare the production rates which were calculated in the preceding sections with some values which have been observed empirically. Since the former are based on hypothetical situations in which all light entering the water is absorbed by plants, the observational data, to be comparable, must be restricted to natural environments in which these conditions are at least closely approximated (for example, in dense plankton blooms, thick stands of benthic algae and rooted plants). In addition to these maximal values, the theoretical potential may be contrasted with average oceanic productivity rates.

We may also extend this comparison to the terrestrial environment, including some of the better agricultural yields, bearing in mind, however, that the physiology and hence, perhaps, the biotic potential of land plants may differ significantly from those of algae.

Finally, we may include the yields of *Chlorella* grown in outdoor mass culture, drawing here upon the excellent, continuing studies of H. Tamiya and his collaborators. These are of particular interest, since the conditions of these experiments were as optimal as possible and since the physiology of *Chlorella* is identical or closely similar to that of the organisms upon which our calculations are based. Thus the *Chlorella* yields will serve as a check for the theoretical production rates.

It is important, in making these comparisons, to keep in mind the distinction

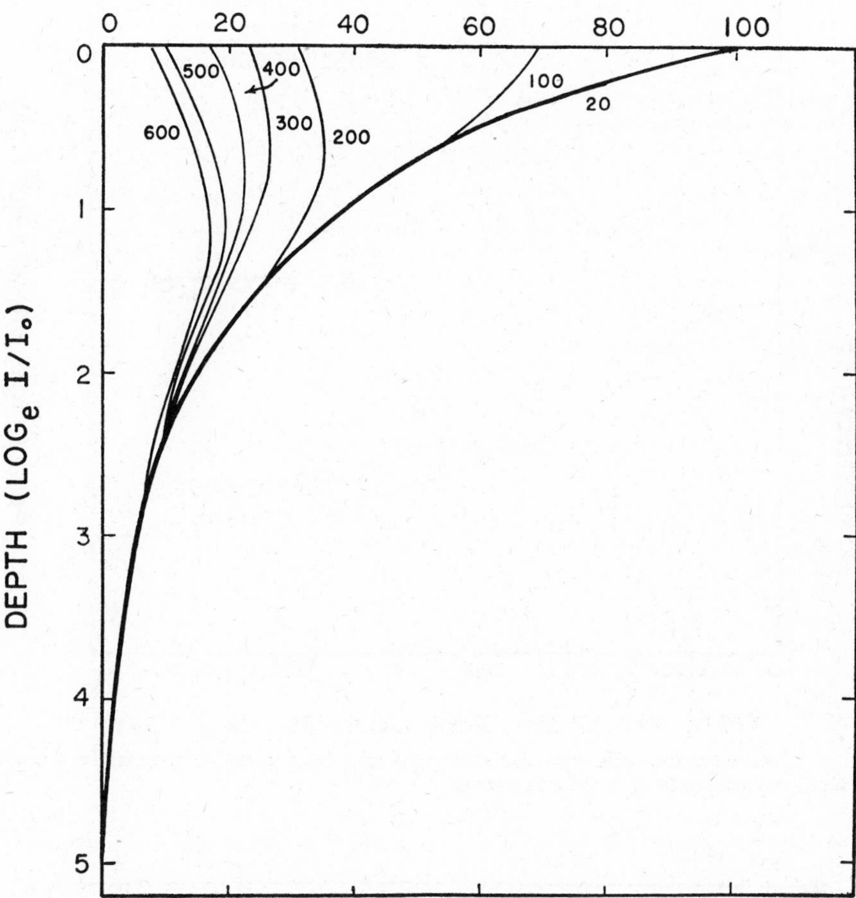

Fig. 4. Relative photosynthesis as a function of water depth for days of different incident radiation. Numbers beside curves show gram calories per square centimeter per day.

between gross and net production as defined above. Some of the data refer to true photosynthesis measurements (gross production) while others, such as the *Chlorella* experiments and the agricultural yields, are based on the actual harvest of organic matter (net production). In those cases in which only gross production values are available and where radiation data are given, net production has been obtained from Figure 5 and is shown in parentheses.

The theoretical production potential for average and maximal radiation, and the observational data for both marine and terrestrial environments, are given in Table 1. In each case the original source is given, except for the land values, where reference is made to the recent compilation by Odum (*18*). The various methods by which the values were obtained will not be discussed here except in the case of the unpublished data, in which gross production was calculated from chlorophyll and light, according to the method of Ryther and Yentsch (*19*) and net production was measured by the C^{14} method, uncorrected for respiration as this method is interpreted by Ryther (*20*). Where gross production (photosynthesis) was originally reported as oxygen evolution, this has been converted to carbon assimilation, using an assimilatory quotient

$$\left(\Delta \frac{+O_2}{-CO_2}\right)$$

of 1.25 (see Ryther, *20*). Carbon uptake, in turn, has been converted to total

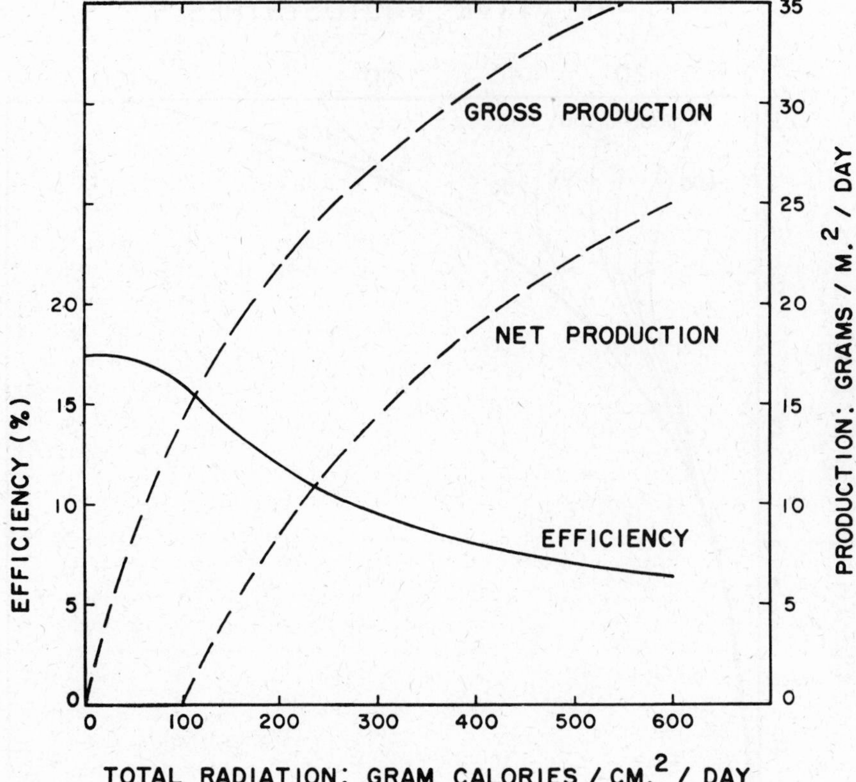

Fig. 5. Photosynthetic efficiency and theoretical maximum potential gross and net production as a function of incident radiation.

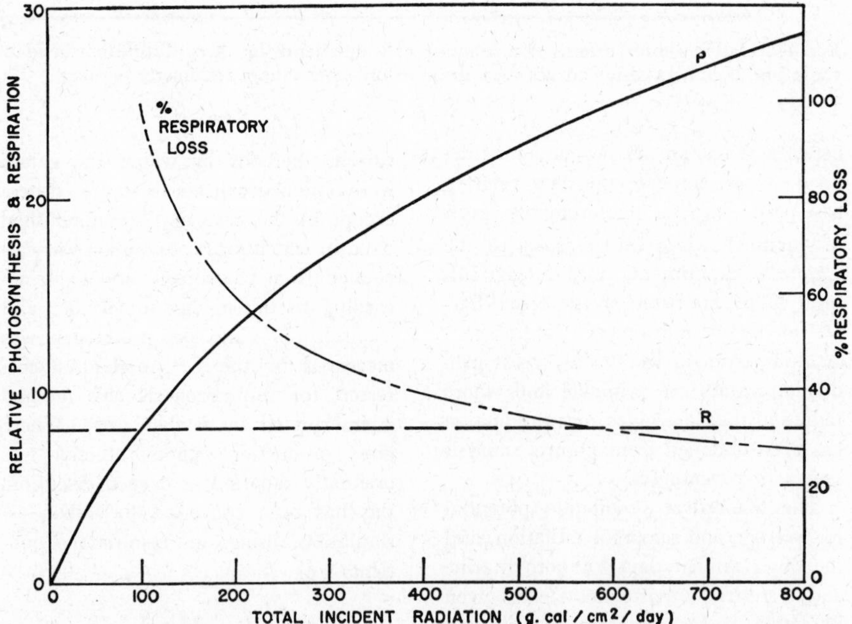

Fig. 6. Relative photosynthesis, respiration, and percentage of respiratory loss as a function of incident radiation.

organic production by assuming that the latter is 50 percent carbon by weight.

The maximal values for the marine environment represent the seven highest such values known to me. In addition to these, data are given for three regions (one inshore, one coastal, and one offshore) which have been studied over long enough periods of time to justify the calculation of annual means.

Discussion

The mean yield of *Chlorella* obtained by the Japanese workers is almost identical to the mean theoretical production for days of average radiation (12.4 versus 13.5 g/m^2 day). These yields of *Chlorella* were produced only during the warmer part of the year, presumably owing to the poor growth of *Chlorella* at low temperatures. The highest yields of *Chlorella* (up to 28 g/m^2 day) were, according to Tamiya, "obtained on fair days in the warmer months." This maximum is approximately the same as the theoretical net production for days of maximum radiation. Thus, the *Chlorella* yields agree very well with the theoretical productive potential of the sea.

The land values for net production quoted from Odum's tables range from 18.4 g/m^2 day for the highest yields of sugar cane to 0.2 g/m^2 day for deserts. The best agricultural yields are generally of the same order of magnitude as the theoretical net production of the sea, as are the values for the salt marsh and the pine forest (during its years of best growth). Uncultivated grasslands range from 3.0 for tall prairie to 0.2 for desert conditions. Because of the extreme contrasts among terrestrial environments, mean values for the land as a whole are difficult to determine and would have little meaning. It is interesting, however, that Schroeder's estimate (*21*) of the annual production of all the land is equivalent to a mean daily production of 0.55 g/m^2, roughly the same as the value given in Table 1 for short prairie grass.

With regard to the marine data, it is perhaps surprising that net production rates differ by less than a factor of 2 in such diverse environments as a coral reef, a turtle grass flat, a polluted creek, and the Grand Banks. This alone would indicate that production in each case is limited by the same basic factor, the photosynthetic potential of the plants, and indeed these and the other high values in *D* in Table 1 all closely approach the theoretical potential.

Seasonal studies have been made of three marine areas, Long Island Sound, the continental shelf off New York, and the Sargasso Sea off Bermuda. In each case temporary rates of production were observed during the spring flowering which approached the theoretical maximum, but the annual means were more than an order of magnitude lower (*E* in Table 1). True, these regions do not, throughout the year, satisfy the postulated conditions necessary to obtain this maximum, namely, that all light entering the water be absorbed by plants. For example, in his Long Island Sound studies, Riley (*22*) found that no more than one-third of the incident radiation was utilized by plants, the remainder presumably being absorbed by nonliving particulate and dissolved materials. Using Riley's techniques, I estimated that only 25 to 40 percent of the light penetrating the continental shelf waters was absorbed by the phytoplankton. This alone, however, is insufficient to account for the discrepancy between observed and potential production rates. In the clear waters of the Sargasso Sea only 10 to 20 percent of the light is absorbed by the phytoplankton during most of the year. But there is little if any other particulate matter present; the remainder of the light is absorbed by the water itself. This is not a cause but an effect of low production. The underlying reason for low production rates here and in most parts of the ocean is the limitation of essential nutrients in the upper, euphotic layers and the inadequacy of vertical mixing processes in bringing deep, nutrient-rich water to the surface.

With the exception of the three planktonic communities which have been discussed, the seasonal cycles of marine production are largely unknown and can only be surmised. Probably high levels may be maintained throughout the year in benthic populations such as the coral reef, the turtle grass flats (see *D* in Table

1) and in thick beds of seaweeds, provided that seasonal temperature extremes do not impair growth. While the concentrations of nutrients in the surrounding waters may be very low, the fact that they are continually being replenished as the water moves over the plants probably prevents their ever being limiting. Plankton organisms, on the other hand, suspended as they are in their milieu, can probably never maintain high production rates in a given parcel of water, for their growth rapidly exhausts the nutrients from their surrounding environment and any mixing process which enriches the water must, at the same time, dilute the organisms. However, high plankton production may be sustained in a given geographic area (a polluted estuary, a region of permanent upwelling of deep water, and so forth), which is continually replenished with enriched water. In these situations, the productive capacity of the sea may be sustained for long periods, perhaps permanently.

For most of the ocean, as stated above, no such mechanism for nutrient replenishment is available. The combined meteorological and hydrographic conditions which produce the typical spring flowering of the phytoplankton over much of the oceans have been adequately described elsewhere and need not be discussed here. Suffice it to say that, in the oceans as a whole, as seasonal studies have demonstrated, high production approaching the theoretical maximum under optimal conditions is restricted to periods of a few days or, at most, weeks, per year.

Steemann Nielsen (*23*) has recently estimated the net production of the entire hydrosphere as 1.2 to 1.5×10^{10} tons of carbon per year, roughly one-tenth the earlier estimates made by Riley (*24*) and others, and about comparable to Schroeder's figure (*21*) for the land. Our production estimates are somewhat higher than those of Steemann Nielsen, the annual mean net production of organic matter for the Sargasso Sea (0.40 g/m^2 day) being about 6 times as great as his value for the same area, and twice his average for the oceans as a whole. This discrepancy appears to be largely due to the fact that Steemann Nielsen's values are based on single observations which probably seldom included seasonal maxima. His observations in the Sargasso Sea, for example, were made in June and did not differ greatly from our June values, which were the seasonal minima. If the Sargasso Sea is one of the less fertile parts of the ocean, as is generally believed, then our data would indicate that the seas are more than twice as productive as the land (*25*).

References and Notes

1. A. Krogh and K. Berg, *Intern. Rev. ges. Hydrobiol. Hydrog.* 25, 205 (1931).
2. B. H. Ketchum and A. C. Redfield, *J. Cellular Comp. Physiol.* 33, 281 (1949).
3. B. Kok, *Acta Botan. Neerl.* 1, 445 (1952).
4. H. G. Aach, *Arch. Mikrobiol.* 17, 213 (1952).
5. E. C. Wassink, B. Kok, J. L. P. van Oorschot, "The efficiency of light-energy conversion in *Chlorella* cultures as compared with higher plants," in "Algal Culture from Laboratory to Pilot Plant," *Carnegie Inst. Wash. Publ. No. 600* (1953), pp. 55–62.
6. W. M. Powell and G. L. Clarke, *J. Opt. Soc. Am.* 26, 111 (1936).
7. C. L. Utterback and W. Jorgensen, *ibid.* 26, 257 (1936).
8. E. O. Hulburt, *ibid.* 35, 698 (1945).
9. R. Emerson and C. M. Lewis, *Am. J. Botany* 30, 165 (1943).
10. T. Tanada, *ibid.* 39, 276 (1951).
11. P. Moon, *J. Franklin Inst.* 230, 583 (1940).
12. K. Kalle, *Ann. Hydrog. mar. Meteor.* 66, 1 (1938).
13. J. H. Ryther *et al., Biol. Bull.* 115, 257 (1958).
14. E. Steemann Nielsen and E. A. Jensen, *Galathea Repts.* 1, 49 (1957).
15. J. H. Ryther, *Deep-Sea Research* 2, 134 (1954).
16. E. I. Rabinowitch, *Photosynthesis and Related Processes* (Interscience, New York, 1956), vol. 2, part 2, pp. 1925–1939.
17. H. H. Kimball, *Monthly Weather Rev.* 56, 393 (1928).
18. E. P. Odum, *Fundamentals of Ecology* (Saunders, Philadelphia, ed. 2, 1959).
19. J. H. Ryther and C. S. Yentsch, *Limnol. Oceanog.* 2, 281 (1957).
20. ———, *ibid.* 1, 72 (1956).
21. H. Schroeder, *Naturwissenschaften* 7, 8 (1919).
22. G. A. Riley, *Bull. Bingham Oceanog. Coll.* 15, 15 (1956).
23. E. Steemann Nielsen, *J. conseil, Conseil permanent intern. exploration mer* 19, 309 (1954).
24. G. A. Riley, *Bull. Bingham Oceanog. Coll.* 7, 1 (1941).
25. This paper is contribution No. 1016 of the Woods Hole Oceanographic Institution. The work was supported in part by research grant G-3234 from the National Science Foundation and under contract AT (30-1)-1918 with the Atomic Energy Commission.
26. H. Tamiya, *Ann. Rev. Plant Physiol.* 8, 309 (1957).
27. H. T. Odum and E. P. Odum, *Ecol. Monographs* 25, 291 (1955).
28. H. T. Odum, *Limnol. Oceanog.* 2, 85 (1957).
29. J. H. Ryther *et al., Biol. Bull.* 115, 257 (1958).
30. J. H. Ryther and C. S. Yentsch, unpublished data.
31. J. H. Ryther and D. W. Menzel, unpublished data.
32. G. A. Riley, *Bull. Bingham Oceanog. Coll.* 15, 324 (1956).

PART V

COMMUNITY STRUCTURE

COMMUNITY STRUCTURE, POPULATION CONTROL, AND COMPETITION

NELSON G. HAIRSTON, FREDERICK E. SMITH, AND LAWRENCE B. SLOBODKIN

Department of Zoology, The University of Michigan, Ann Arbor, Michigan

The methods whereby natural populations are limited in size have been debated with vigor during three decades, particularly during the last few years (see papers by Nicholson, Birch, Andrewartha, Milne, Reynoldson, and Hutchinson, and ensuing discussions in the Cold Spring Harbor Symposium, 1957). Few ecologists will deny the importance of the subject, since the method of regulation of populations must be known before we can understand nature and predict its behavior. Although discussion of the subject has usually been confined to single species populations, it is equally important in situations where two or more species are involved.

The purpose of this note is to demonstrate a pattern of population control in many communities which derives easily from a series of general, widely accepted observations. The logic used is not easily refuted. Furthermore, the pattern reconciles conflicting interpretations by showing that populations in different trophic levels are expected to differ in their methods of control.

Our first observation is that the accumulation of fossil fuels occurs at a rate that is negligible when compared with the rate of energy fixation through photosynthesis in the biosphere. Apparent exceptions to this observation, such as bogs and ponds, are successional stages, in which the failure of decomposition hastens the termination of the stage. The rate of accumulation when compared with that of photosynthesis has also been shown to be negligible over geologic time (Hutchinson, 1948).

If virtually all of the energy fixed in photosynthesis does indeed flow through the biosphere, it must follow that all organisms taken together are limited by the amount of energy fixed. In particular, the decomposers as a group must be food-limited, since by definition they comprise the trophic level which degrades organic debris. There is no a priori reason why predators, behavior, physiological changes induced by high densities, etc., could not limit decomposer populations. In fact, some decomposer populations may be limited in such ways. If so, however, others must consume the "left-over" food, so that the group as a whole remains food limited; otherwise fossil fuel would accumulate rapidly.

Any population which is not resource-limited must, of course, be limited to a level *below* that set by its resources.

Our next three observations are interrelated. They apply primarily to terrestrial communities. The first of these is that cases of obvious depletion of green plants by herbivores are exceptions to the general picture, in which

Reproduced with permission from The American Naturalist, XCIV: 421-425, 1960.
Published by The American Society of Naturalists, Tempe, Arizona.

the plants are abundant and largely intact. Moreover, cases of obvious mass destruction by meteorological catastrophes are exceptional in most areas. Taken together, these two observations mean that producers are neither herbivore-limited nor catastrophe-limited, and must therefore be limited by their own exhaustion of a resource. In many areas, the limiting resource is obviously light, but in arid regions water may be the critical factor, and there are spectacular cases of limitation through the exhaustion of a critical mineral. The final observation in this group is that there are temporary exceptions to the general lack of depletion of green plants by herbivores. This occurs when herbivores are protected either by man or natural events, and it indicates that the herbivores are able to deplete the vegetation whenever they become numerous enough, as in the cases of the Kaibab deer herd, rodent plagues, and many insect outbreaks. It therefore follows that the usual condition is for populations of herbivores *not* to be limited by their food supply.

The vagaries of weather have been suggested as an adequate method of control for herbivore populations. The best factual clues related to this argument are to be found in the analysis of the exceptional cases where terrestrial herbivores have become numerous enough to deplete the vegetation. This often occurs with introduced rather than native species. It is most difficult to suppose that a species had been unable to adapt so as to escape control by the weather to which it was exposed, and at the same time by sheer chance to be able to escape this control from weather to which it had not been previously exposed. This assumption is especially difficult when mutual invasions by different herbivores between two countries may in both cases result in pests. Even more difficult to accept, however, is the implication regarding the native herbivores. The assumption that the hundreds or thousands of species native to a forest have failed to escape from control by the weather despite long exposure and much selection, when an invader is able to defoliate without this past history, implies that "pre-adaptation" is more likely than ordinary adaptation. This we cannot accept.

The remaining general method of herbivore control is predation (in its broadest sense, including parasitism, etc.). It is important to note that this hypothesis is not denied by the presence of introduced pests, since it is necessary only to suppose that either their natural predators have been left behind, or that while the herbivore is able to exist in the new climate, its enemies are not. There are, furthermore, numerous examples of the direct effect of predator removal. The history of the Kaibab deer is the best known example, although deer across the northern portions of the country are in repeated danger of winter starvation as a result of protection and predator removal. Several rodent plagues have been attributed to the local destruction of predators. More recently, the extensive spraying of forests to kill caterpillars has resulted in outbreaks of scale insects. The latter are protected from the spray, while their beetle predators and other insect enemies are not.

Thus, although rigorous proof that herbivores are generally controlled by predation is lacking, supporting evidence is available, and the alternate hypothesis of control by weather leads to false or untenable implications.

The foregoing conclusion has an important implication in the mechanism of control of the predator populations. The predators and parasites, in controlling the populations of herbivores, must thereby limit their own resources, and as a group they must be food-limited. Although the populations of some carnivores are obviously limited by territoriality, this kind of internal check cannot operate for all carnivores taken together. If it did, the herbivores would normally expand to the point of depletion of the vegetation, as they do in the absence of their normal predators and parasites.

There thus exists either direct proof or a great preponderance of factual evidence that in terrestrial communities decomposers, producers, and predators, as whole trophic levels, are resource-limited in the classical density-dependent fashion. Each of these three can and does expand toward the limit of the appropriate resource. We may now examine the reasons why this is a frequent situation in nature.

Whatever the resource for which a set of terrestrial plant species compete, the competition ultimately expresses itself as competition for space. A community in which this space is frequently emptied through depletion by herbivores would run the continual risk of replacement by another assemblage of species in which the herbivores are held down in numbers by predation below the level at which they damage the vegetation. That space once held by a group of terrestrial plant species is not readily given up is shown by the cases where relict stands exist under climates no longer suitable for their return following deliberate or accidental destruction. Hence, the community in which herbivores are held down in numbers, and in which the producers are resource-limited will be the most persistent. The development of this pattern is less likely where high producer mortalities are inevitable. In lakes, for example, algal populations are prone to crash whether grazed or not. In the same environment, grazing depletion is much more common than in communities where the major producers are rooted plants.

A second general conclusion follows from the resource limitation of the species of three trophic levels. This conclusion is that if more than one species exists in one of these levels, they may avoid competition only if each species is limited by factors completely unutilized by any of the other species. It is a fact, of course, that many species occupy each level in most communities. It is also a fact that they are not sufficiently segregated in their needs to escape competition. Although isolated cases of non-overlap have been described, this has never been observed for an entire assemblage. Therefore, interspecific competition for resources exists among producers, among carnivores, and among decomposers.

It is satisfying to note the number of observations that fall into line with the foregoing deductions. Interspecific competition is a powerful selective force, and we should expect to find evidence of its operation. Moreover, the evidence should be most conclusive in trophic levels where it is necessarily present. Among decomposers we find the most obvious specific mechanisms for reducing populations of competitors. The abundance of antibiotic substances attests to the frequency with which these mechanisms have been developed in the trophic level in which interspecific competition is inevitable. The producer species are the next most likely to reveal evidence of competition, and here we find such phenomena as crowding, shading, and vegetational zonation.

Among the carnivores, however, obvious adaptations for interspecific competition are less common. Active competition in the form of mutual habitat-exclusion has been noted in the cases of flatworms (Beauchamp and Ullyott, 1932) and salamanders (Hairston, 1951). The commonest situation takes the form of niche diversification as the result of interspecific competition. This has been noted in birds (Lack, 1945; MacArthur, 1958), salamanders (Hairston, 1949), and other groups of carnivores. Quite likely, host specificity in parasites and parasitoid insects is at least partly due to the influence of interspecific competition.

Of equal significance is the frequent occurrence among herbivores of apparent exceptions to the influence of density-dependent factors. The grasshoppers described by Birch (1957) and the thrips described by Davidson and Andrewartha (1948) are well known examples. Moreover, it is among herbivores that we find cited examples of coexistence without evidence of competition for resources, such as the leafhoppers reported by Ross (1957), and the psocids described by Broadhead (1958). It should be pointed out that in these latter cases coexistence applies primarily to an identity of food and place, and other aspects of the niches of these organisms are not known to be identical.

SUMMARY

In summary, then, our general conclusions are: (1) Populations of producers, carnivores, and decomposers are limited by their respective resources in the classical density-dependent fashion. (2) Interspecific competition must necessarily exist among the members of each of these three trophic levels. (3) Herbivores are seldom food-limited, appear most often to be predator-limited, and therefore are not likely to compete for common resources.

LITERATURE CITED

Andrewartha, H. G., 1957, The use of conceptual models in population ecology. Cold Spring Harbor Symp. Quant. Biol. 22: 219–232.

Beauchamp, R. S. A., and P. Ullyott, 1932, Competitive relationships between certain species of fresh-water triclads. J. Ecology 20: 200–208.

Birch, L. C., 1957, The role of weather in determining the distribution and abundance of animals. Cold Spring Harbor Symp. Quant. Biol. 22: 217–263.

Broadhead, E., 1958, The psocid fauna of larch trees in northern England. J. Anim. Ecol. 27: 217–263.

Davidson, J., and H. G. Andrewartha, 1948, The influence of rainfall, evaporation and atmospheric temperature on fluctuations in the size of a natural population of *Thrips imaginis* (Thysanoptera). J. Anim. Ecol. 17: 200–222.

Hairston, N. G., 1949, The local distribution and ecology of the Plethodontid salamanders of the southern Appalachians. Ecol. Monog. 19: 47–73.

1951, Interspecies competition and its probable influence upon the vertical distribution of Appalachian salamanders of the genus Plethodon. Ecology 32: 266–274.

Hutchinson, G. E., 1948, Circular causal systems in ecology. Ann. N. Y. Acad. Sci. 50: 221–246.

1957, Concluding remarks. Cold Spring Harbor Symp. Quant. Biol. 22: 415–427.

Lack, D., 1945, The ecology of closely related species with special reference to cormorant (*Phalacrocorax carbo*) and shag (*P. aristotelis*). J. Anim. Ecol. 14: 12–16.

MacArthur, R. H., 1958, Population ecology of some warblers of northeastern coniferous forests. Ecology 39: 599–619.

Milne, A., 1957, Theories of natural control of insect populations. Cold Spring Harbor Symp. Quant. Biol. 22: 253–271.

Nicholson, A. J., 1957, The self-adjustment of populations to change. Cold Spring Harbor Symp. Quant. Biol. 22: 153–172.

Reynoldson, T. B., 1957, Population fluctuations in *Urceolaria mitra* (Peritricha) and *Enchytraeus albidus* (Oligochaeta) and their bearing on regulation. Cold Spring Harbor Symp. Quant. Biol. 22: 313–327.

Ross, H. H., 1957, Principles of natural coexistence indicated by leafhopper populations. Evolution 11: 113–129.

HOMAGE TO SANTA ROSALIA
or
WHY ARE THERE SO MANY KINDS OF ANIMALS?*

G. E. HUTCHINSON

Department of Zoology, Yale University, New Haven, Connecticut

When you did me the honor of asking me to fill your presidential chair, I accepted perhaps without duly considering the duties of the president of a society, founded largely to further the study of evolution, at the close of the year that marks the centenary of Darwin and Wallace's initial presentation of the theory of natural selection. It seemed to me that most of the significant aspects of modern evolutionary theory have come either from geneticists, or from those heroic museum workers who suffering through years of neglect, were able to establish about 20 years ago what has come to be called the "new systematics." You had, however, chosen an ecologist as your president and one of that school at times supposed to study the environment without any relation to the organism.

A few months later I happened to be in Sicily. An early interest in zoogeography and in aquatic insects led me to attempt to collect near Palermo, certain species of water-bugs, of the genus Corixa, described a century ago by Fieber and supposed to occur in the region, but never fully reinvestigated. It is hard to find suitable localities in so highly cultivated a landscape as the Concha d'Oro. Fortunately, I was driven up Monte Pellegrino, the hill that rises to the west of the city, to admire the view. A little below the summit, a church with a simple baroque facade stands in front of a cave in the limestone of the hill. Here in the 16th century a stalactite encrusted skeleton associated with a cross and twelve beads was discovered. Of this skeleton nothing is certainly known save that it is that of Santa Rosalia, a saint of whom little is reliably reported save that she seems to have lived in the 12th century, that her skeleton was found in this cave, and that she has been the chief patroness of Palermo ever since. Other limestone caverns on Monte Pellegrino had yielded bones of extinct pleistocene Equus, and on the walls of one of the rock shelters at the bottom of the hill there are beautiful Gravettian engravings. Moreover, a small relic of the saint that I saw in the treasury of the Cathedral of Monreale has a venerable and

*Address of the President, American Society of Naturalists, delivered at the annual meeting, Washington, D. C., December 30, 1958.

petrified appearance, as might be expected. Nothing in her history being known to the contrary, perhaps for the moment we may take Santa Rosalia as the patroness of evolutionary studies, for just below the sanctuary, fed no doubt by the water that percolates through the limestone cracks of the mountain, and which formed the sacred cave, lies a small artificial pond, and when I could get to the pond a few weeks later, I got from it a hint of what I was looking for.

Vast numbers of Corixidae were living in the water. At first I was rather disappointed because every specimen of the larger of the two species present was a female, and so lacking in most critical diagnostic features, while both sexes of the second slightly smaller species were present in about equal number. Examination of the material at leisure, and of the relevant literature, has convinced me that the two species are the common European *C. punctata* and *C. affinis*, and that the peculiar Mediterranean species are illusionary. The larger *C. punctata* was clearly at the end of its breeding season, the smaller *C. affinis* was probably just beginning to breed. This is the sort of observation that any naturalist can and does make all the time. It was not until I asked myself why the larger species should breed first, and then the more general question as to why there should be two and not 20 or 200 species of the genus in the pond, that ideas suitable to present to you began to emerge. These ideas finally prompted the very general question as to why there are such an enormous number of animal species.

There are at the present time supposed to be (Muller and Campbell, 1954; Hyman, 1955) about one million described species of animals. Of these about three-quarters are insects, of which a quite disproportionately large number are members of a single order, the Coleoptera.[1] The marine fauna although it has at its disposal a much greater area than has the terrestrial, lacks this astonishing diversity (Thorson, 1958). If the insects are excluded, it would seem to be more diverse. The proper answer to my initial question would be to develop a theory at least predicting an order of magnitude for the number of species of 10^6 rather than 10^8 or 10^4. This I certainly cannot do. At most it is merely possible to point out some of the factors which would have to be considered if such a theory was ever to be constructed.

Before developing my ideas I should like to say that I subscribe to the view that the process of natural selection, coupled with isolation and later mutual invasion of ranges leads to the evolution of sympatric species, which at equilibrium occupy distinct niches, according to the Volterra-Gause principle. The empirical reasons for adopting this view and the correlative view that the boundaries of realized niches are set by competition are mainly indirect. So far as niches may be defined in terms of food, the subject has been carefully considered by Lack (1954). In general all the indirect evi-

[1]There is a story, possibly apocryphal, of the distinguished British biologist, J. B. S. Haldane, who found himself in the company of a group of theologians. On being asked what one could conclude as to the nature of the Creator from a study of his creation, Haldane is said to have answered, "An inordinate fondness for beetles."

dence is in accord with the view, which has the advantage of confirming theoretical expectation. Most of the opinions that have been held to the contrary appear to be due to misunderstandings and to loose formulation of the problem (Hutchinson, 1958).

In any study of evolutionary ecology, food relations appear as one of the most important aspects of the system of animate nature. There is quite obviously much more to living communities than the raw dictum "eat or be eaten," but in order to understand the higher intricacies of any ecological system, it is most easy to start from this crudely simple point of view.

FOOD CHAINS

Animal ecologists frequently think in terms of food chains, of the form *individuals of species* S_1 *are eaten by those of* S_2, *of* S_2 *by* S_3, *of* S_3 *by* S_4, etc. In such a food chain S_1 will ordinarily be some holophylic organism or material derived from such organisms. The simplest case is that in which we have a true *predator chain* in Odum's (1953) convenient terminology, in which the lowest link is a green plant, the next a herbivorous animal, the next a primary carnivore, the next a secondary carnivore, etc. A specially important type of predator chain may be designated Eltonian, because in recent years C. S. Elton (1927) has emphasized its widespread significance, in which the predator at each level is larger and rarer than its prey. This phenomenon was recognized much earlier, notably by A. R. Wallace in his contribution to the 1858 communication to the Linnean Society of London.

In such a system we can make a theoretical guess of the order of magnitude of the diversity that a single food chain can introduce into a community. If we assume that in general 20 per cent of the energy passing through one link can enter the next link in the chain, which is overgenerous (cf. Lindeman, 1942; Slobodkin in an unpublished study finds 13 per cent as a reasonable upper limit) and if we suppose that each predator has twice the mass, (or 1.26 the linear dimensions) of its prey, which is a very low estimate of the size difference between links, the fifth animal link will have a population of one ten thousandth (10^{-4}) of the first, and the fiftieth animal link, if there was one, a population of 10^{-49} the size of the first. Five animal links are certainly possible, a few fairly clear cut cases having been in fact recorded. If, however, we wanted 50 links, starting with a protozoan or rotifer feeding on algae with a density of 10^6 cells per ml, we should need a volume of 10^{26} cubic kilometers to accommodate on an average one specimen of the ultimate predator, and this is vastly greater than the volume of the world ocean. Clearly the Eltonian food-chain of itself cannot give any great diversity, and the same is almost certainly true of the other types of food chain, based on detritus feeding or on parasitism.

Natural selection

Before proceeding to a further consideration of diversity, it is, however, desirable to consider the kinds of selective force that may operate on a food chain, for this may limit the possible diversity.

It is reasonably certain that natural selection will tend to maintain the efficiency of transfer from one level to another at a maximum. Any increase in the predatory efficiency of the nth link of a simple food chain will however always increase the possibility of the extermination of the $(n-1)^{th}$ link. If this occurs either the species constituting the nth link must adapt itself to eating the $(n-2)^{th}$ link or itself become extinct. This process will in fact tend to shortening of food chains. A lengthening can presumably occur most simply by the development of a new terminal carnivore link, as its niche is by definition previously empty. In most cases this is not likely to be easy. The evolution of the whale-bone whales, which at least in the case of *Balaenoptera borealis*, can feed largely on copepods and so rank on occasions as primary carnivores (Bigelow, 1926), presumably constitutes the most dramatic example of the shortening of a food chain. Mechanical considerations would have prevented the evolution of a larger rarer predator, until man developed essentially non-Eltonian methods of hunting whales.

Effect of size

A second important limitation of the length of a food chain is due to the fact that ordinarily animals change their size during free life. If the terminal member of a chain were a fish that grew from say one cm to 150 cms in the course of an ordinary life, this size change would set a limit by competition to the possible number of otherwise conceivable links in the 1-150 cm range. At least in fishes this type of process (metaphoetesis) may involve the smaller specimens belonging to links below the larger and the chain length is thus lengthened, though under strong limitations, by cannibalism.

We may next enquire into what determines the number of food chains in a community. In part the answer is clear, though if we cease to be zoologists and become biologists, the answer begs the question. Within certain limits, the number of kinds of primary producers is certainly involved, because many herbivorous animals are somewhat eclectic in their tastes and many more limited by their size or by such structural adaptations for feeding that they have been able to develop.

Effects of terrestrial plants

The extraordinary diversity of the terrestrial fauna, which is much greater than that of the marine fauna, is clearly due largely to the diversity provided by terrestrial plants. This diversity is actually two-fold. Firstly, since terrestrial plants compete for light, they have tended to evolve into structures growing into a gaseous medium of negligible buoyancy. This has led to the formation of specialized supporting, photosynthetic, and reproductive structures which inevitably differ in chemical and physical properties. The ancient Danes and Irish are supposed to have eaten elm-bark, and sometimes sawdust, in periods of stress, has been hydrolyzed to produce edible carbohydrate; but usually man, the most omnivorous of all animals, has avoided almost all parts of trees except fruits as sources of food, though various individual species of animals can deal with practically every tissue of many arboreal species. A major source of terrestrial diversity was thus introduced by the evolution of almost 200,000 species of flowering plants, and the three quarters of a million insects supposedly known today are in part a product of that diversity. But of itself merely providing five or ten kinds of food of different consistencies and compositions does not get us much further than the five or ten links of an Eltonian pyramid. On the whole the problem still remains, but in the new form: why are there so many kinds of plants? As a zoologist I do not want to attack that question directly, I want to stick with animals, but also to get the answer. Since, however, the plants are part of the general system of communities, any sufficiently abstract properties of such communities are likely to be relevant to plants as well as to herbivores and carnivores. It is, therefore, by being somewhat abstract, though with concrete zoological details as examples, that I intend to proceed.

INTERRELATIONS OF FOOD CHAINS

Biological communities do not consist of independent food chains, but of food webs, of such a kind that an individual at any level (corresponding to a link in a single chain) can use some but not all of the food provided by species in the levels below it.

It has long been realized that the presence of two species at any level, either of which can be eaten by a predator at a level above, but which may differ in palatability, ease of capture or seasonal and local abundance, may provide alternative foods for the predator. The predator, therefore, will neither become extinct itself nor exterminate its usual prey, when for any reason, not dependent on prey-predator relationships, the usual prey happens to be abnormally scarce. This aspect of complicated food webs has been stressed by many ecologists, of whom the Chicago school as represented by Allee, Emerson, Park, Park and Schmidt (1949), Odum (1953) and Elton (1958), may in particular be mentioned. Recently MacArthur (1955) using an ingenious but simple application of information theory has generalized the points of view of earlier workers by providing a formal proof of the increase in stability of a community as the number of links in its food web increases.

MacArthur concludes that in the evolution of a natural community two partly antagonistic processes are occurring. More efficient species will replace less efficient species, but more stable communities will outlast less stable communities. In the process of community formation, the entry of a new species may involve one of three possibilities. It may completely displace an old species. This of itself does not necessarily change the stability, though it may do so if the new species inherently has a more stable population (cf. Slobodkin, 1956) than the old. Secondly, it may occupy an unfilled niche, which may, by providing new partially independent links, increase stability. Thirdly, it may partition a niche with a pre-existing species. Elton (1958) in a fascinating work largely devoted to the fate of species accidentally or purposefully introduced by man, concludes that in very diverse communities such introductions are difficult. Early in the history of a community we may suppose many niches will be empty and invasion will proceed easily; as the community becomes more diversified, the process will be progressively more difficult. Sometimes an extremely successful invader may oust a species but add little or nothing to stability, at other times the invader by some specialization will be able to compete successfully for the marginal parts of a niche. In all cases it is probable that invasion is most likely when one or more species happen to be fluctuating and are underrepresented at a given moment. As the communities build up, these opportunities will get progressively rarer. In this way a complex community containing some highly specialized species is constructed asymptotically.

Modern ecological theory therefore appears to answer our initial question at least partially by saying that there is a great diversity of organisms because communities of many diversified organisms are better able to persist than are communities of fewer less diversified organisms. Even though the entry of an invader which takes over part of a niche will lead to the reduction in the *average* population of the species originally present, it will also lead to an increase in stability reducing the risk of the original population being at times underrepresented to a dangerous degree. In this way loss of some niche space may be compensated by reduction in the amplitude of fluctuations in a way that can be advantageous to both species. The process however appears likely to be asymptotic and we have now to consider what sets the asymptote, or in simpler words why are there not more different kinds of animals?

LIMITATION OF DIVERSITY

It is first obvious that the processes of evolution of communities must be under various sorts of external control, and that in some cases such control limits the possible diversity. Several investigators, notably Odum (1953) and MacArthur (1955), have pointed out that the more or less cyclical oscillations observed in arctic and boreal fauna may be due in part to the communities not being sufficiently complex to damp out oscillations. It is certain that the fauna of any such region is qualitatively poorer than that of warm temperate and tropical areas of comparable effective precipitation. It is probably considered to be intuitively obvious that this should be so, but on analysis the obviousness tends to disappear. If we can have one or two species of a large family adapted to the rigors of Arctic existence, why can we not have more? It is reasonable to suppose that the total biomass may be involved. If the fundamental productivity of an area is limited by a short growing season to such a degree that the total biomass is less than under more favorable conditions, then the rarer species in a community may be so rare that they do not exist. It is also probable that certain absolute limitations on growth-forms of plants, such as those that make the development of forest impossible above a certain latitude, may in so acting, severely limit the number of niches. Dr. Robert MacArthur points out that the development of high tropical rain forest increases the bird fauna more than that of mammals, and Thorson (1957) likewise has shown that the so-called infauna show no increase of species toward the tropics while the marine epifauna becomes more diversified. The importance of this aspect of the plant or animal substratum, which depends largely on the length of the growing season and other aspects of productivity is related to that of the environmental mosaic discussed later.

We may also inquire, but at present cannot obtain any likely answer, whether the arctic fauna is not itself too young to have achieved its maximum diversity. Finally, the continual occurrence of catastrophes, as Wynne-Edwards (1952) has emphasized, may keep the arctic terrestrial community in a state of perennial though stunted youth.

Closely related to the problems of environmental rigor and stability, is the question of the absolute size of the habitat that can be colonized. Over much of western Europe there are three common species of small voles, namely *Microtus arvalis*, *M. agrestis* and *Clethrionomys glareolus*. These are sympatric but with somewhat different ecological preferences.

In the smaller islands off Britain and in the English channel, there is only one case of two species co-occurring on an island, namely *M. agrestis* and Clethrionomys on the island of Mull in the Inner Hebrides (Barrett-Hamilton and Hinton, 1911–1921). On the Orkneys the single species is *M. orcadensis*, which in morphology and cytology is a well-differentiated ally of *M. arvalis*; a comparable animal (*M. sarnius*) occurs on Guernsey. On most of the Scottish Islands only subspecies of *M. agrestis* occur, but on Mull and Raasay, on the Welsh island of Skomer, as well as on Jersey, races of Clethrionomys of somewhat uncertain status are found. No voles have reached Ireland, presumably for paleogeographic reasons, but they are also absent from a number of small islands, notably Alderney and Sark. The last named island must have been as well placed as Guernsey to receive *Microtus arvalis*. Still stranger is the fact that although it could not have got to the Orkneys without entering the mainland of Britain, no vole of the *arvalis* type now occurs in the latter country. Cases of this sort may be perhaps explained by the lack of favorable refuges in randomly distributed very unfavorable seasons or under special kinds of competition. This explanation is very reasonable as an explanation of the lack of Microtus on Sark, where it may have had difficulty in competing with *Rattus rattus* in a small area. It would be stretching one's credulity to suppose that the area of Great Britain is too small to permit the existence of two sympatric species of Microtus, but no other explanation seems to have been proposed.

It is a matter of considerable interest that Lack (1942) studying the populations of birds on some of these small British islands concluded that such populations are often unstable, and that the few species present often occupied larger niches than on the mainland in the presence of competitors. Such faunas provide examples of communities held at an early stage in development because there is not enough space for the evolution of a fuller and more stable community.

NICHE REQUIREMENTS

The various evolutionary tendencies, notably metaphoetesis, which operate on single food chains must operate equally on the food-web, but we also have a new, if comparable, problem as to how much difference between two species at the same level is needed to prevent them from occupying the same niche. Where metric characters are involved we can gain some insight into this extremely important problem by the study of what Brown and Wilson (1956) have called *character displacement* or the divergence shown when two partly allopatric species of comparable niche requirements become sympatric in part of their range.

I have collected together a number of cases of mammals and birds which appear to exhibit the phenomenon (table 1). These cases involve metric characters related to the trophic apparatus, the length of the culmen in birds and of the skull in mammals appearing to provide appropriate measures. Where the species co-occur, the ratio of the larger to the small form varies from 1.1 to 1.4, the mean ratio being 1.28 or roughly 1.3. This latter figure may tentatively be used as an indication of the kind of difference necessary to permit two species to co-occur in different niches but at the same level of a food-web. In the case of the aquatic insects with which I began my address, we have over most of Europe three very closely allied species of Corixa, the largest *punctata*, being about 116 per cent longer than the middle sized species *macrocephala*, and 146 per cent longer than the small species *affinis*. In northwestern Europe there is a fourth species, *C. dentipes*, as large as *C. punctata* and very similar in appearance. A single observation (Brown, 1948) suggests that this is what I have elsewhere (Hutchinson, 1951) termed a fugitive species, maintaining itself in the face of competition mainly on account of greater mobility. According to Macan (1954) while both *affinis* and *macrocephala* may occur with *punctata* they never are found with each other, so that all three species never occur together. In the eastern part of the range, *macrocephala* drops out, and *punctata* appears to have a discontinuous distribution, being recorded as far east as Simla, but not in southern Persia or Kashmir, where *affinis* occurs. In these eastern localities, where it occurs by itself, *affinis* is larger and darker than in the west, and superficially looks like *macrocephala* (Hutchinson, 1940).

This case is very interesting because it looks as though character displacement is occurring, but that the size differences between the three species are just not great enough to allow them all to co-occur. Other characters than size are in fact clearly involved in the separation, *macrocephala* preferring deeper water than *affinis* and the latter being more tolerant of brackish conditions. It is also interesting because it calls attention to a marked difference that must occur between hemimetabolous insects with annual life cycles involving relatively long growth periods, and birds or mammals in which the period of growth in length is short and of a very special nature compared with the total life span. In the latter, niche separation may be possible merely through genetic size differences, while in a pair of ani-

TABLE 1

Mean character displacement in measurable trophic structures in mammals (skull) and birds (culmen); data for Mustela from Miller (1912); Apodemus from Cranbrook (1957); Sitta from Brown and Wilson (1956) after Vaurie; Galapagos finches from Lack (1947)

	Locality and measurement when sympatric	Locality and measurement when allopatric	Ratio when sympatric
Mustela nivalis	Britain; skull ♂ 39.3 ♀ 33.6 mm.	(*boccamela*) S. France, Italy ♂ 42.9 ♀ 34.7 mm.	
		(*iberica*) Spain, Portugal ♂ 40.4 ♀ 36.0	♂ 100:128 ♀ 100:134
M. erminea	Britain; " ♂ 50.4 ♀ 45.0	(*hibernica*) Ireland ♂ 46.0 ♀ 41.9	
Apodemus sylvaticus	Britain; " 24.8	unnamed races on Channel Islands 25.6–26.7	100:109
A. flavicollis	Britain; " 27.0		
Sitta tephronota	Iran; culmen 29.0	races east of overlap 25.5	100:124
S. neumayer	Iran; " 23.5	races west of overlap 26.0	
Geospiza fortis	Indefatigable Isl.; culmen 12.0	Daphne Isl. 10.5	100:143
G. fuliginosa	Indefatigable Isl.; " 8.4	Crossman Isl. 9.3	
Camarhynchus parvulus	James Isl.; " 7.0	N. Albemarle Isl. 7.0	James 100:140:180
	Indefatigable Isl.; " 7.5	Chatham Isl. 8.0	100:129
C. psittacula	S. Albemarle Isl.; " 7.3	Abington Isl. 10.1	Indefatigable 100:128:162
	James Isl.; " 9.8	Bindloe Isl. 10.5	100:127
	Indefatigable Isl.; " 9.6		
C. pallidus	S. Albemarle Isl.; " 8.5		
	James Isl.; " 12.6	N. Albemarle Isl. 11.7	S. Albemarle 100:116:153
	Indefatigable Isl.; " 12.1	Chatham Isl. 10.8	100:132
	S. Albemarle Isl.; " 11.2		
			Mean ratio 100:128

mals like *C. punctata* and *C. affinis* we need not only a size difference but a seasonal one in reproduction; this is likely to be a rather complicated matter. For the larger of two species always to be larger, it must never breed later than the smaller one. I do not doubt that this is what was happening in the pond on Monte Pellegrino, but have no idea how the difference is achieved.

I want to emphasize the complexity of the adaptation necessary on the part of two species inhabiting adjacent niches in a given biotope, as it probably underlies a phenomenon which to some has appeared rather puzzling. MacArthur (1957) has shown that in a sufficiently large bird fauna, in a uniform undisturbed habitat, areas occupied by the different species appear to correspond to the random non-overlapping fractionation of a plane or volume. Kohn (1959) has found the same thing for the cone-shells (Conus) on the Hawaiian reefs. This type of arrangement almost certainly implies such individual and unpredictable complexities in the determination of the niche boundaries, and so of the actual areas colonized, that in any overall view, the process would appear random. It is fairly obvious that in different types of community the divisibility of niches will differ and so the degree of diversity that can be achieved. The fine details of the process have not been adequately investigated, though many data must already exist that could be organized to throw light on the problem.

MOSAIC NATURE OF THE ENVIRONMENT

A final aspect of the limitation of possible diversity, and one that perhaps is of greatest importance, concerns what may be called the mosaic nature of the environment. Except perhaps in open water when only uniform quasi-horizontal surfaces are considered, every area colonized by organisms has some local diversity. The significance of such local diversity depends very largely on the size of the organisms under consideration. In another paper MacArthur and I (Hutchinson and MacArthur, 1959) have attempted a theoretical formulation of this property of living communities and have pointed out that even if we consider only the herbivorous level or only one of the carnivorous levels, there are likely, above a certain lower limit of size, to be more species of small or medium sized organisms than of large organisms. It is difficult to go much beyond crude qualitative impressions in testing this hypothesis, but we find that for mammal faunas, which contain such diverse organisms that they may well be regarded as models of whole faunas, there is a definite hint of the kind of theoretical distribution that we deduce. In qualitative terms the phenomenon can be exemplified by any of the larger species of ungulates which may require a number of different kinds of terrain within their home ranges, any one of which types of terrain might be the habitat of some small species. Most of the genera or even subfamilies of very large terrestrial animals contain only one or two sympatric species. In this connection I cannot refrain from pointing out the immense scientific importance of obtaining a really full insight into the ecology of the large mammals of Africa while they can still be studied under natural conditions. It is indeed quite possible that the results of studies on these wonderful animals would in long-range though purely practical terms pay for the establishment of greater reservations and National Parks than at present exist.

In the passerine birds the occurrence of five or six closely related sympatric species is a commonplace. In the mammal fauna of western Europe no genus appears to contain more than four strictly sympatric species. In Britain this number is not reached even by Mustela with three species, on the adjacent parts of the continent there may be three sympatric shrews of the genus Crocidura and in parts of Holland three of Microtus. In the same general region there are genera of insects containing hundreds of species, as in Athela in the Coleoptera and Dasyhelea in the Diptera Nematocera. The same phenomenon will be encountered whenever any well-studied fauna is considered. Irrespective of their position in a food chain, small size, by permitting animals to become specialized to the conditions offered by small diversified elements of the environmental mosaic, clearly makes possible a degree of diversity quite unknown among groups of larger organisms.

We may, therefore, conclude that the reason why there are so many species of animals is at least partly because a complex trophic organization of a community is more stable than a simple one, but that limits are set by the tendency of food chains to shorten or become blurred, by unfavorable physical factors, by space, by the fineness of possible subdivision of niches, and by those characters of the environmental mosaic which permit a greater diversity of small than of large allied species.

CONCLUDING DISCUSSION

In conclusion I should like to point out three very general aspects of the sort of process I have described. One speculative approach to evolutionary theory arises from some of these conclusions. Just as adaptative evolution by natural selection is less easy in a small population of a species than in a larger one, because the total pool of genetic variability is inevitably less, so it is probable that a group containing many diversified species will be able to seize new evolutionary opportunities more easily than an undiversified group. There will be some limits to this process. Where large size permits the development of a brain capable of much new learnt behavior, the greater plasticity acquired by the individual species will offset the disadvantage of the small number of allied species characteristic of groups of large animals. Early during evolution the main process from the standpoint of community structure was the filling of all the niche space potentially available for producer and decomposer organisms and for herbivorous animals. As the latter, and still more as carnivorous animals began to appear, the persistence of more stable communities would imply splitting of niches previously occupied by single species as the communities became more diverse. As this process continued one would expect the overall rate of evolution to have increased, as the increasing diversity increased the probability of the existence of species preadapted to new and unusual niches. It is reasonable to suppose that strong predation among macroscopic metazoa did not begin until the late Precambrian, and that the appearance of powerful predators led to the appearance of fossilizable skeletons. This seems the only reasonable hypothesis, of those so far advanced, to account for the relatively sudden appearance of several fossilizable groups in the Lower Cambrian. The process of diversification would, according to this argument, be somewhat autocatakinetic even without the increased stability that it would produce; with the increase in stability it would be still more a self inducing process, but one, as we have seen, with an upper limit. Part of this upper limit is set by the impossibility of having many sympatric allied species of large animals. These however are the animals that can pass from primarily innate to highly modifiable behavior. From an evolutionary point of view, once they have appeared, there is perhaps less need for diversity, though from other points of view, as Elton (1958) has stressed in dealing with human activities, the stability provided by diversity can be valuable even to the most adaptable of all large animals. We may perhaps therefore see in the process of evolution an increase in diversity at an increasing rate till the early Paleozoic, by which time the familiar types of community structure were established. There followed then a long period in which various large and finally large-brained species became dominant, and then a period in which man has been reducing diversity by a rapidly increasing tendency to cause extinction of supposedly unwanted species, often in an indiscriminate manner. Finally we may hope for a limited reversal of this process when man becomes aware of the value of diversity no less in an economic than in an esthetic and scientific sense.

A second and much more metaphysical general point is perhaps worth a moment's discussion. The evolution of biological communities, though each species appears to fend for itself alone, produces integrated aggregates which increase in stability. There is nothing mysterious about this; it follows from mathematical theory and appears to be confirmed to some extent empirically. It is however a phenomenon which also finds analogies in other fields in which a more complex type of behavior, that we intuitively regard as higher, emerges as the result of the interaction of less complex types of behavior, that we call lower. The emergence of love as an antidote to aggression, as Lorenz pictures the process, or the development of cooperation from various forms of more or less inevitable group behavior that Allee (1931) has stressed are examples of this from the more complex types of biological systems.

In the ordinary sense of explanation in science, such phenomena are explicable. The types of holistic philosophy which import *ad hoc* mysteries into science whenever such a situation is met are obviously unnecessary. Yet perhaps we may wonder whether the empirical fact that it is the nature of things for this type of explicable emergence to occur is not something that itself requires an explanation. Many objections can be raised to such a view; a friendly organization of biologists could not occur in a universe in which cooperative behavior was impossible and without your cooperation I could not raise the problem. The question may in fact appear to certain types of philosophers not to be a real one, though I suspect such philosophers in their desire to demonstrate how often people talk nonsense, may sometimes show less ingenuity than would be desirable in finding some sense in such questions. Even if the answer to such a question were positive, it might not get us very far; to an existentialist, life would have merely provided yet one more problem; students of Whitehead might be made happier, though on the whole the obscurities of that great writer do not seem to generate unhappiness; the religious philosophers would welcome a positive answer but note that it told them nothing that they did not know before; Marxists might merely say, "I told you so." In spite of this I suspect that the question is worth raising, and that it could be phrased so as to provide some sort of real dichotomy between alternatives; I therefore raise it knowing that I cannot, and suspecting that at present others cannot, provide an intellectually satisfying answer.

My third general point is less metaphysical, but not without interest. If I am right that it is easier to have a greater diversity of small than of large organisms, then the evolutionary process in small organisms will differ somewhat from that of large ones. Wherever we have a great array of allied sympatric species there must be an emphasis on very accurate interspecific mating barriers which is unnecessary where virtually no sympatric allies occur. We ourselves are large animals in this sense; it would seem very unlikely that the peculiar lability that seems to exist in man, in which even the direction of normal sexual behavior must be learnt, could have developed to quite the existing extent if species recognition, involving closely related sympatric congeners, had been necessary. Elsewhere (Hutchinson, 1959) I have attempted to show that the difficulties that *Homo sapiens* has to face in this regard may imply various unsuspected processes in human evolutionary selection. But perhaps Santa Rosalia would find at this point that we are speculating too freely, so for the moment, while under her patronage, I will say no more.

ACKNOWLEDGMENTS

Dr. A. Minganti of the University of Palermo enabled me to collect on Monte Pellegrino. Professor B. M. Knox of the Department of Classics of Yale University gave me a rare and elegant word from the Greek to express the blurring of a food chain. Dr. L. B. Slobodkin of the University of Michigan and Dr. R. H. MacArthur of the University of Pennsylvania provided me with their customary kinds of intellectual stimulation. To all these friends I am most grateful.

LITERATURE CITED

Allee, W. C., 1931, Animal aggregations: a study in general sociology. vii, 431 pp. University of Chicago Press, Chicago, Illinois.

Allee, W. C., A. E. Emerson, O. Park, T. Park and K. P. Schmidt, 1949, Principles of animal ecology. xii, 837 pp. W. B. Saunders Co., Philadelphia, Pennsylvania.

Barrett-Hamilton, G. E. H., and M. A. C. Hinton, 1911-1921, A history of British mammals. Vol. 2. 748 pp. Gurney and Jackson, London, England.

Bigelow, H. B., 1926, Plankton of the offshore waters of the Gulf of Maine. Bull. U. S. Bur. Fisheries 40: 1-509.

Brown, E. S., 1958, A contribution towards an ecological survey of the aquatic and semi-aquatic Hemiptera-Heteroptera (water-bugs) of the British Isles etc. Trans. Soc. British Entom. 9: 151-195.

Brown, W. L., and E. O. Wilson, 1956, Character displacement. Systematic Zoology 5: 49-64.

Cranbrook, Lord, 1957, Long-tailed field mice (Apodemus) from the Channel Islands. Proc. Zool. Soc. London 128: 597-600.

Elton, C. S., 1958, The ecology of invasions by animals and plants. 159 pp. Methuen Ltd., London, England.

Hutchinson, G. E., 1951, Copepodology for the ornithologist. Ecology 32: 571-577.

1958, Concluding remarks. Cold Spring Harbor Symp. Quant. Biol. 22: 415-427.

1959, A speculative consideration of certain possible forms of sexual selection in man. Amer. Nat. 93: 81-92.

Hutchinson, G. E., and R. MacArthur, 1959, A theoretical ecological model of size distributions among species of animals. Amer. Nat. 93: 117-126.

Hyman, L. H., 1955, How many species? Systematic Zoology 4: 142-143.

Kohn, A. J., 1959, The ecology of Conus in Hawaii. Ecol. Monogr. (in press).

Lack, D., 1942, Ecological features of the bird faunas of British small islands. J. Animal Ecol. London 11: 9-36.

1947, Darwin's Finches. x, 208 pp. Cambridge University Press, Cambridge, England.

1954, The natural regulation of animal numbers. viii, 347 pp. Clarendon Press, Oxford, England.

Lindeman, R. L., 1942, The trophic-dynamic aspect of ecology. Ecology 23: 399-408.

Macan, T. T., 1954, A contribution to the study of the ecology of Corixidae (Hemipt). J. Animal Ecol. 23: 115-141.

MacArthur, R. H., 1955, Fluctuations of animal populations and a measure of community stability. Ecology 35: 533-536.

1957, On the relative abundance of bird species. Proc. Nat. Acad. Sci. Wash. 43: 293-295.

Miller, G. S., Catalogue of the mammals of Western Europe. xv, 1019 pp. British Museum, London, England.

Muller, S. W., and A. Campbell, 1954, The relative number of living and fossil species of animals. Systematic Zoology 3: 168-170.

Odum, E. P., 1953, Fundamentals of ecology. xii, 387 pp. W. B. Saunders Co., Philadelphia, Pennsylvania, and London, England.

Slobodkin, L. B., 1955, Condition for population equilibrium. Ecology 35: 530-533.

Thorson, G., 1957, Bottom communities. Chap. 17 *in* Treatise on marine ecology and paleoecology. Vol. 1. Geol. Soc. Amer. Memoir 67: 461-534.

Wallace, A. R., 1858, On the tendency of varieties to depart indefinitely from the original type. *In* C. Darwin and A. R. Wallace, On the tendency of species to form varieties; and on the perpetuation of varieties and species by natural means of selection. J. Linn. Soc. (Zool.) 3: 45-62.

Wynne-Edwards, V. C., 1952, Zoology of the Baird Expedition (1950). I. The birds observed in central and southeast Baffin Island. Auk 69: 353-391.

ON THE RELATIVE ABUNDANCE OF SPECIES

ROBERT MACARTHUR

Department of Zoology, University of Pennsylvania,
Philadelphia, Pennsylvania

This paper will contain a discussion of the ecological consequences which can be deduced from data on the comparative abundances of species found together.

Let $N_i(t)$ be the abundance of the i-th species at time t. Then if $r_i(t)$ is defined by

$$r_i(t) = \frac{1}{N_i(t)} \frac{dN_i(t)}{dt},$$

integrating, we obtain

$$\log N_i(t) = \log N_i(O) + \int_o^t r_i(t)dt. \quad (1)$$

Notice that r is permitted to vary. There are two opposed schools in ecology, one maintaining that the integral in equation (1) is important compared with log $N_i(O)$ and the other maintaining that it is unimportant. These two views may lead to different ideas of the relative sizes of the $N_i(t)$ and so they will be discussed separately.

OPPORTUNISTIC SPECIES

Opinion 1: $\int_o^t r_i(t)dt$ *is important compared with log* $N_i(O)$. Such species are essentially opportunistic, being common when conditions have been good for some time; no equilibrium populations are maintained except perhaps as long-term averages. Basically, in this case, relative abundance is of little biological interest, because it is controlled by the vagaries of the climate and other aspects of the environment affecting r. However, it is often, but not always, possible to predict the relative abundance directly from equation (1). For, when the r_i vary completely independently, their accumulated integrals undergo "random walks" and will become normally distributed (Feller, 1950; Margalef, 1957, has already pointed this out.) And, by our assumption, the log $N_i(t)$ will be normally distributed and the $N_i(t)$ will therefore be log-normally distributed. A difficult and perhaps more important case leading to a log-normal distribution is discussed later. Notice that this distribution reflects nothing about the structure of the community; common species are those which lately have had large r's; at different times, or different places (within the same habitat) different species will be the most abundant. These conclusions form the easiest way to recognize opportunistic species. Thus, diatom species in polluted rivers show a log-normal distribution of abundances, and have common species with large r and with ir-

Reproduced with permission from The American Naturalist, XCIV: 25-36, 1960. Published by The American Society of Naturalists, Tempe, Arizona.

regular distribution (Patrick, 1954, and personal communication). The insects studied by Ross (1957) had common species unpredictable in space and time; they too must be opportunistic. In fact, it is reasonable to suppose that many terrestrial invertebrates (Andrewartha and Birch, 1954) and plants (at least those characteristic of early stages in succession; Salisbury, 1942) fall in this category 1. And at least some vertebrates (for example, Cape May and bay-breasted warblers; MacArthur, 1958) are also opportunistic.

EQUILIBRIUM SPECIES

Opinion 2: $\int_0^t r_i(t)dt$ *is unimportant compared with log* $N_i(O)$. This is the case of species in some sort of population equilibrium. Here, the study of relative abundance is important and may reveal structural features of the whole community. In this case, there will be as many models of relative abundance as there are models of species population interactions, and the results require a more elaborate discussion. The total abundance of a species over its whole range is different from its density in a local habitat, and the relative abundances of species over a large area will thus be quite different from those in a small section of the area. Which will be easier to understand? Two features will often make the relative abundances over a small area easier to understand. First, the environmental changes are relatively great in a large area; no theory of relative abundance can be expected to predict these. Second, there is some evidence on the evolution of population size (Fisher, 1958, p. 112). The population unit which undergoes natural selection is the hypothetical deme, even though this can not be delimited sharply. Thus, if relative abundances are measured on areas of size comparable to that usually occupied by a deme, then we may expect an evolutionary law of relative abundance of the type qualitatively outlined by Fisher. Such a theory would be very interesting. Fisher suggests that common species will increase faster than rare ones. If, as a first approximation, we assume that the rate of fixation of beneficial genes is proportional to the population size, so that the improvement each year is about proportional to population size, then as shown by Cramer (1946, pp. 218–221), population sizes will become log-normally distributed. This conclusion is of interest since one of the prominent theories of relative abundance, due to Preston (1948), shows that this curve fits observed data fairly well. However for ecological purposes it is useful to try to avoid the genetic assumptions involved in an evolutionary theory, and thereby to make alternative hypotheses which have a more purely ecological meaning. There are two principal alternatives.

(a) *The total number of individuals of all species together is essentially constant*, so that increases in the populations of some must result in decreases in others. There is a fairly natural model for this alternative. It will be illustrated with an example. Suppose there are ten individuals and four species; represent the individuals by ten i's in a row. We can then draw five vertical bars between the letters in any positions such that at least one bar is at each end of the row: ||ii |iiiii |iii |. There are now four spaces between bars; these represent the four species, and the number of i's in the spaces are the numbers of individuals in the species. In the example, the left-hand species has no individuals, that is, is not represented in the census, and the other species have two, five and three individuals. The essential characteristic of this model is that an increase in one species' abundance, that is, a change in the position of one of the vertical bars, automatically involves a corresponding decrease in the abundances of other species.

Here, and for the rest of this paper, it is assumed that the species whose abundances are being compared are of roughly equal size, so that an individual of one species is comparable to an individual of any of the others. It is thus reasonable to consider the relative abundances of the bird species feeding on defoliating insects, and, separately, to consider the relative abundances of the parasitic insects. It is, however, both unreasonable and uninteresting to consider the relative abundances of the combined populations.

(b) *The abundances of different species are truly independent.* Here, an increase in the abundance of one species has no necessary effect on that of any others. The appropriate model in this case is a sequence of i's with a pair of vertical bars determining the abundance of each species; the position of each pair of bars is independent of that of the pairs of bars which determined the abundances of the other species.

These alternatives do not yet unambiguously determine relative abundances. Relative abundances are precisely determined, however, if we can assume that the bars are placed randomly among the i's. Mathematically, this is equivalent to having all positions of the bars equally probable. Now it is well known that a given species is usually common in one or two of the many habitats present in a region. In others it will be rare or absent and in still others it will have intermediate abundance. It is also well known that the different species have different habitat choices. Thus a census taker by a change in choice of homogenous habitat is quite likely to have many species change radically in abundance. And thus, in any given habitat the abundances are likely to be quite random.

These models, combined with the random element due to the census-taker, should determine the relative abundance of species, of approximately the same sizes, in communities obeying one of the two alternatives, a or b.

In an earlier paper (MacArthur, 1957), the formula for the expected abundance of the r–th rarest species was shown to be, for alternative a,

$$\frac{m}{n}\sum_{i=1}^{r}\frac{1}{n-i+1} \tag{2}$$

where there are n species and m individuals, and for alternative b,

$$(3) \qquad \frac{\sqrt{n-r+1} - \sqrt{n-r}}{\sqrt{n}}$$

Alternative a (total number of individuals constant) was shown to be closer to the truth, for birds at least, than alternative b (species abundances determined independently). This suggests that the subdivided segments of the sequence of i's in alternative a should correspond to a useful biological property of the organisms. Hutchinson (1957) defined "niche" in very elegant terms and was able to show that his "niche" and the non-overlapping segments of alternative a are closely related. It is thus appropriate to refer to a as "niches non-overlapping" and b as "niches overlapping."

Before passing on to a more detailed discussion of the evidence bearing on these alternatives, a different way of describing the same alternatives will be mentioned. If instead of ranking the species according to abundance and calculating the expected abundance of the r'th rarest species as was done in equations 2 and 3, one calculates the expected number of species with a given abundance (that is, the number of species with one individual, the number of species with two individuals, . . , the number of species with i individuals, etc.) the following formulae result (see appendix for proofs):

For alternative a, non-overlapping niches, the most probable number g_i of species with i individuals is given by the solution of

$$(2a) \qquad \log_e g_i + 1/2g_i = \lambda i + \mu$$

where λ and μ are undetermined constants. This implies that if alternative a is holding, a graph of $\log_e g_i + 1/(2g_i)$ against i should yield a straight line. For alternative b, overlapping niches, the expected number g_i of species with i individuals is given by

$$(3a) \qquad g_i = a - bi$$

where a and b are constants. Thus a graph of g_i against i should yield a straight line. The formulations of the results of alternatives a and b given in equations 2a and 3a are the same as those usually given to studies of relative abundance, but to the present author it is easier to think in terms of the formulation of equations 2 and 3, which dealt with ranked species.

In figure 1, alternatives a and b are compared with a bird census (Saunders, 1936) covering all of Quaker Run Valley in New York; in figure 2, the censuses of the component habitats (pasture, orchards, mature oak-hickory, etc.) are plotted. The expected curves for the two alternatives, based on equations 2 and 3, are plotted for comparison in figure 1. It is immediately clear that while as expected the total population of the valley fits neither alternative, the small, more homogenous habitats plotted in figure 2 are in very close agreement with alternative a as expressed by equation 2. (Any curve parallel to that for alternative a in figure 1 shows agreement with alternative a). The general close agreement is also very evident from figure 3 which is compiled from large tracts of virgin areas (three in Mexico

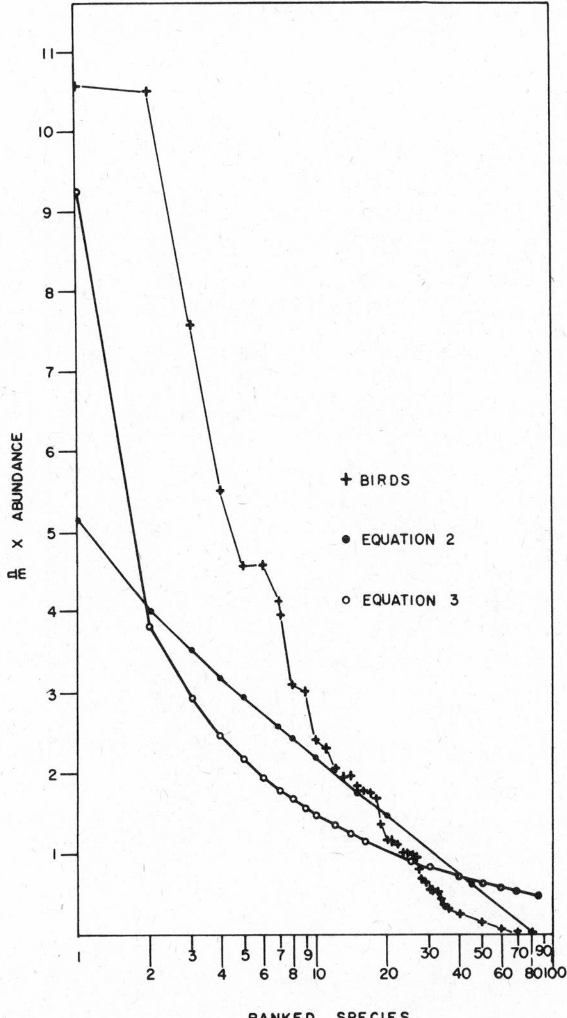

FIGURE 1. The abundances of the various bird species throughout Quaker Run Valley are ranked from commonest, on the left, to rarest, on the right, and plotted for comparison with the abundances expected from alternatives (a) and (b), which are given in equations 2 and 3.

[Davis, 1953, 1954, 1955], four in U.S.A. [Fables, 1957; Pugh, 1957; Longley, 1944; Hensley, 1954] and two in Canada [Stewart, 1955]).

These are all the censuses from virgin stands in extensive areas of that type which were analyzed. When bird censuses from mixed habitats are studied they reveal a divergence from the prediction of equation 2, however. This discrepancy is nearly always of the same type—common species are commoner than predicted and rare species are rarer—as was observed when the whole of Quaker Run Valley was compared with the formula of alternative a. Although two causes of this discrepancy will be discussed, the im-

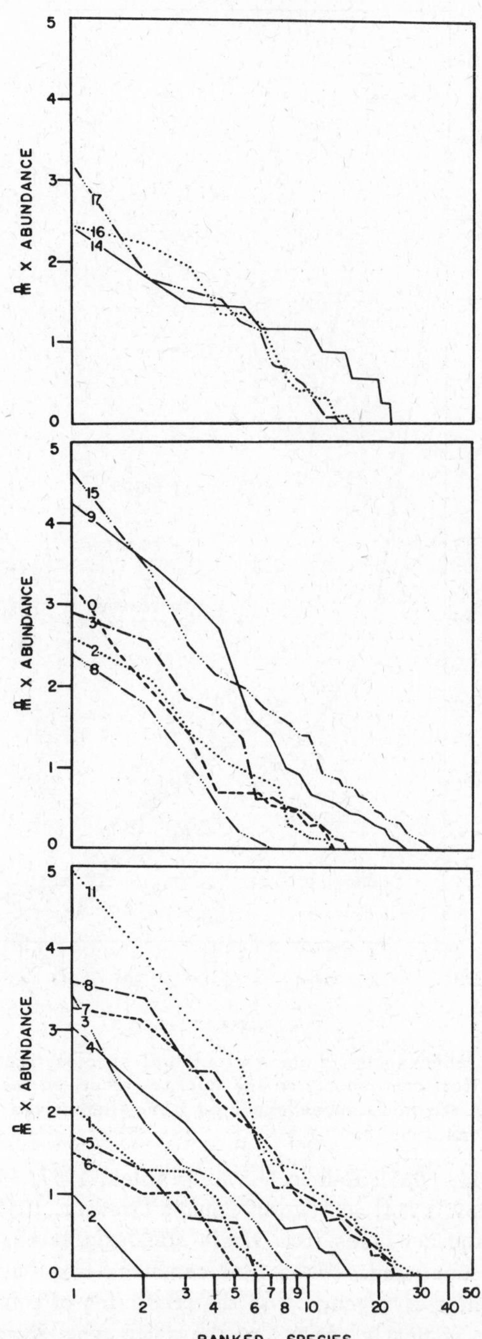

FIGURE 2. The bird species abundances of the component habitats of Quaker Run Valley are plotted separately, in the manner used in figure 1. A good fit to alternative (a) (equation 2) is indicated by the observed relative abundance curve being parallel to that curve in figure 1 which was calculated from equation 2.

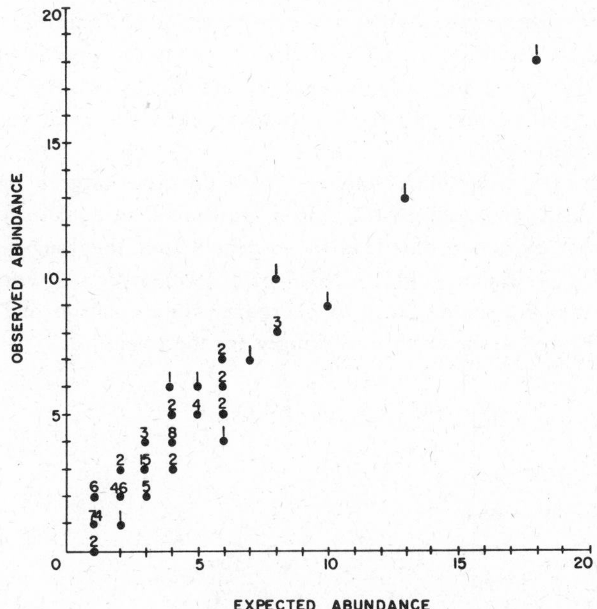

FIGURE 3. The observed abundances of species in nine tracts of virgin forest from Canada to Mexico are compared with the expected abundances calculated from equation 2. The expected abundances are taken as the nearest integer to the value predicted by the equation, and the parentheses enclose the number of species represented by the neighboring point on the graph.

portant thing to note is that it is always easier, that is, requires less information, to make a random system show excessive clumping than to make it excessively uniform. By moving any pair of points very close together one can always increase the clumping; to increase the uniformity one must have some knowledge of the configuration of nearby points, and move the pair accordingly. Thus any disturbance causing a departure from randomness is more likely to cause it in the direction of excessive clumping. Clumping in our model means clumping of the bars placed among the i's, which implies common species too common and rare too rare, as frequently observed. From a biological viewpoint, there seem to be two principal causes: (1) If the mean abundance of the species is different in two habitats, then the relative abundance in the combined area will depart from the expected. Thus, inclusion of an "edge" is likely to cause discrepancies. Hutchinson (1957) has appropriately called this phenomenon "heterogeneous diversity" and has discussed it thoroughly. (2) Empirically, common species in one habitat are more likely than rare ones to be common or at least present in neighboring habitats. For this reason, too, combining censuses from nearby habitats results in common species being unexpectedly common and rare species unexpectedly rare. Both of these causes operate in Quaker Run Valley where the individual habitats fitting equation 2 (and thus also 2 a) combine to give a total census deviating greatly. Thus for birds at least it appears that the postulates of alternative a—that the total number of individuals is roughly constant and the individuals are partitioned among the species present—are correct and that when the census-taker, by his choice of small homogeneous census area, makes the partitioning random, then the relative abundances conform to equation 2.

So far, in comparing bird censuses with the alternatives of equilibrium species, it has been assumed that birds are indeed in equilibrium. Perhaps the most direct evidence that this is so comes from the long-term censuses carried out by Williams (1947, 1948, 1949, 1950) over 18 years. These show that birds are more likely to decrease when common and to increase when rare. Figure 4 shows this strikingly for the ovenbird.

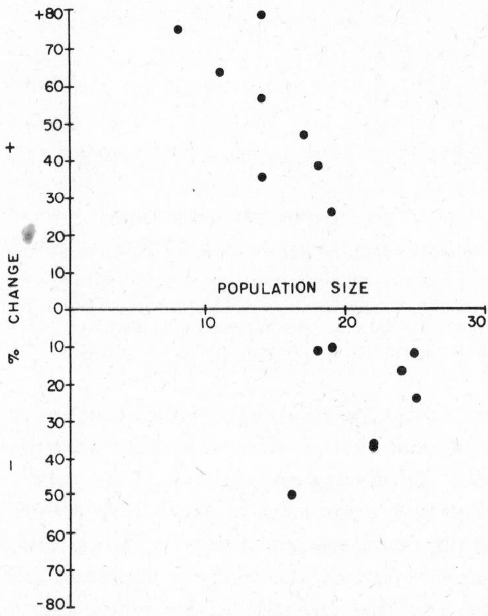

FIGURE 4. Increases and decreases over an 18-year period in the ovenbird population of a wood near Cleveland, Ohio, are plotted against the population size preceding the increase or decrease.

Data for other taxonomic groups are less convincing. Kohn (1959) has shown that Conus snails on Hawaiian reefs may agree closely with alternative a and equation 2, but otherwise, censuses of trees, fish, soil arthropods and other organisms deviate greatly from the expectation of alternative a and equation 2. Hairston and Byers (1954) feel that some species of soil arthropods show a local clumping and claim that this is not due to environmental heterogeneity. In this case, the environment is not being fully utilized and the postulates of alternative a, of course, fail to hold. Any closer agreement obtained by combining censuses from different areas is thus probably spurious. In the case of the trees, fish and perhaps some soil arthropods too, the census-taker almost certainly fails to effect the random subdivision of the individuals among the species, so that even if alternative a still holds for these groups, the relative abundances from censuses would not be expected to fit equation 2. Many of the censused areas are probably heterogeneously diverse also, so that an attempt to deduce ecological properties of these groups from their relative abundances cannot be made along these lines.

SUMMARY

1. A distinction is made between opportunistic and equilibrium species.
2. There is little ecological interest in the relative abundances of opportunistic species, but such species abundances should frequently have a log-normal distribution.
3. The relative abundances of equilibrium species are of considerable ecological interest and frequently can be deduced from the assumption that increase in one species population results in a roughly equal decrease in the populations of other species. To make the formulae well-defined it is necessary to assume that the census-taker has sampled a small area and thus achieved a certain sort of randomness.
4. For bird populations, at least, discrepancies between observations and predictions are negligible except when the censused area is compounded from different habitats. The discrepancy is then partly due to the fact that common species in one habitat are more likely to be present in adjacent habitats than are rare ones.

ACKNOWLEDGMENTS

G. E. Hutchinson has provided a continuous stream of good ideas on the subject for seven years since he first drew the author's attention to it. Drs. Peter Klopfer, Monte Lloyd, and David Lack made valuable comments and criticisms. The work was supported in part by a regular postdoctoral fellowship of the National Science Foundation which the author spent at the Edward Grey Institute of Field Ornithology at Oxford, England.

LITERATURE CITED

Andrewartha, H. G., and L. C. Birch, 1954, The distribution and abundance of animals. University of Chicago Press, Chicago, Ill.

Cramer, H., 1946, Mathematical methods of statistics. Princeton University Press, Princeton, N. J.

Davis, L. I., 1953, Census 31. Audubon Field Notes 7: 352-353.

1954, Census 40. Audubon Field Notes 8: 384.

1955, Census 27. Audubon Field Notes 9: 425-426.

Fables, S., and D. Fables, 1957, Census 9. Audubon Field Notes 11: 440.

Feller, W., 1951, Probability theory and its applications. John Wiley & Sons, Inc., New York, N. Y.

Fisher, R. A., 1958, The genetical theory of natural selection. Dover Publications, Inc., New York, N. Y.

Hairston, N. G., and G. W. Byers, 1954, Soil arthropods of a field in southern Michigan: a study in community ecology. Cont. Lab. Vert. Biol. 64. 37 pp.

Hensley, M. M., 1954, Ecological relations of the breeding bird populations of the desert biome of southern Arizona. Ecol. Mon. 24: 185-207.

Hutchinson, G. E., 1957, Concluding remarks. Cold Spring Harbor Symp. Quant. Biol. XXII: 415-427.

Kohn, A., 1959, The ecology of Conus in Hawaii. Ecol. Mon. 29: 47-90.

Longley, W. H., 1944, Census 27. The Season (Suppl. to Audubon Mag.) CLI: 24.

MacArthur, R. H., 1957, On the relative abundance of bird species. Proc. Nat. Acad. Sci. 45: 293-295.

1958, Population ecology of some warblers of northeastern coniferous forests. Ecol. 39: 599-619.

Margalef, R., 1957, La teoria de la informacion en ecologia. Memorias de la Real Academia de Ciencias y Artes de Barcelona. XXXII, No. 13. 79 pp.

Patrick, R., 1954, A new method for determining the pattern of the diatom flora. Notulae Naturae of Acad. Nat. Sci. Philadelphia. No. 259: 1-12.

Preston, F. W., 1948, The commonness, and rarity, of species. Ecol. 29: 254-283.

Pugh, E., and R. Pugh, 1957, Census 10. Audubon Field Notes 11: 440-441.

Ross, H. H., 1957, Principles of natural coexistence indicated by leafhopper populations. Evolution 11: 113-129.

Salisbury, E. J., 1942, The reproductive capacity of plants. Bell, London.

Saunders, A. A., 1936, Ecology of the birds of Quaker Run Valley, Alleghany State Park, New York. The State University of New York, Albany, New York.

Stewart, R. W., 1955, Censuses 9, 10. Audubon Field Notes 9: 415-416.

Williams, A. B., 1947, Climax beech-maple forest with some hemlock (15 year summary). Audubon Field Notes 1: 205-210.

1948, Census 8. Audubon Field Notes 2: 231.

1949, Census 14. Audubon Field Notes 3: 262-263.

1950, Census 7. Audubon Field Notes 4: 297-298.

APPENDIX

Suppose there are n species and m individuals. Let g_i be the number of species with i individuals. The *most probable* values of g_i will be computed for each type of randomness and for alternative a and b. To simplify manipulations it is useful to remember that, by Stirling's formula (cf. Feller, 1950, p. 43) $\log_e n!$ is very closely approximated by $\log_e (2)^{1/2} + (n + 1/2)\log_e n - n$, and thus the derivative of $\log_e n!$ is very nearly

$$(4) \qquad \frac{d}{dn} \log_e n! = \log_e n + \frac{1}{2n}.$$

Consider now the various cases.. First, suppose total abundance is constant (niches non-overlapping) and the bars dividing the i's are moved randomly (niches continuous). As pointed out earlier, this means the i's are indistinguishable, and distinguishable combinations of i's and bars are equally probable. The number of distinguishable arrangements producing g_1 species of abundance 1, g_2 with two individuals, . . . g_i with i individuals, . . . , is

$$\frac{n!}{g_1!\, g_2! \ldots g_i \ldots},$$

and since there are, in all, n species and m individuals,

$$(4') \qquad \sum_i i g_i = m, \quad \text{and} \quad \sum_i g_i = n.$$

By Lagrange's method of undetermined multipliers the state of greatest probability will be given by the solution for g_i (8 = 1, 2, ...)

$$(5) \qquad \frac{\partial}{\partial g_i}\left(\log_e \frac{n!}{g_1!\, g_2! \ldots g_i! \ldots} + \lambda \sum_i i g_i + \mu \sum_i g_i\right) = 0;$$

In view of 2, this is equivalent to

$$(6) \qquad \log_e g_i + \frac{1}{2 g_i} = \lambda i + \mu .$$

It would be possible to solve for λ (approximately $-m/n$) and for μ (approximately $\log (n^2/m)$) because of conditions 4′, but this seems unnecessary since equation 6 implies that a graph of $\log_e g_i + \frac{1}{2 g_i}$ against i will be a straight line, provided the hypothesis (continuous, non-overlapping niches) is valid.

Consider, next, alternative b. Here the species abundances are determined independently, or equivalently, two bars are placed randomly among the i's and the number lying between them represents the abundance of a species; the process is repeated for each species. The total number of i's in the sequence is clearly not equal to the total number of individuals in the census, this time; it is an independent parameter, but fortunately one which has little effect on the relative abundances predicted. The problem is most easily solved as follows. Suppose, for instance, that there are ten i's. Construct a square array of 100 i's.

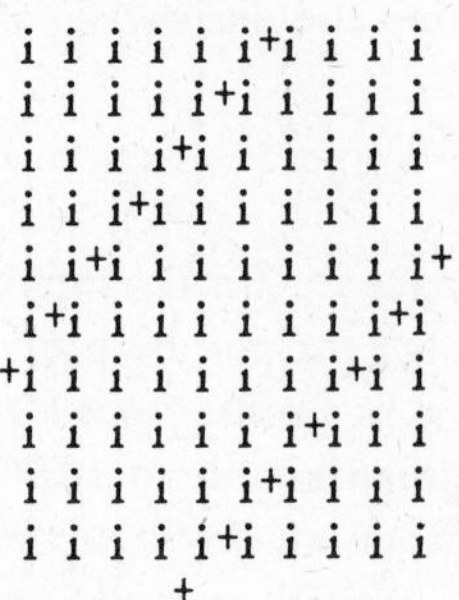

Now two bars determined the abundance of the species in question; draw a vertical bar in the array in the position of the first bar determining the abundance, and a horizontal bar through the array in the position of the second bar determining abundance. Since each bar falls with uniform probability in each of the 11 positions available to it, all $11^2 = 121$ positions of the point of intersection of the two bars are equally probable. The probability that the two bars in the original sequence or the two coordinates in the square array differ by precisely four i's is then the fraction of the 121 coordinate points which satisfy this condition. The coordinates marked with a + sign are the ones, and their number is clearly $2(11 - 4) = 14$. In general, if there are p i's, the probability that two randomly placed bars enclose q i's is clearly given by

$$\frac{2(p + 1 - q)}{(p + 1)^2}.$$

When this probability is plotted against q, a straight line results. Therefore, since the expected number of species with q individuals under this alternative is proportional to the probability of q individuals, the number of species with q individuals would, if alternative b holds, be linearly related to q. Notice that the state of maximum probability was computed for alternative a while the mean or expected state was computed for alternative b. Presumably both distributions are sufficiently symmetrical so that the mean is approximately the state of maximum probability and conversely.

SPECIES ABUNDANCE AND COMMUNITY ORGANIZATION

Nelson G. Hairston
Department of Zoology, University of Michigan

The prevalent conviction among ecologists that natural communities represent important and meaningful assemblages of organisms has prompted a diverse series of analyses. The present paper is an examination of some of the analyses as applied primarily to soil arthropods, with an explanation of some of the difficulties that have been encountered. The thesis contained herein is that the numerical abundance and spatial distribution of all species found must be taken into account before an understanding of community organization can be obtained.

Analyses and definitions of the community have been used to approach the subject from several more or less distinct points of view—function, location, and biotic composition. Most studies have dealt with only one of these aspects, but some assumption has usually been made about the others. Macfadyen (1957) has recently reviewed the various community definitions that have been offered. In the present paper, particular attention is paid to the aspects of community structure that can be discovered from the occurrence and relative abundance of species, usually confined to a taxonomic group not larger than a phylum.

The species composition of communities has been used as an approach to community analysis for at least 50 years. The data have been viewed from the standpoints of species frequency, species per unit of area, the spatial distribution of individuals, and the numerical abundance of species. In all of these, attempts have been made, graphically and mathematically to express some aspect of community structure.

Species Frequency

The regular arrangement of species in a community was apparently first observed by plant ecologists (Raunkiaer 1909, 1918, 1934; Gleason 1920). In Raunkiaer's analysis, the frequency of occurrence of each species in a series of samples provides the basic data. When the number of species in each frequency class is plotted, there usually results a curve more or less resembling a reversed "J" (Kenoyer 1927). The original interpretation was that the short arm of the curve, representing species present in 80% or more of the samples, were the dominant forms which were able to prevent immediate competitors from occupying the area, while the long arm of the curve consisted of non-dominants that did not offer competition. It was eventually shown, however, that the shape of the curve depended upon sample size, and that species tended to shift position between the two arms as the samples were made larger or smaller (Romell 1930).

Association of Common Species

As an outgrowth of the species frequency studies, there has developed a school of "biocoenology," which uses differential association of a number of relatively ubiquitous species in order to delimit communities. The details of the method vary with different workers, some using numerical abundance in addition to common presence. Because of the dependence of ubiquity on sample size, the selection of the species used must be somewhat arbitrary, and to this extent the method is artificial, although interesting results may be obtained (Macfadyen 1954, 1957; Kontkanen 1957, Whittaker and Fairbanks 1958). Conventionally, the results are expressed in a "trellis diagram," which is obtained by rearranging the list of samples until the maximal affinities between samples are obtained.

An alternate method of using the association of relatively ubiquitous species to delimit communities has been described by Hairston and Byers (1954).

Species per Unit of Area

In order to avoid the arbitrary restriction imposed by selecting common species, a number of plant ecologists have concentrated upon the relationship between the number of species found and the area covered. This has resulted in the "species area curve" (Arrhenius 1921, Gleason 1922, Cain 1938). Using the curve, an approach can be made to the most favorable size of sample for the conditions of any given study. The number of species found apparently increases linearly with the logarithm of the area studied over a wide range of sample sizes, and the slope of the line thus formed has been used as a measure of community diversity (Margalef 1957), although the relationship does not hold for very small samples (Hairston and Byers 1954), and is claimed not to hold for very large ones (Preston 1948). Shinozaki (1955) and Shinozaki and Urata (1953) have expressed doubts as to the ecological significance of the relationship.

Reproduced with permission from Ecology, 40: 404-416, 1959. Published by The Ecological Society of America and The Duke University Press, Durham, North Carolina.

Spatial Distribution

Although some earlier workers were aware that the obvious non-random distribution of organisms in nature must have an effect upon the results of sampling, Cole (1946 a and b) was apparently the first ecologist to attempt a measurement of the nature of the distribution of animals, and of the interspecific associations that could be discovered by appropriate statistical tests. A series of authors (Neyman 1939, Anscombe 1948, 1949; Thomas 1949, Thomson 1952, Bliss and Fisher 1953) have reported mathematical descriptions of observed distributions. The underlying causes of the observed non-random distributions are different from species to species, and therefore none of the mathematical formulae are valid for all cases. The negative binomial has certain practical advantages for the ecologist, who may have neither the time nor the inclination to do more than use the formulae as presented. Its usefulness lies in the fact that there are published formulae for estimating the necessary terms (Bliss and Fisher 1953, Bliss and Calhoun 1954). This distribution contains a constant (k), the value of which can range from zero at maximal clumping to infinity at completely random distribution. It is thus of considerable value in estimating the relative degree of clumping shown by different species.

Another method of expressing the spatial distribution of organisms is as the mean distance to the nearest individual of the same species (usually referred to as the "nearest neighbor" method) (Dice 1952, Clark and Evans 1954, Thompson 1956, Blackith 1958). The technique is especially applicable to distributions of plants and of those animals having nests or burrows.

The influence of the spatial distribution of constituent species on analyses of community structure was pointed out by Hairston and Byers (1954), who interpreted the failure of indices of diversity to remain constant with increasing sample size as being due to the clumping of rare species. More information will be given on this point below.

Numerical Abundance

The first important attempt to interpret animal community structure from the relationship between the numbers of individuals and of species obtained by sampling was that of Fisher, Corbet, and Williams (1943). These authors started from the observations that a regular curve results whenever sampling data are plotted so as to compare the number of species in the successive abundance categories. There are many species with a single individual, fewer with two individuals, and so on to higher numbers, only a few species being represented by very large populations. Thus, in their large collection of moths from light traps, consisting of 15,609 individuals distributed among 240 species, the 12 species represented by 282 or more individuals constituted over half of the collection, while over half of the species were represented by 13 or fewer individuals. The arithmetic plot of the data resembles a hyperbola, but on a geometric plot, the hyperbola can be shown not to apply.

Fisher concluded that the logarithmic series provided an adequate description of the data. The logarithmic series is a special case of the negative binomial distribution in which k is assumed to be equal to zero. As he points out, it is possible to make this assumption if the number of undiscovered species is unknown and the series cannot go below one individual per species. This requires the addition of a new constant *alpha,* and the relationship between the number of species S and the total number of individuals N can be expressed by the formula

$$S = \alpha \ln \left(1 + \frac{N}{\alpha}\right) \qquad (1)$$

The constant, α, thus becomes an expression of the diversity of species in relation to the total number of individuals. Fisher, Corbet, and Williams found that for the light trap data the value of α was more or less constant over a range of sample sizes, and concluded that it was a valuable index of the diversity of species in a natural community.

The logarithmic series was later applied to a variety of situations by Williams. Some of these situations were the number of species per genus in a taxonomic group (Williams 1944, 1947a), the number of publications per scientific author (Williams 1947b) and many other similar series. The curve seems to apply to almost any situation involving duplication, selection, and dispersal.

Preston (1948) proposed a different method of representing the same data. Objecting to that feature of the logarithmic series requiring more species of minimal abundance (one individual) than any other category, he pointed out that for such well known groups as birds, there appear to be no more very rare species than very abundant ones, and that most species seem to have an intermediate position. He found that when the species in a census are grouped into abundance categories (octaves) representing all of the numbers between successive powers of 2, the number of species in the octave form part of a normal curve, which can be expressed as

$$S_r = S_0 e - (ar)^2 \qquad (2)$$

where S_o is the number of species in the modal octave, S_r is the number of species r octaves from the mode, and a is a constant calculated from the data. Complete data being unobtainable in most cases, the curve obtained is truncated at the rare end, but the complete form is predictable, and hence the total number of species, including those as yet undiscovered. In a later paper, Williams (1953) accepted the greater utility of Preston's lognormal analysis, although the logarithmic series is preferable mathematically. Brian (1953) has observed that the curve obtained from Preston's method is, in many cases, more similar to the negative binomial than to the normal. In the present author's opinion, however, the fit is seldom sufficiently good to make the distinction.

A number of other indices of diversity have also been proposed (Numata 1950, Margalef 1951, 1956).

Hairston and Byers (1954) attempted the analysis of extensive data on soil arthropods by both the logarithmic series and the lognormal method. They concluded that both indices of diversity were related to sample size, a feature that renders impossible the comparison of different communities. The suggested reason was the clumping of rare species so that, with repeated or enlarged samples, there is more likelihood of encountering new rare species than additional specimens of species already found. The phenomenon was more apparent in their data than in the earlier publications because the samples came from fixed points in the community, whereas the clumping of individual species is largely obscured in their passage to a light trap.

Information Theory and Community Analysis

In a long and thoughtful article that will repay careful reading, Margalef (1957) has considered the possibilities of analyzing natural communities by the approach of information theory. Information in this sense is a function of the number of possible choices between equally probable states required for a complete understanding of the level of organization under consideration. The assumption of equally probable states is, of course, entirely too restrictive for serious use in most ecological studies, but the theory contains certain concepts that will be used below, and that make it worthwhile presenting in some detail. Thus, we may consider the information in a community, as based upon counting the number of species present, or we may consider at a different level the amount of information as based upon placing all individuals in their proper species, or, finally, we may consider the total possible information in the system, considering each individual as separately identifiable and localizable in space. In each case, what is measured is a function of the number of choices required to reduce the total number to a given lower level, and in the final case to reduce it to a single choice. Since the possible number of combinations among N individuals is N!, the total measured information would be a function of this, or expressed in "bits" (the usual unit in information theory),

$$I = 1.443 \ln N! \qquad (3)$$

In most cases, the data are such that this is not very meaningful, since we know too little about the spatial arrangement of individuals, to say nothing of their individual identification. The placing of individuals in species is usually the most that can be hoped for, and the information in the system is:

$$I = 1.443 \ln \frac{N!}{N_1!\,N_2!\ldots N_S!} \qquad (4)$$

in which N_1, N_2, etc. are the numbers of individuals in the different species. Information theory thus makes no pretense of providing an explanation for observed phenomena, but only tells how much information is required to explain them. It will be recognized immediately that this is a very large amount, and in practice becomes impossible to calculate for samples of any respectable size. Various approximations have been proposed to circumvent the factorials.

One of the most important points in Margalef's paper concerns the concept of redundancy. This derives from the obvious fact that the information at the level of placing individuals in their proper species depends upon the relative abundance of the species. In the improbable event that all are equally abundant, the denominator is small and the measured information is maximal; if individuals are distributed completely at random among the species, the information is less but still considerable, and if, as is usually the case, the abundances are very unequal, the denominator of the fraction is large, and the information in the system is much less.

The inequality of abundance constitutes repetition for the common species, and since this increases the probability that an individual belongs to a species already recognized, the amount of information per individual is relatively small. This repetition is what is meant by redundancy. We come at this point to a stumbling block caused by the restricted use of the familiar word "information." It is difficult, as Margalef says, to visualize how a random arrangement could contain more information than a non-random one, but if it is remembered that information is measured as a function of the number of choices required to reduce the system to a given level of organization, then it is clear that more choices are needed to describe a random arrangement than an organized one. The difference between the two can be considered as a measure of the degree of organization that has gone into setting up the observed system, although it is a weakness of the information theory approach that it is not possible to say anything about the system prior to its organization, and assumptions either of randomness or of some other arrangement are necessary.

Margalef rightly considers that the direct formulae are unworkable, and uses instead a simple index of diversity derived from the above-mentioned linear relationship between number of species and the logarithm of the size of sample (or of total individuals). Thus,

$$d = \frac{S - 1}{\ln N} \quad (5)$$

He makes a comparison between the results obtained with this formula and 2 others derived from information theory, and concludes that the simple index will give satisfactory results. The comparison is based not on an actual series of species counts, but on the frequencies of letters in a sentence in Spanish, part of a sentence in English, and a series of random numerals. His justification of the simple index is based upon the fact that all 3 indices become stable after a sharp rise in response to a new system of symbols. The comparison between the letters in a language and the arrangement of organisms in a community is not valid, however, as will be shown below.

Models Derived from Biological Premises

Dissatisfied with empirical mathematical descriptions, MacArthur (1957) proposed that the situation be viewed from the standpoint of what is or could be happening biologically in the community. Using the relative sizes and possible arrangements of niches held by the species in a community, he pointed out that conceivably these could be completely separate, adjacent, or overlapping. On the assumption that the total number of individuals is equivalent to the occupancy of the whole environment, and that the species represent the niches, MacArthur presented mathematical models representing the functional community as broken at randomly distributed points into contiguous, non-overlapping niches for one hypothesis, or by randomly distributed pairs of points into overlapping niches for a second hypothesis, or into separate units of randomly distributed sizes (discrete niches) for a third hypothesis. He gave data from a bird census (and mentioned others) that the first hypothesis fits. The second and third hypotheses do not appear to have validity in any situation yet tested.

For the first hypothesis, the predicted abundance of the rth rarest species may be calculated as:

$$\frac{N}{S} \sum_{i=}^{r} \frac{1}{(S-i+\ )} \quad (6)$$

where N is total individuals, S is total species, i is the interval between successively ranked species and the rarest, and r is rank in rareness.

With regard to the first hypothesis, MacArthur found that bird censuses from large areas departed from the model in that common species were more common than predicted, and rare species rarer. When small parts of the large area (individual habitats) were censused, the fit was considerably better. He postulated that a non-fit of the sort that he found represents heterogeneity, while in homogeneous habitats the relationships conform to his hypothesis. A few other kinds of data have been applied to the hypothesis (Hutchinson 1957), and some seem to fit, particularly marine gastropods of the genus *Conus* (Kohn, quoted by Hutchinson).

Observations

Most of the data used in this study concern soil arthropods, obtained by Tullgren extraction. The site of the collections is an abandoned field on the Edwin S. George Reserve of the University of Michigan. It had remained undisturbed by man for at least 25 years and unploughed for 50 years prior to the sampling. Deer pressure has apparently prevented succession to woody vegetation. The otherwise quite uniform area is interrupted by 12 small depressions, referred to hereafter as "swales," characterized by a dense mat of blue grass (*Poa pratensis*), in contrast with the upland which is dominated by *Poa compressa* and *Aristida purpurascens*. For a more detailed description of the vegetation, see Evans and Cain (1952), and Cain and Evans (1952). The microarthropods were extracted from 2 series of samples, one taken at random over the upland part of the field, and the other taken at random from the swales. All samples consisted of cylindrical cores, 5 inches in diameter and 8½ inches deep. The complete data from 38 of the upland samples are given in Hairston and Byers (1954). Five samples from one of the 2 largest swales have now been sorted and counted, and the results are

TABLE I. Number of specimens of all microarthropods obtained by Tullgren extraction of samples from upper 8½ inches of soil in a single swale. Collections made 1949-1950

Species		Date of Sampling				
		Sep. 9	Oct. 20	Nov. 17	Dec. 8	Jan. 12
Araneida	U4	2	0	0	0	0
	U7	0	1	0	0	1
Pseudoscorpionida	U1	1	2	4	1	0
Acarina	P1	6	0	71	206	128
	P3	0	0	0	0	1
	P4	0	2	0	0	0
	P5	4	1	7	4	10
	P8	0	2	0	0	0
	P10	9	0	0	0	0
	P11	13	51	0	2	1
	P13	1	1	1	0	3
	P14	24	0	1	3	1
	P15	1	0	0	0	0
	P16	1	0	4	1	0
	P17	44	0	0	0	0
	P18	0	0	15	48	0
	O1	260	67	15	608	240
	O2	505	21	140	87	40
	O4	0	0	0	31	12
	O5	52	3	135	39	2
	O6	0	0	0	404	134
	O7	6	1	0	0	0
	O9	355	122	119	534	340
	O11	0	0	0	8	22
	O12	37	0	1	6	0
	O14	3	0	0	0	0
	O18	0	0	0	55	21
	O20	0	1	0	0	0
	O23	28	98	17	32	49
	O31	61	21	0	19	44
	O32	21	26	3	2	3
	O33	30	162	121	108	59
	O34	2	1	0	2	0
	O35	475	774	2286	493	775
	O36	0	0	5	4	0
	O37	1	0	2	8	0
	O38	1	0	0	0	0
	O39	0	0	174	12	0
	O40	0	0	11	2	30
	O41	0	0	1	0	0
	O42	0	0	3	0	27
	O43	4	0	1	24	1
	O44	0	0	0	1	0
	O45	0	0	0	6	12
	O46	0	0	0	0	2
	O47	0	0	0	0	2
	S2	0	0	0	0	36
	S5	8	2	33	55	25
	S6	0	0	59	0	4
	T1	0	0	0	2	5
	T7	1	1	0	5	11
	T10	0	2	0	10	1
	T12	54	49	0	18	6
	T13	0	1	1	0	1
	T14	0	0	0	7	3
	E1	73	31	104	112	99
	E2	49	9	106	26	66
	E3	0	3	0	0	0
	E4	0	0	0	5	0
	E5	0	11	0	0	0
	E6	4	9	6	44	120
	E8	15	9	1	0	3
	E11	0	1	0	0	1
	E13	9	0	0	11	3
	E18	0	0	0	6	10
	E24	0	0	0	5	2
	E27	13	18	11	9	27
	E34	1	0	12	0	0
	E38	0	8	26	10	3

TABLE I—(Continued)

Species		Date of Sampling				
		Sep. 9	Oct. 20	Nov. 17	Dec. 8	Jan. 12
	E42	0	0	4	0	0
	E43	0	0	2	0	0
Diplopoda	U1	1	0	1	0	0
Pauropoda	1	4	35	4	3	0
Symphila	1	0	0	1	1	5
Hexapoda Protura	1	0	15	9	9	1
	2	0	0	2	0	0
	3	0	0	5	0	1
	4	1	0	0	0	0
Thysanura	J1	0	2	0	1	0
Collembola	P1	0	8	0	5	1
	P2	13	6	10	5	154
	P4	0	0	0	3	4
	P5	0	0	0	18	15
	P14	0	1	1	24	6
	P15	0	1	0	0	0
	P16	20	0	6	21	16
	P17	0	0	8	420	42
	E1	1	0	0	3	5
	E2	0	0	0	6	11
	E4	57	26	16	0	58
	E5	0	0	9	4	23
	E6	0	0	0	1	3
	S3	0	1	0	0	6
	S4	0	0	0	1	0
	S5	9	0	4	0	0
Corrodentia	A1	2	0	0	0	0
Thysanoptera	6	33	0	0	8	6
	11	5	1	0	2	2
	16	2	0	0	0	0
Hemiptera	L1	0	0	1	0	0
	D1	0	0	0	0	1
Homoptera	Ny1	0	2	1	1	0
	Ny3	0	1	0	0	0
	Ny9	0	0	3	0	0
Coleoptera	St6	1	0	1	0	0
	St7	0	0	1	0	0
Larva	4	0	0	0	0	1
	15	0	7	12	2	1
	16	2	0	2	2	0
Lepidoptera	L10	13	10	22	3	1
Diptera	L11	2	0	0	0	2
	L12	1	0	1	0	0
Hymenoptera	F1	0	1	0	0	0
	F3	0	1	0	0	0
	F4	0	1	0	0	0
# OF SPECIES		54	51	57	66	69
# OF INDIVIDUALS		2341	1631	3622	3618	2757

given in Table I. The unconventional classification has been described and defended in the paper referred to. As will be shown below, this classification yields data that have the same characteristics as more conventional and time-consuming methods. The same designations are used in Table I that were used in the earlier publication, the numerical series being continuous with the designations already used.

The data, as might be expected, resemble those from the upland samples taken at the same time. There are more species and more individuals than are found in the samples from the upland, but there is overlap in the values for individuals.

Clumping and Abundance

In analyzing the upland samples by the logarithmic series and the lognormal distribution, Hairston and Byers found that the results depended upon the size of the sample under consideration, and, as noted above, postulated that clumping of the rare species could account for this, since new rare species would then be more likely to be added than individuals of other rare species already encountered. They were able to show that some of the rare species were clumped, but were unable to obtain estimates of the degree of clumping. Reasonable methods for estimating the constants of the negative binomial distribution are now available (Bliss and Fisher 1953), and the constant k has been estimated for all species represented by two or more individuals (Figure 1). It should be pointed out that the estimates are less than 90% efficient in many cases, but the trend of the values in relation to mean abundance is so apparent that the low efficiency cannot be considered a series objection to the conclusions.

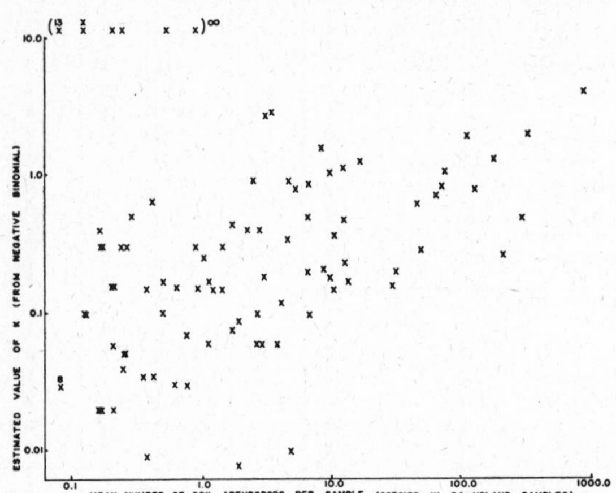

Fig. 1. The inverse relation between abundance and clumping as measured by the constant k in the negative binomial distribution. Data from Hairston and Byers (1954).

Since a small value of k denotes clumping, and a value of infinity denotes randomness, 83% of the species show some degree of clumping, and there is a definite, even trend toward more intense clumping as rarer and rarer species are considered. It will also be observed that all of the randomly distributed species are relatively rare, all having means of less than one individual per sample. Two thirds are represented by only 2 individuals each. This suggests that with further sampling many of them would also be found to be clumped.

The data from the 5 swale samples have been treated in the same fashion (Figure 2). As might be expected from the smaller number of samples, the points on the chart are more scattered, but the same trend is evident, being significant at the 1% level when tested by tetrachoric r (Dixon and Massey 1951, p. 233).

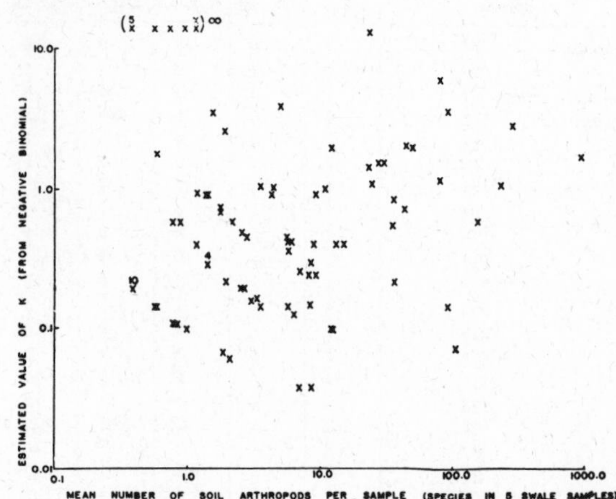

Fig. 2. The inverse relation between abundance and clumping as measured by the constant k in the negative binomial distribution. Data on swale samples from Table I.

The progressive clumping of rarer species gives an indication of the structure and organization of the communities studied. It appears that the suitability of the different parts of the community is far from uniform when the different levels of abundance are considered. The more nearly the whole community is suitable for a species, the more abundant that species is, and the more likely it is to have a random distribution. Conversely, the rarer a species is, the more likely it is to be strongly clumped because it only finds suitable habitat in a few places in the community. Between the extremes, a complete series of intermediates is found. It is this continuous series that has caused considerable disagreement among ecologists concerning the structure and even the objective existence of communities. Some have been impressed with the homogeneity of the community, and they were influenced by the common presence of the abundant species over the whole community; others have been impressed by the mosaic nature of the community, and were influenced by the strongly clumped distributions of the less abundant species. The picture is more likely one of a continuous series of mosaics, each overlapping the others and with larger and larger pieces, until for the most abundant species the whole community is one piece—a part of a mosaic biosphere.

Comparison of the Two Communities

If the above interpretation is correct, an examination of the fates of the species common to the 2 communities should yield interesting information. For the months for which swale data are available (September to January), 90 species were recorded from the 5 upland samples nearest the swale, and 116 species were recorded from the 5 swale samples. There were 43 species common to the two communities, which amounts to 48% of the upland species and 37% of the swale species. This result might have been anticipated, as the swales are moist, rich islands in the sandy upland. It is of greater interest to note that the relation between numerical abundance of the different species in the 2 communities (Figure 3) is weak, although it is significant statistically. This is to be expected if the general conditions in the 2 places are somewhat different. Species adapted to conditions in the swale would be able to find suitable habitats only in restricted parts of the upland, and vice-versa. This is borne out by comparing the abundances and the values of k for each species in the 2 communities. The comparison is meaningless for species which have only 1-3 individuals in one or both communities, but 21 of the 27 species with better representation in both communities show greater clumping in the community of less abundance (Table II). The table also shows that the tendency is strongest where differences in abundance are greatest, and hence least likely to be artifacts of sampling error. This indicates that the degree of clumping is not necessarily a character of the species, but also depends upon the kind of community in which it is being studied. The foregoing conclusion would probably not hold, of course, for social or territorial species.

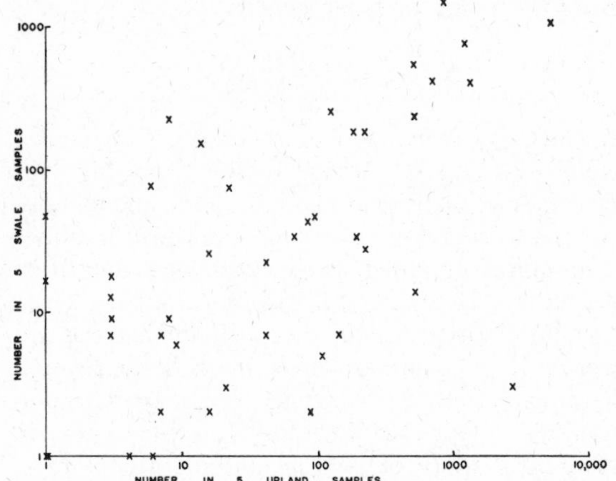

FIG. 3. The relative abundance of species in two similar adjacent communities. Each point represents one species found in both swale and upland.

TABLE II. The relation between relative abundance and relative degree of clumping in 27 species of soil arthropods found in 2 communities. For the value of N_1/N_2, the smaller number was chosen for the numerator, regardless of community. This operation fixed the positions of k_1 and k_2. A lower value of k denotes greater clumping.

Relative abundance (N_1/N_2)	Number of cases	Number of Cases in Which k_1/k_2 Was:	
		Greater than 1	Less than 1
0 -0.33	11	0	11
0.34-0.66	10	3	7
0.67-1.00	6	3	3
Totals	27	6	21

Diversity, Heterogeneity, and Community Identification

Using equation (5) above, Margalef has made some interesting interpretations of his data on marine phytoplankton. He recognized that, like other indices of diversity, this one shows an increase with enlarged samples. He did not regard this as a serious objection, and pointed out the circular argument accompanying descriptions of most such indices. These are judged valid when they can be shown to remain stable in "reasonably homogeneous" communities, but there is no criterion of homogeneity other than the index that is described. He attributes the increase in the value of the index with increased sample size to a real heterogeneity.

Margalef's justification for the use of his index is based upon the frequently-noted similarity between the distributions of letter frequencies in a language and species frequencies in samples from communities. Selecting most of a sentence from his own text, he calculated the index of diversity for successively larger samples, starting with a single letter. The index rose rapidly at first, but after 30 or 40 letters it became quite stable. In addition to his own index, he used 2 others derived directly from information theory, and he considered that the fact that all 3 indices followed the same pattern in analyzing the languages constituted justification for their use in analyzing data from natural communities. The analogy with language is interesting, but unless common or similar underlying causes can be shown for the organization of languages and communities, any similarities must remain interesting coincidences, and must not be used in interpretation or in the foregoing kind of justification.

In the present case, the most likely reason for an apparent increase in heterogeneity with an increase in sample size lies in the spatial distribution of the species concerned, and the inverse relation between clumping and abundance. Accordingly, if the arrangement of letters in a language is to be used for justifying a system of analyzing a community, the distribution of the letters should show the same characteristics as the distribution of species. This is obviously not the case, but if mathematical evidence is required, it is given in Figure 4. In this case, 10 lines taken at random from Margalef's paper were used as "samples."

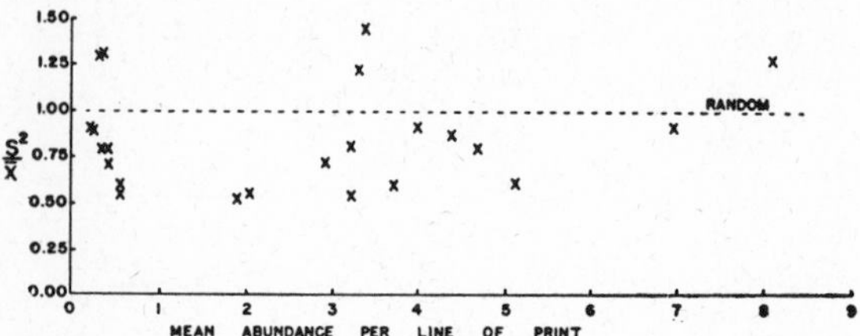

FIG. 4. The relation between clumping and abundance of 23 letters in 10 lines of Spanish text, taken at random from Margalef (1957).

Only 5 of the 23 letters showed any evidence of clumping, the remainder being slightly more uniform than random in distribution. This means that the constant k in the negative binomial cannot be used, since its value becomes meaningless for most letters. Instead, the ratio of variance to mean abundance has been used. They are equal and the ratio equal to unity when the distribution is random. Higher values denote clumping, lower ones more uniform distribution. It is clear that no relation exists between the abundance of a letter and its spatial distribution. Hence, we should expect that an index of diversity would not be related to sample size as it is for most field data, since repeats of letters already encountered would be relatively as frequent as new letters. This accounts for the stabilization of the 3 indices of diversity in Margalef's analysis. The large proportion of letters that are uniformly distributed suggests a similarity with the distribution of birds, which tends to be uniform because of their territories. Bird censuses have been particularly attractive in the justification of indices of diversity (Preston) and models (MacArthur), and it seems likely that there is a relationship between their use in such cases and their unusual spatial distribution.

Although the justification for their use is not valid, these indices gave interesting results when used to analyze plankton communities. Margalef was able to show regular gradients in diversity in an estuarine river, and found that the distribution of the gradients corresponded to the influence of incursions of water from the open Atlantic. Since the data presented in Table I above and by Hairston and Byers represent two quite different communities with two subdivisions of the upland community, attempts were made to discover whether Margalef's indices of diversity and heterogeneity could be used to separate the 3 in a completely objective manner. The method used was to calculate the diversity of pooled pairs of samples, on the theory that pairs from different communities should show greater diversity than pairs from the same community. For this purpose, 14 samples were selected: 5 from the swale, 7 from the central part of the upland, and 2 from the peripheral part of the upland. Eight of the 9 upland samples could be classified as coming from homogeneous material, since all combinations among them gave low indices of diversity.

Another series of calculations was also made, using the index of heterogeneity

$$H = \frac{d_{AB}}{d_A + d_B} \qquad (7)$$

in which d_{AB} is the index of diversity of the pooled samples A and B. These indices were high for all combinations between swale and upland samples, and lower for all combinations within either community. Neither index gave any indication of a difference among the upland samples.

It thus appears valid to conclude that the approach is adequate to effect a crude separation of samples from 2 distinct but fairly similar communities. This accounts for its effectiveness in Margalef's study of phytoplankton. In his case, of course, there would be no method of estimating beforehand which samples came from which community. In the case of the terrestrial communities, a glance at the vegetation effects an immediate preliminary classification that is as accurate as the rather laborious calculations reported.

The Biological Model

The development of a model based upon biological premises is an encouraging advance over empirical descriptions. A comparison of expected values with the observed data on soil arthropods (Figure 5) is disappointing at first glance. The fit is poor both for single samples and for pooled samples. In all cases, the observed curves are too steep—rare species are too rare and abundant species are too abundant to conform to expectations. Lest the reader conclude that the failure is due to the unconventional taxonomy, a similar set of calculations has been made for the data reported by Kontkanen (1957) on beetles, in which there appears to be no question of the taxonomic certification (Figure 6). The same kinds of deviations from the expected are found in these data, particularly for the abundant species. The apparently closer fit at the rare end of the curve is due to the fact that a number of the less abundant species were omitted from Kontkanen's table. One of 5 samples from his Community I does show an excellent fit, but this can scarcely be regarded as anything more than a statistical accident, as it is clearly the exception rather than the rule.

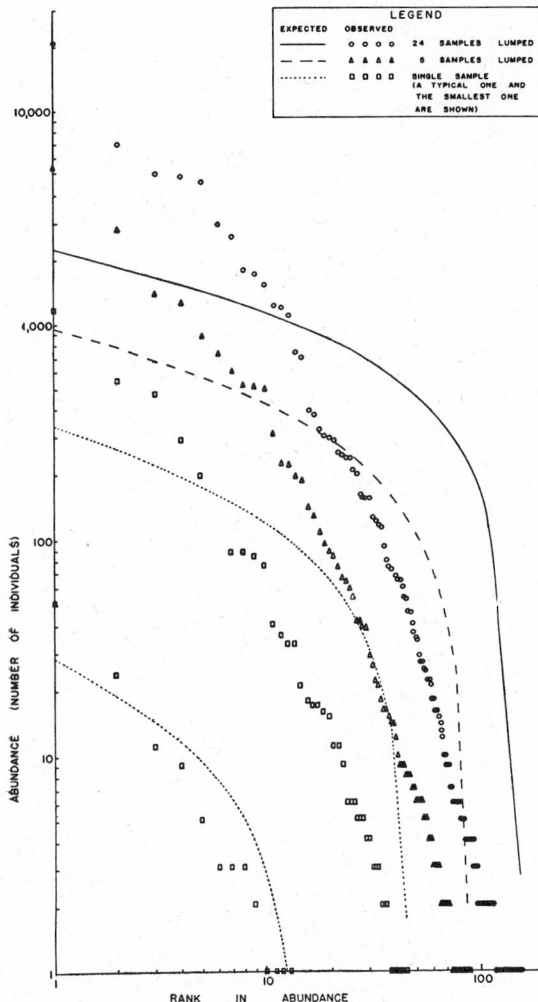

FIG. 5. The relation between abundance and rank in abundance of soil arthropods for samples of various sizes, compared with expectations based on MacArthur's first hypothesis. Data from Hairston and Byers (1954).

An examination of Figure 5 shows that there is apparently a relationship between the size of the sample and the departure from expectations. This observation is in agreement with MacArthur's statement that bird censuses from large areas show a greater departure from expectation than do those from small areas. MacArthur attributes this effect to the greater heterogeneity of the large area, and concludes that heterogeneity is indicated whenever data show this kind of departure from expectations.

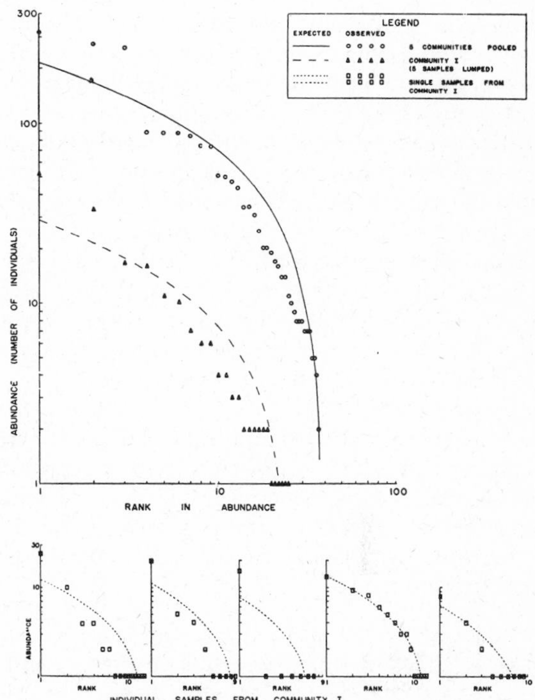

FIG. 6. The relation between abundance and rank in abundance of beetles, compared with expectations based on MacArthur's first hypothesis. Data from Kontkanen, 1957.

There are, however, certain difficulties with this interpretation, especially as regards the present data. First, although the idea that the large area represents greater heterogeneity than smaller ones is logical in the case of birds, it is less acceptable for the soil arthropods, both because the samples were selected for homogeneity on an independent basis, and because the conclusion of marked heterogeneity within a community violates well-founded ideas to the contrary. Second, there is a more general objection to the assumption of randomness in MacArthur's model. If the natural community is a meaningful assemblage of organisms, the arrangement and relative abundance of these would not be expected to be random. At this point, it is well to recall the concept of redundancy in information theory. Redundancy was shown to be indicative of organization, and also to represent departure from randomness. Thus, if the community is an organized system, one would not expect the relative abundance of the species in it to conform to a random series.

Fortunately, there is a test that can resolve the question. This is based upon the implied predictions in the two interpretations. MacArthur's explanation predicts that if we deliberately add heterogeneous data (as from another community) to the system, the departure from expectation will be greatly increased. The prediction implied in the *a priori* assumption of organization is exactly the opposite; if data from another community are added, the organization is less, and a nearer approach to expectations based on randomness is achieved than when an equivalent amount of data from the same community is added. If we return to Figure 6, it can be seen that lumping the 5 communities present in Kontkanen's data yields a curve that seems to come closer to the expected than does data from a single community. In the absence of an objective means of comparison, however, the difference is not very convincing.

I am indebted to Mr. Peter H. Ovenburg for the suggestion that an accurate objective estimate of the deviation of a set of data from expectation can be obtained by comparing the observed with the expected variance. He has also provided the formula for calculating the expected variance in MacArthur's model:

$$s^2 = \left[\frac{N^2}{S^3}\Sigma\left(\sum_{i=1}^{r}\frac{1}{(S-i+1)}\right)^2\right] - \frac{N^2}{S^2} \qquad (8)$$

the terms being the same as in equation (6) above. This expression is a measure of the expected deviation from a hypothetical uniform distribution, and hence the comparison with the observed variance is a valid one. Unfortunately, the expected variance cannot be assigned a probability, and the worth of the comparison is thus somewhat subjective (Craig, personal communication). It does yield results that are internally consistent.

The ratio $\frac{\text{observed variance}}{\text{expected variance}}$ was calculated for a series of single and pooled samples as follows: the 5 upland samples nearest the swale in space and covering the same months as the swale samples were selected as being most appropriate for the desired comparison. The ratio of variances was calculated for each of these samples, and also for the larger sample formed by pooling them. The ratio for the larger sample is considerably greater than the average of the 5 individual ratios. When 5 additional upland samples are added, the ratio of variances is found to increase in an apparently linear fashion with the number of samples pooled (Figure 7). A similar relationship holds for the 5 swale samples.

The critical test of the 2 hypotheses can be made by comparing the ratios between variances obtained by pooling 5 upland and 5 swale samples and the ratio obtained by pooling the 10 upland samples. MacArthur's explanation predicts that the ratio obtained by pooling samples from the 2 communities will be the higher, whereas the explanation propounded above predicts that the ratio obtained by pooling the 10 upland samples will be greater because a greater degree of organization has been revealed. The results are given in Figure 7. Introducing heterogeneity clearly

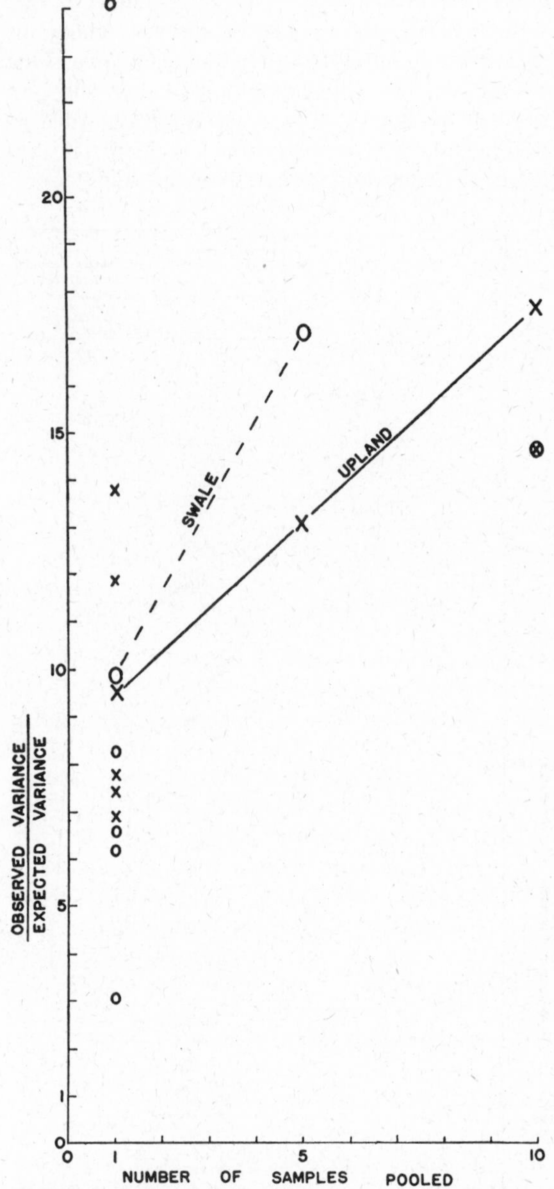

FIG. 7. The relation between amount of departure from MacArthur's model (ratio of variances) and sample size in 2 communities of microarthropods, and in a sample formed by pooling the 2 communities. Small symbols represent variance ratios for individual samples in upland (crosses) and swale (circles). Large crossed circle represents ratio of variances for a sample formed by pooling 5 swale and 5 upland samples.

reduces the ratio between variances and thus approaches more nearly the expectation of a random distribution of species populations. Adding more samples from the same community causes the deviation from randomness to increase linearly with the number of samples pooled.

The effect is even more dramatic when two completely unrelated samples are pooled. For this purpose, Margalef's Sample A of marine phytoplankton and Hairston and Byers' Sample P7-5857 of soil arthropods were used. The former consists of 1032 specimens in 21 species, and the latter consists of 494 specimens in 25 species. The observed variance is 62.36 times as great as expected for the plankton sample, and 11.76 times as great as expected for the soil arthropods. For the two samples pooled, the ratio is 7.87. Thus the more complete the heterogeneity that is added the nearer the approach to expectation based on the assumption of randomness.

Discussion

Perhaps the most satisfying means of expressing community organization would be through directly observed actions of all species present upon each other. This kind of information is not available for any community, and while such data as we have are valuable, they are much too fragmentary to allow the construction of more than the most general kind of model based on food relationships (Lindeman 1942, Macfadyen 1957). Other relationships, such as competition, are even more imperfectly known, especially in the field.

It therefore seems worthwhile to approach the subject from the viewpoint of the distribution and relative abundance of the different species, with the assumption that the 2 approaches must be interrelated in ways not immediately apparent, but ultimately discoverable. The merit of MacArthur's analysis lies in the implied relationship of species abundance to community energetics. His demonstration that the model based on the assumption of contiguous but non-overlapping niches fits the data better than models based on alternative assumptions is of considerable interest, since it implies that the factor determining population size is something that cannot be shared, but is completely utilized. Space, in the sense of "habitat niche" does not qualify, since species do share the same space and do not occupy all of it, although in a few cases 2 species have been shown to occupy virtually non-overlapping stations along an environmental gradient (Beauchamp and Ullyott 1932, Hairston 1951). Food would appear to be the only factor likely to qualify. At first thought, the apparent excess of many kinds of food (Andrewartha 1957) would appear to contradict the foregoing statement, but if we recognize that food not consumed by herbivores or carnivores is ultimately used by reducers, it is clear that the objection is not valid for the community as a whole, and that in any balanced state, such as we assume communities to be, the food is completely consumed by some species or other. In fact, this is axiomatic in biogeochemistry. Moreover, although the same species may be shared as food, a single item can only be consumed by one individual at a time. The most perplexing aspect of the analysis based on MacArthur's hypothesis is that it should be applicable to restricted taxonomic groups, so that it is apparently not necessary to consider all species in the community at once. This implies that each taxonomic group consumes all of the food that is available to it. Carrying this line of reasoning to the species level, the hypothesis of contiguous but non-overlapping niches makes good biological sense, in that no species can eat more food than is available.

If these conclusions are valid, there are implications concerning the importance of competition between species in the community. It would appear to be true that the process of adaptation of each species towards the maximal utilization of resources has resulted in innumerable competitive situations which have been resolved in various ways. If the outcome has been the elimination of some species from the system, there would be no way to demonstrate the event, and observations of this sort of outcome have rarely if ever been made in nature, although it is the usual thing in laboratory experiments. The events in succession might be considered as providing exceptions, since species are replaced during succession, but it is difficult to demonstrate that the replacement is due to competition. It has frequently been claimed that empty niches must abound in view of the ability of certain introduced species to succeed in establishing themselves. Such introductions, however, result in a decrease in numbers of some previously established species, as is shown dramatically in the history of oceanic islands. The author knows of no adequate data contrary to the generalization that successful introductions reduce the populations of one or more indigenous species. The implication that natural communities contain no unoccupied niches is clear.

The situation in an undisturbed natural community, then, illustrates the outcome of selection and interspecific competition. The species that are less successful in competition are not only less abundant, but are able to maintain populations only in restricted parts of the community to which they are particularly well adapted. This accounts for the increasingly clumped distributions with decreasing abundance. Successful species are more numerous and occur throughout the communities to which they are well adapted, but the degree of success is not entirely uniform over the community, and we find that they are also clumped, but to a lesser degree than the rare species. Although the preceding sentences might be interpreted as indicating a sharp distinction between the two kinds of species, such is not the case. The continuous inverse relationship between clumping and abundance provides no validation for the concept that dominance and nondominance are distinct and separable characteristics of the different species of soil arthropods studied. Hence, there is no justification other than convenience for omitting any species from an analysis of a community. The importance of knowing the relative abundance of the species is shown both in the demonstration that it provides a valid method of showing the amount of organization present and in the comparison between the 2 communities, where the same species assume very different degrees of importance. A mere statement of the presence of these species or even the frequency of occurrence in a given series of samples could easily lead to wrong conclusions about them.

Summary

The organization of natural communities was studied from the standpoint of the relative abundance of the species of microarthropods in the soil of 2 similar communities on a long-abandoned field. An examination of the details of distribution shows a continuous inverse relationship between abundance and clumping of the more than 100 species studied. This observation provides a basis for explaining why various empirically determined "indices of diversity" are not constant when increasingly large samples from the same community are analyzed. The strong clumping of the rare species means that with increased sampling new rare species are more likely to be added to the total than are additional specimens of rare species already recorded.

In spite of the dependence of the index of diversity on sample size, it can be used to show some interesting relationships, including a crude but completely objective separation of samples from similar communities. It is thus quite useful in situations such as plankton studies where there is no *a priori* separation of samples on the basis of the appearance of the area from which they came.

The most important use of data of this kind is in MacArthur's model based upon the biological hypothesis that the niches represented by different species abundances are contiguous but non-overlapping. This implies that food determines the abundance of all species, since it is the only factor that is completely utilized and cannot be shared by different species. MacArthur's assumption that the sizes of the niches conform to a random distribution is not confirmed. The departure from randomness is found to be greater with increased sample size as long as the samples come from the same community, but decreases if heterogeneous material is added in the form of samples from another community. These results indicate the degree of organization of the community, since, from information theory, it follows that organization is measured as departure from randomness. The organization of a community results from the outcome of interspecific competition for the available resources, and is expressed both in the relative abundance and the spatial distribution of the constituent species.

Acknowledgments

Part of the data were obtained on a grant from the Horace H. Rackham School of Graduate Studies: Faculty Research Fund, Project No. 739. The author also wishes to acknowledge the stimulating discussion by his colleagues in the seminar on population ecology. These discussants were F. E. Smith, L. B. Slobodkin, D. W. Hayne, J. T. Armstrong, M. D. Engelmann, D. D. Hurst, L. J. Laux, P. H. Ovenburg, and R. B. Root. It is a pleasure to thank Mr. T. Uyeno for a translation of a review of the Shinozaki articles, which were otherwise unavailable.

References

Andrewartha, H. G. 1957. The use of conceptual models in population ecology. Cold Spring Harbor Symp. Quant Biol. **22**: 219-232.

Anscombe, F. J. 1948. The transformation of poisson, binomial, and negative binomial data. Biometrika **35**: 246-254.

———. 1949. The statistical analysis of insect counts based on the negative binomial distribution. Biometrics **5**: 165-173.

Arrhenius, O. 1921. Species and area. Jour. Ecol. **9**: 95-99.

Beauchamp, R. S. A., and **P. Ullyott.** 1932. Competitive relationships between certain species of freshwater triclads. Jour. Ecol. **20**: 200-208.

Blackith, R. E. 1958. Nearest-neighbor distance measurements for the estimation of animal populations. Ecology **39**: 147-150.

Bliss, C. I., and **D. W. Calhoun.** 1954. An outline of biometry. New Haven. Yale Cooperative Corp.

Bliss, C. I., and **R. A. Fisher.** 1953. Fitting the negative binomial distribution to biological data. Biometrics **9**: 176-200.

Brian, M. V. 1953. Species frequencies in random samples from animal populations. Jour. Anim. Ecol. **22**: 57-64.

Cain, S. A. 1938. The species-area curve. Amer. Midl. Nat. **19**: 573-581.

———, and **F. C. Evans.** 1952. The distribution patterns of three plant species in an old-field community in southeastern Michigan. Contrib. Lab. Vert. Biol. Univ. Mich. **52**: 1-11.

Clark, P. J., and **F. C. Evans.** 1954. Distance to nearest neighbor as a measure of spatial relationships in populations. Ecology **35**: 445-453.

Cole, L. C. 1946a. A study of the cryptozoa of an Illinois woodland. Ecol. Monogr. **16**: 49-86.

———. 1946b. A theory for analyzing contagiously distributed populations. Ecology **27**: 329-341.

Dice, L. R. 1952. Measure of spacing between individuals within a population. Contrib. Lab. Vert. Biol. Univ. Mich. **55**: 1-23.

Dixon, W. J., and **F. J. Massey, Jr.** 1951. Introduction to statistical analysis. New York. McGraw-Hill.

Evans, F. C., and **S. A. Cain.** 1952. Preliminary studies on the vegetation of an old-field community in southeastern Michigan. Contrib. Lab. Vert. Biol. Univ. Mich. **51**: 1-17.

Fisher, R. A., A. S. Corbet, and **C. B. Williams.** 1943. The relation between the number of species and the number of individuals in a random sample from an animal population. Jour. Anim. Ecol. **12**: 42-58.

Gleason, H. A. 1920. The applications of the quadrat method. Bull. Torrey Bot. Club **44**: 463-481.

———. 1922. On the relation between species and area. Ecology **3**: 158-162.

———. 1929. The significance of Raunkiaer's law of frequency. Ecology **10**: 406-408.

Hairston, N. G. 1951. Interspecies competition and its probable influence upon the vertical distribution of Appalachian salamanders of the genus Plethodon. Ecology **32**: 266-274.

———, and **G. W. Byers.** 1954. The soil arthropods of a field in southern Michigan. A study in community ecology. Contrib. Lab. Vert. Biol. Univ. Mich. **64**: 1-37.

Hutchinson, G. E. 1957. Concluding remarks. Cold Spring Harbor Symp. Quant. Biol. **22**: 415-427.

Kenoyer, L. A. 1927. A study of Raunkiaer's law of frequence. Ecology **8**: 341-349.

Kontkanen, P. 1957. On the delimitation of communities in research on animal biocoenotics. Cold Spring Harbor Symp. Quant. Biol. **22**: 373-375.

Lindeman, R. L. 1942. The trophic-dynamic aspect of ecology. Ecology **23**: 399-417.

MacArthur, R. H. 1957. On the relative abundance of bird species. Proc. Nat. Acad. Sci. U. S. **43**: 293-295.

Macfadyen, A. 1954. The invertebrate fauna of Jan Mayen Island (East Greenland). Jour. Anim. Ecol. **23**: 261-297.

———. 1957. Animal Ecology. Aims and Methods. London. Sir Isaac Pitman and Sons, Ltd.

Margalef. R. 1951. Diversidad de especies en las comunidades naturales. P. Inst. Biol. Apl. **9**: 5-27.

———. 1956. Informacion y diversidad espicifica en las cominudades de organismos. Inv. Pesq. **3**: 99-106.

———. 1957. La teoria de la informacion en ecologia. Mem. Real Acad. Ciencias y Artes de Barcelona **32**: 373-449.

Neyman. J. 1939. On a new class of "contagious" distributions, applicable in entomology and bacteriology. Ann. Math. Stat. **10**: 35-57.

Numata, M. 1950. The homogeneity of plant communities—Studies on the structure of plant communities VI. Bot. Mag. (Tokyo) **63**: 203-309.

Preston, F. W. 1948. The commonness, and rarity, of species. Ecology **29**: 254-283.

Raunkiaer, C. 1909. Formationsundersögelse og Formationsstatistik. Bot. Tidsske. **30**: 20-132.

———. 1918. Recherches statistiques sur les formations vegetales. Det. Kgl. Danske Videnskabens Selskab. Biol. Meddel. **1**: 1-80.

———. 1934. The life forms of plants and statistical plant geography. Oxford. Clarendon Press.

Romell, L. G. 1930. Comments on Raunkiaer's and similar methods of vegetation analysis and the law of frequency. Ecology **11**: 589-596.

Shinozaki, K. 1955. Several problems on the law of geometrical progression. Physiology and Ecology **6**: 127-144.

———, and **N. Urata.** 1953. Apparent abundance of different species. Res. Pop. Ecol. **2**: 8-21.

Thomas, M. 1949. A generalization of Poisson's binomial limit for use in ecology. Biometrika **36**: 18-25.

Thompson, H. R. 1956. Distribution of distance to Nth neighbor in a population of randomly distributed individuals. Ecology **37**: 391-394.

Thomson, G. W. 1952. Measures of plant aggregation based on contagious distributions. Contrib. Lab. Vert. Biol. Univ. Mich. **53**: 1-17.

Whittaker, R. H., and **C. W. Fairbanks.** 1958. A study of plankton copepod communities in the Columbia Basin, southeastern Washington. Ecology **39**: 46-65.

Williams, C. B. 1944. Some applications of the logarithmic series and the index of diversity to ecological problems. Jour. Ecol. **32**: 1-44.

———. 1947a. The generic relations of species in small ecological communities. Jour. Anim. Ecol. **16**: 11-18.

———. 1947b. The logarithmic series and its application to biological problems. Jour. Ecol. **34**: 253-272

———. 1953. The relative abundance of different species in a wild animal population. Jour. Anim. Ecol. **22**: 14-31.

THE ROLE OF SOIL ARTHROPODS IN THE ENERGETICS OF AN OLD FIELD COMMUNITY

MANFRED D. ENGELMANN

*Department of Zoology, University of Michigan, Ann Arbor, Mich.**

INTRODUCTION

In a very stimulating paper (1942), the late R.L. Lindeman brought the problem of community energetics to the attention of the biologist, especially the ecologist. The study of this important problem did not spread, as one might have expected it to do, to all kinds of natural communities but remained focused upon the marine and fresh-water habitats. There are two reasons for the continued emphasis upon the aquatic habitats, the first and most important being the fact that the animal groups from these environments are comparatively well known taxonomically. Secondly, most of the support for studies in community energetics has come from various government and private agencies, who have recognized the implications of such work for fish production purposes. However, a critical evaluation of the general validity of Lindeman's concepts cannot be undertaken until data are obtained from a much wider spectrum of community types. This study is an attempt to apply the principles of community energetics to a terrestrial community with the intention of eventually broadening the scope of our knowledge in the area of community metabolism.

There are two aspects to any study of energetics: the field survey and the laboratory experiment. This division has led to two separate approaches to the problem which are ultimately dependent upon each other for the final answer. A field survey employs numerous methods to ascertain the density of each population present in the area. Such a study relies heavily upon the literature for information about the physiology and life history of various animals and plants in the community. An energy flow scheme is then constructed from the field data and the information in the literature. A few examples of this type of investigation are those of Lindeman (1942), and more recently Odum (1957) and Teal (1957). A laboratory study, on the other hand, focuses attention upon the life history, physiology, and population dynamics of selected species under controlled conditions. The results of these investigations give information about the various efficiencies of which the species is capable. Examples of this type of study are those by Slobodkin (1959), Richman (1958), Trama (1957), and Armstrong (1960).

Several investigations have been concentrated upon the organisms living in various types of soil. Birch & Clark (1953) considered the status of the forest soil organisms as a study unit. Faunas of forest soils, especially in Europe, have been examined to a greater extent than those of prairie soils. Bornebusch (1930) pioneered with a study of several forest soils, ranging from pine woods to beech stands. He sampled the numbers and kinds of individuals in the soil, compared both species composition and numbers from the different stands, and attempted some studies of respiration and biomass on the soil animals. The sampling methods used by Bornebusch were inadequate, and his density estimates are low (Birch & Clark, 1953). Van der Drift (1950) has made one of the more recent studies on the forest arthropods, and this work contains an extensive bibliography. The work is mainly concerned with numbers of individuals and taxa, with the addition of some biomass estimates. Wallwork (1959) deals with several aspects of the population dynamics of some forest soil mites found in the United States. Extensions of the forest floor (such as tree holes) and specialized habitats have been considered by Park and his students (Park *et al.* 1950, Park & Auerbach 1954, Winston 1956).

Soil communities of fields and pastures have been studied by Salt *et al.* (1948), MacFadyen (1952), and Hairston & Byers (1954). Their papers are mainly concerned with numbers of individuals and distribution of animals in the community, although MacFadyen gives biomass data where possible. The Europeans have done more work on the soil arthro-

* Present address: Department of Natural Science, Michigan State University, East Lansing, Mich.

Reproduced with permission from Ecological Monographs, 31: 221-238, 1961. Published by The Duke University Press, Durham, North Carolina.

pods because the taxonomy of their soil groups is relatively well known. The taxonomic work on these same groups in America has been neglected, with many groups unworked for 40 years or more.

The soil arthropods of an abandoned field were chosen for the study discussed in this paper. Both laboratory and field studies were undertaken. The field chosen for study is located on the University of Michigan's Edwin S. George Reserve, 4.5 mi west of Pinckney, Livingston Co., Mich. Evans & Cain (1952) and Evans & Dahl (1955) have described the vegetation of this field; Talbot (1953, 1954) has investigated the ant populations; Hairston & Byers (1954) have sampled the soil arthropods; and Evans & Lanham (1960) have examined the insect fauna of the herbaceous stratum. According to Evans & Dahl, the climate is a humid, mesothermal one, with mean monthly temperatures ranging from —4°C in January to 23°C in July, with a mean annual precipitation of 78 cm well distributed throughout the year. The soil is a sandy loam with very good drainage. The humus layer of the soil ranges from 2.5 to 3.6 cm in depth. Vegetation of the field consists of grasses (*Poa, Aristida, Setaria,* and *Leptoloma*), forbs (*Antennaria, Lespedeza, Rumex,* and *Solidago*), mosses (*Ceratodon* and *Polytrichum*), and lichens (*Cladonia*). The field has 2 distinct vegetation types or associations. Several depressions or swales are found in various areas of the field. These depressions have a dense cover of Kentucky blue grass, *Poa pratensis,* interspersed with the common milkweed, *Asclepias syriaca.* The rest of the field is higher and generally dominated by Canadian blue grass, *Poa compressa,* although there are patches of other grasses which displace the Canadian blue grass. Hairston (1959) found a difference in the soil fauna between the upland and the swales; therefore, these 2 areas are considered to be separate communities. In the present study only the upland community was considered.

The major goals of this study were (1) to determine the position of the oribatid mites in the food web, and (2) to indicate their role in the soil industry. Secondary goals included (3) determination of the ecological efficiency value for the soil herbivores, (4) comparison of this value with those obtained from aquatic studies, and (5) evaluation of the hypothesis that all communities operate on the same energetic principles.

I wish to acknowledge the following persons for their assistance during the course of my work: I. J. Cantrall, for permission to work on the Edwin S. George Reserve; F. E. Smith and P. Ovenberg, for their help with the regression calculations; L. B. Slobodkin, for advice on ecological efficiencies; and G. H. Lauff, for his sponsorship of the radioactive-labeling work. Special thanks are due my wife, Patricia, who typed the manuscript and helped with the editing; the members of my doctoral committee, W. R. Dawson, F. C. Evans, and A. H. Smith, who gave assistance during the course of the investigation and in the writing of the manuscript; and my chairman, N. G. Hairston, who gave encouragement and valuable help through the entire period of this endeavor.

MATERIALS AND METHODS

In evaluating the role of the arthropods in the soil of the old field, the following information was considered necessary to make up an energy balance sheet: the number of individuals present during the year; their reproductive rates and generation times; their body weights, and the amount of energy represented by these weights; and their metabolic energy. Despite the number of soil sampling studies, information about the soil arthropods is scanty. Data necessary to draw up the energy balance sheet were obtained by the following sampling and experimental techniques.

Sampling

A sampling program was employed to obtain estimates of the numbers of individuals present in the soil during the year. Hairston & Byers (1954) carried out an extensive program on the old field during the years 1949 and 1950; therefore, only a limited sampling program was undertaken in 1958. Sampling tubes 6.3 cm in diameter and 12.5 cm long were employed once each month to remove 3 plugs of soil from the central part of the old field. The sampling sites were chosen at random before the time of collection. The soil plugs were kept in the sample tubes and transported to the laboratory in plastic bags. This technique minimized moisture loss and kept the soil plug intact.

Extraction and Identification

Tullgren extraction (Park & Auerbach 1954) was used to remove the arthropods from the soil plugs. The soil plug in its sample tube was placed upside down in the Tullgren funnel. A 40-watt bulb furnished the heat and light source. The arthropods were caught in a jar containing 70% alcohol. The animals were then counted under a dissecting microscope.

The oribatid mites were the most intensively studied group of the soil arthropods found in the old-field samples. These small mites are found in forest and prairie soils all over the world; those found on the old field ranged from .1 to .9 mm. in length. Some of these mites are soft-bodied in all stages; however, most of the individuals from the samples studied were of species in which the adult has a thick chitinous exoskeleton and differs in appearance from the immature stages.

Taxonomically this group has received little attention. Although in Europe the taxonomic relationships of these mites are relatively well-known because of the work of men like Grandjean, work to date on forms from the Western Hemisphere has been of a pioneer nature. In recent years Dr. Tyler Woolley has begun a detailed study of the systematics of the Oribatidae, but the task is a very complicated one, and it will be a long time before the picture is in any way complete. Hence, for the purpose of the research reported in this paper, a numbering device was substituted for species designations. The system was modeled after the one used by Hairston & Byers in their work on the field populations and proved a convenient tool for preliminary identification of different groups. Each recognized kind of mite was given a number and specimens were sent to specialists for future study. The immature forms which differ from the adults in appearance were probably placed in a different category. The immature forms, however, are rather infrequent in the samples. Therefore this source of error is probably not a major concern.

Live arthropods were caught in jars containing water (Engelmann 1956). The animals were cultured in jars which had a flooring of plaster of paris and charcoal (Rohde 1956). The jars were supplied with various types of food, and the plaster was kept moist. The most successful diet for the arthropods in culture consisted of washed, pulverized organic material found on the surface of the soil, supplemented with dried yeast (*Saccharomyces*) which had been suspended in water. The yeast was dropped onto the bottom of the "nest" in very small quantities. Funga (*Mycena, Aspergillus, Agaricus,* and others) were also used as a source of food at various times.

Weight and Respiration

A quartz-helix balance sensitive to 2.5 μg was used to weigh the arthropods. Many of the animals weighed less than a microgram, so that a number of individuals had to be weighed at one time in order to register on the scale; the weights are therefore averages in most cases. The animals were killed by immersion in alcohol for a few minutes. They were then transferred to weighing pans and placed in a desiccator for 24 hours or more. When removed from the desiccator, the dried animals began to take up water from the air at a rapid rate, until an equilibrium was reached in about 5 minutes. Consequently some moisture was probably taken up by the animals during this weighing procedure, which required approximately 1.5 minutes per measurement.

Respiration data for the soil arthropods were obtained with the Warburg respirometer (Umbreit 1949) and a modification of the insect respirometer of Smith & Douglas (1949). This latter apparatus proved to be most convenient and was used most frequently. The Smith-Douglas respirometer was modified by substituting small glass vials with ground glass necks for the large brass chamber of the original model. The bottom half of the vial was lined with moist filter paper and closed with a piece of sterile cotton after the arthropods had been placed

Table 1. Numbers of individuals of the oribatid mite species found in 22 soil samples from an old field, Edwin S. George Reserve, Livingston Co., Mich.
? indicates sample destroyed before species was counted.

Oribatid mite species no.	Dates of Samples																						Totals
	Dec. 1, '57	Dec. 1, '57	Jan. 3, '58	Feb. 8, '58	Mar. 3, '58	Apr. 13, '58	Apr. 13, '58	May 4, '58	June 6, '58	July 7, '58	Aug. 8, '58	Aug. 8, '58	Sept. 2, '58	Sept. 2, '58	Oct. 4, '58	Oct. 4, '58	Oct. 31, '58	Oct. 31, '58	Dec. 12, '58	Dec. 12, '58	Jan. 9, '59	Jan. 9, '59	
101	31	12	12	19	25	37	14	4	27	19	28	79	0	13	5	0	5	7	5	20	26	12	400
102	0	0	2	10	1	50	1	2	1	0	0	0	0	0	4	0	12	3	16	2	1	4	109
103	7	2	4	0	0	0	0	0	0	0	0	0	0	1	0	0	0	0	1	0	0	0	15
105	171	16	15	17	99	14	35	40	10	5	47	181	6	6	6	13	247	0	35	66	138	15	1182
108a	4	4	2	2	2	7	3	1	9	0	0	17	1	0	2	8	6	1	6	4	13	5	97
108c	3	6	0	11	0	25	5	0	0	0	0	1	0	1	1	1	19	6	12	2	1	0	94
108d	2	0	1	3	3	7	9	8	0	0	3	2	1	7	6	2	5	0	13	0	5	0	77
108e	0	0	0	0	0	4	?	1	0	0	1	0	0	0	0	0	6	0	0	1	0	0	13
109	0	0	1	2	0	2	0	0	0	0	0	0	0	0	0	0	0	1	23	0	1	0	30
110	0	13	2	0	0	0	2	0	2	0	0	0	0	4	1	1	0	2	0	0	5	1	33
111	0	0	0	0	0	0	0	0	0	0	0	10	0	0	1	0	1	0	0	0	0	0	12
112a	0	0	0	9	6	17	0	0	7	0	0	0	0	1	6	0	7	0	17	0	1	6	77
112b	0	0	0	0	0	0	0	2	7	2	0	3	0	3	3	0	0	0	0	0	0	0	20
113	0	0	0	0	11	0	0	1	0	0	0	1	0	0	0	2	0	1	0	0	0	0	16
114	4	4	17	7	1	1	2	0	0	0	1	8	0	1	0	15	0	0	1	0	0	6	68
115	0	0	0	0	0	1	0	0	0	0	0	0	0	0	0	0	0	0	0	0	0	0	1
116	0	0	0	0	0	0	0	0	2	0	0	4	0	1	2	0	3	0	1	0	0	0	13
117	3	0	4	8	0	0	0	1	2	0	0	0	0	0	4	2	1	1	25	14	6	3	74
118	0	0	1	0	0	0	0	0	0	0	0	0	0	0	0	0	0	0	0	0	0	0	1
119	0	0	0	1	0	2	0	3	0	0	0	0	0	0	0	0	1	0	2	2	0	0	11
120	0	0	0	25	8	66	?	11	7	31	37	54	27	31	35	5	47	3	26	37	4	2	456
121	10	5	0	0	0	0	0	4	2	0	0	0	0	0	2	1	4	2	1	0	0	0	31
126	?	?	7	89	6	42	?	1	4	3	2	5	10	30	8	3	48	9	60	0	61	20	408
128	?	?	0	0	4	0	?	32	7	4	15	8	0	8	155	11	46	0	139	153	0	2	584
Total...	235	62	68	203	166	275	71	111	87	64	134	373	45	107	241	64	458	36	383	301	262	76	3822

on the filter paper. A roll of filter paper soaked in .1 molar NaOH was placed in the upper end of the vial. The manometer consisted of a length of thick-walled capillary tubing with a bore of .5 mm. Colored water containing a detergent was used as manometer fluid. The respirometers were immersed in a water bath which maintained a temperature of 24°-25° C during the course of the experiment.

Feeding and Assimilation

A radioactive labeling technique was used to make estimates of food ingestion and assimilation (Trama 1957). Yeast was labeled with radioactive glycine C^{14}. A known quantity of the yeast was plated on a counting planchet and radioactivity determined in a gas flow geiger counter. This procedure yielded an estimate of the number of disintegrations per unit of time per unit of weight of yeast. The yeast was then presented to the animals for a period of time, the animals were killed and dissolved in hot formamide and plated on a planchet. The disintegrations per unit of time obtained from the dissolved animals were then translated into grams of yeast contained in the body of the animal at the time of death. When the animals were allowed to post-absorb before being killed, an assimilation rate was estimated.

A bomb calorimeter was used to obtain estimates of the caloric contents of various substances including vascular plant material, fungi, and insect larvae (Richman 1958).

PRESENTATION AND ANALYSIS OF DATA

The numbers of oribatid mites in the various species categories found in 22 samples taken over a 13-month period are given in Table 1. Species categories 101, 105, and 120 are found in most of the samples and are probably the more characteristic species of the field's upland. Species 115 and 118 were found only once and are most likely to be "accidentals". Yearly population patterns fell into 3 main types: populations with a relatively constant level through the year, populations largely restricted to the summer months, and populations showing increased numbers in both spring and fall. Species 101, 105, and 120 show no marked population peak, species 112b and 116 were taken only in summer, and the rest of the species show a spring population peak and a fall population peak. The fall population peak is usually greater than the one in the spring. This double peak has been observed in other oribatid populations (Sengbusch 1954) and has implications for the turnover rate of the populations concerned. Sengbusch believes that this double peak can be explained by the presence of two reproductive periods each year, one in the spring and one in the fall. Hairston & Byers (1954) give good evidence for the vertical migration of soil arthropods; therefore, the spring peak could also be explained by the return of the adults to the surface layers of the soil.

The total numbers of each species of mite in the 22 samples were divided by the number of samples to secure "average sample" figures for the thirteen months (Table 2). Weights were also obtained for each mite species. These figures were used to calculate the biomass of the oribatids found in an average sample (Table 2).

Table 2. Numbers, weights, and biomasses of the oribatid mites found in an average soil sample (area 31.2 cm^2) from an abandoned field in southeastern Michigan, 1958.

Species Category	Mean No. of Individuals Per Sample	Mean Wt. of Individual (µg)	Species Biomass (mg/m²)
101	18.20	1.50	8.750
102	5.00	2.00	3.205
103	0.68	15.60	3.397
105	53.70	0.70	12.019
108a	4.40	1.00	1.410
108c	4.30	0.51	0.705
108d	3.50	0.43	0.481
108e	0.60	0.33*	0.064
109	1.40	2.43	1.090
110	1.50	5.00	2.404
111	0.50	12.00*	1.923
112a	3.50	0.74*	0.833
112b	0.90	0.89*	0.250
113	0.70	0.71*	0.151
114	3.10	5.49	5.449
115	0.05	4.00*	0.074
116	0.60	0.33*	0.077
117	3.40	1.00	1.090
118	0.05	2.00*	0.029
119	0.50	0.20*	0.035
120	21.70	3.50*	2.436
121	1.40	7.15	3.205
126	21.50	0.31*	2.147
128	30.70	0.27	2.660
Totals	181.88	—	53.884

* Weight derived from regression equation.

Biomass

Fig. 1 shows, on a double log plot, the relationship of the length-width index, i.e., the length times the width of the animal measured in microns, to the weight of the animal, in micrograms. The line was fitted to the points by means of the standard regression technique (the least squares method). The correlation coefficient of the points to the line is .85, and a t value of 12.0 is significant at a probability of less than .01. The animals were measured after they had been mounted on slides in balsam. This point is important, for there is some compression of the animal on the slide which increases the lateral dimensions, thus increasing the frontal area about 20%. The weight of slide-mounted animals was estimated from the following formula: Log weight of animal in micrograms = 1.32 [log length + log width (in microns)] — 5.87. Neither length nor volume measurements showed a linear relationship when plotted against weight. The explanation for this is that the exoskeleton and muscles attached to it comprise most of the weight of these arthropods. Dry weight, therefore, becomes some function of the surface area rather than of volume. The length-

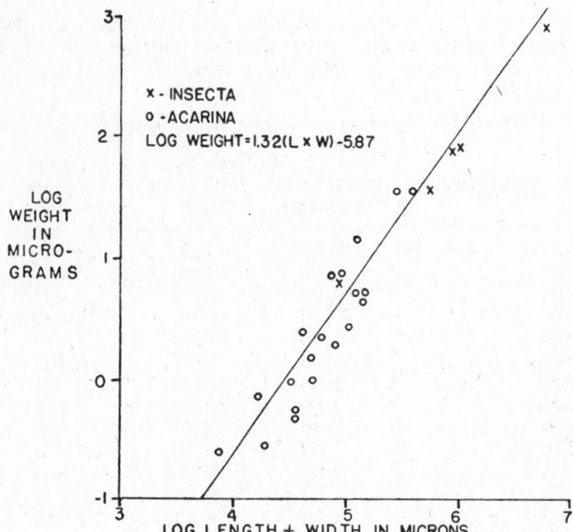

Fig. 1. The relationship of weight to length-width index in twenty five terrestrial arthropods. Data from Acarina (o) and Insecta (x) were used to make the plot.

width index is apparently some constant proportion of the total surface area (about 40%) and can therefore be used as a satisfactory measure.

The biomass for each species category was calculated from the weights obtained by direct weighing or from the regression equation (Table 2). A total of about 54 milligrams of oribatid mites was estimated for each square meter of upland of the old field. This estimate of standing crop was then converted into energy units by the assumption that a gram of arthropod protoplasm is equivalent to 5000 gram calories of energy. Culture methods did not allow the accumulation of enough material to make an actual assay of oribatid protoplasm; however, some calorimetry was done on fourth instar larvae of *Tenebrio molitor.* Larvae taken directly from culture and homogenized had a caloric content of 6578.9 cals/gm; fat-extracted individuals had a caloric content of 4858.1 cal/gm, and the exoskeletons (formamide-treated larvae) contained 4978.0 cals/gm. In a table compiled by Golley (1959), caloric values for the animal material tested ranged from 1900 cals/gm to 6200 cals/gm, with most of the values falling between 4000 and 5500 cals/gm. The assumption of 5000 cals/gm is, therefore, not an unreasonable approximation at the present time. The product of the total estimated standing crop (54 mg) times the mean caloric content (5000 cals/gm) gives an estimate of 270 cals of oribatid mites found to a depth of 12.5 cm on each square meter of upland.

When a population is in a "steady state" condition the total production biomass will remain the same from year to year, although during the year the standing crop biomass may fluctuate around some mean value. However, the standing crop gives little indication *per se* of the energy flow through the population. Energy flows into the population in the form of food and flows out of the population in the form of respiration and dead individuals. As far as the population is concerned, egested or defecated food has never entered the protoplasm of the population. In this sense, then, the digestive tract of the animal can be considered an extension of the external environment. Therefore, only the functions of respiration rate, feeding rate, and death rate need be estimated to describe the basic energy characteristics of the population.

Oxygen Consumption

Data on oxygen consumption by various arthropods were obtained with the aid of respirometers (Table 3). Technical difficulties prevented acquisition of respiration information from all of the soil arthropods; therefore, some other approach was needed to obtain estimates of the respiration of these animals. Data of Bornebusch (1931) were used with the data from Table 3 to plot the log of the total respiration of the individual against the log of the total body weight (Fig. 2). The slopes for the 2 sets of points are .74 and .85. The common regression line for all the points has a slope of .84. There is no significant difference between the 3 lines. A slope of .85-.90 is common for a great number of invertebrates (Zeuthen 1953). The *t* test values for each of the regressions are highly significant (P less than .01). The following formula was used to estimate the respiration of an animal when the weight was known:

Log respiration ($\mu l \; 10^{-3}$) = .85 (log weight in micrograms) + .44.

Table 3. Respiration of soil arthropods at 25°C in the laboratory.

Species	Weight µg	µl/ ind./hr. (Mean)	Range	s	Coeff. of variation	Avg. µl/ mg. per hour
Oribatidae *Oppia nova*	1.0	.0065	.0227-.0013	.0066	1.01	6.5
Oribatidae species 101	1.5	.0024	—	—	—	1.6
Oribatidae Species 102	2.0	.0044	.0041-.0050	.00052	.118	2.2
Acaridae *Tyroglyphus linteri*	2.3	.017	.0035-.0110	.01085	.61	7.4
Oribatidae Species 15	11.05	.0215	—	—	—	1.95
Scydmaenidae Species 7 Larva	13.6	.08	—	—	—	5.9
Oribatidae *Casmia* (mixed instars)	15.56	.0138	—	—	—	0.89
Oribatidae Species 12	26.52	.0107	—	—	—	0.4
Mesostigmata Species 14	40.1	.0305	—	—	—	0.76
Scydmaenidae Species 1 larva	45.25	.140	—	—	—	3.1
Pselaphidae *Reichenbachia*	76.6	.145	—	—	—	1.9
Staphylinidae Species 4	86.25	.215	—	—	—	2.5
Staphylinidae Species 3	88.75	.061	—	—	—	0.7
Staphylinidae Species 6	96.5	.18	—	—	—	1.9
Formicidae *Ponaria* (worker)	187.3	.24	—	—	—	1.3
Isopoda *Armadillidium vulgare* (Juvenal)	636.2	1.118	—	—	—	1.8
Carabidae Species 2	891.0	.238	—	—	—	0.27
Scarabaeidae *Geotrupes*	160300.0	120.5	—	—	—	0.75

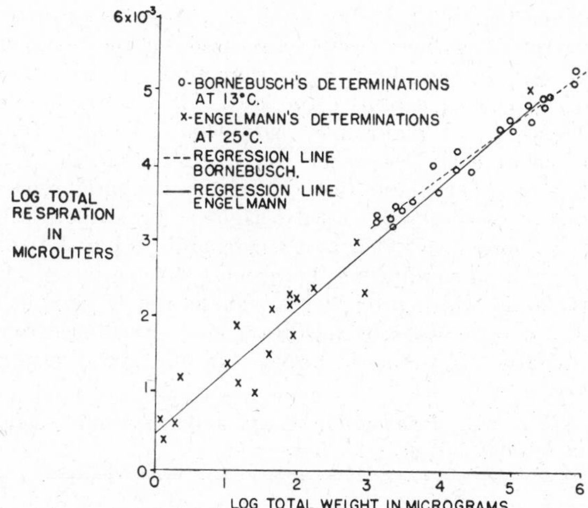

FIG. 2. Respiration-weight relationship in forty terrestrial arthropods. Data from the study of Bornebusch (1930) and from the present study were used to make the plot.

If the rates of oxygen consumption obtained from the respiration studies or from the regression equation are multiplied by the number of individuals in each species category, we obtain estimates of the amount of oxygen used by the population each hour, and these can be extrapolated to the daily oxygen consumption (Table 4). The total oribatid oxygen consumption per day was estimated at 3424 microliters. The caloric values of the oxygen consumed can be obtained if the RQ is known (Brody 1945: 310). Although no RQ is known for oribatid mites, the RQ of a resting insect is .82 (Roeder 1953), and the caloric equivalent of a microliter of oxygen at this RQ is .0048 cals. If this factor is applied to the data, an estimated 16.5 cals per day are burned by the total oribatid fauna (Table 4). Since these animals are poikilotherms, they will not function at the same rate throughout the year. The respiration-temperature curve of Krogh (1941: 6) and the monthly mean air temperatures of Ann Arbor (Clim. data, 1958) were used to determine the rates of respiration of the mites for each month. This was equivalent to 4 months of metabolic rate of 25° C. These calculations yield an estimate of 1965 calories respired by the oribatids over the period of a year (Table 4). An estimate of respiration based upon Krogh's curve may be too low, because many invertebrates are capable of some metabolic adjustment (Uvarov 1931, Agrell 1947, Bullock 1955, Fry 1958). Such adjustment could be advantageous to a soil dwelling organism, since the moist part of the year is usually the cold part of the year (spring, fall and winter). The soil arthropods require moist surroundings both because they are subject to desiccation, and because their food source requires moisture.

TABLE 4. Oxygen consumed and calories burned by the oribatid mites found in an average sample of 12.5 cm depth extrapolated to an area of 1 m², from an abandoned field in southeastern Michigan, 1958.

Species category	Oxygen consumption** for total population µl O_2/day	ENERGY EXPENDITURE OF TOTAL POPULATION	
		gm cal per 24 hours†	gm cal per year
101	336.205*	1.62173	192.98
102	169.224*	0.81728	97.25
103	302.873	1.46148	173.91
105	838.428	4.04471	481.30
108a	145.507*	0.70190	83.52
108c	50.639	0.24358	28.98
108d	26.602	0.12820	15.26
108e	4.808	0.02244	2.67
109	127.559	0.61536	73.22
110	124.675	0.60254	71.70
111	84.933	0.41024	48.82
112a	58.331	0.28204	33.56
112b	16.987	0.08333	9.92
113	8.654	0.04167	4.96
114	279.156	1.34610	160.18
115	3.846	0.01923	2.29
116	5.769	0.02885	3.43
117	72.113	0.34935	41.57
118	1.603	0.00641	0.76
119	2.885	0.01282	1.53
120	216.658	1.04483	124.32
121	126.277	0.60895	72.46
126	205.120	0.98714	117.46
128	214.735	1.03522	123.19
Totals:	3423.587	16.51538	1965.24

* From actual respiration measurement.
** Recorded at 25°C.
† Assuming an average value of .0048 calories per microliter.

ANNUAL CALORIC FLOW THROUGH THE MITE POPULATION

Information on the feeding rates of the oribatid mites came from two sources: direct weight experiments and radioactive tracer studies. The 2 methods yielded different results. The radio-tracer work gave an estimate of 40% body weight ingested at the end of a 24-hour feeding period, while the direct weighing technique gave estimates of from 90-110% body weight ingested after the same time interval. This discrepancy was explained when it became evident that the mites were contaminating their food source by fungi carried into the culture in their digestive tracts or on their bodies. The growing fungi as well as the mites consumed the food, and, therefore, the loss of weight in the food planchet was more than doubled. The use of food by both mites and fungi produced the apparent high ingestion rate of the weight experiments. Radiotracer work gave an estimate of 8% body weight assimilated at the end of 24 hrs. The direct weighing technique gave an estimate of 13% body weight egested per day. Since the contamination factor would also affect the latter estimate, this should be multiplied by a factor of 2.3 (the rate of consumption of mite feces by fungi in the cultures). Thus the more probable value is approximately 30% of the body weight egested by the mites each day.

Using a respiration factor of 4 months of full activity as a year's activity and a value of 4000 calories per gram of food material, it was estimated that 10,248 calories are ingested by 54 mg of mites (the mite biomass in an average square meter) during a year. Caloric values of 3713 and 3999 calories per gram for the puff ball (*Astreus hygrometricus*) cortex were obtained by bomb calorimetry during the course of this study. Dried *Leptoloma* leaves gave values of 3825-4248 calories per gram. These figures agree with those compiled by Golley for the caloric values of plant material. Values for seeds in Golley's compilation, however, ran higher, ranging up to 6000 calories per gram.

An estimated 7686 calories are egested annually by the oribatid population. This figure was obtained by using the 30% egestion estimate and the same monthly factor and caloric values used in calculating ingestion rates above. If the animals assimilate 8% of their body weight per day, they will assimilate about 2058 calories each year, or 20% of the food ingested. Of these 2058 calories, 1965 are used in respiration.

Life cycle data become essential if we are to make estimates of the energies lost to the population through mortality. The complete life history of one oribatid mite, *Oppia nova,* was observed. In culture both adults and young fed upon yeasts and fungal mycelia. At 24° C the egg stage lasted 6-8 days, the larval instar lasted 8-9 days, first nymphal instar lasted 4-5 days, and the second nymphal instar 7-8 days. From the time of oviposition to the time of the emergence of the adult took 25-30 days. There was a 15-day maturation period before the adult laid its first egg; therefore, the minimum generation time would be 45 days. The adults lay about 1 egg every 7-10 days. This rate was obtained from a culture of several individuals which were allowed to oviposit for several days. The culture included both male and female individuals and the total number of eggs was averaged for the total number of individuals; therefore, 1 egg per 10 days per individual is an average population rate.

The long generation time and field data on the fluctuation of populations support the hypothesis that the oribatids completely replace their population once, or at the most twice each year if, as seems likely, reproduction is limited to the warmer months. If a yearly turnover rate is assumed, then 54 mg of mites, equal to 270 gram calories, will go to the next trophic level as dead adults. Adults, however, are not the only individuals which die in the course of the year, and in fact, the young are extremely vulnerable to predators. In culture, for example, the hard-bodied adults are almost ignored by predaceous mites and beetles, while the soft-bodied immature stages are attacked vigorously. Some estimate of the mortality of immature individuals must be attempted before the energy picture of the oribatids is complete. It has already been observed that the adults of *Oppia nova* lay, on the average, 1 egg every 10 days. The egg is about 3% of the body weight of the adult (Table 5). In an attempt to define the length of the breeding period, the cleared, mounted specimens were scrutinized for the presence of eggs in the uteri. Eggs were found in the uteri of specimens captured in April, 1958 through late November of that same year. One individual captured in early December had a gravid uterus. On the basis of these observations a 6-month reproductive period is proposed. Eighteen eggs, then, will be produced each year by a single adult. In a state of population equilibrium, 1 egg must survive to replace the adult which produced it. Therefore, 17 eggs will die in some stage of the life cycle. Mortality from predation is probably heaviest in the larval instar.

TABLE 5. Relationship of egg weight to adult weight in selected mites.

Species category	Average Weight Determined by Regression				Egg wt as % adult wt
	Egg wt μg	s	Adult wt μg	s	
Tyroglyphus linteri	.085	.0068	1.750	.093	4.9
Oribatid-102	.174	.0180	4.423	.521	3.9
Oribatid-109	.187	.0570	9.34	—	2.0
Oribatid-110	.185	.0000	7.28	—	2.5
Oribatid-111	.337	.1880	12.52	—	2.7
Oribatid-114	.204	—	9.16	—	2.2
Oppia nova	.080	—	1.77	—	4.5
				Avg. Oribatid	3.0%
				Acarid	5.0%

The actual caloric value of the eggs is unknown; however, these structures are undoubtedly supplied with a quantity of "yolk" material which is in the form of fats and oils. The fat-laden fourth instar larva of *Tenebrio* yielded a caloric value of 6000 gram calories per gram, and this value was arbitrarily used for the caloric value of the mite eggs. The resulting quantity of energy passing out of the population in the form of dead "young" is therefore about 160 calories per year.

The caloric balance sheet for the oribatid biomass in an average square meter for 1 year may be summarized as follows: ingested—10,248 calories; egested—7,686 calories, or 75% of the ingested material; assimilated—2,058 calories, or 20% of the ingested material; respired—1,965 calories, or 96% of the assimilated calories; adult mortality—270 calories, or 13% of the assimilated calories; egg (young) mortality—160 calories, or 7.8% of the assimilated calories. Ninety-five % of the ingested calories has been accounted for in the number of calories egested and assimilated. Five %, or 504 calories, is unaccounted for; this is within the range of experimental error. One hundred and seventeen % of the assimilated calories is accounted for in respiration and total mortality, resulting in a surplus of 17% or 337 calories. Each figure was attained independently from various experimental and field data; none was derived from working only with "known" figures

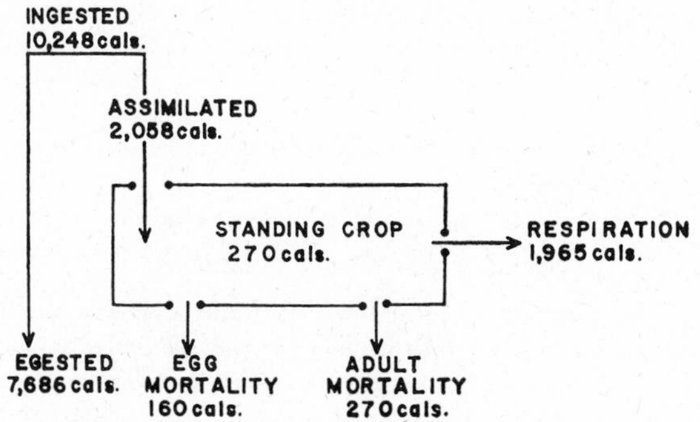

7,686+2,058=9,744 (504 CALS. UNACCOUNTED FOR)
1,965+270+160=2395 (337 CALS. OVERESTIMATED)

FIG. 3. Annual energy balance sheet for the oribatid mites found on a square meter of an abandoned field in Michigan, 1958. The arrows indicate the direction of energy flow. The rectangle represents the protoplasm of the oribatid population.

and solving for "unknowns". Hence, though there are arithmetical discrepancies, each estimate is a fairly close one, and all are supported by combined field and laboratory data. The caloric balance data are also summarized in Fig. 3.

CHANGES IN SPECIES COMPOSITION

When this study was originally undertaken, it was hoped that the extensive collecting data of Hairston & Byers could be employed in a complete analysis of the energetics of the soil fauna. After careful comparison of the 1949-50 fauna and the 1958 fauna, it became clear that the oribatid mite populations had undergone a radical change in the years between 1950 and 1958. This change affected not only the species composition of the upland field, but also the biomass and respiration energies of the oribatid mites involved.

An analysis of the oribatid species composition of the field for the years 1949-50 and 1958 showed that only 5 species were common to the field during both samplings. Twenty-three species categories disappeared from the field after 1950 and were replaced by 19 new species. Numbers of individuals showed a similar decrease, since 33% fewer individuals were found per square meter in 1958. An analysis of the 5 species categories is made in Table 6. It is evident that 2 species have increased their numbers and biomass, 2 have decreased in numbers and biomass, and 1 has remained at about the same level. In spite of the decrease in the total numbers of individuals, there has been doubling of the biomass over the 1950 figure, and a near doubling of the respiration rate (Table 7). The increase in the biomass could be accounted for by the fact that the average individual in 1958 was heavier than the average individual of 1949-50; this is illustrated in Table 8, where an analysis is made of the portion of the total biomass contributed by individuals of various weight categories. Individuals in the .1-.49 and 5.0-9.9 microgram categories make up the greater part of the 1950 biomass, while the .5 through 9.9 microgram classes make up the greater proportion of the 1958 biomass. The milligram per square meter figures indicated that a greater number of heavier individuals produced the greater biomass in the 1958 samples. Apparently, the lighter species of 1949-50 have been replaced by heavier species in 1958.

TABLE 6. Comparison of the five species categories common to the old field in the years 1949-1950 and 1958.

SPECIES CODE NUMBER		NO. OF IND./M²		BIOMASS IN MG./M²		Population trend
'49-'50	'58	'49-'50	'58	'49-'50	'58	
5	120	6410.3	6954.8	1.733	2.436	+
6	105	3449.9	17210.9	2.471	12.019	+
7	115	46.6	16.0	0.311	0.074	–
9	126	21173.3	6890.8	3.815	2.147	–
10	109	170.9	448.7	0.956	1.090	+

\+ represents an increase from 1950 to 1958.
– represents a decrease from 1950 to 1958.

TABLE 7. Comparison of various population characteristics of the oribatid mites in the top 12.5 cm of one square meter of the old field for the years 1949-1950 and 1958.

Characteristic	Years '49-'50	Year 1958	% increase (+) or decrease (–) '58 over '50
Total number of individuals......	87449.20	58293.10	– 33.2
Total biomass in mgs.	26.96	53.88	+100.0
Total standing crop in calories.......	134.75	269.48	+100.0
Respiration in µl's per total population per day.....	1843.25	3423.59	+ 92.0
Gm. cals. burned per day per total pop.	8.85	16.52	+ 92.0
Gm. cals. per year per population...	1052.82	1965.24	+ 92.0

TABLE 8. Comparison of the biomass and weight of individual oribatid mites from the old field for the years 1949-1950 and 1958.

Weight of individuals µg	BIOMASS '49-'50		BIOMASS 1958	
	mg/m²	%	mg/m²	%
.1 and below..........	2.857	10.6	0.000	0.0
.1-.49................	9.564	35.5	7.900	14.7
.5-.99................	2.615	9.7	13.958	25.9
1.0-4.99..............	1.661	6.2	14.558	27.0
5.0-9.99..............	7.856	29.1	12.148	22.5
10.0-14.99............	2.409	8.9	1.923	3.6
15.0 and greater.......	0.000	0.0	3.397	6.3
Total..............	26.962	100.0	53.884	100.0

It is evident then, that over this 8-year period, the oribatid populations have not been in a state of equilibrium, but have been undergoing marked change. The species present on the field during 1949-50 have disappeared, presenting certain difficulties in reconstructing the energy flow picture at that time. Nevertheless, a reasonable approximation of this energy flow system can be reached by studying the slides of the animals and using the area-weight equation and the weight-respiration equation.

The increase in oribatid biomass does not necessarily mean that the rest of the soil fauna has also increased. Evidence from 3 samples from the 1958 field in which all the animals were counted indicates that other groups have declined in numbers of species and numbers of individuals. There were no new species of eupodids and Collembola, but many of the species collected in 1949 and 1950 had disappeared. The implication is that the oribatids have replaced some of the other herbivores found in the old field soil.

It is possible that these drastic changes in the oribatid populations were correlated with corresponding changes in the above-ground system. The component of the latter most likely to exhibit significant modification is the vegetation. The plant cover of the old field was surveyed by Evans & Cain (1952) during the 1949-50 season; they recorded a total of 92 vascular plant species and an average of 148.2 g of air-dried vegetation per m^2. No formal plant investigation was undertaken in 1958, but clip-plot studies made in July of that year by U. N. Lanham (personal communication) yielded an average of 119.2 g of air-dried vegetation, and casual observations indicated that the same species reported by Evans & Cain and by Evans & Dahl (1954) were still present. That old-field production may remain fairly constant over a considerable period of time is also suggested by Odum's (1960) 6-yr study of abandoned fields on the Savannah River, Georgia, in which the net production underwent no significant change despite considerable alteration in species composition. Such evidence as is available, then, indicates that there has been no radical change in the old-field vegetation to correlate with changes in the oribatid populations.

Trophic Efficiencies

In theory the radiant energy taken up by a community is eventually given off as heat or respiration. If one could measure the total energy utilized by a particular community, one could use this as a basis for the comparison of communities. All too often, however, a total energy measurement is impractical, and therefore Lindeman (1942) proposed a series of efficiencies by which the various trophic levels within the community may be evaluated. These efficiencies have been summarized by Patten (1959: 227). The efficiency which is probably the most significant for use in the comparison of trophic levels of different communities is called the "efficiency of transfer of ingested energy" by Patten and the "ecological efficiency" by Slobodkin (1960). For the purposes of the present study this efficiency is defined as the ratio of the calories ingested by the carnivore level to the number of calories ingested by the herbivore level:

$$\text{EF} = \frac{\text{cals. ingested by carnivore}}{\text{cals. ingested by herbivore}} \times 100$$

The population figures of Hairston & Byers were used to obtain the data needed for the efficiency equation. The numbers of individuals listed in Table 1 of Hairston & Byers were averaged, and then extrapolated to numbers of individuals per square meter. (In this case the depth of the square meter is 20.8 cm, rather than the 12.5 cm used by the present author in his study of the oribatid mite populations.) The mounted individuals were measured, and weight and oxygen consumptions were estimated by means of the regression equations.

It is evident that some of the animals found in the Hairston & Byers samples are not members of the soil community: e.g. thrips, true bugs, etc. Indeed, the classification of animals as members of the soil community presented several problems. Many animals appear to belong to the soil fauna but in actuality may not. The ants, carabid and staphylinid beetles, and dipteran larvae will be used as examples to illustrate this point. The most common ant on the field (*Lasius niger neoniger*) was observed to forage for dead animals, feed upon insects, root secretions and stem aphids (Talbot 1953). Plant material collected consisted of seeds, nectar and flower parts. The ants were parasitized by mites, and preyed upon by spiders, tiger beetles, and the flicker. Even though the ants burrow in the soil, their livelihood comes from the above-ground community, and from an energetics point of view they therefore are best considered part of the above-ground edaphon. The staphylinid and carabid beetles present greater problems, when an attempt is made to assign them to a particular community. In culture they have been observed to feed upon Collembola and mites, as well as upon meal worms, flies, leafhopper nymphs, etc. Occasionally in culture, they have even been observed to feed upon apple and banana (Needham *et al.* 1937)! A similar type of difficulty is presented by the small spiders and fly larvae found on the old field. A great amount of field and laboratory study is needed before these relationships can be resolved. These animals were eliminated from the efficiency analysis because of the lack of quantative data. It was decided to limit inclusion in the category of soil arthropods to the mites, Collembola, Protura, Symphyla, Pauropoda, and Japygida.

Knowing the food habits of an animal is of prime importance to an analysis of ecological efficiency. The literature on the food habits of the soil arthropods is indeed scant and extremely diffuse. Many times on the basis of one observation of one species a whole family has been assigned a particular food habit. This practice is deplorable but often leaves no alternative. The group called eupodoid by Hairston & Byers has proved to be a composite including members of the Acaridae, Trombididae and Eupodidae. In many cases the feeding habits of these animals were assigned on the basis of the mouth parts, and they were placed in questionable categories by the present author (Table 9). The japygids,

TABLE 9. Average numbers of individuals, biomass, and respiration of the soil arthropods found on 1 m^2 x 20.3 cm of the old field in the years 1949-1950.

Category	Average number	Biomass in Mg.	Standing Crop Energy Gm. cals.	Resp. in cals.	Food habits
ACARINA					
Parasitoid.......	12414.8	9.330	46.650	354.37	Carn.
Oribatid........	87582.6	28.596	142.980	1115.96	Herb.
Sarcoptoid......	4721.8	3.466	17.330	138.66	Herb.
Trombidoid.....	1797.8	1.722	8.610	53.33	Carn.
Eupodoid.......	9191.0	3.262	16.310	136.42	Herb.
	20396.4	5.204	26.025	233.32	Herb.?
	2543.0	1.974	9.870	67.06	Carn.
	236.4	0.042	0.210	2.57	Carn.?
Pauropoda......	679.9	0.244	1.220	10.73	Herb.
Symphyla.......	51.3	0.418	2.090	11.52	Herb.
Protura.........	662.1	2.387	11.935	66.53	Herb.
INSECTA					
Japygida........	388.5	13.472	67.365	298.78	???
Podurid.........	7764.2	7.534	37.670	274.81	Herb.
Entomobryid....	243.2	2.095	10.475	53.60	Herb.
Sminthurid......	175.7	0.121	0.605	3.64	Herb.

which make up a considerable portion of the energy and biomass of the field soil arthropods, gave the most trouble. There is one citation in the literature given by Kühnelt in *Soil Zoology* (Kevan ed. 1955) in which he states that japygids are predators; however, intestinal analysis revealed both plant and animal substances. When observed in the laboratory during this investigation these animals huddled in cracks and crevices of the culture jars and slowly died off. They were never observed to feed. For this reason 3 separate analyses were made of the total data: 1), considering the japygids as herbivores; 2), considering them as carnivores; and 3), omitting the group entirely (Table 10).

As indicated above, ecological efficiency can be calculated if the numbers of calories ingested by both the herbivores and carnivores are known. Since feeding experiments were not carried out on the carnivores, the ingestion rates of these animals are not known. Nevertheless, an estimate of the calories involved can be obtained in the following way: if a steady-state condition is assumed, the respiration of the population plus the egestion-excretion of the population will equal the calories ingested. If the population is being preyed upon, then the calories respired and egested-excreted by the predators represent a portion of the ingested calories of the prey population. Therefore, these calories must be included with the egestion and respiration calories of the prey population. Assimilation rates vary with

TABLE 10. Ecological efficiency of the soil herbivores of the old field.

ASSIMILATION %		EFFICIENCY %		
Carn.	Herb.	Without *Japex*	*Japex* Carn.	*Japex* Herb.
32	32	18.9	27.5	16.9
	25	15.4	22.9	13.7
	14	9.6	14.7	8.5
25	32	23.0	32.7	20.7
	25	18.9	27.5	16.9
	14	12.0	18.1	10.6
14	32	32.9	45.4	30.1
	25	28.1	39.4	25.5
	14	18.9	27.5	16.9

the amount of food available, and since the food level of the soil herbivores is unknown for the field during 1949-1950, efficiencies for several assimilation rates have been calculated (Table 10). Richman found that *Daphnia* assimilated from 14 to 32% of the food ingested, depending upon the food level. The figure of 25% was selected as being a convenient number near the middle of that range. The ecological efficiencies were calculated by the following formula:

$$EF = \frac{Rc + Rc\left(\frac{100-A'}{A'}\right)}{Rh + Rh\left(\frac{100-A''}{A''}\right)}$$

where Rc is the respiration of the carnivore, Rh is the respiration of the herbivore, A′ is the % assimilation of the carnivore, A″ is the % assimilation of the herbivore, and EF stands for ecological efficiency. In applying the data of this study to the formula given above, two variables were considered: (1) the assimilation rate of the herbivores and carnivores, and (2) the uncertain feeding status of the japygids. Hence, instead of obtaining a single efficiency, a range of efficiencies resulted from the several possible combinations of the variables.

The number of calories respired by the herbivores was 2045.19 when the japygids were omitted and also when they were included as carnivores, and 2343.97 when the japygids were considered to be herbivores. The numbers of calories respired by the carnivores was 477.33 when the japygids were omitted and also when they were included as herbivores, and 776.10 when the japygids were considered to be carnivores. Thus the total amount of respiration for combined herbivore and carnivore populations was 2522.52 calories when the japygids were omitted from both groups and 2821.30 calories when they were included in either herbivore or carnivore group. The above values are based upon the number of animals found in 1 square meter of soil, 20.8 cm deep, and over a year's period of time. The efficiencies range from 45.5% to 8.5% depending upon the various assimilation efficiencies proposed for the components of the system and the position of the japygids in the trophic scheme. It will be noted that wherever the assimilation rate for the carnivore and the herbivore is the same, i.e., 32%, 25%, 14%, for each, the EF for that column is the same: i.e., 18.9, 27.5, or 16.9. When A′ and A″ in the above equation are equal, EF becomes a ratio of the 2 respiration rates, thereby giving the same efficiency for all assumed assimilations.

Table 11 gives the range of the total calories consumed by the herbivores used in calculating the efficiencies found in Table 10. It will be noted that not only are there different caloric values for the same efficiency, but there are also the same caloric values for different efficiencies. Which value or values are the most reasonable? One approach is to determine how many calories the herbivores can produce over a year's time. Life history information showed that the acarid mites (*Caloglyphus* and *Tyroglyphus*) were capable of 2-3 generations per month (Table 12), and that they could deposit 56-235 eggs per lifetime per female. The oribatids have a lower reproductive rate and longer development time. It was found that the egg weight of

TABLE 11. Caloric consumption and ecological efficiency calculated for the soil herbivores found on the old field during 1949-1950.

Consumption by herbivores cals.	Ecological efficiency %	Consumption by herbivores cals.	Ecological efficiency %
7882.89	18.9	11713.09	45.4
8300.54	23.0	12174.25	28.1
8816.57	27.5	13369.81	25.5
8816.57	16.9	13502.65	39.4
9234.23	20.7	15515.87	9.6
9495.66	32.7	15933.53	12.0
9699.74	15.4	16449.56	14.7
10090.11	18.9	17128.65	18.1
10385.03	32.9	17564.65	8.5
10606.13	22.9	17982.31	10.6
10867.56	13.7	18103.38	18.9
11285.21	16.9	19346.08	27.5
11285.21	27.5	20152.27	16.9
11318.83	30.1		

Tyroglyphus linteri was about 5% of the adult weight (Table 5). Using this information it was calculated that the herbivore population could produce 1928-3390 calories in eggs and adults for the maintenance of the predator populations. Most of the caloric requirements calculated for the carnivores in constructing Table 10 fell between 1260 and 3360 calories. However, the set of "*Japex* carn." efficiencies calculated at an assimilation level of 14% depended on a value of 5325 calories consumed each year by the carnivores. This value is more than the herbivores can possibly produce during a year, and the dependent set of efficiencies is therefore not a reasonable one.

Another way to try to narrow the choice of the

TABLE 12. Life cycle information of several herbivorous mites.

Genus and species	Length of life	Eggs produced during life	Development time	Reference
Tetranychus telarus....	20-40 days	70	—	Metcalf & Flint 1939
Tarsonemus pallidus...	14 days	—	—	Metcalf & Flint 1939
Rhizoglyphus hyacinthi.	30-60 days	50-100	—	Metcalf & Flint 1939
Rhizoglyphus echinopus.	17-27 days	—	—	Baker & Wharton 1952
Phyllocoptis oleivorus..	7-14 days	—	—	Metcalf & Flint 1939
Paratetranychus pilosus	21 days	30-35	—	Metcalf & Flint 1939
Paratetranychus citrii..	—	—	21- 35 days	Metcalf & Flint 1939
Halotydeus destructor..	25-50 days	—	—	Baker & Wharton 1952
Caloglyphus mycophagus	18-23 days	235	4-9 days	Rohde 1959
Tyroglyphus linteri....	32-84 days	56-214	14- 25 days	Engelmann
Oppia nova..........	—	.12 egg per day	25- 30 days	Engelmann
Pseudotritia sp........	—	—	56 days (average)	Rohde 1955
Euphthiracarus flavum.	—	—	60 days	Rohde 1955
Galumna elimatus.....	—	—	72-107 days	Sengbusch 1954
Galumna nervosus.....	—	—	45- 50 days	Sengbusch 1954
Galumna longiplume...	—	—	58- 66 days	Sengbusch 1954

various efficiencies would be to calculate the amount of food material coming into the herbivore population. At the beginning of this study, it was believed that the population of herbivores fed upon the dead plant and animal material of the old field. It soon became evident that this was not so, and that the herbivores were feeding upon the organisms which were attacking the dead material; i.e., the mites were feeding upon the fungi and bacteria, and incidentally upon some of the dead material. If the various ecological efficiencies that were found for the herbivores are assumed to be the same for the bacteria and fungi, the result will be a series of estimated amounts of food available to the mites. The 148 grams of vascular plants which were found on 1 square meter of old field make up the greatest part of the dead material which falls to the decomposers each year. This amount of plant material is equivalent to 620,000 calories. If the lowest EF of 8.5 is used, the result will be an estimated 22,134 calories of fungi and bacteria ingested by the herbivores. This efficiency will adequately fill the needs for all the efficiencies calculated for the soil herbivores (Table 11). However, the 20,152.27 caloric value at 16.9% EF comes the closest to the 22,134 caloric estimate. One must keep in mind that other animals such as nematodes, rotifers, and protozoa also feed upon bacteria and fungi. Nematodes and rotifers were found in the soil of the old field, and it was estimated that the nematodes accounted for only about 360 calories per year. However, this is a very crude estimate, made on the basis of only 1 sampling, and they may consume more. The 16.9% efficiency was obtained by assuming a 14% assimilation rate for both herbivore and carnivore.

In a final attempt to narrow the range of ecological efficiencies the figure of 40% body weight ingested by the oribatid mites was applied to the total biomass of the herbivores. This weight, when converted into calories, gave estimates of 10,150.88 calories consumed when the japygids were omitted and 12,712.74 calories consumed when the japygids were included as herbivores. Using the 2 extremes in assimilation rate for the carnivores (i.e. 14% and 32% assimilation) the following efficiencies were obtained: when the japygids were considered to be herbivores, the ecological efficiency was 8-32%; when the japygids were considered to be carnivores, the ecological efficiency was 12-47%. It can be seen that even with 1 variable—the assimiliation efficiency of the predator—the range of possible ecological efficiencies is considerable. The 47% value is once again too high because it required 4,620 calories of ingested herbivore to support the carnivore population, 1230 calories greater than can be produced by the herbivores during the year. Even the 32% efficiency may be too high, for it required 4074 calories to support the carnivores.

At the present stage of knowledge, therefore, any ecological efficiency between 8% and 30% may be considered reasonable for soil herbivores.

DISCUSSION

To create the proper setting for the discussion to follow, the use of the word "community" must be clarified. In most texts the community concept is supported and discussed with such assurance that the reader is led to believe that the concept is a rule in ecology. MacFadyen (1957: 238) points out that "the term community is a shibboleth and a label for a working hypothesis." Therefore, the discussion and re-definition of the term is not out of order. The definition of community used in this paper is as follows: an assemblage of populations coexisting in time and space, mutually regulative and interdependent, and depending ultimately upon some common energy source. This definition contains elements from several sources, principally Allee *et al.* (1949) and MacFadyen (1957). The stipulation about the energy source is lacking in most definitions; yet, it would seem that this requirement is basic to understanding of the community. The food web, if known, can be used to delimit one community from another. A common energy source, however, does not necessarily have to be solar radiation, but can be another form of energy, such as organic materials of various kinds, or even various simple chemical compounds which are capable of being broken down by microorganisms (e.g., sulphur and iron bacteria).

If there is a basic trophic scheme for all communities, then the energy relationships should be reflected in the community structure. Community structure has been approached from several points of view. Physical description came first, but this approach cannot be tested by the application of mathematical processes, and thus relies solely upon the acuity of the observer. Hairston (1955) has summarized another line of approach, that of comparing species abundance with mathematical models. Of all the models used, the ones by MacArthur (1957) are most appealing because they are based upon biological principles rather than upon some theoretical mathematical curve. Data of relative species abundance best fit the MacArthur model which assumes that the niches are continuous but not overlapping. When the number of individuals per species (relative abundance) is plotted against the predicted curve, however, biological data do not fall along the predicted curve. Hairston attributed this difference between observed and expected plots to the fact that niche size is not determined randomly as suggested by MacArthur's model, but rather, niche size is a function of an organized system—the community. Hairston further pointed out that food is the one constituent of the community that will fit this model. Since, in all analyses mentioned by Hairston, numbers of individuals were used, it is possible to plot an energy function of these animals as related to their food (i.e., calories respired) against the theoretical curve. Figs. 4, 5, and 6 show the form of the observed data with respect to the predicted curves when numbers of individuals, biomass, and calories respired for a year are plotted for the oribatid mites found on the old-field in 1958. The observed curve for numbers of individuals is similar to those presented by Hairston (1959). Biomass gives a smoother curve, with a shape similar to that of the predicted curve, but still exhibiting the same

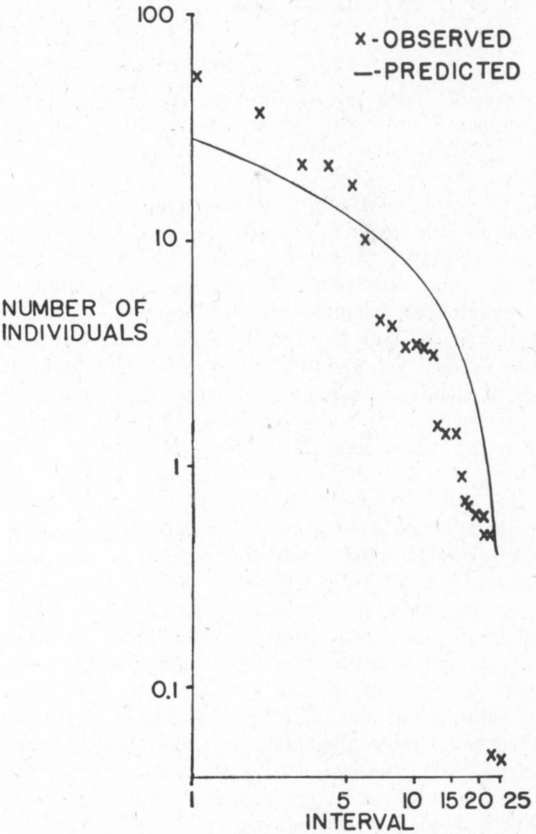

FIG. 4. Number of individuals of each species of oribatid mite found on the old field in 1958, compared with the model of MacArthur.

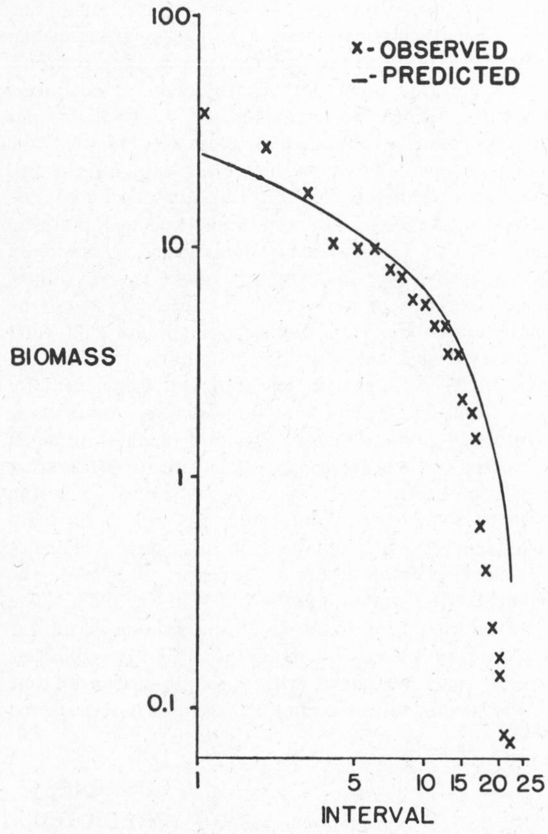

FIG. 5. Total biomass of each species of oribatid mite found on the old field in 1958, compared with the model of MacArthur.

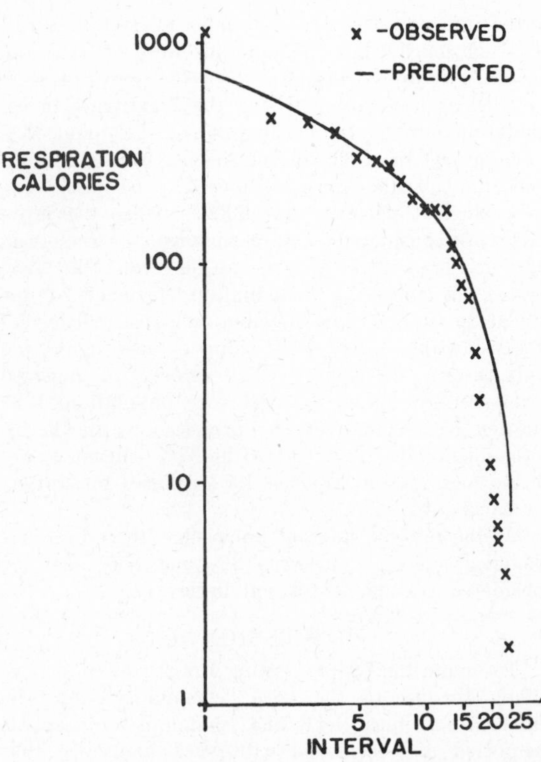

FIG. 6. Total respiration of each species of oribatid mite found on the old field in 1958, compared with the model of MacArthur.

distortions as did the previous curve. When respiration calories are plotted, the top half of the curve conforms to prediction, but the bottom half of the curve still falls away. This curve could be interpreted as meaning that the common organisms fit the model and have their niche size determined in a random manner, while the rare individuals do not fit the model and do not have their niche size determined at random. However, when the respirations for all of the soil arthropods found on the old field during 1949 and 1950 were plotted, the curve still showed the deviations of the plot for numbers of individuals. This may reflect the fact that several trophic levels are included in the total analysis of arthropods, while only part of one trophic level was considered in the analysis of the oribatids. It seems that for a single trophic level, at least, energy units more nearly fit the predicted curves. There is indication, then, that Hairston's assumption has validity and that the niche or status of an animal in the community might therefore be defined in terms of the amount and kind of food it eats, hence ultimately in terms of energy consumed.

The food web of the community is one of the more important concepts of community organization, and its complete qualitative and quantitative description should be the ultimate goal of the community ecologist. The food web of the soil community is poorly understood. The role of the soil arthropods in this food web will be considered next, because these organisms hold a key position in the soil community.

It is generally accepted that the soil arthropods play an important role in the soil-building process. Allee *et al.* (1949) review the classification of the soil organisms according to their food habits. This classification, based mostly upon the ideas of Fenton and Jacot, divided the soil organisms into 5 major groups: 1), chemical agents (bacteria and fungi); 2), ectophagous agents (species which eat whole green leaves and perform some chemical breakdown); 3), endophagous agents (agents which "mine" leaves and roots); 4), predators; and 5), shelterers (animals which use the soil as a retreat only). A common description of the process of soil building is as follows: first, the dead material falls to the ground; then the arthropods grind the material into small bits; and finally the bacteria and fungi attack the "grindings" and break the material down to an elemental state, which can once more be exploited by the plants. Many of the observations on food habits of soil arthropods seem to support this view. When van der Drift (1950) fed millipeds very moist leaf litter, they assimilated about 6% of the material. Gere (1956) fed millipeds as well as isopods on litter. He noted however, that the animals did much better on the litter from the Fx layer, or decomposed material just above the mineral soil, than they did on the newly fallen dead leaves. Wallwork (1958) and Rohde (1955) raised and maintained oribatid mites on leaf litter or decayed wood. Birch & Clark (1953) report Riha as stating that the oribatids feed upon wet dead leaves, wet dead wood, and that two species feed upon fungal mycelia.

In this study, however, the soil arthropods would not culture upon fresh dead, or dried plant material, even after it was wetted. Green plant material did not seem acceptable. *Oppia nova* was finally cultured on yeast. It was observed then that several other species of oribatid mites (family Eremaeidae) fed upon yeast, (*Saccharomyces cerevisiae*), mushrooms (*Mycena fibula, Agaricus campestris* and others) and the hyphae of *Aspergillus inornata*. A belbid mite specialized upon a mold (an imperfect) which grew upon decaying arthropod muscles. The particular fungus was very sticky and smaller mites would become trapped if they tried to cross it, but the long-legged belbid had no such difficulty and fed exclusively upon this mold in culture. Further search of the literature disclosed observations similar to those cited above. Van der Drift (1950) cites Dr. Rooseboom's observation that *Oppia neerlandica, Oribatula tibialis, Chamobotes schultze,* and *Galumna* cf. *dorsalis* all fed upon molds. Wallwork (1958) found fungal mycelia in the guts of most of the mites that he inspected. The guts were also filled with other material. Sengbusch found that the young of *Galumna* (several species) would feed on the alga *Protococcus,* while the adult fed upon moss. Rohde (1959) raised the mite *Caloglyphus* on fresh hamburger, and the same mite was cultured by D. Pimentel (personal communications) on *Neurospora*. Metcalf & Flint (1939) review the life histories of several mites which are pests on agricultural plants. Representatives of the same families including the agricultural pests are found in the soil of the old field. Finally, the volume edited and compiled by Needham *et al.* (1937) gives numerous culture methods of invertebrates. The food recommended for the milliped *Euryurus erythropygus* is moist decayed sapwood; for oribatids, and tyroglyphids, lichen, mosses, cheese mold, and moist dead wood. The mushroom mite, *Tyroglyphus linteri,* various Collembola (*Achorutes armatus, Proisotoma minuta, Lipidocyrtus cyaneus, L. albus,* and *Sminthurus caecus*), Diptera larva (*Sciara coprophila, Neosciara pauciseta, Calliceras* sp., and members of the Cecidomyidae) have all been raised on commercial mushroom spawn. Yeast has been used to culture *Proisotoma minuta* (Auerbach *et al.* 1957), and *Tyroglyphus linteri* (present author). Similar references on the food habits of soil-dwelling arthropods may be found in the work of Cloudsley-Thompson (1953), and Kevan (1955).

The question raised here is, do soil arthropods actually feed upon dead material, as has been so often reported, or are these animals actually deriving their nourishment from mycelia of fungi within the decaying litter? The definition of the word "feed" in the above question creates the problem, because an animal may ingest material and yet not be able to assimilate it. The majority of the dead matter falling to the floor stratum of a community is in the form of plant material, most of which is cellulose and hemicellulose. The starches and sugars contained in the living leaves of the plant have undoubtedly been used up by the cells of the plant as the leaves died, have been transported to other parts of the plant for storage, or have been leached from the leaf or oxidized before the leaf fell to the ground. Therefore, an organism must have cellulase in order to break down the cellulose for use as a food source. The lower plants (bacteria and fungi) are well-supplied with cellulase, as are many of the parasitic protozoa. However, when the metazoa are surveyed for the presence of cellulase (Prosser *et al.* 1950) it is found only in various Mollusca and the earthworm (*Lumbricus*). Symbiotic bacteria and/or protozoa are the usual source of cellulase in most wood-eating insects. Brues (1946) has shown dramatically the dependence of insects upon microorganisms. Using the fruit fly as an example, he points out that although the larvae appear to be feeding upon the banana medium, they are actually feeding upon yeasts growing in the medium. If the culture is kept completely sterile, the fly larvae die. In the same line, a soil arthropod may be *ingesting* dead plant material; however, it is *digesting* the living bodies of the fungal hyphae which are attacking the dead material. In each case where the food habits of a soil arthropod have been explored fully, it has been shown that fungus is a suitable food material. It is possible that the soil arthropods possess cellulase, but in view of the lack of the enzyme in the rest of the Metazoa, this possibility seems to be slight. Some soil arthropods may, of course, have intestinal symbionts. Rohde (1955) reports that the young of the box mite (*Pseudotritia* sp.) consume the feces of the adult, and that the adult's digestive tract is filled with rod-shaped bacteria. This feces-eating habit is common of other wood-feeding arthropods such as the passalid beetles and termites. New enzymes for the soil arthropods do not have to be postulated however, to allow for the break down of the dead plant material in the soil community. The bacteria and fungi already possess the necessary cellulases. These plants digest their food extracellularly and then absorb the dissolved sugars. An arthropod feeding upon the dead material, then, has access to the sugars digested by the fungus as well as to the fungal protoplasm. In culture glucose crystals were fed upon by galumnid and eremaeid mites, indicating that these animals were attracted to sugars.

Not all of the soil arthropods are herbivores; some are known to be carnivorous. All of the Parasitidae and Trombididae feed upon mites and Collembola or are parasitic upon vertebrates and large insects. These animals presumably act as population controls on the herbivores or upon the animals which they parasitize.

This review of the feeding habits of the soil arthropods, and especially of the food preferences of the mites, suggests that the traditional role of these animals in the soil community needs some revision. It follows from the above observations that the role of the soil arthropods is not merely that of a grinding mill. Rather, they form a control mechanism upon the fungus populations. The soil arthropods affect the fungi in at least three different ways. First, the arthropods feed directly upon fungi, thereby cutting the biomass of the plants in the immediate area. In this sense the arthropods act as a depressing factor upon the fungal population. Secondly the arthropods clear away material penetrated by hyphae, exposing new material to the action of the fungi. The oribatid mites also have a third important effect upon the fungi, since they defecate while they are feeding. The feces of these animals are usually filled with spores from some previous meal. The mite feces then inoculate newly-exposed material with new fungal spores. This action tends to accelerate the breakdown of the material in the immediate area, for it is known that the respiration of a rapidly growing fungus colony is greater that that of a mature colony (James 1953). Finally, of course, there is a certain amount of grinding or reduction of particle size in the feeding process, as well as the seeding of the feces with microorganisms. The reduction of particle size would seem more important for the bacteria, which can work only on the surfaces of materials, than for the fungi, which are capable of penetrating materials.

This analysis of community energetics further suggests that soil arthropods do not fit precisely into Lindeman's original scheme, or at least that they have not been properly elaborated upon in that scheme. A schematic representation of the energy flow of the old field is given in Fig. 7. Lindeman's symbols are retained in the interest of standardization and clarity. For each trophic level (capital lambda) there is a flow of energy into the level (small lambda) in the form of food or radiation depending upon the level, and the energy leaves that level in the form of respiration (R), decomposition (D), and energy consumed by the next level (small lambda). Each level is given a number: 1 for the green plants, 2 for the herbivores, 3, primary carnivores, and so forth. In the Lindeman scheme the "D" of decomposition of the trophic level either embraces the whole soil fauna, or it includes only the bacteria and fungi, thereby omitting the herbivores and carnivores which are directly dependent upon these plants for food. In the present modification of the scheme, the soil complex is represented by the double numbers: 11 for the fungi and bacteria, 22 for the herbivorous mites, Collembola, round worms, etc., and 33 for the carnivorous mites.

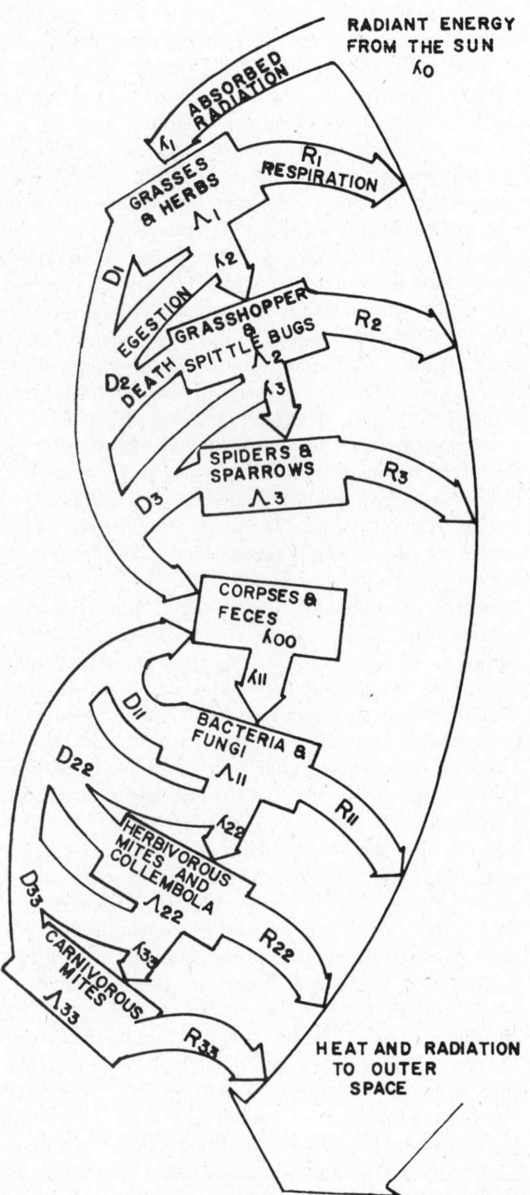

FIG. 7. A schematic energy flow diagram for the upland of an old field in Michigan. The symbols used are those of Lindeman. Note that "D" represents decomposition; this includes egestion, which has never become part of the protoplasm of the population, and death, which has been part of the protoplasm of the population.

This trophic diagram of the old field indicates 2 major flows of energy, one above-ground and the other one in the soil. The above-ground system is powered directly by the sun's energy, captured by the green plants, while the soil system is powered directly by the dead bodies and feces of the above-ground members. The dead material, of course, was originally produced by the green plants. The soil plants can be placed in trophic levels equivalent to those of the above-ground system, and given a supply of energy, the soil system will continue to operate. The fact that the oribatid population underwent such a complete change, while the above-ground community changed little, tends to support the idea that the soil system is a separate community from the above-ground community. The surface of the soil then becomes an ecotone and animals such as spiders, staphylinids, and carabids can be considered ecotonal animals. These facts support the views of Birch & Clark (1953) that the soil is an ecological community in its own right.

The diagram depicts the energy flow of the old field only in its broadest outlines and is admittedly an over-simplification of the true picture. A single animal may not fall into a single trophic level, or may change food habits according to season: e.g., the chipping sparrow, which feeds mostly upon arthropods during the breeding season and mostly upon plant seeds during the rest of the summer. Imports and exports have also been ignored. In the old field, for example, windborne seeds and flying arthropods, are continually emigrating or immigrating. Rains leach materials from the soils. Carnivores often feed from several different trophic levels, thus complicating the picture further. Without information on these unknowns, the scheme is probably best left in simplified form.

A value of the Lindeman scheme is that it will allow the comparison of communities at all levels. At present this comparison is fairly rough because of imperfect methods of collecting needed data. On the population level the results for the oribatids compare favorably with those of Richman (1958) and Slobodkin (1959) for *Daphnia,* the water flea. The only outstanding difference between the two kinds of organisms involves the amount of energy put into reproduction by the populations. The *Daphnia* have a high reproductive rate, while the oribatids have a low rate. Assimilation rates and respiration vs. growth calories for non-reproductive adults of *Daphnia* and *Oppia* are all in the same range. Richman has shown that the growth rates and assimilation rates of *Daphnia* are similar to those found for other animals including vertebrates. He reiterates that the basic biochemistry of all animals is very similar. When the ecological efficiency of the soil arthropods is compared with that of organisms in aquatic communities, the efficiencies also fall in the same range. The ecological efficiencies for the herbivores of several fresh water communities are summarized by Patten (1959). These efficiencies range from 5.5% to 21.0%. From the numerous efficiencies found for the soil arthropods it appears that anything from 8.5% to 30% would be a reasonable estimate. It may disturb some persons to have the ecological efficiency rating so variable. If one considers the efficiency of a population at monthly intervals, it will be seen that there are fluctuations which reflect food levels and predator levels. The overall yearly estimate, then, is an average of the population's efficiencies over the 12-month period. When food supply is abundant, per cent assimilation is low and more calories are "wasted" (defecated) by the population. At the other extreme, when food is scarce, greater amounts of food are assimilated and less is wasted. The ecological efficiency is variable just as a respiration rate is variably, but it should vary within a limited range. Slobodkin (1960) believes 5-15% to be the reasonable limits of this range. However, the data for the soil arthropods suggest that the upper limit may be 20% or higher.

Another efficiency that is a valuable tool in the comparison of several communities is the "efficiency of transfer to each level in terms of original input" (Patten 1959). If the above-ground system and the soil system are considered to be a single community, the primary energy source for the community, is, of course, the sun. The calculated efficiency of transfer of solar energy to the herbivore level of the soil arthropods is .02-.03%. The reason for such a low efficiency is that the soil arthropods are at least 3 trophic levels away from the original energy source. If, however, we consider the soil system to be a separate community, then the energy source and original input for the community is the amount of dead material available. This places the soil herbivores on a par with the above-ground herbivores with respect of trophic level within their communities. The efficiency of transfer thus calculated for the trophic level of the soil arthropods is in this instance 1.5-2.0%. Patten's summarized values for the efficiency of transfer to the herbivore level in aquatic communities ranged from .05 to 6.8%. The efficiency values for the soil arthropods fall well within this range.

In short, these data on the efficiencies of the soil arthropods, both at the population level and at the trophic level, lend support to the hypothesis that all communities function according to the same energetic principles.

SUMMARY

1. In 1958 a field sampling program and laboratory studies were undertaken with the soil arthropods of an old field in south-eastern Michigan to elucidate the energy dynamics of the soil system. Laboratory methods involved Tullgren extraction, biomass determination, respiration studies and calorimetry.
2. An energy balance sheet was drawn up for the oribatid mites. It was calculated that these mites in 1 square meter 12.5 cm deep consumed 10,248 calories of food each year and assimilated 2,058 calories or 20% of the food ingested. Respiration accounted for 96%, and mortality for 20% of the assimilated material. The error for the calculation was 13%.
3. When comparison was made with the data obtained by Hairston & Byers (1954) on the same field, it was found that the oribatid mite populations had changed markedly. The species composition had changed completely save for 5 species. Numbers of individuals had decreased 33% between 1950 and 1958, but the biomass and calories of respiration had doubled or almost so. It is suggested that the oribatid fauna has probably

displaced other components of the soil, and that the total arthropod biomass has remained at a constant level.

4. The ecological efficiency was calculated for the soil arthropods. Due to the lack of certain feeding information, reasonable efficiencies ranged from 8% to 30% for the soil herbivores.
5. When energy units (respiration calories) were used in place of numbers of individuals in one of MacArthur's models, the observed curves more nearly fit the predicted curves, lending support to the idea that the niche is the amount and kind of food a population consumes.
6. The main role of the soil herbivores was found to be that of controlling the fungal and bacterial populations which are breaking down the dead materials. These arthropods can both accelerate and retard the growth of the decay organisms. The soil carnivores serve as population controls on the herbivores.
7. The soil system is considered for two reasons to be a community separate from the above-ground system. First, it has a trophic level system similar to that of the above-ground system, and secondly, changes in species composition in the soil arthropods are apparently independent of changes in the above-ground system.
8. Data on *Daphnia pulex,* the water flea, and *Oppia nova,* an oribatid mite, compared favorably with respect to their respiration and assimilation efficiencies. The range of ecological efficiencies (8.5-30%) for the soil herbivores compared favorably with ecological efficiencies for the same trophic level in the aquatic communities, and the 1.5-2.0% efficiency of transfer to each level in the soil community also fell within the range of efficiencies found for the aquatic communities. These data lend support to the hypothesis that all communities operate on the same energetic principles.

LITERATURE CITED

Agrell, I. 1947. Some experiments concerning thermal adjustment and respiratory metabolism in insects. Arkiv. Zool. 39: 1-48.

Allee, W. C., A. E. Emerson, O. Park, T. Park, & K. P. Schmidt. 1949. Principles of Animal Ecology. Philadelphia: Saunders.

Armstrong, J. T. 1960. The dynamics of *Daphnia pulex* and of *Dugesia tigrina* populations as modified by immigration. Ph.D. Dissertation, Univ. of Mich.

Auerbach, S. I., D. A. Crossley, Jr., & M. D. Engelmann. 1957. Effects of gamma radiation on Collembola population growth. Science **126**: 614.

Baker, E. W., & G. W. Wharton. 1952. An Introduction to Acarology. New York: Macmillan Company.

Birch, L. C., & P. D. Clark. 1953. Forest soil as an ecological community with special reference to the fauna. Quart. Rev. Biol. **28**: 13-36.

Bornebusch, C. H. 1930. The Fauna of the Forest Soil. Copenhagen.

Brody, S. 1945. Bioenergetics and Growth, with Special Reference to the Efficiency Complex in Domestic Animals. New York: Reinhold.

Brues, C. T. 1946. Insect Dietary. Cambridge: Harvard U. Press

Bullock, T. H. 1955. Compensation for temperature in metabolism and activity of poikilotherms. Biol. Rev. **30**: 311-342.

Cloudsley-Thompson, J. L. 1958. Spiders, Scorpions, Centipedes, and Mites. New York: Pergamon Press.

Engelmann, M. D. 1956. Observations on the feeding behavior of several pselaphid beetles. Ent. News **67**: 19-24.

Evans, F. C., & S. A. Cain. 1952. Preliminary studies on the vegetation of an old-field community in southeastern Michigan. Cont. Lab. Vert. Biol. Univ. Mich. **51**: 1-20.

Evans, F. C., & E. Dahl. 1955. The vegetational structure of an abandoned field in southeastern Michigan and its relation to environmental factors. Ecology **36**: 685-706.

Evans, F. C. & U. N. Lanham. 1960. Distortion of the pyramid of numbers in a grassland insect community. Science **131**: 1531-1532.

Fry, F. E. J. 1958. Temperature compensation. Ann. Rev. Phys. **20**: 207-224.

Gere, G. 1956. The examination of the feeding biology and the humificative function of Diplopoda and Isopoda. Acta Biol. Hung. **6**: 258-271.

Golley, F. B. 1959. Table of caloric equivalents. Mimeographed sheet. Available from the author, Dept. of Zool., Univ. of Georgia, Athens, Georgia.

Hairston, N. G. 1959. Species abundance and community organization. Ecology **40**: 404-416.

Hairston, N. G., & G. W. Byers. 1954. A study in community ecology: the soil arthropods in a field in southern Michigan. Cont. Lab. Vert. Biol. Univ. Mich. **64**: 1-37.

James, W. O. 1953. Plant Respiration. London: Oxford Press.

Kevan, D. K. McE. (ed.), 1955. Soil Zoology. London: Butterworths.

Krogh, A. 1941. The Comparative Physiology of Respiratory Mechanisms. Philadelphia: University of Pennsylvania Press.

Lindeman, R. L. 1942. The trophic-dynamic aspect of ecology. Ecology **23**: 399-418.

MacFadyen, A. 1952. The small arthropods of a Molinia fen at Cothill. J. Anim. Ecol. **21**: 87-117.

———. 1957. Animal Ecology; Aims and Methods. London: Pitman.

MacArthur, R. H. 1957. On the relative abundance of bird species. Proc. Nat. Acad. Sci. U. S. **43**: 293-295.

Metcalf, C. L. & W. P. Flint. 1939. Destructive and Useful Insects. New York: McGraw-Hill.

Needham, J. G., F. E. Lutz, P. L. Welch, & P. S. Galtsoff. 1937. Culture Methods for Invertebrate Animals. New York: Dover.

Odum, E. P. 1960. Organic production and turnover in old field succession. Ecology **41**: 34-49.

Odum, H. T. 1957. Trophic structure and productivity of Silver Springs, Florida. Ecol. Mono. **27**: 55-112.

Park, O., S. Auerbach, & G. Corley. 1950. The tree-hole habitat with emphasis on the pselaphid beetle fauna. Bull. Chicago Acad. Sci. **9**: 19-57.

Park, O., & S. I. Auerbach. 1954. Further study of the tree-hole complex with emphasis on quantitative aspects of the fauna. Ecology **35**: 208-222.

Patten, B. C. 1959. An introduction to the cybernetics of the ecosystem: the trophic-dynamic aspect. Ecology **40**: 221-231.

Prosser, C. L. (ed.), 1950. Comparative Animal Physiology. Philadelphia: Saunders.

Richman, S. 1958. The transformation of energy by *Daphnia pulex*. Ecol. Mono. **28**: 273-291.

Roeder, K. D. (ed.), 1953. Insect Physiology. New York: Wiley.

Rohde, C. J., Jr. 1955. Studies on arthropods from a moss habitat with special emphasis on the life history of three oribatid mites. Ph.D. Dissertation, Northwestern Univ. Evanston, Illinois.

———. 1956. A modification of the plaster-charcoal technique for rearing of mites and other small arthropods. Ecology **37**: 843-844.

———. 1959. Studies on the biologies of two mite species, predator and prey, including some effects of gamma radiation on selected developmental stages. Ecology **40**: 572-579.

Salt, G., F. S. J. Hollick, F. Raw, & M. V. Brian. 1948. The arthropod population of pasture soil. J. Anim. Ecol. **17**: 139-150.

Sengbusch, H. 1954. Studies on the life histories of three oribatid mites with observations on other species. Ann. Ent. Soc. Amer. **47**: 646-668.

Slobodkin, L. B. 1959. Energetics in *Daphnia pulex* populations. Ecology **40**: 232-243.

———. 1960. Ecological energy relationships at the population level. Amer. Naturalist. **94**: 213-236.

Smith, A. H., & J. R. Douglas. 1949. An insect respirometer. Ann. Ent. Soc. Amer. **42**: 14-18.

Talbot, M. 1953. Ants of an old-field community on the Edwin S. George Reserve, Livingston county, Michigan. Cont. Vert. Lab. Biol. Univ. Mich. **63**: 1-13.

———. 1954. Populations of the ant *Aphaenogaster* (*Attomyrma*) *treatae* Forel on abandoned fields on the Edwin S. George Reserve. Cont. Vert. Lab. Biol. Univ. Mich. **69**: 1-9.

Teal, M. J. 1957. 'Community metabolism in a temperate cold spring. Ecol. Mono. **27**: 283-302.

Trama, F. 1957. The transformation of energy by an aquatic herbivore *Stenonema pulchelium* (Ephemeroptera). Ph.D. Dissertation, Univ. of Mich.

Umbreit, W. W., R. H. Burris, & J. F. Stauffer. 1949. Manometric techniques and tissue metabolism. Minneapolis: Burgess Pub. Co.

United States Dept. Commerce. 1958. Climatological Data: Annual Summary. **73**.

Uvarov, B. P. 1931. Insects and climate. Trans. Royal Ent. Soc. London **79**: 1-247.

van der Drift, J. 1950. Analysis of the Animal Community in a Beech Forest Floor. Wageningen.

Wallwork, J. 1958. Notes on the feeding behavior of some forest soil acarina. Oikos **9**: 260-271.

———. 1959. The distribution and dynamics of some forest soil mites. Ecology **40**: 557-563.

Winston, P. W. 1956. The acorn microsere, with special reference to arthropods. Ecology **37**: 120-132.

Zeuthen, E. 1953. Oxygen uptake as related to body size in organisms. Quart. Rev. Biol. **28**: 1-12.

BIRD POPULATIONS OF THE HIGHLANDS (NORTH CAROLINA) PLATEAU IN RELATION TO PLANT SUCCESSION AND AVIAN INVASION[1]

Eugene P. Odum

Department of Biology, University of Georgia, Athens, Georgia

Birds, during the breeding season at least, are proving to be favorable subjects for the study of population dynamics in nature. Their conspicuousness and territorial behavior aid population measurements and make birds especially promising material for the study of competition, habitat selection, niche relations, and the relation of population density to plant succession, distributional changes, and to speciation. The study of wild bird populations in North America in recent years has been influenced by two important trends: (1) the development of the spot-mapping technic (see summary by Williams, '47), and (2) the increasing emphasis on population measurements of definitely delimited areas which are ecologically uniform or represent single, rather than mixed, communities. The annual "Breeding Bird Census" sponsored by Audubon Magazine, and subsequently Audubon Field Notes, for the past 12 years has particularly accelerated the latter trend. Although population estimates made with comparable technic are now available for a variety of communities in many biotic regions of North America, many gaps, both regional and ecological, must be filled before the student of populations can profitably analyze the results for elucidation of the basic problems mentioned above. Population measurements of major communities of the southeastern United States are especially needed, since few censuses from this region have been published. During the 12-year period previously mentioned, censuses from only 13 community areas have been published for the entire southeastern region (10 states): several states in other regions have contributed this number in a single year.

As part of a regional program of research on the comparative vertebrate ecology of mountains, piedmont, and coastal plain of southeastern United States, the objectives of the present study were threefold: (1) to determine bird population density of important communities of a high altitude region representative of the southern end of the Appalachians; (2) to relate bird populations to plant succession; and (3) to compare these data with those from other regions. An added incentive for this study arose from our desire to see if the density of population, or "population pressure," had any bearing on, or was correlated with, the recent rather spectacular invasion of several species from the mountains to piedmont (Odum and Burleigh, '46; Odum, '48).

The Highlands Plateau

The Highlands Plateau is a high-altitude region with an elevation averaging approximately 4,000 ft. located on the main Blue Ridge of the Appalachian Mountains where North Carolina joins Georgia and South Carolina. The Blue Ridge extends into Georgia as a rugged ridge with a number of peaks between 4,000 and 5,000 ft., but there are no extensive, relatively flat areas at high elevations south of the Highlands Plateau, which thus occupies a strategic position near the end of the mountain salient which "funnels northern species into the heart of the southland," as it were. For this reason and because of the facilities offered by the Highlands Biological Lab-

[1] This study was aided by a grant from the Leonce Fremeaux Wall Fellowship administered by the Highlands Biological Laboratory. The writer is indebted to Miss Thelma Howell, Resident Director of the Laboratory, for help in many ways and to Mr. Henry Wright for location of areas of undisturbed vegetation.

Fig. 1. Vegetative zonation on the Highlands Plateau. The lower dark belt is a mature hemlock-northern hardwood stand while the upper lighter colored area is an oak-chestnut forest growing on the drier slopes and summits.

oratory, the Highlands region was selected as a suitable region for the study of bird populations under mountain conditions.

The general plant ecology of the region is well illustrated by figure 1. There is no spruce zone at Highlands such as is present further north on the Blue Ridge or on the Great Smoky Mountains. The peaks (several exceeding 5,000 ft., elevation) and steeper slopes are covered with a deciduous forest, largely oak-chestnut, which is the probable climatic climax. The communities containing plants and animals with northern affinities are found in ravines, moist areas along streams, and high, level parts of the plateau. Hemlock is the chief dominant of this second major climax, probably to be considered a post-climax (Oosting and Billings, '39). The reason for this seemingly reversed zonation, which, incidentally, is characteristic of the southern Appalachians south of the spruce range, is that the relatively great difference in moisture between peaks and ravines is more important as a limiting factor for plants and animals than is the relatively small difference in temperature. Thus, red-breasted nuthatches and brown creepers, so-called Canadian Zone species, are to be found breeding in the lower, dark (hemlock) belt in figure 1, while birds of more southern origin may be found in the deciduous growth above them (light colored in fig. 1). Biotic communities, then, on the Highlands Plateau may be conveniently arranged in two series: (1) communities leading to the climax of oak-chestnut, the oak-chestnut sere, and (2) communities leading to the climax of hemlock or hemlock-birch, the hemlock sere. The former is largely deciduous throughout its development. Early successional stages in the latter may be entirely deciduous, but conifers develop at least a two-thirds dominance in the later stages of succession. The plant ecology of the virgin hemlock forests of the region has been studied by Oosting and Billings ('39), the occurrence and distribution of summer birds by Stevenson ('41), and distribution of small mammals by Odum ('49).

Methods

Three areas representing early, intermediate, and late or climax stages of succession were selected for each of the two principal seres of the region, making a total of 6 areas on which breeding bird populations were measured. Each of the areas is shown in figures 2 to 7 and they are designated in the subsequent discussion as follows: In the mesic or hemlock sere, (1) mesic shrubland (2) intermediate hemlock-hardwood (3) climax virgin hemlock; in the oak-chestnut sere, (4) xeric shrubland (5) intermediate deciduous forest (6) climax oak-chestnut. All of the plots have roughly the same altitude, between 3,800 and 4,100 feet, so that altitude is not a factor in determining differences in populations. Each plot selected was mapped, and outline maps were mimeographed. The area of each plot in acres was determined from the completed map by the use of a planimeter. Bird populations were determined by the spot-mapping or territory-mapping technic as follows: Each plot was visited in rotation for 3–4 hours in the morning and birds seen and heard while slowly cruising the plot were recorded on a fresh copy of the base map. Afternoon visits were also made to check questionable records and look for nests. Each area was visited from 4 to 6 times with total of 16 to 30 hours of observation. Total populations were calculated from the number of occupied territories plotted on composite maps. Each plot was censused for two successive seasons, except the oak-chestnut climax, which was censused only in one season. In 1946, observations were made between June 12 and July 4 and in 1947 between May 31 and June 25.

The size of some of the plots, especially the early seral stages, was smaller than originally planned because I was unable to locate large areas of uniform composition of desired stage in succession. In heavily forested mountain regions the total amount of early seral vegetation may be quite large, but it consists of numerous small areas, such as roadsides, small abandoned fields, etc. Plots of shrubland or young forest 25 or 30 acres in extent and of uniform composition just did not exist in the high altitude region. Consequently, since the object was to determine the population of specific communities for comparative purposes, it seemed desirable to select uniform, even though small, areas rather than diverse, but larger ones. Stewart and Aldrich ('49) report that extensive census work done on the Patuxent Refuge has shown that results from small uniform areas are more reliable than from larger mixed ones. However, small quadrats admittedly introduce errors in estimating abundance of less common species or those with large territories. Likewise, total density calculations may be exaggerated. Specifically, to test these possibilities for the region being studied, a 10-acre plot was measured in the center of the completed census map of the 25-acre oak-chestnut plot ac-

Table I. *The relation of plot size to density calculations in an oak-chestnut forest*

	Pairs per 100 acres based on: A 25-acre sample	A 10-acre sample
Ovenbird*	38	45
Black-throated blue warbler	24	25
Blue-headed vireo	22	30
Red-eyed vireo	12	15
Veery	12	10
Chestnut-sided warbler	8	15
Wood thrush	8	0
Towhee	6	0
White-breasted nuthatch	4	10
Downy woodpecker	4	5
Hairy woodpecker	4	0
Bl. and white warbler	4	5
Hummingbird	4	5
Ruffed grouse	2	5
Tufted titmouse	2	0
Carolina chickadee	2	0
Wood pewee	2	0
Robin	2	5

Total species, large area—18; small area—12

Total density (pairs per 100 acres), large area, 160.

Total density (pairs per 100 acres), small area, 175.

* For scientific names see table III.

tually censused. Populations were then calculated in pairs per 100 acres for both 10- and 25-acre plots, the results being shown in table I. It will be seen that the density of the five most abundant species is approximately the same whether calculated from the large or small area. For the less common and larger species the small plot either gives too high a figure or fails to record them at all. The total density as determined from the 10-acre plot is roughly 10% greater than for the large area. In conclusion, it appears that small plots may be used to determine density of the most common species but are less reliable for the less common species. If results from small plots are to be compared with those from larger ones, density calculations based on small plots should be corrected. Accordingly, in the data presented in tables II and III a 10% reduction in the density calculation of each species has been made, where plots were 10 acres or less in size. Where a pair's territory was not wholly on the study area, the appropriate fraction was carefully estimated from field observation and calculated density figure in pairs per hundred acres rounded off to the nearest whole number as further precaution against distortion of figures based on different sized samples.

The Study Plots

1. *Mesic shrubland* (fig. 2).—Size 6.4 acres, located four miles east of Highlands on Route 64 opposite and with similar topographic location as the plot of virgin hemlock (No. 3). The small stream which flows through the virgin area continues through the shrubland. The vegetation consists of shrubs and small trees chiefly alders, willows, and brambles (*Rubus*) which form dense thickets interspersed with more open areas dominated by grasses and herbs. Huge stumps of hemlock and thickets of laurel (*Kalmia*) and *Rhododendron* remain from the original hemlock forest which occupied the area. The plot has never been cultivated, but has apparently been subjected to some grazing in the past.

Fig. 2. Mesic shrubland which has developed after the logging of the climax hemlock-hardwood forest. Virgin undisturbed forest may be seen in the background.

FIG. 3. Interior of the intermediate hemlock-hardwood forest. Note hemlock and birch trees and well developed shrub understory.

2. *Intermediate hemlock-hardwood forest* (fig. 3).—Size 15 acres, located around the Highlands Biological Laboratory building and Lake Ravenel. Some of the hemlocks in the western and eastern portions are very large and probably are a part of the original forest, but most of the area is covered with a second growth, dominant trees averaging 6–10 inches D.B.H. The deciduous elements, chiefly birch and maple, and the coniferous elements, hemlock and white pine, are approximately equal in dominance. The understory is well developed and varies from pure *Rhododendron* along small streams to witch hazel and *Azalea* in the drier portions. The clearings immediately around the Laboratory building and between the Laboratory and Museum Building are not included in the area censused since they obviously represent an entirely different community.

3. *Virgin hemlock* (fig. 4).—Size 12 acres, located four miles east of Highlands on Route 64, opposite plot 1. This plot is owned and preserved by Mr. Henry Wright and is a remnant of the once extensive virgin hemlock forest known as the "Primeval Forest" or "Ravenel's Woods." Hemlock, with trees 3 to 4 feet in diameter and 400 years or more old, comprise ¾ of the stand by basal area.

FIG. 4. Interior of the virgin hemlock forest with dense understory of Rhododendron.

Black birch, many reaching very large size, red maple, Frazier's magnolia, red oak, and other deciduous trees are widely scattered in the stand. The understory over most of the area is a mass of *Rhododendron maximum,* often almost impenetrable. Oosting and Billings ('39) in their study of the "Primeval Forest" before its destruction found that hemlock was the chief dominant in all the vast area, but there were two distinct types based on the composition of the understory: *Rhododendron* type and *Polycodium* type, the latter having a greater percentage of deciduous elements and occurring on higher ground. The present study plot is typical of the *Rhododendron* type.

4. *Xeric shrubland* (fig. 5).—Size 4.3 acres, located on a hillside sloping up from Highway 64 three and a half miles east of Highlands. Vegetation is typical of that which follows, within a few years, the removal the oak-chestnut forest. Brambles (*Rubus*), black locust, sumac, and cherry are the most numerous species of shrubs and small trees which occur in dense thickets interspersed with more open places dominated by grasses and herbs.

5. *Intermediate* (*second growth*) *deciduous forest* (fig. 6).—Size 10 acres,

Fig. 5. Xeric shrubland which has followed the logging of the climax oak-chestnut forest. Black locust, brambles (*Rubus*), sumac, and a large chestnut stump with a few chestnut sprouts may be seen in the picture.

Fig. 6. Interior of the intermediate or second-growth deciduous forest. The study plot contains a few large trees but is largely covered with a dense stand of small trees and saplings.

FIG. 7. Interior of the mature oak-chestnut study area, showing large mature oaks and a fallen chestnut tree in foreground. In the background the death of a group of chestnuts (killed by chestnut bark fungus disease) has created a sun-lit, shrub-filled opening. This particular study plot, while modified by the chestnut blight in common with all the Appalachian oak-chestnut forests, has been little disturbed by man.

located on a steeply sloping hillside four and a half miles east of Highlands near plots 1 and 3. Vegetation consists of a rather uniform stand of oaks, hickories, maples and other deciduous trees 4–10 inches D.B.H. There is a well developed herb layer and less dense shrub layer. A few small hemlocks, a few chestnut sprouts, and one or two patches of *Rhododendron* occur. The plot is a good example of a young forest which has developed after the clear cutting of the original oak-chestnut forest on the mountain slope.

6. *Mature oak-chestnut* (*climax*) *forest* (fig. 7).—Size 25 acres, located on a steeply sloping hillside near plot 4, three and one-half miles east of Highlands. Vegetation is typical of the mature mountain slope forest relatively undisturbed by man. However, since all large chestnuts have been killed by the blight, openings have been created in the otherwise continuous canopy with the result that patches of young vegetation, along with vigorous chestnut sprouts, occur scattered throughout the stand. Shrub and herb layers are well developed. Hemlock and *Rhododendron,* which are so characteristic of the mesic forests, are of very minor importance on the plot.

RESULTS

Densities calculated in pairs per 100 acres for each of the six study areas are given in tables II and III. Except for plot 6, studied for one season only, figures represent averages of both the 1946 and 1947 census results, there being very little difference in the two years. In the two shrubland plots and the intermediate deciduous forest area a 10% reduction was made to correct for small size of plot as previously explained. In the tables, the data are arranged so as to show successional changes occurring during the development of forest from shrubland stages in each of the two seres. These data clarify and make quantitative the relation between common breeding birds of the region and major plant communities, even though it should be emphasized that they do not give a complete picture of successional changes.

Total populations

The density of birds differs rather strikingly in the two community series. In the upland oak-chestnut sere, populations are high in the shrub stage and decrease as the forest matures, even though the chestnut blight has created considerable "edge effect" in the mature forest. In the hemlock sere, on the other hand, the high density in the shrub stage is maintained or even increased with the development of the climax. The greater density in forests of hemlock sere is correlated with (1)

TABLE II. *The hemlock sere*

	Pairs per 100 acres		
	Mesic shrubland (plot 1)	Intermediate hemlock-hardwood (plot 2)	Virgin hemlock (plot 3)
Song Sparrow (*Melospiza melodia*)	126	—	—
Chestnut-sided Warbler (*Dendroica pensylvanica*)	49		
Catbird (*Dumatella carolinensis*)	42	25	16
Field Sparrow (*Spizella pusilla*)	22		
Towhee (*Pipilo erythrophthalmus*)	14		
Goldfinch (*Spinus tristis*)	14		
Brown Thrasher (*Toxostoma rufum*)	14		
Indigo Bunting (*Passerina cyanea*)	7		
Wood Thrush (*Hylocichla mustelina*)		42	10
Black-throated Blue Warbler (*Dendroica caerulescens*)		40	75
Blue-headed Vireo (*Vireo solitarius*)		30	25
Black-and-white Warbler (*Mniotilta varia*)		27	12
Rose-breasted Grosbeak (*Pheucticus ludovicianus*)		17	2
Blackburnian Warbler (*Dendroica fusca*)		10	49
Flicker (*Colaptes auratus*)		10	—
Red-breasted Nuthatch (*Sitta canadensis*)		8	17
Junco (*Junco hyemalis*)		8	—
Veery (*Hylocichla fuscescens*)		8	—
Wood Pewee (*Contopus virens*)		8	6
Scarlet Tanager (*Piranga olivacea*)		7	27
Cedar Waxwing (*Bombycilla cedrorum*)		7	—
Ovenbird (*Seiurus aurocapillus*)		5	—
Carolina Chickadee (*Parus carolinensis*)		5	8
Red-eyed Vireo (*Vireo olivaceus*)		3	—
Cardinal (*Richmondena cardinalis*)		3	—
Parula Warbler (*Parula americana*)		3	17
Hooded Warbler (*Wilsonia citrina*)		2	—
Robin (*Turdus migratorius*)		2	—
Canada Warbler (*Wilsonia canadensis*)			33
Hairy Woodpecker (*Dendrocopus villosus*)			10
Brown Creeper (*Certhia familiaris*)			8
White-breasted Nuthatch (*Sitta carolinensis*)			8
Crested Flycatcher (*Myiarchus crinitus*)			4
Tufted Tutmouse (*Parus bicolor*)			2
Broad-winged Hawk (*Buteo platypterus*)			2
Totals	288	270	331

TABLE III. *The oak-chestnut sere*

	Pairs per 100 acres		
	Xeric shrubland (plot 4)	Intermediate deciduous forest (plot 5)	Mature climax* (plot 6)
Chestnut-sided Warbler (*Dendroica pensylvanica*)	108	—	8
Towhee (*Pipilo erythrophthalmus*)	108	—	6
Catbird (*Dumatella carolinensis*)	68	—	—
Field Sparrow (*Spizella pusilla*)	45	—	—
Golden-winged Warbler (*Vermivora chrysoptera*)	18	—	—
Brown Thrasher (*Toxostoma rufum*)	18	—	—
Indigo Bunting (*Passerina cyanea*)	18	—	—
Goldfinch (*Spinus tristis*)	9	—	—
Flicker (*Colaptes auratus*)	4	—	—
Ovenbird (*Seiurus aurocapillus*)		50	38
Red-eyed Vireo (*Vireo olivaceus*)		45	12
Blue-headed Vireo (*Vireo solitarius*)		38	22
Black-throated Blue Warbler (*Dendroica caerulescens*)		23	24
Black-and-white Warbler (*Mniotilta varia*)		15	4
Wood Pewee (*Contropus virens*)		15	2
Scarlet Tanager (*Piranga olivaceus*)		15	—
Wood Thrush (*Hylocichla mustelina*)		8	8
Robin (*Turdus migratorius*)		8	2
Downy Woodpecker (*Dendrocopus pubescens*)		2	4
Hairy Woodpecker (*Dendrocopus villosus*)		2	4
Carolina Chickadee (*Parus carolinensis*)		1	2
Veery (*Hylocichla fuscescens*)			12
White-breasted Nuthatch (*Sitta carolinensis*)			4
Ruby-throated Hummingbird (*Archilochus colubris*)			4
Tufted Titmouse (*Parus bicolor*)			2
Ruffed Grouse (*Bonasa umbellus*)			2
Totals	396	222	160

* Modified by chestnut blight, see text.

greater moisture content and (2) presence of both coniferous and deciduous life forms. How these factors may influence the bird population will be discussed later in this paper.

Species differences

Species composition of comparable communities in the two seres was not greatly different, there being very few species that nest exclusively in only one sere, but the relative abundance and consequent importance of many species was found to be different in the two community series. In other words, the two seres appear to differ quantitatively much more than qualitatively.

Observation in the region as a whole has indicated that red-breasted nuthatch, brown creeper, blackburnian warbler, and perhaps parula warbler and song sparrow nest entirely or very largely in the moist communities of the hemlock sere. All other common species of hemlock sere have been found at least sparingly in the oak-chestnut series even though not all were, necessarily recorded in the small sample areas actually censused. Conversely, the xeric communities apparently have no exclusive species.

While it is thus difficult to find species differences in the two seres, the abundance of many species proved to be quite different. The Cairns's or mountain subspecies of the black-throated blue warbler (*Dendroica coerulescens cairnsi*) ranked near the top in forest stages of both seres, the density, however, being greater in the forest stages of the hemlock sere, averaging 57 pairs per 100 acres for the two forest plots of the former and about 24 pairs per 100 acres for comparable stages in the oak-chestnut series. These measurements provide definite statistics to support the impression which one gets from general observation in the region, namely, that the Cairns's warbler is the most abundant forest bird of the region. The solitary or mountain subspecies of the blue-headed vireo (*Vireo solitarius alticola*) was one of the few species which showed the same abundance in the two seres, averaging 28 and 30 pairs per 100 acres, respectively. This species probably can be considered the second most common bird of forests in general, although it is outranked in one or other of the seres by several species.

In contrast to the blue-headed vireo, the blackburnian and Canada warblers showed a high abundance in hemlock forests and were absent in the xeric communities . Conversely, the ovenbird and red-eyed vireo were very important members of the oak-chestnut forests and of minor importance in the hemlock-hardwood forests. These four species were responsible for a large part of the difference in bird populations of the forest stages of the two community series.

In the shrubland communities, the chestnut-sided warbler was very abundant in both seres, and, with an average abundance of 79 pairs per 100 acres, can be rated the most abundant species of the early stages of succession generally. The greatest difference in the two seres at the shrubland stage resulted from the fact that the song sparrow was prominent in the mesic community and the towhee correspondingly abundant in the xeric community, these two species being responsible for most of the difference in the two populations (see tables II and III).

Comparison of study plots by means of percentage differences

In addition to revealing specific differences and similarities in populations of different areas, as had been done in the preceeding paragraphs, some statistical means of comparing the *total* population, including species composition and density as well as total density, would be desirable. While the methods and results of field censuses are not yet precise enough, nor the variables sufficiently well known to warrant refined statistical analysis, percentage comparisons would seem to be justified, as an aid, at least, in comparing one community with another. In table IV each of the six plots is compared with every other one by means of "percentage differences." These percentages are calculated as follows: The difference in density (in pairs per 100 acres) for each species occupying the two areas being compared is determined. Thus, if species

TABLE IV. *Percentage difference in the breeding bird population of the six study plots compared with each other*

	Mesic Shrubland (plot 1)	Intermediate Hemlock (plot 2)	Virgin Hemlock (plot 3)	Xeric Shrubland (plot 4)	Intermediate Oak-chestnut (plot 5)
Intermediate Hemlock (plot 2)	95.8				
Virgin Hemlock (plot 3)	97.9	50.5			
Xeric Shrubland (plot 4)	51.8	95.6	97.8		
Intermediate Oak-chestnut (plot 5)	100.0	60.9	65.5	100.0	
Mature Oak-chestnut (plot 6)	93.8	63.7	68.6	96.9	39.6

one has 20 pairs in plot A and 10 in plot B, the difference is 10 pairs; or if species B has 10 pairs in plot A and none in plot B the difference is also 10 pairs. All these differences are then added and the total divided by the total number of pairs on both areas to determine the percentage difference between the two populations. The procedure is worked out in detail in table V. This "percentage difference" (or its complement "percentage similarity") thus is a rough index of difference (or similarity) in species composition and in density, the commonest species having the greatest weight in determination of the figure. A percentage difference of 100 indicates that the populations of the areas being compared are entirely different, with no species in common. A figure of less than 50% indicates a close similarity in two populations. Since even plots of the same community side by side

TABLE V. *Breeding bird population of Highlands, North Carolina, hemlock-hardwood forest (A) compared with West Virginia spruce-hardwood (B), and New York hemlock-beech (C)*

	A	B	Diff. A-B	C	Diff. A-C	Diff. B-C
Black-throated Blue Warbler*	57	16	41	9	48	7
Blackburnian Warbler	30	55	25	14	16	41
Blue-headed Vireo	28	26	2	1	27	25
Wood Thrush	26	3	23	1	25	2
Black and White Warbler	20	—	20	2	18	2
Catbird	20	—	20	—	20	0
Canada Warbler	16	16	0	10	6	6
Scarlet Tanager	17	7	10	5	12	2
Parula Warbler	10	3	7	—	10	3
Rose-breasted Grosbeak	10	3	7	—	10	3
Red-breasted Nuthatch	12	7	5	—	12	7
Chickadee (Carolina or Black-cap)	6	2	4	9	3	7
Wood Pewee	7	—	7	—	7	0
Hairy Woodpecker	5	3	2	3	2	0
Flicker	5	—	5	—	5	0
Brown Creeper	4	7	3	—	4	7
White-breasted Nuthatch	4	—	4	5	1	5
Junco	4	21	17	—	4	21
Veery	4	7	3	5	1	2
Ovenbird	2	3	1	32	30	29
Crested Flycatcher	2	—	2	1	1	1
Red-eyed Vireo	2	10	8	1	1	9
Robin	1	3	2	—	1	3
Hooded Warbler	1	—	1	—	1	0
Cardinal	1	—	1	—	1	0
Tufted Titmouse	1	—	1	—	1	0
Blue Jay	1	3	2	2	1	1
Magnolia Warbler (*Dendroica magnolia*)		45	45	25	25	20
Golden-crowned Kinglet (*Regulus satrapa*)		32	32	—	—	32
Black-throated Green Warbler (*D. virens*)		31	31	32	32	1
Olive-backed Thrush (*Hylocichla ustulata*)		13	13	—	—	13
Hermit Thrush (*Hylocichla guttata*)		3	3	6	6	3
Winter Wren (*Troglodytes troglodytes*)		3	3	—	—	3
Purple Finch (*Carpodacus purpureus*)		3	3	—	—	3
	296	325	353	163	331	258

Percentage diff. A-B $\frac{\text{AB diff. } 353}{\text{A} + \text{B } 621} = 56.8.$

Percentage diff. A-C $\frac{\text{AC diff. } 331}{\text{A} + \text{C } 459} = 72.1.$

Percentage diff. B-C $\frac{\text{BC diff. } 258}{\text{B} + \text{C } 488} = 52.9.$

* For scientific names see table II.

would show at least small differences, a figure of zero would probably not be obtained in actual practice.

In table IV it will be seen that populations of the shrubland areas show a 94 to 100% difference from forest plots in either or both seres, a reflection of the fundamental importance of vegetational life-form. The two plots which are most alike are the second-growth and the mature oak-chestnut with a 39.6 percentage difference. This small difference in avifauna is clearly correlated with the results of chestnut blight which has "opened up" the mature stand until it resembles a younger forest, or even a shrubland, into which chestnut-sided warblers and towhees, birds of early seral stages, have reinvaded. Eventually, the openings created by death of the chestnuts will be filled, but for the time being the vigor of the chestnut sprouts produces a sort of shrub disclimax (see Odum and Burleigh, '46) within the forest. The bird population reflects very well the mixture of open shrub and closed forest vegetation and illustrates how well birds may serve as indicators to ecological conditions and changes.

When similar stages in the two seres are compared a gradual divergence in bird population is indicated, that is, mature communities differ from each other more than the young communities. Thus, the percentage difference between the two shrubland stages is 51.8, between the two young forests 60.9 and between the mature stages 68.6. The latter figure might possibly be somewhat different without the disturbing influence of the chestnut blight.

Comparison with other Appalachian regions

In table V the bird population of the hemlock-northern hardwood forest on the Highlands Plateau (column A) is compared with the population of a spruce-northern hardwood forest in the Cheat Mountains of West Virginia (column B) censused by Stewart and Aldrich ('49) and the population of a hemlock-beech forest on the Helderberg Plateau of east-central New York (column C) censused by Kendeigh ('46). In column A, the virgin and the intermediate plots at Highlands are combined to give an average picture of the hemlock-hardwood forest and to make the total sample (27 acres) similar in size to that in the other studies. Hawks, owls, the pileated woodpecker and the ruffed grouse are omitted from the tabulation since none of the study plots are large enough adequately to census these large birds.

All three of these localities lie in the ecotone between the Northern Coniferous Forest (or Taiga) Biome and the Eastern Deciduous Forest Biome, the plant community of the West Virginia mountains being more closely allied floristically to the Northern Coniferous Forest. Average summer temperatures are about the same for the three regions but rainfall is much heavier in the southern Appalachians as shown by the following data:[2]

	Average temperature, ° F.		Total annual precipitation, inches
	Jan.	July	
Highlands, N. C.	39.7	70.5	82.6
Cheat Mts., W. Va.	30.9	68.6	68.7
Helderberg Pl., N. Y.	22.3	68.6	34.9

Referring to table V, it will be noted, first, that the total population density of the North Carolina and West Virginia plots is similar and both have nearly twice as many birds as the New York plot. This is correlated with the higher rainfall and the greater development and diversification of the forest understory in the two southern regions, the New York forest being rather open with scant under-

[2] Data taken from U. S. Dept. Agriculture Yearbook of 1941, *Climate and Man.* Weather stations at Highlands and West Berne, N. Y., are close to study areas. For Cheat Mountains, the Pickens (Randolph County) data are used, which according to Maurice Brooks (personal communication) may be considered average for the higher altitude regions.

growth. This difference in the understory is a regional one, and not just local. For example, Brooks ('43) states that "in the southern Appalachians the development of a rich and varied shrub understory . . . is, perhaps, the most prominent characteristic of the vegetation" and serves to distinguish these mountain forests from similar ones farther north.

As shown by the percentage-difference figures, species composition in the three plots is remarkably similar, considering the great distance separating them. Thus, the North Carolina hemlock-hardwood forest and West Virginia spruce-hardwood forest showed only a 56.8 per cent difference, and the West Virginia forest was likewise not greatly different from the New York hemlock-hardwood forest (52.9%). The extremes in the series, the North Carolina and the New York plots, geographically the farthest apart, showed a greater percentage difference (72.1%), as might be expected.

In general, five or six species are chiefly responsible for the north-south difference in Appalachian coniferous-hardwood forests, as far as the sample plots are concerned. The Highlands plot lacks three species that are very important in the areas to the north, namely, golden-crowned kinglet and magnolia and black-throated green warblers. Highlands is south of the range of the magnolia warbler and virtually south of the range of the golden-crowned kinglet. The latter has been reported from the Highlands region in summer by T. D. Burleigh and A. H. Howell (Stevenson, '41) and may breed there rarely, but I was unable to find it in the course of the present study. On the other hand, the range of the black-throated green warbler continues into Georgia and Alabama, far south of Highlands; hence its absence on the Highlands Plateau is puzzling. A few individuals of this species appear in mid- or late summer, but I found no evidence that the species breeds anywhere in the area in any kind of habitat, this being also the experience of previous observers in the region (Stevenson '41). Southwest of Highlands in Gilmer and Pickens County, Georgia, the species is a locally common breeding bird. In this region, as elsewhere in the southern Appalachians, it has become adapted to deciduous forests, especially those with a mixture of Virginia or scrub pine (*Pinus virgianana*), and often breeds at low altitudes (Odum, '45); where available, it also occupies hemlock or hemlock-white pine stands along with the blackburnian warbler, its common associate in the north. The best explanation for the absence of the black-throated green warbler at Highlands seems to lie in the historical factor rather than any climatic or habitat limiting factors. The southern part of the range of this bird is "split" or bifurcate. There is a coastal population, *Dendroica virens waynei* breeding south to South Carolina and a mountain population, *D. v. virens* breeding south to Alabama, with an area in between not occupied by either race. Apparently, the high plateau on which Highlands is located and the adjacent areas in northeast Georgia have been bypassed and not yet occupied by the mountain race which is common to the west. Recently, the birds breeding in western South Carolina have been referred to the coastal race, *waynei* (see Sprunt and Chamberlain, '49). If this is verified by further taxonomic study, then Highlands would appear to be located in the hiatus between the two populations. In the forests of Highlands Plateau the particular niche of the black-throated green, the medium level stratum, is apparently not occupied by any other warbler or species with similar ecological requirements. If the black-throated green warbler were present in numbers, say, 30 pairs per hundred acres, the percentage difference between the Highlands study areas and those further north would be greatly reduced.

Looking at table V from the other view, that is, species present in the southern end of the Appalachian chain but not present in the northern portion, we find that no species of primarily southern distribution (for example, hooded warbler) figured prominently in the population of the hemlock-hardwood forest; rather, the black-throated blue warbler, wood thrush, black and white warbler, and catbird, all of which breed throughout the Appalachian region, were more abundant in the southern end and largely compensated for the absence of the three species mentioned above. The greater abundance of the black-throated blue warbler in the central and especially in the southern Appalachians seems well correlated with the rich development of the shrub understory (as previously described) which provides its particular niche within the forest. The Appalachian subspecies, *cairnsi,* is especially associated with (but not restricted to) *Rhododendron,* a characteristic shrub constituent not only of the mixed forest but the moister portions of the oak-chestnut and other deciduous forests as well.

The catbird, generally considered a bird of the forest edge or early seral stages, was not restricted to these habitats at Highlands, but occupied *Rhododendron* thickets at some distance from the forest edge wherever there was a small opening in the canopy left by a fallen tree. This species, incidentally, was the only one occurring in all three stages of succession in the hemlock sere (table II).

While the birds of the hemlock-hardwood forests at Highlands have thus been shown to be closely allied both qualitatively and quantitatively to those of more northern forests in the coniferous-deciduous forest ecotone, the population of the Highlands oak-chestnut forests, although representing a mature climax community growing at the same or greater altitude, appears to be more closely related to forest populations of Eastern Deciduous Forest Biome. Thus, the ovenbird and red-eyed vireo, among the four most abundant species at Highlands, rank as the two most abundant species in a series of eight mature deciduous forests located in Virginia, West Virginia, New York, and Ohio as summarized by Kendeigh ('44, table 20). Likewise, general species composition is similar. As far as birds are concerned, therefore, the classification of the oak-chestnut association as a sub-division of the Eastern Deciduous Forest Biome seems justified. The oak-hickory climax forest of the piedmont plateau of North Carolina and Georgia, as censused at Chapel Hill (H. T. Odum, '46) and Athens (E. P. Odum, '47), differs chiefly from the southern Appalachian oak-chestnut forest in having (1) fewer or no ovenbirds, (2) more wood thrushes, (3) the summer tanager replacing the scarlet tanager, (4) hooded warblers, yellow-throated vireos, and Carolina wrens in moderate numbers, and (5) no black-throated blue warblers, veerys, or blue-headed vireos (see, however, subsequent discussion of recent invasion of latter species into the piedmont). Otherwise, there are many similarities, including the fact that the red-eyed vireo ranks first or second in abundance in both regions. Detailed percentage analyses and a more precise evaluation of the ecological relations of the bird populations of the mountain deciduous forests must await the gathering of additional quantitative data from the southeastern region generally.

Discussion

Population density and plant succession

In his pioneer study of the "ecological succession of birds" on Isle Royale, C. C. Adams ('08) stated that as far as the number of species occupying successive vegetative stages was concerned, there was a "development of diversity from simplicity and a later return to simplicity." Population density seems often to show a similar trend, especially in secondary seres on the upland, in which a peak in population is reached somewhere in the middle of the successional series.

On the Highlands Plateau bird population density in the oak-chestnut sere followed the trend indicated in the previous paragraph. Very early vegetation stages, or grassland communities, developing on cleared land are but poorly developed at high altitudes and were not censused in this study, but were observed to be thinly occupied by birds. Typical grassland species of lower altitudes and the piedmont region (meadowlark and grasshopper sparrow, for example) are largely absent from Highlands. When the development of the vegetation reaches the shrub and young forest stages, the communities are well occupied by birds, and, as already indicated, population density decreases as the forest matures, even with disturbing influence of the chestnut blight.

In the hemlock sere, on the other hand, this "typical" population density-succession curve is modified, since the high populations of shrubland stages are maintained or increased as the forest matures, even including very old virgin tracts. Moisture may be the key to this difference. So much emphasis has been placed on temperature as a factor controlling distribution and abundance of birds, that the importance of the water factor has often been overlooked. Since Highlands is near the center of an area which has the highest annual rainfall in the eastern United States (80 inches or more as previously indicated), moisture is an especially important ecological factor. The high water content of the forests of the hemlock sere could conceivably result in increased populations both directly by providing more available water and by moderating temperature changes, and indirectly by producing a more luxuriant vegetation with consequent greater variety of niches and, perhaps, a greater amount of food. At present, there is no way to evaluate accurately the importance of these possibilities.

Comparison with adjacent biotic regions

Following Stewart and Aldrich's census of the West Virginia spruce-hardwood forest in 1947 (Stewart and Aldrich, '49) DeGarmo repeated the study on the same area in 1948 (DeGarmo, '48). He found the population to be very similar to that of the previous year (as shown in Table V), but the total density was even greater —381 pairs per 100 acres. This two-year coverage by different observers plus our two year coverage of two different plots at Highlands seems to indicate that the high population density reported for these areas was not temporary or local in nature only. Thus, it can be tentatively concluded that the bird population density of the mixed coniferous-hardwood forests of the southern Appalachians is very high for forest communities, higher than has been generally reported for climax forests in the adjacent Deciduous Forest Biome. Thus, Kendeigh ('44) reports that the average density for 8 climax deciduous forest communities scattered widely over eastern North America is 221 pairs per 100 acres as compared with 300 or over for the Appalachian area. On the Georgia piedmont, 100 miles south of Highlands, our two-year study of an oak-hickory climax forest yielded an average of 225 pairs per 100 acres. The question then arises as to whether the higher density is due to high rainfall as previously discussed, or partly, at least, to the mixed composition of the forest, a sort of "ecotone" or "edge effect," as it were. In other words, the mixed forest provides habitat both for species adapted to coniferous and deciduous life-forms and thus the forest as a whole might support a greater population than pure stands of either. In this connection, the comparison between the New York beech-hemlock forest and the Highlands hemlock-hardwood forest is of interest (table V). Both forests are mixed and both have about the same two to one dominance of hemlock, yet Highlands' forests, located in a region of greater rainfall and having a more luxuriant understory, have twice as large a bird population (as is also true of the West Virginia plot). The results of the annual breeding-bird censuses in Audubon Field Notes provide further evidence that moist communities support high populations since swamp, bog, floodplain, and coastal hammock forests as well as marshes consistently show high densities.

Another factor that should not be overlooked is a historical one which has been advanced by Brooks ('47), who suggests that during glacial times northern birds were crowded into the unglaciated southern Appalachians where they were forced to seek out all possible niches in order to survive, thus explaining the diverse and atypical habitat choice of some species. This might also be a factor in the present high population density although it would seem that it would have more influence on the richness of the avifauna rather than on the number of individuals; the latter would more likely be controlled by the present day carrying capacity of the habitat. Actually, however, all of the suggestions in this section can only be considered as suggestions; what is needed are more data, especially more comparative analyses of populations of different communities and regions.

Population density and avian invasion

During the past forty years, at least four species of birds, the robin, song sparrow, chestnut-sided warbler and blue-headed vireo, have made rather rapid and spectacular extensions of range in the southern Appalachian region (Odum and Burleigh, '45; Odum, '48). The robin, song sparrow and blue-headed vireo have invaded the piedmont region from the mountains, the latter two having only barely entered this region during the past 5 to 10 years. The chestnut-sided warbler has extended its breeding range to the end of the main Blue Ridge (Pickens County, Georgia) which was not occupied prior to 1910. These invasions seem to have resulted from wholesale habitat changes by man and the chestnut blight, but as was pointed out in a previous paper (Odum and Burleigh, '46) a build-up in population, or some degree of population pressure, might be expected to occur before a species, otherwise able to breed in new territory, would actually invade it. The present study provides some evidence to support this contention, since the song sparrow, chestnut-sided warbler, and blue-headed vireo proved to be extremely abundant birds in the sample areas of their habitat located in the general region from which invasion of the Piedmont or more southern mountain areas must have been launched. The robin's forest-edge habitat was not sampled in this study, but there can be little doubt that this species also became very abundant within its range prior to and during the southward range extension. It should be emphasized that, as here conceived, some degree of population pressure might precede or accompany an invasion of new territory, but in itself does not necessarily *cause* an invasion; thus, many other species are abundant in the region in question, the black-throated blue warbler, for example, but have shown no recent invasion tendencies. Climate or habitat limiting factors in most cases presumably prevent an extension of the range even when a species becomes very successful within its original range.

Summary

1. Breeding bird populations were measured on six plots representing shrubland, intermediate forest, and mature or climax forest stages in each of two community series, the hemlock and the oak-chestnut seres, located on the Highlands Plateau, a high altitude region on the main Blue Ridge of the Appalachian mountains located where North Carolina joins Georgia and South Carolina. All plots were between 3,800 and 4,100 ft. altitude and, with one exception, were censused for two consecutive breeding seasons (1946, 1947) by the use of the "spot-mapping" or "territory mapping" method. In size, plots ranged from 4.6 to 25 acres. Density calculations on plots 10 acres or less were corrected to compensate for small size of sample (table I). Data were tabulated to show successional trends in the two seres (tables II and III).

2. Population density was high in the shrubland stages of both seres (288 and 396 pairs per 100 acres). In the oak-chestnut series density was less in the forest stages (222 and 160 pairs per 100 acres, table III), while in hemlock sere high populations were maintained or were increased in the mature stages (270 and 331 pairs per 100 acres, table II).

3. In species composition, communities of the two seres were similar, only a few species (red-breasted nuthatch, and brown creeper, for example) being restricted to communities in the moist series. The abundance of many species differed greatly, however. In the forest stages, the black-throated blue, blackburnian, and Canada warbler were much more abundant in the hemlock sere and red-eyed vireo and ovenbird were much more abundant in the oak-chestnut sere. The blue-headed vireo showed an approximately equal abundance in both. In the shrubland stages the chestnut-sided warbler was abundant in both, but the song sparrow was abundant in and restricted to the mesic shrubland and the towhee more abundant in the xeric shrubland.

4. The total populations of all six plots were compared with each other by means of "percentage differences" (table IV). Populations of the mature forest communities in the two seres showed a greater percentage difference (68.6) than did the two shrubland communities (51.8%). Shrubland communities in general showed a 93.8 to 100 per cent difference from forest communities. The two plots which were least different in bird population were the intermediate and mature forests of the oak-chestnut series (39.6 percentage difference), this being correlated with the effect of the chestnut blight which has created openings and patches of younger vegetation in the mature forest into which species of earlier seral stages have re-invaded.

5. The population of the Highlands hemlock-northern hardwood forest (intermediate and virgin plots combined) is compared with a spruce-hardwood forest in West Virginia and a hemlock-beech forest on Helderberg Plateau of New York (table V). In species composition the three areas were remarkably similar, only 7 species found in one or the other of the northern areas being absent at Highlands. The density of many species was also similar, but in other species there were important differences. The magnolia warbler, golden-crowned kinglet and black-throated green warbler were important constituents of the population of one or both of the more northern plots and absent (possibly very rare in the case of the kinglet) at Highlands. The black-throated blue warbler, wood thrush, black-and-white warbler and several others, although present in the northern areas, were much more abundant at the southern end of the Appalachian chain. Percentage difference for total populations between N. C. and W. Va. plots was 56.8, between W. Va. and N. Y., 52.9, and between N. C. and N. Y., 72.1.

6. Since the black-throated green warbler breeds much farther south and at lower altitudes than Highlands, it is concluded that its absence in the region is due to a historical factor rather than to any climate or habitat limiting factor. It is suggested that the Highlands Plateau may have been by-passed and not yet occupied and may now be a part of a hiatus between breeding ranges of the two races, *D. v. virens* and *D. v. waynei.*

7. Greater moisture and greater development of the forest shrub understory are believed to be the key factors which produce the higher populations found in the mature forests of the hemlock sere as compared with the comparable stages of the oak-chestnut sere. Likewise, higher rainfall and greater understory development in the southern Appalachians generally are correlated with the fact that both Highlands and the West Virginia coniferous-hardwood forest had higher populations than the New York mixed forest or climax deciduous forests as reported in the literature. Mixed life form and post-glacial history are also discussed as pos-

sible factors contributing to high forest populations.

8. The census results provided some evidence to support the contention mentioned in a previous paper (Odum and Burleigh, '46), that a build up in population, or some "population pressure," may precede or accompany (although not necessarily cause) the extension of a bird species' breeding range. Three species, the song sparrow, blue-headed vireo, and chestnut-sided warbler, which are now known to be actively invading the lower mountain regions and the piedmont plateau (in case of the former two), proved to be extremely abundant birds on the Highlands Plateau.

Literature Cited

Adams, C. C. 1908. The ecological succession of birds. Auk, **25**: 109–153.

Brooks, Maurice. 1943. Birds of the Cheat Mountains. Cardinal, **6**: 25–44.

——. 1947. Breeding habitats of certain wood warblers in the unglaciated Appalachian region. Auk, **64**: 291–295.

DeGarmo, W. R. 1948. Breeding-bird population studies in Pocahontas and Randolph counties, West Virginia. Aud. Field Notes, **2** (6) : 219–222.

Kendeigh, S. Charles. 1944. Measurement of bird populations. Ecol. Monogr., **14**: 67–106.

——. 1946. Breeding birds of the beech-maple-hemlock community. Ecology, **27**: 226–245.

Odum, Eugene P. 1945. Northern species summering at the end of the Blue Ridge. Oriole, **10**: 45–52.

——. 1947. Breeding-bird census: climax southern oak-hickory forest. Aud. Field Notes, **1** (6) : 213–214.

——. 1948. Nesting of the mountain vireo at Athens, Ga., conclusive evidence of a southward invasion. Oriole, **13**: 17–20.

——. 1949. Small mammals of the Highlands (North Carolina) Plateau. Jour. Mammalogy, **30**: 179–192.

Odum, Eugene P., and Thomas D. Burleigh. 1946. Southward invasion in Georgia. Auk, **63**: 288–401.

Odum, Howard T. 1946. Breeding-bird census: young upland oak-hickory forest. Aud. Magazine (Sect. II), **48**: 139–140.

Oosting, Henry J., and W. D. Billings. 1939. Edapho-vegetational relations in Ravenel's woods, a virgin hemlock forest near Highlands, North Carolina. Amer. Midland Nat., **22**: 333–350.

Sprunt, Alexander, and E. Burnham Chamberlain. 1949. South Carolina bird life. Charleston, Univ. of S. C. Press, 585 pp.

Stevenson, Henry M. 1941. Summer residents of the Highlands, North Carolina region. Oriole, **6**: 41–48.

Stewart, Robert E., and John W. Aldrich. 1949. Breeding bird populations in the spruce region of the central Appalachians. Ecology, **30**: 75–82.

Williams, Arthur B. 1947. Breeding-bird census: climax beech-maple forest with some hemlock (15 year summary). Audubon Field Notes, **1** (6) : 205–210.

A STUDY OF PLANKTON COPEPOD COMMUNITIES IN THE COLUMBIA BASIN, SOUTHEASTERN WASHINGTON[1]

R. H. Whittaker and C. Warren Fairbanks

Biology Department, Brooklyn College, Brooklyn 10, N. Y., and Chief Park Naturalist, Crater Lake National Park, Ore.

The Study Area

Between the Northern Rocky and Cascade Mountains a great lava sheet, of about 250,000 km^2, forms the Columbia Plateau (Fenneman 1931). One area of this plateau in southeastern Washington—south and east of the Columbia River, north of the Snake River, and west of the Palouse Prairie country of easternmost Washington—is the Coulee District. Although the Coulee District is a dissected plateau in its topography, it lies at low elevations and is widely known as the "Columbia Basin." The surface of the plateau in the Basin slopes from northeast to southwest, and elevations decline from 700-760 m in the north to near 100 m msl at its southern tip near Pasco (Bretz 1923). Most of the stream channels, and most of the lakes studied, have in consequence a northeast-southwest orientation.

[1] A contribution from the Department of Zoology, Washington State College, and the authors' present institutions. Cost of water analyses was supported by the funds for biological and medical research of the State of Washington Initiative Measure No. 171; the analyses were carried out at the Washington State Institute of Technology, Division of Industrial Research. The authors are indebted to H. C. Yeatman, T. Kincaid, and R. W. Kiser for determinations of copepods, to R. W. Dexter for determinations of phyllopods, to B. G. Chitwood for determination of tardigrades, and to W. T. Edmondson, R. W. Pennak, and Mildred W. Wilson for comments on the manuscript. Application to microcrustaceans of the polyvinyl alcohol technique was suggested by D. S. Farner.

The Plateau was formed by lava which spread out over the region in successive flows from the Miocene into the Pliocene, burying the underlying topography and forming a sheet, locally more than 1000 m deep, of layered, columnar lava. The great weight of the lava sheet caused some subsidence, bringing the plateau surface down to its present low level in the Basin. During the Pleistocene the windblown, loess soils which still form the hills of the Palouse country and of part of the Basin itself were deposited on top of the plateau surface. Streams from melting glaciers, of the Spokane ice primarily, later flowed south and west across the area, eroding through the loess and into the underlying lava, forming a braided network of stream channels across the Columbia Basin. Disappearance of the glaciers and the streams which had flowed from them left the channels as the dry "coulees" of today, largest and best known of which is Grand Coulee. These channels and canyons with their walls of lava, and the buttes and loess-topped mesas which rise above them, form a most distinctive landscape, the "channeled scablands" of the Columbia Basin (Bretz 1923, 1928). The total area of these scablands is somewhat over 5000 km^2. While natural lakes are absent from the mature topography of the Palouse country and the loess islands in the Basin, the scabland channels contain a large number of smaller lakes and ponds.

Because of the rain-shadow effect of the Cascade Mountains, climate and vegetation of the area are semi-desert. Annual precipitation values range from approximately 41 cm in the northeastern to 15 cm in the southwestern part of the Basin, generally declining toward the west into the more intense rain-shadow closer to the Cascade Mountains. There is thus a marked climatic gradient within the limits of the Basin, with climates ranging from subhumid at the eastern edge, through semi-arid over most of the area, to arid in the southwest (Thornthwaite 1931). The precipitation regime is maritime, with 64 to 70% of total precipitation falling in the winter months, October through March. The dry summers are a limitation on plant growth in the area (Daubenmire 1942), and result in lowering the levels and drying out of many water bodies by summer evaporation. Temperatures are relatively cool, microthermal by Thornthwaite's (1931) classification (but mesothermal by the classification of Thornthwaite 1948); mean monthly temperatures (Fisher 1941) are from —3 to 0° C for January, 21 to 26° for July. Vegetation of the area has been described by Daubenmire (1942). Prevailing climax communities change toward the west along the climatic gradient: from *Pinus ponderosa* forest in the northeastern corner, and Palouse Prairie (*Festuca idahoensis-Agropyron spicatum* zone) along the eastern edge, through bunchgrass prairie (*Agropyron spicatum-Poa secunda* zone) to sagebrush scrub (*Artemesia tridentata-Agropyron spicatum* zone) in the drier western part. Predominant vegetation in the scabland channels is a sparse grassland, more or less mixed with sagebrush (*Artemesia tridentata*) and somewhat disturbed by grazing; in the eastern channels the grass predominates with scattered sagebrush, but toward the west the sagebrush and other shrubs increase to form the northern desert scrub vegetation of the Grand Coulee and other channels.

Most of the lakes and ponds studied lie in depressions in the basic lava or basalt of the scabland channels. The western part of the area also includes extensive areas of sand dunes with many small ponds (Harris 1954; Johnsgard 1956), represented by Pothole No. 1 of the present study. There are a few lakes (*e.g.* Rock and Falls Lakes) which are relatively deep, with shores of vertical or steeply sloping basalt, and are in most cases oligotrophic. Most of the water bodies are shallow and eutrophic, and the area contains hundreds of the smaller ponds which are locally known as "potholes." The larger lakes with stream outlets and some of the ponds are fresh-water bodies. Most of the potholes lose water only by evaporation, however; and in many of them the accumulation of salts has led to conditions of moderate to intense salinity. Salinity conditions vary widely in a single group of ponds; but there is a general tendency of increasing salinity toward the more arid climates of the western part of the area. The most intensely saline bodies encountered were in the Grand Coulee and toward the southwestern corner of the Basin. In some cases a single chain of lakes lying close together show increasing salinities downward along the coulee; the most notable example of this is the chain in the Grand Coulee from the freshwater Falls, Deep, Park, and Blue Lakes to the saline Lenore and Soap Lakes. In salinity conditions the Columbia Basin resembles arid regions described by Decksbach (1924), Young (1924), Gauthier (1928), Stanković (1931), Hutchinson *et al.* (1932), Naumann (1932: 52-4), Beadle (1932, 1943), Jenkin (1932, 1936), and Hutchinson (1937a, 1937b), and especially semi-arid Saskatchewan as described by Rawson & Moore (1944) and Moore (1952). The large number of water bodies of all degrees of salinity offer a particularly favorable opportunity to study effects of salinity on the life of lakes and ponds.

The Columbia Basin has been a sparsely populated area, but an extensive development program centered on Grand Coulee Dam is now affecting it. An extensive area is to be irrigated, and a whole system of man-made lakes and reservoirs has been developed in the western part of the Basin. Many smaller water bodies have been submerged by these, and a number of bodies sampled for the present study no longer exist as such. The extensive reservoirs are resulting also, through rising ground water levels, in higher water levels and lower salinities in many water bodies not actually submerged (Johnsgard 1956). The lakes of the Grand Coulee area are intensively fished; and increasing recreational use of water bodies and increasing change in the natural life of the area by human exploitation are to be expected with increasing populations. The present study began as one of a series of studies of the biology of the Columbia Basin and the impact of human development upon it, then planned at Washington State College. Its objective was to obtain, through samples from a wide variety of water bodies, some information on limnological conditions in the area as expressed in the group of organisms chosen for study, the plankton copepods.

Methods

Plankton samples were taken from 56 water bodies; of these 40 were chosen for microcrustacean population analysis. The bodies studied may be grouped in relation to five areas of the Basin. One group (Medical, Willow or Murphy, Silver and Clear Lakes and Clear Lake pothole) were from the northeastern and least arid section of the Basin, near the city of Spokane. Also on the eastern edge of the Coulee District, farther south, were the group near Rock Lake and the town of Ewan (Rock and Ledge Lakes, Rock, North Rock, Crescent, Lily Pad, Grass, Tree, Sunken, and Ewan ponds). To the west of these toward the center of the District, and near the towns of Sprague and Ritzville, were a third group (Sprague or Colville Lake, Cow Lake, and Three-inch, East Twin, Marsh, Pear, Disappointment, and Clear ponds). A fourth group (Falls, Deep, Park, Blue, Lenore, Soap, South Tule, and Alkali Lakes, Yellowhead, North Tule, and Avocet ponds) were in the Grand Coulee in the western part of the Basin; and a fifth (Moses Lake, O'Sullivan, Upper and Lower Crab potholes and Pothole No. 1) were south of this in the area of Moses Lake and the Drumheller channels. Names of ponds have been coined by the authors. Locations and summary descriptions of these water bodies are given by Fairbanks (1950); information essential to the present account is compiled in Tables I and II.

These water bodies were visited three times, in spring, summer, and fall—between late March and early May, in July, and in October or November, 1949. Some of the seasonal ponds could be sampled only once or twice. Ten samples of 15 liters each were taken at different points along the shore of a given water body, at depths of 1 m or a little less, above the level of bottom vegetation, if any, and poured through a net of No. 20 bolting silk. Most of the samples thus represent free-swimming, shallow-water or shore plankton. In the lakes, however, both shore and open water plankton were sampled, the latter with oblique hauls of a Clarke & Bumpus (1950) sampler.

Information on water bodies included water temperatures, turbidity readings with a Secchi disk, alkalinity determinations with an electrometric pH meter, areas determined from maps or direct measurements, and depth soundings. A reversing thermometer was used to determine occurrence of stratification during the July visits; only two bodies (Deep and Clear Lakes) possessed a thermocline at that time. Water samples were taken for total salt concentrations and analyses of 12 elements (Na, K, Ca, B, Mg, P, Fe, Cu, Mo, Mn, Sr, and Ag) which could be determined to parts per million or per billion (milliard) by spetrometric and flame photometric methods (Table II).

Plankton samples were killed and preserved in 70% alcohol and set aside until the copepods had lost the red pigments which characterize many of them in this area. Samples were then concentrated into 25 ml of alcohol by means of a miniature plankton net, and fractions of this plankton concentrate were removed for population counts. Two independent counts from the concentrate were made in each case, the two together representing in most cases one-fifth of the original sample, 30 l of lake water. Copepods were tallied in three age groups, as nauplii, copepodids, and adults; the last were determined to species and recorded by sex. Other zooplankters were tallied: Cladocerans to species or genus (except Chydorinae), rotifers, ostracods, and various miscellaneous groups.

The method of handling these population samples, regarded as highly successful, involved mounting fractions of the plankton concentrate on microscope slides in polyvinyl alcohol (PVA). The sample fraction, usually about 1 ml of the concentrate, was transferred by a large-mouth pipette into a rectangular frame on the slide, excess alcohol removed by a blotter, and 4 or 5 drops of PVA added. Large cover slips were then placed, and the slides were heated over a flame until bubbles were removed from the medium and organisms were cleared by blowing out of the internal organs. The PVA mounting renders microcrustaceans transparent and makes visible the fifth feet of copepods; it thus permits determination of these without individual handling and dissection, when sufficient familiarity with the forms being dealt with has been attained. It also provides a permanent reference mount of an actual population sample, in a form in which most adult microcrustaceans may be determined to species. Only by the use of this method, permitting the tallying by species of thousands of copepods, was the population approach of this study possible.

Relations to Salinity and Ion Gradients

The most challenging problem and greatest deterrent to synecological study of plankton is the combination of temporal instability with spatial irregularity of plankton populations. The samples of the present study cannot offer a complete picture of plankton populations, as might be sought from weekly samples from all parts of a given water body. Populations of microcrustacea are less wildly erratic than are those of some smaller plankters, however; and copepod populations showed in the present study a fair degree of consistency through the three seasonal samples from lakes and larger, permanent ponds. Moreover, the approach toward control of population irregularity in the analysis of data was through

TABLE I. Summary of Water Bodies and Microcrustacean Populations

Water body	Total salts, ppm[1]	Area, in hectares	Seasonal relation[2]	COPEPOD POPULATIONS, PERCENT OF SAMPLES[3]													Adult copepods per liter (excluding Harpacticoids)[4]	Adult Harpacticoids per liter[5]	Total copepods per liter[6]	Total cladocerans per liter[6]	Total microcrustacea per liter[7]
				Epischura nevadensis	Diaptomus sicilis	Diaptomus sanguineus	Diaptomus ashlandi	Diaptomus novamexicanus	Diaptomus shoshone	Diaptomus leptopus	Cyclops bicuspidatus	Cyclops vernalis	Cyclops varicans	Eucyclops agilis	Tropocyclops prasinus	Macrocyclops albidus					
Park Lake Group	*244*			*10*			*54*				*36*			*.4*							*6.1*
Rock Lake	170	860	P				100										.15		1.2	.3	1.5
Deep Lake	235	39	P	37			32				30			.6			3.6	.02	6.8	.8	7.6
Park Lake	265	140	P	.4			44				56						.13		3.4	1.5	4.9
Blue Lake	305	210	P	1			41				58			1			.37		6.4	4.1	10.5
Sprague Lake Group	*397*				*5*			*8*			*81*	*4*		*2*							*45.9*
Falls Lake	230	27	P								88			12			1.6		63.2	13.3	76.5
Silver Lake	1000	86	P								93			6			3.6		37.4	12.2	49.6
Clear Lake pothole	330	.4	T								100						1.0	.1	22.1	.9	23.0
Cow Lake	250	85	P		28			1			71						6.1	.07	32.5	45.2	77.7
Moses Lake	210	2060	P		10			9			81						3.5		44.2	138.4	(182.5)[9]
Sprague Lake	335	735	P					21			79						1.4	.9	5.7	17.0	22.7
Clear Lake	425	97	P					34			66			.1			9.9	.07	47.4	10.9	58.3
Yellowhead pond	(7150)[8]	25	S								67	33					0.9		8.5	5.8	14.2
Lake Lenore Group	*2935*				*97*						*1*	*2*	*.04*	*.1*							*72.5*
South Tule Lake	2350	225	P		91						9						11.0		38.8	14.6	53.4
North Tule pond	1040	25	S		98						2						10.2		16.2	10.0	26.2
Willow Lake	4270	36	S		98						1	1		.3			54.2		78.3	11.4	89.7
Granite Lake	4290	43	P		98						.1			1			65.0		94.3	14.9	109.2
Ewan pond	875	4.4	S		99						.1		.4				81.0		130.1	38.6	168.7
Lake Lenore	12100	963	P		100												16.3		76.8	6.1	82.8
Crescent pond	325	.23	T		100												8.0	1.1	64.0	3.4	67.4
Clear pond	620	2.5	T		100												15.0		42.7	15.1	57.8
Three-Inch pond	1190	48	S		97							3					12.3		43.7	4.0	47.8
Medical Lake	2290	43	P		87							13					18.2	.07	20.7	.9	21.6
O'Sullivan Pond Group	*2256*				*4*					*14*	*3*	*24*	*.3*	*51*		*4*					*175.8*
East Twin pond	415	48	S							65		20				15	10.0		22.0	18.8	40.8
O'Sullivan pothole	8710	1.5	S											100			226.5		302.6	7.8	310.4
Avocet pond	610	1.2	T											100			14.0		43.4	42.8	86.2
Sunken pond	310	1.3	S							18		27		46		9	1.1	.8	11.2	3.0	14.2
Upper Crab pothole	2245	1.5	S		22						17	.3	2	58			38.0		233.9	155.5	389.4
Pothole No. 1	1245	.2	T									100					18.0		57.8	151.7	209.5
Disappointment Group	*731*					*88*			*4*		*4*	*1*	*1*	*.5*		*2*					*13.0*
Disappointment pond	390	.01	T			100											0.4		1.0	.2	1.2
Tree pond	290	2.4	T			91					6			3			3.5	.1	17.9	2.4	20.3
Grass pond	670	.54	T			97			3								10.3	.2	22.5	1.8	24.3
Pear pond	1305	.6	T			94					6						6.4		8.4	5.5	13.9
North Rock pond	1320	.4	T			69			19		12						1.6	.1	4.3	6.3	10.6
Marsh pond	410	14	S			75						5	8			12	4.0		6.2	1.3	7.5
Ledge Pond Group	*400*					*12*			*14*		*27*		*36*	*5*		*6*					*56.0*
Ledge "Lake"	370	200	S			25					15		39	10		11	7.2	.3	21.2	4.5	25.7
Rock pond	430	.8	T						27		39		34				5.1	2.1	24.6	61.8	86.4
Lily Pad pond	155	8.5	S								.6	1			99		14.2	2.0	50.6	20.8	71.4
Soap Lake	38700	340	P																	64.7	64.7
Lower Crab pothole	88030	3.0	S																		(24.0)[7]

[1]Total salt determinations are from July water samples in all cases except vernal ponds.
[2]P=permanent and stable; S=semi-permanent ponds, with fluctuating water level and area; T=temporary or seasonal ponds, dry at the time of the summer or fall samples.
[3]Percentages of "Adult copepods per liter," from which average numbers of adults per liter for a given species may be computed.
[4]Average numbers of adult copepods per liter per sampling visit when plankton samples could be taken.
[5]Average numbers of adults per liter per sampling visit, mostly from spring samples. Most or all Harpacticoids are *Canthocamptus vagus*.
[6]Average numbers of copepods, or cladocerans, of all ages per liter per sampling visit when plankton samples could be taken.
[7]Average numbers per liter of copepods plus cladocerans, excluding small numbers of ostracods and phyllopods. The bracketed figure for Lower Crab pothole, however, is for 6.2 adult and 17.8 immature *Artemia salina* per liter on July 29, 1949.
[8]Value probably in error, excluded from group average.
[9]Excluded from group averages. (Moses Lake as a relatively young, dammed lake, the only artificial body sampled, had a very high plankton productivity at the time of the study.)

comparison of groups of samples from several lakes, to permit some averaging out of time-to-time and lake-to-lake variation. Arrangement in relation to the salinity gradient of a small number of water bodies which are not uniform in other conditions may produce a very deceptive picture. When plankton populations may be averaged in groups of several lakes for each interval of the gradient studied, however, there is some hope of distinguishing effects of salinity from those of water-body size and other factors.

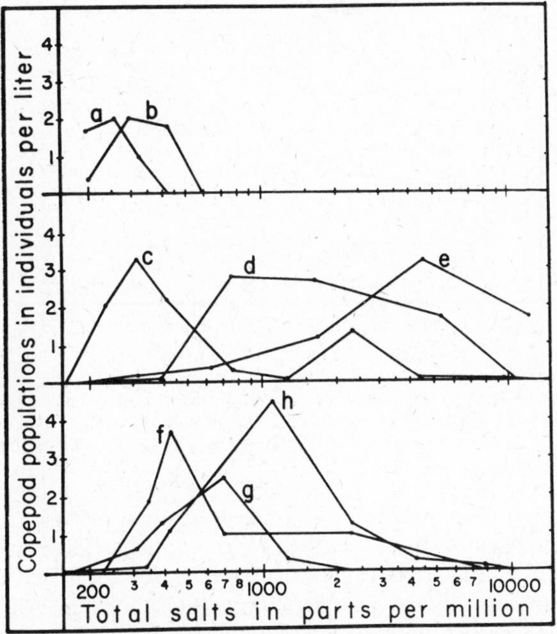

FIG. 1. Distributions of copepod populations in relation to salinity. Points are plotted for average numbers of adult copepod individuals per liter of water per sampling visit, against average total salt contents, for groups of 2 to 6 water bodies. Above: two species of lakes, *Diaptomus ashlandi* (a) and *D. novamexicanus* (b). Middle: three species of both lakes and ponds, *Cyclops bicuspidatus* ×0.5 (c), *Eucyclops agilis* (d), and *Diaptomus sicilis* ×0.1 (e). Below: three species of ponds, *Cyclops varicans* ×10 (f), *Diaptomus sanguineus* (g), and *Cyclops vernalis* (h).

Figure 1 represents the relation to the gradient of total salt concentrations, in parts per million, of species populations expressed as average numbers of adult copepod individuals per liter of water per sampling visit when the lake depression contained water. The groups of water bodies within which populations are averaged include both lakes and ponds for species which occur in both, but include lakes or ponds only for species restricted to one type of water body or the other. The forms of the population figures approximate in some cases a bell-shaped or binominal curve, which has been suggested as the predominant form of population distribution along an environmental gradient (Gause 1930; Whittaker 1951, 1956; Brown & Curtis 1952; *cf.* data of Pennak, 1942, 1951). Use of a linear salinity scale as the horizontal axis results in highly skewed distributions. These become more nearly symmetrical on the log scale of Figure 1, and a "lognormal" relation to the salinity gradient is thus suggested. The manner in which populations relate to a logarithmic gradient further suggests (in analogy with the Weber-Fechner law) that the biological effect of salinity increments is proportional not to absolute magnitudes in parts per million, but to the increment in relation to the salinity to which it is added—$\Delta s/s$.

As may be judged from Figure 1, *Diaptomus ashlandi* is a species of the least saline, oligotrophic lakes; *D. novamexicanus* is a species of eutrophic, fresh to slightly saline lakes. The three species of both lakes and ponds show a sequence along the salinity gradient: *Cyclops bicuspidatus* predominantly in fresh to slightly saline bodies, *Eucyclops agilis* predominantly in mildly to moderately saline bodies, and *D. sicilis* in moderately saline ones. The population of *C. bicuspidatus* shows a second mode in moderately saline bodies. The significance of this is uncertain; but it is of interest that the fresh-water peak of the population is in lakes while the saline peak is in ponds, and it is possible that the two peaks represent two ecotypes within the population of this species. A sequence of sorts appears for the pond species, with *C. varicans* predominantly in fresh to slightly saline, *D. sanguineus* in mildly saline, and *C. vernalis* in moderately saline ponds. The overlaps of these species in relation to salinity are very broad, however, and factors other than salinity seem most critical in determining the presence of one or another in a given pond.

It is consequently impossible to predict the plankton population of a pond from its position on the salinity gradient. For the lakes a clearer sequence appears, but still with considerable irregularity and overlap. Because of this irregularity and overlap, and because the change of populations along the gradient appears to be continuous when groups of water bodies are averaged together, it is difficult to specify particular numbers as limits of fresh-water and saline conditions and of different degrees of salinity. Division between fresh-water and saline bodies at approximately 300 ppm has been suggested by Hesse (1937) and Rawson & Moore (1944). The boundary between fresh-water and saline conditions is presumably to be set where plant and animal populations characteristic of fresh-water conditions are replaced by those characteristic of saline conditions. Apparently all the copepods of saline conditions in the Columbia Basin occur also in fresh-water conditions there or elsewhere. A distinction between fresh-water and saline communities must consequently be based, not on general distributions of species, but on their distributions and numerical relations within the particular group of water bodies being studied. For copepods of lakes in the Columbia Basin, the fresh-water to saline transition may be marked by change of dominance from *C. bicuspidatus* to *D. sicilis.* The highest salinities in which the former is dominant in lakes are 425 and 1000 ppm, the lowest for the latter 875 and 1040 ppm. No definite boundary between fresh-water and saline copepod communities can be specified, but for most bodies the transition is somewhere between 425 and 875 ppm.

All ponds sampled except one are saline, if a limit of 300 ppm is accepted; but those of lower salinities do not have distinctively saline faunas. No feature as simple as dominance of *D. sicilis* permits characterization of saline ponds and definition of their lower salinity limit; most of the ponds sampled may well be regarded as a single complex of fresh to moderately saline conditions. A distinction may be drawn, however, between fresh-water or slightly saline bodies, with salinities of 310-430 ppm and mixed populations of various combinations of *C. varicans, E. agilis, C. bicuspidatus, C. vernalis, D. leptopus,* and *D. shoshone,* and a group of more distinctly saline bodies, mostly above 410 ppm, in each of which a single copepod species (*D. sicilis, E. agilis, C. vernalis*) was strongly preponderant. All the species involved occurred on both sides of the transitional salinities of about 400-450 ppm, and one pond of 325 ppm contained only *D. sicilis.* A transition, by no means clearly defined, may be suggested, however, between the richer copepod communities of fresh-water or slightly saline ponds below 400-450 ppm and the more restricted and often single-species communities of higher salinities.

Limits in parts per million of fresh-water and saline conditions are clearly variable and indefinite, subject to exceptions in both directions, so far as faunal characterization is concerned, and somewhat different for ponds, with their seasonal intensification of salinity, and for lakes. Limits of salinity classes can in the end only be set arbitrarily, though with regard for what seem to be average salinities at which faunal changes occur. In the Columbia Basin it appears that above 300 ppm a few, above 400-450 ppm the majority, and above 800-1000 ppm almost all, copepod communities are saline in character. The terminology of salinity suggested for the present paper differs from that of Rawson & Moore (1944): 300-450 ppm is regarded as transitional from fresh to slightly saline, 450-1000 ppm as mildly saline, and above 1000 ppm as moderately saline. No upper limit of moderate salinity can be determined from the present data; but Lake Lenore at 12,100 ppm is faunistically in the moderately saline grouping while Soap Lake at 37,800 and Lower Crab pothole at 88,030 ppm have distinctive crustacean communities of high salinities.

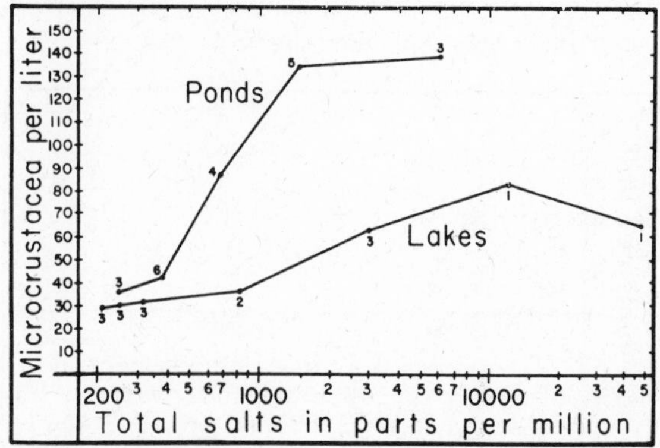

FIG. 2. Standing crops of microcrustaceans in relation to salinity in lakes and in ponds. Points are plotted for average numbers of adult and immature copepods and cladocerans per liter per sampling visit against average total salt contents for groups of water bodies; small figures above and below points are numbers of water bodies averaged.

In Figure 2 microcrustacean standing crops are diagrammed in relation to the salinity gradient. Marked correlations of standing crop, and hence presumably of productivity, with salinity are apparent for both lakes and ponds. Great differences in standing crops appear among water bodies of a given salinity, and in statistical terms the correlation is not high (coefficients of correlation of standing crop *vs.* log salinity of 0.50 for lakes and 0.56 for ponds). It is believed, however, that this means not that the correlation itself is weak, but that standing crops are affected also by many other factors statistical control of which is not possible with the present data. Microcrustacean populations declined at higher salinities from Lake Lenore to Soap Lake, and no microcrustaceans were collected from still more saline Lower Crab pothole. It is unlikely that this limitation of microcrustaceans implies lower productivities at higher salinities in the range sampled. Lower Crab pothole contained a dense population of *Artemia salina* (Table I), and the intense *Artemia* and *Ephydra* production of Great Salt Lake (Hesse 1937) occurs at more than 200,000 ppm.

It is doubtful that the "salinity gradient" has direct, biological meaning to account for its relation to copepod populations and productivity. The salinity gradient may seem little more than a congeries of factor gradients for various ions and compounds which, however, are complexly intercorrelated and may be variously interrelated in physiological implications. In addition to these chemical gradients there is distinct differentiation of biological communities along the salinity gradient, and consequently differences in characteristics of communities and competitive relations affecting species populations. Taken all together, in both chemical and biological features, the salinity gradient is a "complex-gradient" (Whittaker 1954, 1956), a complex of factor gradients or a gradient of total environmental complexes affecting organisms in biological communities. As such, the salinity gradient may be studied not for any assumption of its direct, causal significance, but only for the significant correlations of chemical and biological characteristics of water bodies which it represents.

It is further indicated by Figure 2 that, on the average, ponds are more productive than lakes at all salinity levels compared. Comparing shore samples for all lakes, with areas over 30 hectares and substantial depths, with ponds of either smaller or shallow basins, average microcrustacean standing crops were 44.5 ± 8.7 and 80.9 ± 21.2 individuals per liter per sampling visit (with standard errors of means for 15 and 22 bodies, respectively). Ponds thus supported on the average 1.8 times as dense a microcrustacean population as the shore communities of lakes. A further breakdown compared eutrophic lakes (excluding the Park Group) with larger, permanent and semi-permanent ponds, and smaller, temporary ponds; average numbers of microcrustacea were 58.4 ± 8.0, 107.2 ± 37.2, and 39.1 ± 9.6 for 11, 11, and 10 water bodies. The figures for temporary ponds are for standing crops when there was water to be sampled; they do not reflect the further limitation of annual productivity by disappearance of the aquatic communities during part of the season.

The water analyses (Table II) were obtained to determine whether more direct effects on copepod populations could be established for the various metallic ions, at least. All water bodies were ranked according to content of Na, Mg, K, Ca, B, Mn, Fe, and Cu; and tables were prepared showing the relations of copepod populations to these ion gradients. It is in some cases relatively easy to obtain graphs resembling Figure 1 by suitable grouping of the water bodies, but the significance of such results in questionable. Concentrations of most of the elements studied are correlated with one another and with total salt content; and it is impossible to manipulate the material in such a way as to establish distributional relations to a single element while others and total salts are held constant. Because a given population declines in both directions from its mode along a gradient, this is not a problem to which multiple and partial correlations are suited.

Limited conclusions are possible from inspection of the distributions. An ion whose concentration is more critical in its effect on copepod faunas than total salinity might result in clearer segregation of fresh-water and saline faunas. Sensitivity might be expressed in narrow restriction and insensitivity in broad spread of a species population in relation to a given ion; and relative spread of species along the various ion gradients can be approached as dispersion. None of the ions studied permitted a clearer segregation of fresh-water and saline faunas than did total salt content. For no species was there a clear and unquestionable response of its distribution to a particular metallic ion. There is a suggestion that copper might significantly affect population levels within the range of concentrations represented (0.4 to 212 ppb). High populations of *C. biscuspidatus* and *C. vernalis* were more narrowly confined to the fresh-water end of the gradient (below 4.0 and 4.5 ppb) by copper content than by total salts; high populations of *E. agilis,* in contrast, occurred only in the range of relatively high copper content (17 to 41 ppb). In each case the species population occurred at lower levels along almost the whole range of concentrations represented (highly saline bodies excluded), and it cannot be established that the relation is more than coincidental.

No efforts toward characterizing ponds with different faunas by relative contents of different elements were successful. Ranking of all water bodies by the ratio of Mg to Na (suggested by work of Boone & Baas-Becking 1931) gave striking results: high *D. sicilis* populations occurred only at low values of the ratio (below 0.2), *E. agilis, C. vernalis,* and *D. sanguineus* were concentrated at intermediate values (0.02 to 0.3), and *C. bicuspidatus* at high values (above 0.02). Further scrutiny of the data revealed that, because Na was strongly correlated with total salts and Mg was not, low values of the ratio occurred in saline and high values in fresh to mildly saline bodies. Treatment in terms of the Mg/Na ratio thus simply reproduced the distributional relation of these five species to the salinity gradient and other ions correlated with it. The analysis of Mg/Na ratios may serve mainly to illustrate the perils of unwary interpretation of such material.

Correlation of standing crops with concentrations of various elements is also evident in the data; and coefficients of correlation of standing crop *vs.* log concentration were computed for 9

TABLE II. Concentrations of metallic elements and phosphorus

Water body	Total salts, ppm	Major Elements in Parts Per Million					Minor Elements in Parts Per Billion (10^9)						
		Na	Mg	K	Ca	B	P	Fe	Mo	Cu	Mn	Sr	Ag
Lily Pad pond	155	35	13	6.8	3.2	0.24	115	105	....	5	7	41	..
Rock Lake	170	15	5	4.8	0.7	0.16	141	144	....	9	10	74	19
Moses Lake	210	40	11	11.2	1.8	1.12	....	40	2	1	0.5	195	..
Falls Lake	230	34	15	6.4	1.6	1.04	....	37	0.2	1	2	....	..
Deep Lake	235	26	11	7.6	1.4	0.64	....	17	2	4	4	....	..
Cow Lake	250	26	13	12.0	2.6	0.21	....	32	....	11	15	16	..
Park Lake	265	48	13	11.0	2.3	0.87	..	84	....	5	4	....	..
Tree pond	290	45	22	24.8	2.0	0.29	383	290	....	33	19	59	29
Blue Lake	305	70	24	13.2	4.0	0.85	....	50	3	5	2	....	..
Sunken pond	310	49	6	22.8	2.0	1.13	98	101	....	25	3	19	..
Crescent pond	325	21	10	6.6	2.6	0.50	....	46	....	12	17	227	..
Clear Lake pothole	330	46	27	5.0	3.4	0.68	155	251	3	15	4	50	18
Sprague Lake	335	24	19	9.4	1.4	0.29	....	70	....	4	0.8	253	..
Ledge "Lake"	370	66	28	18.0	2.7	0.05	207	133	....	17	3	....	..
Disappointment pond	390	59	26	61.0	2.8	0.72	....	15	....	13	...	26	..
Marsh pond	410	33	11	8.6	3.9	0.09	....	150	....	0.4	3	....	..
East Twin pond	415	96	32	15.2	2.8	0.20	....	67	....	4	15	25	..
Clear Lake	425	94	7	21.2	6.3	0.08	....	21	....	1	0.5	....	..
Rock pond	430	130	3	32.0	5.3	0.28	....	....	....	5	4	....	..
Avocet pond	610	126	34	19.2	9.0	1.07	226	390	14	18	5	451	..
Clear pond	620	126	23	55.2	5.4	0.35	....	9	....	0.6	8	....	..
Grass pond	670	200	29	33.8	7.6	0.72	....	78	1109	112	3	315	..
Ewan pond	875	302	15	42.4	11.4	0.41	384	416	9	33	9	301	3
Silver Lake	1000	(61)[1]	94	22.0	4.9	1.95	318	750	....	10	85	....	..
North Tule pond	1040	268	14	29.6	12.2	1.85	1529	578	21	11	36	....	..
Three-Inch pond	1190	166	21	35.0	7.2	3.13	1547	595	4	113	...	....	..
Pothole No. 1	1245	224	66	131.0	12.4	1.86	....	234	....	2	93	....	..
Pear pond	1305	365	16	124.0	16.0	0.38	....	37	....	4	39	....	..
North Rock pond	1320	84	63	18.8	6.4	4.28	1611	1320	16	32	125	1016	..
Upper Crab pothole	2245	(2070)[1]	56	192.0	48.0	0.53	....	10	27	41	...	....	..
Medical Lake	2290	715	10	54.0	30.0	0.76	....	55	....	2	2	....	..
South Tule Lake	2350	705	10	122.0	28.0	1.64	....	336	63	212	11	....	..
Willow Lake	4270	1480	6	210.0	57.0	0.63	....	54	83	4	5	....	..
Granite Lake	4290	1480	7	169.0	28.0	1.60	....	81	....	15	4	....	..
Yellowhead pond	(7150)[1]	202	1	23.0	8.5	1.57	214	242	15	17	31	....	..
O'Sullivan pothole	8710	2600	283	210.0	98.0	3.70	....	113	118	20	...	....	..
Lake Lenore	12100	4140	38	364.0	148.0	9.07	....	181	81	200	...	....	..
Soap Lake	38700	13000	22	1190.0	470.0	8.28	....	390	....	49	...	....	..
Lower Crab pothole	88030	27500	599	1105.0	870.0	24.7	....	1101	1207	194	...	....	..

[1]Value probably in error.

elements in lakes, in ponds, and in all water bodies together. The coefficients for Na (0.50 for lakes, 0.53 for ponds, 0.36 for both together) were almost identical with those for total salts. Positive coefficients of 0.3 to 0.7 were obtained also for K, Ca, Cu, Mg, and B *vs.* standing crops of ponds, for B *vs.* standing crops of lakes; lower and probably non-significant correlations were obtained for K, Ca, Cu, and Mg in lakes and for Fe, Mn, and P in all water bodies. Although significant correlations of standing crops with concentrations of various elements occur in these lakes, causal meaning is hardly to be assumed for most of them. The salinity gradient reflects the accumulation in water bodies of many substances, of which some are among the factors influencing productivity; concentrations of most of these substances are consequently correlated with total salts and with standing crops whether or not they influence productivity. No metal showed evident effect in limiting microcrustacean populations at high concentrations. Two of the most highly productive ponds (O'Sullivan and Upper Crab) were among bodies with highest concentrations of almost all ions studied (excluding lakes of intense salinity); and these suggest that microcrustacean productivities were not limited by concentrations of 2900 ppm for Na, 283 ppm for Mg, 210 ppm for K, 98 ppm for Ca, 4 ppm for B, and 41 ppb for Cu.

Extreme sensitivities to certain ions have been shown for phytoplankton species (Rodhe 1948). The attempts to establish effects of metallic ions on copepod populations were, however, consistently inconclusive. To the extent that conclusions may be drawn from them, these conclusions (except for the circumstantial suggestion that copper might be significant) are negative.

Community-Types and Their Relations

The first attempts to group plankton samples into community-types were based on the salinity gradient and the contrast of lakes and ponds. A sequence of lake types in relation to salinity may, in fact, be recognized. No comparable series of pond types could be established by simple inspection of the data, however; and an alternative approach to classification was explored: grouping of water bodies by measurement of relative similarities of their plankton communities into community-types, which could then be compared with one another and given limnological characterization.

The techniques employed have been developed by ecologists studying terrestrial communities—by phytosociologists (Kulczyński 1928; Motyka 1947; Motyka *et al.* 1950; Matuszkiewicz 1948, 1950, 1952; Sørensen 1948; Poore 1955; Culberson 1955; Bray 1956; Koch 1957), and by animal ecologists (Renkonen 1938, 1944; Agrell 1941, 1945; Forsslund 1945; Brink & Wingstrand 1949; Kontkanen 1950a; Odum 1950; Whittaker 1952), most of whom are Continental students of the "biocenotics" of terrestrial arthropod communities. Two basic types of measurement are used in such work (Williams 1944, 1949 and Hughes & Lindley 1955, have suggested other possibilities; see also Goodall 1952). The *coefficient of community,* originally used by Jaccard (1902, 1908, 1912, 1932) measures the percentage of species shared by two community samples, community-types, or floristic lists among the total number of species represented in one or both:

$CC = \frac{c}{a + b - c}$, in which a is the number of species in the first sample, b in the second sample, and c the number of species occurring in both. Other means of measurement modify the coefficient of community to compare samples in terms of relative abundance or importance of species—by frequencies or constancies in the case of plants (Kulczyński 1928; Gleason 1920; Tüxen & Ellenberg 1937; Raabe 1952). The most widely used measurement for animal communities compares them by numbers of individuals of species, within the group being studied:

$$PS_c = 100 - .5\Sigma|a - b| = \Sigma \min (a, b),$$

in which a and b are, for a given species, the percentages of samples A and B which that species represents. This measurement, some properties and limitations of which were discussed by Whittaker (1952), has been variously named, but may perhaps best be termed *percentage similarity* of community samples. An alternative to these quantitative approaches has been developed among students of biocenotics in central and southern Europe, who consider that grouping of samples by the non-quantitative techniques of *diagnostic species* (see below) is more effective (Kühnelt 1943a, 1943b, 1951a, 1951b; Rabeler 1947; Gisin 1947, 1951; Franz 1943, 1950; Tischler 1951; Strenzke 1952; Quézel & Verdier 1953; see also Brundin, 1934, and reviews of Renkonen, 1949, Kontkanen, 1950b, and Schwenke, 1953).

Of the two quantitative approaches, coefficient of community measures relative similarity in terms of species composition, and may over-value minor species to the neglect of differences in dominance and major species. Percentage similarity, on the other hand, measures relative similarity of numerical composition in terms of species populations and generally leads to grouping of communities by dominants or major species. It may thus over-value the sharing of dominant species to the neglect of differences in over-all community composition. Each measurement has its advantages and limitations under different ecological conditions, and use of both for comparison or their combination may often be appropriate. Kontkanen (1950a) has applied both to insect samples and concluded that coefficient of community gave the more effective grouping. The contrary conclusion was reached in the present study; the relatively small numbers of species dealt with strongly limits the significance of coefficients of community and requires an approach through numerical comparison.

For the percentage similarity treatment, data for copepod populations were totaled for sample visits and, in the case of lakes, for shore and open-water samples, and converted into percentages of total samples represented by each species (Table I). Direct computation of percentage similarities is then possible through either of two procedures. Comparing Deep and Park Lakes, which share the species *Epischura nevadensis, D. ashlandi,* and *C. bicuspidatus:* $PS_c = 100 - .5\Sigma|a - b| = 100 - .5[|37 - .4| + |32 - 44| + |30 - 56| + |.6 - 0|] = 100 - .5 \times 75.2 = 62.4$. Or, more simply, for all species shared by the two samples, the smaller percentage values may be summed: $PS_c = \Sigma \min (a, b) = .4 + 32 + 30 = 62.4$.

Percentage similarities were thus computed for all possible combinations of samples, $n(n - 1)/2$ computations where n is the number of samples, and entered in a Kulczyński triangle or matrix (Table III). In the first such matrix prepared, high and low similarity values were scattered in such a way as to offer no recognizable grouping of samples. In order to reveal such groupings, the sequence of the samples should be so changed as to

TABLE III. Matrix of percentage similarities of copepod community samples

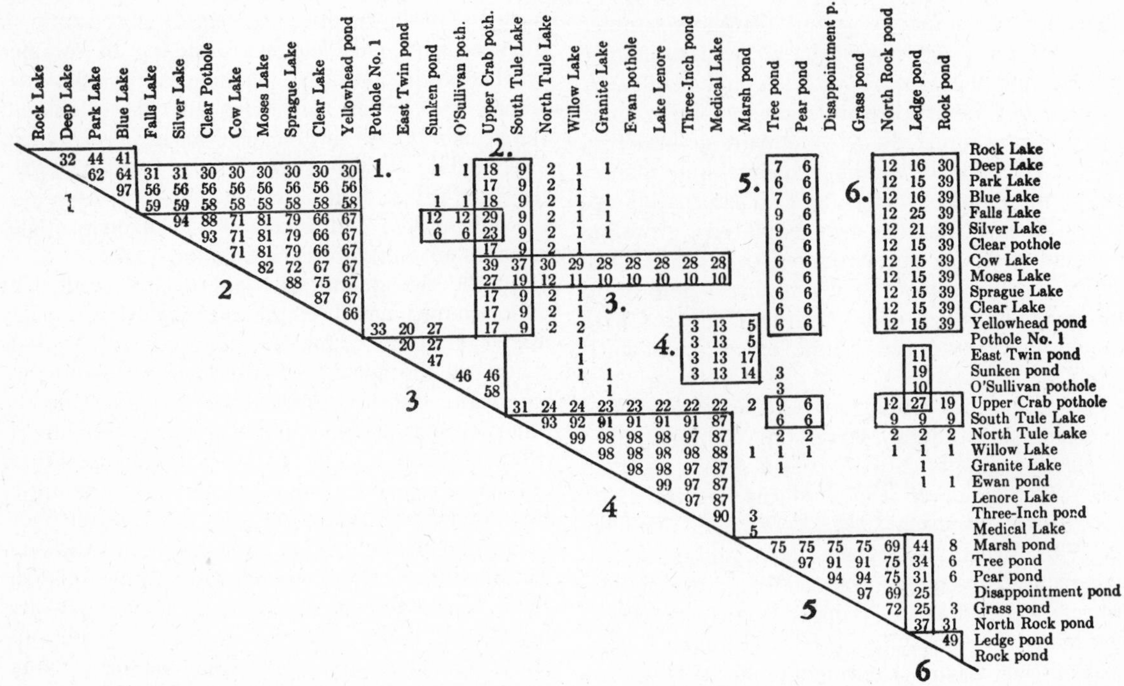

	Rock Lake	Deep Lake	Park Lake	Blue Lake	Falls Lake	Silver Lake	Clear Pothole	Cow Lake	Moses Lake	Sprague Lake	Clear Lake	Yellowhead pond	Pothole No. 1	East Twin pond	Sunken pond	O'Sullivan poth.	Upper Crab poth.	South Tule Lake	North Tule Lake	Willow Lake	Granite Lake	Ewan pothole	Lake Lenore	Three-Inch pond	Medical Lake	Marsh pond	Tree pond	Pear pond	Disappointment p.	Grass pond	North Rock pond	Ledge pond	Rock pond
Rock Lake		32	44	41																													
Deep Lake			62	64	31	31	30	30	30	30	30	30			1	1	18	9	2	1	1						7	6			12	16	30
Park Lake				97	56	56	56	56	56	56	56	56					17	9	2	1							6	6			12	15	39
Blue Lake					59	59	58	58	58	58	58	58			1	1	18	9	2	1	1						7	6			12	16	39
Falls Lake						94	88	71	81	79	66	67			12	12	29	9	2	1	1						9	6			12	25	39
Silver Lake							93	71	81	79	66	67			6	6	23	9	2	1	1						9	6			12	21	39
Clear pothole								71	81	79	66	67					17	9	2	1							6	6			12	15	39
Cow Lake									82	72	67	67					39	37	30	29	28	28	28	28	28		6	6			12	15	39
Moses Lake										88	75	67					27	19	12	11	10	10	10	10	10		6	6			12	15	39
Sprague Lake											87	67					17	9	2	1							6	6			12	15	39
Clear Lake												66					17	9	2	1							6	6			12	15	39
Yellowhead pond													33	20	27		17	9	2	2				3	13	5	6	6			12	15	39
Pothole No. 1														20	27					1				3	13	5							
East Twin pond															47					1				3	13	17						11	
Sunken pond																46	46			1	1			3	13	14	3					19	
O'Sullivan pothole																	58				1						3					10	
Upper Crab pothole																		31	24	24	23	23	22	22	22	2	9	6			12	27	19
South Tule Lake																			93	92	91	91	91	91	87		6	6			9	9	9
North Tule Lake																				99	98	98	98	97	87		2	2			2	2	2
Willow Lake																					98	98	98	98	88	1	1	1			1	1	1
Granite Lake																						98	98	97	87		1					1	
Ewan pond																							99	97	87							1	1
Lenore Lake																								97	87								
Three-Inch pond																									90	3							
Medical Lake																										5							
Marsh pond																											75	75	75	75	69	44	8
Tree pond																												97	91	91	75	34	6
Pear pond																													94	94	75	31	6
Disappointment pond																														97	69	25	
Grass pond																															72	25	3
North Rock pond																																37	31
Ledge pond																																	49
Rock pond																																	

maneuver high percentage similarity values toward the diagonal of the matrix, so far as possible. One may begin with a sample regarded as "extreme"; in this case the most oligotrophic body, Rock Lake, was chosen. This sample must be followed by another with which it has highest similarity (Deep Lake), and this in turn by a third whose highest similarities are with Deep Lake and another sample, which becomes the fourth, and so on.

By this procedure (and, often, more than one trial arrangement), the high similarity values by which samples are to be grouped may be clustered along the diagonal as in Table III. Six community-types are suggested, and are marked by heavy triangles. This published matrix has been shortened by eliminating from it certain water bodies (Lily Pad pond, Soap Lake, and Lower Crab pothole) which do not share species populations with the other bodies in sufficient numbers to permit significant comparisons. Certain samples which were identical with other samples in their single-species composition could be dropped without loss of information; Avocet, Crescent, and Clear ponds were thus deleted.

If a single environmental gradient accounts for most or all of the variation among samples, these will fit into sequence in the matrix; and the similarity values will decrease rather uniformly from the diagonal toward the upper right corner. It is obvious that the samples of the present study do not form a simple sequence related to, say, the salinity gradient. The multi-directional interrelations of samples and groups are indicated by the boxes of intermediate similarity values which are distant from the diagonal. In the present, relatively simple material, the meaning of these is easily interpreted in terms of species composition. Thus the widespread species *C. bicuspidatus* links together the first two groups (box 1), and links both of these to certain ponds of groups 5 and 6 (boxes 5 and 6). *D. sicilis* links certain eutrophic lakes with the saline bodies of group 4 (box 3), *C. vernalis* links ponds of group 3 with bodies transitional to groups 4 and 5 (box 4); and the meaning of smaller boxes marked can be determined from Table I.

Means of diagramming and visualizing the multi-directional relations indicated by the matrix were sought. Percentage compositions of the six groupings derived from Table III were averaged (Table I). These averages, in turn, were compared by percentage similarities; and a matrix of community-types was prepared. The results are diagrammed as a plexus of community-types in Figure 3. All percentage similarities above 6 are represented by lines whose lengths are scaled to 100-PS_c, percentage differences expressing relative dissimilarities or ecological distances of the groups from one another. These lines may be related to the boxes, and contacts along the diagonal, of Table III; but a given pair of community-

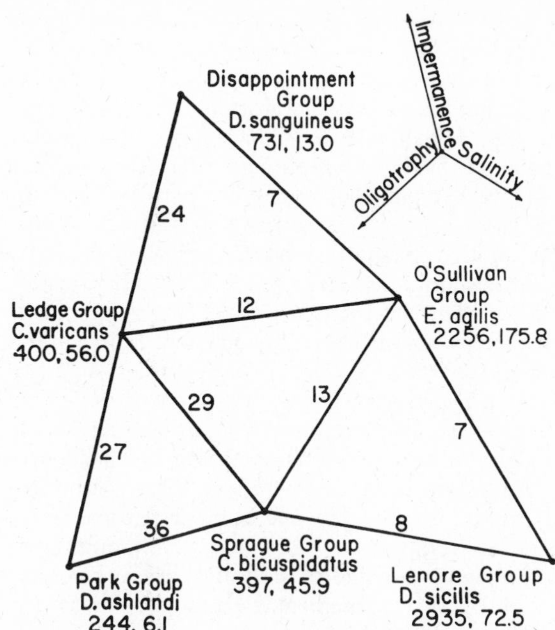

FIG. 3. Plexus of copepod community-types based on measurements of percentage similarity for water-body groupings (see Table I). Percentage similarity values are indicated by the lines; lines are drawn to scale for 100 minus percentage similarity. Information at each point includes a major copepod species by which the community-type may be characterized, average total salt content in ppm (the first number), and average microcrustacean standing crop (the second number) for the water body grouping.

types are generally related by several species. All other relations of community-types, for which no lines are drawn, are expressed in percentage similarities of 6 or less. A generally similar plexus, but with lines of different proportions, results from comparisons by coefficients of community.

The plexus was constructed independently of the authors' interpretations of the environmental relations of these community-types. Its triangular form is contrary to expectation; ecological prepossessions might suggest a square formed by various combinations of fresh-water *vs.* saline and permanent *vs.* temporary conditions. These two gradients are, however, present in the structure of the plexus. The base line from the Park Group to the Lenore Group is in part a salinity gradient; the Park Group are lakes which are both oligotrophic and of low salinity; the Sprague Group is predominantly of eutrophic fresh-water to slightly saline lakes, the Lenore Group predominantly of moderately saline bodies. The larger numbers entered by the names of groups are average total salt contents in parts per million. The vertical axis is, on the whole, but with considerable overlap between groups, one of seasonal regime. The Park Group consists wholly, and the Sprague and Lenore Groups predominantly, of lakes. The Disappointment Group at the upper apex consists of temporary ponds, with one shallow semi-permanent pond (Marsh). The intermediate groups, Ledge and O'Sullivan, include no lakes and are predominantly of semi-permanent ponds—bodies which did not dry during the season of observation but showed marked decrease in depth and area during the summer and fall. Such bodies may dry up in some years, and they subject their communities to greater fluctuations of salinity and other environmental conditions than truly permanent lakes and ponds. (Ewan pond, regarded as a typical "pothole" of this group, showed effects of reduced water volume in salinities of 645, 875, and 1660 ppm in April, July, and October). The plexus thus supports a three-part classification into permanent, semi-permanent, and temporary bodies (*cf.* Gajl 1925 and Decksbach 1929, eustatic, perennial astatic, and temporary astatic).

The plexus represents, not four combinations of salinity and seasonal regime, but three environmental extremes—oligotrophy, salinity, and seasonal instability—and the Ledge, Sprague, and O'Sullivan groups represent various intermediates to these extremes. Relations of these conditions to standing crops of microcrustaceans are indicated by the smaller numbers entered by the groups, averages of microcrustacean populations per liter. Increasing populations toward more saline conditions are indicated for the lakes and suggested for the semi-permanent ponds. Populations of semi-permanent ponds are higher than those of lakes at a given salinity, but temporary ponds have lower populations than either. Both oligotrophy and greatest seasonal instability are reflected in low standing crops; but high salinity, within the range of water bodies represented, is not. The results thus support, from a different grouping of samples and with statistically less effective comparisons, those already discussed.

The community-types may be characterized by species composition as well as limnological conditions (Table I); some major species are indicated on the plexus. In most cases percentage similarities lead to grouping by dominant species; thus the Sprague, Lenore, and Disappointment groups are characterized by dominance of *C. bicuspidatus, D. sicilis,* and *D. sanguineus,* respectively. The Park Group, except Rock Lake, is characterized by sharing of dominance by *D. ashlandi* and *C. bicuspidatus.* The two other pond groupings cannot be characterized by any single dominant species; they appear to be relatively heterogeneous groupings in which *E. agilis, C. vernalis,* and *D. leptopus* are major species for the Sunken Group, *C. varicans* with different combinations of other species for the Ledge Group. It is thus much less easy to generalize about copepod communities of ponds than those of lakes. In general, the smaller the water body, the more is its plankton a shore-plankton community subject to diverse and little-understood influences of shore and bottom properties, and the less easily predicted is the plankton community from knowledge of major water-body characteristics.

It is of interest to compare these results with those which might be obtained by the grouping by diagnostic species which is very widely practiced among Continental phytosociologists and students of biocenotics in southern Europe. Two types of diagnostic species may be distinguished (Braun-Blanquet 1932, 1951): *character-species* (*Charakterarten, Kennarten, Leitarten*) which are largely or wholly restricted to a given community-type, among a group of these being compared, and *differential-species* (*Differentialarten, Trennarten, Scheidearten*) which are usually much more widespread "companions" (*Begleiter*) occurring in many community-types, but are largely or wholly restricted to one of two community-types being compared and may thus serve to distinguish these. All the major species mentioned except *C. bicuspidatus* are character-species for community-types; in most cases a given species characterizes a community-type not only as a dominant (by numerical importance) but also as both character-species (by relative restriction to the type) and constant (by occurrence in most or all of the samples for that type). In addition, *E. nevadensis* becomes a character-species for the Park Group and *D. novamexicanus* for the Sprague Group. No very effective distinctions by differential-species are suggested by the data, except that *C. bicuspidatus* may be treated as a differential-species separating the highly oligotrophic Rock Lake, with its walls of vertical basalt and waters turbid with colloidal clay, from other bodies of the Park Group. For the material studied here, the quantitative approach through dominance and percentage similarities, and the qualitative through diagnostic species, lead to much the same pattern of community groupings. (It cannot be assumed that they will do so under other circumstances.) By the nomenclature which is standardized in phytosociology, the community-types recognized here might be designated either *associations* (defined by character-species) or *sociations* (defined by dominants). Since animals alone, and a single group of these, are in question, they are termed here simply water-body groupings or plankton community-types.

It is felt that these approaches lead to useful and meaningful groupings of water bodies. The groupings overlap extensively in limnological conditions, and this fact must be considered in any interpretation of them. It may be possible in some cases to construct abstract representations like the plexus discussed which have little limnological or biological meaning. Percentage similarity, for example, may give very misleading results if a given species has two ecotypes dominant in two, distantly related, groups of habitats and communities. Experience with other material suggests that the matrix and plexus approach often gives results less clear-cut and easily interpreted than those in the present work. A virtue of these techniques, however, is that they permit grouping of communities by actual similarity in biological characteristics, in relative independence of ecologists' assumptions about how communities ought to relate to one another according to their environments. They may thus sometimes give a better picture of biological relations than one based on environmental characteristics alone, and in the classification and characterization of water bodies they may well supplement more purely limnological considerations.

Distributional Interrelations of Species

Distributional relations of species may also be investigated through the matrix and plexus approach. A larger number of means of measuring the "association" of two species are available to choose from (see also Goodall 1952). Some of these (Forbes 1907, 1925; Shelford 1915; Dice 1945, 1952; Cole 1949, 1957) are based on direct comparison of the number of samples in which two species occur together, in a given sample series, with the number of occurrences together which would be expected by chance. Others employ coefficients of correlation in one form or another (Iljinski & Poselskaja 1929; Stewart & Keller 1936; Tuomikoski 1942, 1948; Cole 1949; Kontkanen 1949; Nash 1950; Goodall 1953, 1954a; de Vries *et al.* 1954; de Vries 1953; Damman & de Vries 1954). Still others are simple expressions of the percentage occurrence together of species in a set of samples (Agrell 1945; Dice 1945, 1952; Whittaker 1952). Distributional associations of plant species have been studied also by Ramensky (1930), Katz (1930), Scheygrond (1932), Iversen (1936, 1954), Matuszkiewicz (1948), Motyka *et al.* (1950), Gardner (1951), Gilbert & Curtis (1953), Hale (1955), Greig-Smith (1952), Bray (1956), and McIntosh (1957), those of animal species by Backlund (1945), Kontkanen (1950a), and Webb (1950).

It is doubtful that correlation in the usual, product-moment, sense is what should be measured in problems like those of the present study (*cf.* Cole 1949, and Bray 1956). It is further doubtful that measurement should be based on comparison of actual co-occurrence with that expected by chance. If, in a given series of lake samples, species *a* occurs in 20 of the 40 and *b* in 30 of the 40, co-occurrence expected by chance is $\frac{20}{40} \times \frac{30}{40} = \frac{3}{8}$, or 15 lakes. Occurrence together of the two species in 15 lakes is, by this standard, non-association; and occurrence together in 10 is negative association. But occurrence together in 10 or 15 lakes may be a matter not of chance, but of distributional amplitudes in relation to environment; there may be 10 or 15 lakes of the 40 in which environmental conditions permit both species to maintain populations.

It is considered that the relation to be measured is not co-occurrence relative to chance expectation, or product-moment correlation, but *relative distributional overlap.* Figure 4 illustrates two species with distributional curves overlapping along an environmental gradient (*cf.* Fig. 1); community samples are assumed to be evenly spaced along the gradient. Two approaches to measurement are possible: (1) The number of samples in which both occur may be compared with the number in which one or both occur; in effect lengths of the gradient representing overlap and total amplitudes are being compared—$\frac{b-c}{a-d}$. (2) The cross-hatched overlap area may be compared with one-half the total areas of the two curves (without assuming these to be of binomial form). If the area under a given curve is treated as the sum of the heights of lines for samples such as are marked out between *a* and *b* (*i.e.* the relative numbers of individuals of the species taken in samples along the gradient), and the sum of these heights for a given species is 100%, then the relation of the cross-hatched area to the total areas of the curves becomes a percentage. Measurements

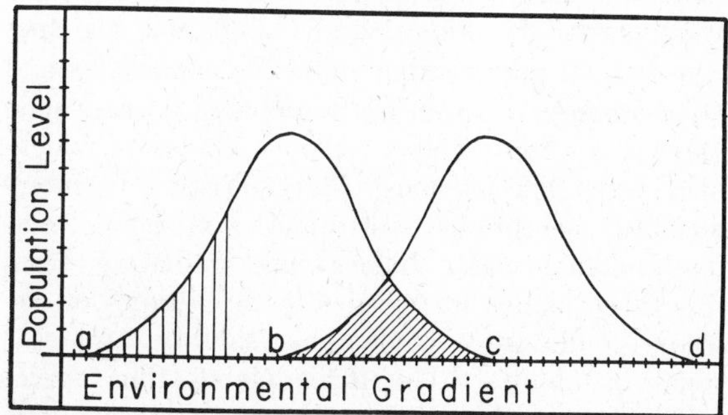

FIG. 4. Distributional overlap of two species in relation to an environmental gradient.

in terms of means and dispersions are easily conceived, but are thought unsuitable to the kind of material with which ecologists must usually deal.

For computation, the first measurement becomes simply the percentage of samples in which both species occur, among samples in which one or both occur: $PC = \frac{c}{a+b-c}$, when *a* is the number of samples containing the first species, *b* the number containing the second, and *c* the number containing both. The most effective means of computing the second measurement is to total the population of a given species in all samples in the series. Numbers of that species in particular samples are then converted to percentages of that total. When all species have been thus treated, a table of percentage distributions corresponding to Table I, but based on vertical computation of totals and percentages, results. From this table the percentage similarities of species distributions may be simply computed for all pairs of species by the same formula as for percentage similarity of community samples.

Of these two measurements the first, which may be termed *percentage co-occurrence,* is analogous to coefficient of community and the second to percentage similarity of community samples. As is the case with the other measurements, they give somewhat different results, and each has its advantages and limitations under different circumstances. Both are, clearly, very strongly influenced by the distribution of samples relative to the total field of occurrence of the species. Rarely are samples taken along a gradient as in Figure 4; often they may be concentrated in the overlap $b-c$ or in one of the non-overlaps $a-b$ and $c-d$. Species populations occur and overlap in relation to many environmental gradients, not one; and rarely can the whole field of occurrence of both be sampled. The measurements cannot in general express the distributional relation of species in the field, only their distributional relation in a particular set of samples. Granting the conspicuous limitations of such measurements, they may still reveal relations of species in samples which are not apparent from simple inspection of tables. As measurements, they are devoid of statistical sophistication, but free also from assumptions about statistical properties of the material and what is to be measured that are embodied in some more formal procedures. For the present, early stage of development of these techniques, they may be preferred as simple and direct expressions of that which an ecologist regards as appropriate to measurement in the distributional relations of species in his samples.

Percentage co-occurrences and percentage similarities of species distributions are given in Table IV. Copepod species occurring in fewer than three water bodies are excluded; distributions of these are discussed in the following section. It is impossible to manipulate the matrices so that all higher values are concentrated along the diagonal, and multi-directional relations among species are indicated by this fact.

TABLE IV. Matrix for relative distributional overlaps of copepod species. Values above the diagonal are percentage co-occurrences, those below are percentage similarities of species distributions. (x = less than 0.5%)

	Epischura nevadensis	Diaptomus ashlandi	Eucyclops agilis	Cyclops bicuspidatus	Diaptomus sicilis	Cyclops vernalis	Macrocyclops albidus	Cyclops varicans	Diaptomus sanguineus	Diaptomus shoshone	Diaptomus novamexicanus
Epischura nevadensis..		75	14	13	..	..	..	..	..	..	..
Diaptomus ashlandi...	29		13	12	..	..	..	..	..	..	..
Eucyclops agilis......	x	x		40	13	15	13	12	11	..	6
Cyclops bicuspidatus..	4	11	11		29	14	4	17	15	8	17
Diaptomus sicilis......	..	..	5	6		21	..	12	..	..	13
Cyclops vernalis......	..	..	3	1	9		27	15	8	..	..
Macrocyclops albidus..	..	..	2	1	..	16		29	22	..	..
Cyclops varicans......	..	..	30	10	16	2	22		20	14	..
Diaptomus sanguineus.	..	..	1	1	..	1	18	11		25	..
Diaptomus shoshone...	..	..	..	1	..	..	..	21	19		..
Diaptomus novamexicanus.....	..	..	x	58	2	..	..	..	..	..	

Of the two measurements, percentage co-occurrence is regarded as providing the better results in the present material; these values are diagrammed as a plexus in Figure 5. The relations cannot be represented effectively in two dimensions. The heavy *E. agilis-C. bicuspidatus* line should be regarded as an axis from which three plane surfaces radiate outward—*D. ashlandi* and *E. nevadensis* in one direction, *C. vernalis, D. sicilis,* and *D. novamexicanus* in a second, and *Macrocyclops albidus, C. varicans, D. sanguineus,* and *D. shoshone* in a third. *C. bicuspidatus* and *E. agilis* are the most widely distributed species in non-saline and mildly saline water bodies; they are consequently distributionally related to every other species in the plexus (except *E. agilis vs. D. shoshone*). The planes extending outward from the *E. agilis-C. bicuspidatus* axis are formed by species which are characteristic of more distinctive environments. The extreme members of two of the planes, *D. ashlandi* and *E. nevadensis,* and *D. sanguineus* and *D. shoshone,* are almost wholly unrelated to species on the other planes; *C. vernalis* and *D. sicilis* are related, however, to *M. albidus* and *C. varicans,* and these relations are not shown. For the most part, positions toward the center of the plexus are occupied by common and widely distributed or cosmopolitan cyclopids;

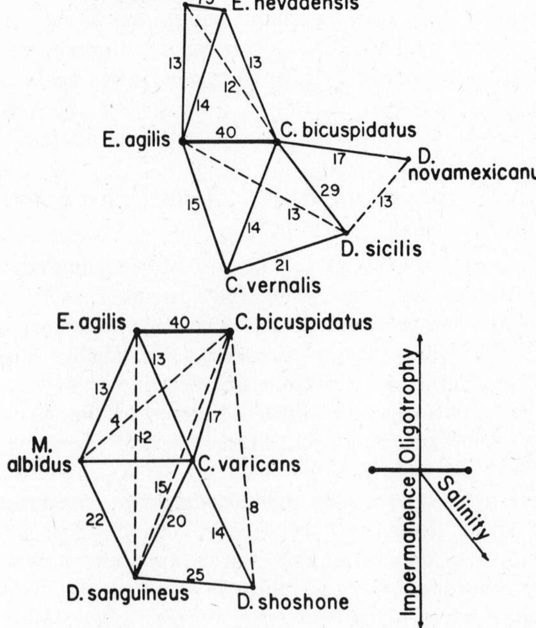

FIG. 5. Plexus of distributional relations of copepod species, based on measurements of percentage co-occurrence (Table IV). Percentage co-occurrence values are indicated by lines connecting species; solid lines are drawn to scale for 100 minus percentage co-occurrence, broken lines are not drawn to scale. The heavy line connecting *E. agilis* and *C. bicuspidatus* is the axis from which radiate three planes for groups of distributionally related species: *D. ashlandi* and *E. nevadensis* in oligotrophic conditions, *C. vernalis and D. sicilis* in saline conditions, *M. albidus, C. varicans, D. sanguineus,* and *D. shoshone* in unstable or temporary ponds.

distal positions are occupied by diaptomids (and the temorid *E. nevadensis*) of more restricted American or western distributions (see also Fig. 3).

Interpretation of the plexus in terms of environmental relations is not difficult. *D. ashlandi* and *E. nevadensis* are the species of oligotrophic lakes, *D. novamexicanus* is a species of eutrophic lakes. *C. vernalis* is a species of slightly to moderately saline ponds, *D. sicilis* a species of saline lakes and ponds. *M. albidus* and *C. varicans* are species of semi-permanent ponds; *D. sanguineus* and *D. shoshone* are species of temporary ponds. The plexus thus represents a central complex of widely distributed species most characteristic of "intermediate" conditions—eutrophic, non-saline, relatively stable water bodies—and radiating from this three planes for species of three types of extreme conditions—oligotrophy, salinity, and seasonal instability. The three planes thus correspond to the three axes of the community-type plexus (Fig. 3).

Distributional Summary

From the preceding and other data, the distribution of zooplankters may be summarized. Nomenclature follows suggestions of Mildred S. Wilson on Diaptomidae, H. C. Yeatman on Cyclopidae, to conform to the forthcoming, new edition of Ward and Whipple (1918); names used in Pennak (1953) are given in parentheses when they differ. Occurrence during all seasons of sampling may be assumed unless otherwise stated.

Cyclops bicuspidatus Claus was the most widely distributed species, occurring in 23 of 40 water bodies with a wide range of ecological conditions—oligotrophic to moderately saline (155 to 4290 ppm), true lakes (both shore and open water) to semi-permanent and temporary ponds, and at all seasons, though maximum population densities were encountered in the spring. It was dominant in many fresh-water lakes and a few saline ponds.

Eucyclops agilis (Koch) was widely distributed with more scattered occurrence (13 water bodies) over the same range of lake and pond conditions. Its population levels were much lower than those of *C. bicuspidatus*—except in certain slightly to moderately saline ponds in which it was dominant. In lakes *E. agilis* occurred in shore samples only.

Diaptomus sicilis Forbes, the third major species, was the principal copepod of a majority of moderately saline bodies (1040 to 12,100 ppm)—both lakes and ponds, and both shore and open waters of lakes—and in some of them was the only copepod. This population of *D. sicilis* (which has been known as *D. natriophilus* Light) is most characteristic of moderately saline conditions; but it was dominant in three ponds in the slight to mild salinity range (325, 620, 875 ppm) and present in two fresh-water lakes (210 and 250 ppm). It was observed in only two temporary ponds; in lakes and semi-permanent ponds it occurred in all seasons, but with densest populations during the fall samples in most cases.

Diaptomus ashlandi Marsh occurred only in the four oligotrophic lakes, and predominantly in open waters of these.

Epischura nevadensis Lillj. was recorded in three of the four oligotrophic lakes, at lower population levels than *D. ashlandi,* also predominantly in open waters.

Diaptomus novamexicanus Herrick (*D. washingtonensis* Marsh) occurred in four eutrophic lakes, in both shore and open waters, associated with *C. bicuspidatus* but at lower population levels than this.

Cyclops vernalis Fischer was the most widely distributed of the species occurring mainly in ponds, collected from 8 of 12 semi-permanent ponds (and in one saline lake and one temporary pond), from fresh-water to moderately saline conditions (155 to 2290 ppm). Although not a species of vernal ponds, it was taken only in the spring in most of these water bodies—but it was recorded also in summer and fall.

Cyclops varicans Sars occurred in four semi-permanent and one temporary pond, slightly to moderately saline (370 to 2245 ppm), and in two of these was a major or dominant species.

Macrocyclops albidus (Jurine) occurred in four semi-permanent, fresh or slightly saline ponds (310 to 415 ppm), in none of which was it the dominant species.

Diaptomus sanguineus Forbes was the major species of temporary ponds; it was the dominant or sole species in six of the 11 temporary ponds studied and occurred in one semi-permanent pond. Like most of the pond species, it occurred over the range from fresh or slightly saline to moderately saline conditions (290 to 1320 ppm). It was collected only in the spring.

Diaptomus shoshone Forbes was the other species of vernal ponds, taken only in the spring from three temporary ponds with salinities from 430 to 1320 ppm. Although occurring at low populations per liter, this species of giants, by the standards of fresh-water copepods, was conspicuous in the plankton wherever it occurred. (Identity of this form is still in doubt; it may be *D. novemdecimus* M. S. Wilson 1953).

Diaptomus leptopus Forbes (= *D. piscinae* Forbes) occurred in only two ponds, 310 and 415 ppm, both semi-permanent; it was the dominant copepod in one.

Tropocyclops prasinus (Fischer) (= *Eucyclops prasinus*) occurred as the dominant species in one strictly non-saline (155 ppm), semi-permanent pond.

Paracyclops fimbriatus (Fischer) was taken in the spring sample from Silver Lake, and *Diaptomus eiseni* Lillj. was taken from Alkali Lake.

Harpacticoid copepods were taken from 14 water bodies, of salinities from 155 to 2290 ppm, in lake shore samples and in semi-permanent and temporary ponds. They were taken in the spring only in most water bodies, and substantial numbers were taken only from shallow ponds. Most, and possibly all, of those tabulated in Table I were *Canthocamptus vagus* (Coker & Morgan).

A considerable number of cladoceran species were recorded in the present study and by Kiser (1939). In general, however, copepods were the predominant microcrustacea. Copepods outnumbered cladocerans by 2.2/1, averaging the whole series of water bodies together, and by a somewhat higher ratio (3.0/1) for 14 lakes excluding Soap Lake. In saline Soap Lake (38,700 ppm) a cladoceran, *Moina hutchinsoni* Brehm, was the sole microcrustacean collected; this species occurred also in Lake Lenore (12,100 ppm) but was outnumbered there by *D. sicilis*.

The samples also included the smaller numbers of ostracods, insects, mites, nematodes, and annelids which enter shore plankton. The most unexpected plankters were the tardigrades which were encountered in three ponds (Rock, Sunken, and Cresecent) and one lake (Cow) and occurred at a population level of slightly more than 1 per liter in Rock pond. The tardigrades from Sunken pond have been determined as *Echiniscus blumi* Richters, those from other bodies as *Macrobiotus macronyx* Dujardin. Rotifers were especially numerous in two saline bodies, Soap Lake and O'Sullivan pothole, but were not abundant in Lake Lenore.

Like other arid and semi-arid areas with many unstable water bodies, the Columbia Basin has a diverse fauna of phyllopods; only a few of these were collected for the present study. *Branchinecta coloradensis* Packard occurred in Willow Lake, and *Eubranchipus serratus* Forbes in Rock pond. The fairy shrimp collected from Alkali Lake, a shallow body of moderate salinity (2180 ppm and pH 9.0) in the Grand Coulee, has recently been described as the new species *Branchinecta mackini* by Dexter (1956). *Lepidurus* sp. was taken from South Tule and Alkali Lakes, where it occurred with *D. sicilis*. *Artemia salina* Leach was the sole crustacean collected from Lower Crab pothole (88,030 ppm) and Soda Lake approximately 100,000 ppm). Conditions of extreme salinity in the Columbia Basin are thus expressed in the crustacean plankton by exclusion of copepods, and single-species communities of other forms—*Moina* in Soap Lake and *Artemia* in some still more intensely saline bodies.

Conclusion

It is possible to treat plankton communities effectively with the procedures of synecology, as distinguished from those of autecology and faunistics. The most formidable problem is that of population irregularity and instability, but this does not preclude synecological research. Comparable problems, if less severe ones, are not unknown in terrestrial communities; they have been observed in such widely different circumstances as tropical rain forest (Aubréville 1938), temperate deciduous forest (Raup 1956), and arctic tundra (Griggs 1934, 1936; Raup 1941). The present study is of limited scale and restricted to a single group of organisms, but may suggest something of what can be done despite the difficulties inherent in plankton synecology.

Much discussion in terrestrial ecology has centered on the nature of community-types—whether these are "real" and natural units, clearly defined in the field and comparable to well-defined species, or are simply produced by ecologists through their classification of the complex and merging patterns of natural communities according to some chosen classificatory criterion (Ramensky 1924, 1930; Gleason 1926, 1939; Lenoble 1927, 1928; Nichols 1929; Raup 1942; Cain 1947; Mason 1947; Whittaker 1951, 1952, 1956; Curtis & McIntosh 1951; Dice 1952; Goodall 1953, 1954b; de Vries *et al.* 1954; Poore 1956). The bases of the latter view were advanced by Ramensky (1924) as two principles: the principle of species individuality—that species are variously and complexly distributed, each according to its own unique physiological and biotic relations to environment and other species, and consequently do not fit into well-defined associations—and the principle of community continuity—that many natural communities intergrade continuously along continuous environmental gradients, so that boundaries between community-types must often be arbitrary.

The material discussed here is not regarded as effective evidence, but it is consistent with the principle of species individuality. Only two of the species had similar distributions (*D. ashlandi* and *E. nevadensis*), and these were not closely similar. What the species-plexus seems to represent is not a number of distinct associations, but a complex pattern of distributional overlaps in which each species has its own, distinctive environmental relation. The treatment of the salinity gradient suggests that, although lakes of similar environmental conditions may have plankton communities sharply different from one another, plankton community-types in general may intergrade continuously along the salinity gradient. The relations of species and community-types to seasonal stability and instability (*cf.* Gajl 1925) suggest that this also may be a complex-gradient in relation to which there is gradation rather than discrete classes of water bodies and communities. The principles of species individuality and community continuity may suggest a very different perspective on what an ecologist is about when he classifies natural communities. They do not imply, however, as some ecologists have felt, that effective study of species interrelation and community classification are impossible.

Geological circumstances of the Columbia Basin have produced a large number of water bodies which will be increasingly used for recreation. Problems of productivity and fish culture are not a primary concern of this study, but certain conclusions are suggested. Salinity should not constitute a major limitation on fish production in the area. Only a few of the lakes have salinities in excess of the limits for fish production, indicated as about 15,000 ppm by Rawson & Moore (1944). For most of the water bodies the principal limitation is likely to be small size, with its implications of seasonal instability and the possibility of winter oxygen exhaustion under an ice cover in a cool climate. Apart from the minority of strongly saline lakes and the large numbers of seasonal ponds, the water bodies of the Columbia Basin are of relatively high productivities, with their productivities enhanced rather than restricted in conditions of mild and moderate salinity.

Summary

1. The channeled scablands of the Columbia Basin contain numerous lakes and ponds; and many of these, in the semi-arid climate, are saline. Forty water bodies ranging from fresh to highly saline and from true lakes to temporary ponds were selected for study of plankton copepod communities.

2. Population samples of shore and open-water plankton were mounted on slides in polyvinyl alcohol, and adult copepods were tallied by species. The population data made possible an approach which was not simply faunistic, but an experiment in plankton synecology or biocenotics.

3. Relations of species to the salinity gradient were investigated. In lakes *Diapotomus ashlandi* and *Epischura nevadensis* were characteristic of oligotrophic conditions, *Cyclops bicuspidatus* and *D. novamexicanus* of eutrophic fresh to mildly saline conditions, and *D. sicilis* of moderately saline conditions. Pond species were less clearly segregated by salinity and more strongly affected by seasonal instability and other factors. Attempts to establish effects of various metallic ions on species populations and plankton community-types gave inconclusive but generally negative results.

4. Although the area contains deep, rock-walled, oligotrophic lakes, the majority of the water bodies are shallow and eutrophic. Productivity, as expressed in microcrustacean standing crops, increased with increasing salinity in both lakes and ponds through most of the range of salinity conditions sampled. Microcrustacean populations per unit volume of water were almost twice as high in ponds as in lakes, but were low in most of the temporary ponds.

5. A matrix and plexus for plankton samples and community-types were prepared by measurements of percentage similarities; six community-types which could be characterized by copepod populations and limnological conditions resulted. Percentage co-occurrences were used to prepare a matrix and plexus of distributional relations of species. Both treatments suggest a central complex of community-types and species characteristic of eutrophic, fresh to mildly saline, relatively stable water bodies, and community-types and species which depart from these in three directions of environmental extremity—oligotrophy, salinity, and seasonal instability.

6. Distributional relations of copepod species are summarized. Copepods are excluded from water bodies of high salinities; these are characterized by dense populations of single crustacean species (*Moina hutchinsoni* at 38,700 ppm in Soap Lake, *Artemia salina* in still more saline bodies).

References

Agrell, I. 1941. Zur Ökologie der Collembolen. Untersuchungen im schwedischen Lappland. Opuscula Entom., Suppl., **3**: 1-236.

———. 1945. The collemboles in nests of warmblooded animals with a method for sociological analysis. K. Fysiogr. Sällsk. i Lund, Handl., N.F., **56**(10): 1-19.

Aubréville, A. 1938. La forêt coloniale (Les forêts de l'Afrique Occidentale Française). Acad. des Sci. Colon., Paris, Ann., **9**: 1-244.

Backlund, H. O. 1945. Wrack fauna of Sweden and Finland, ecology and chorology. Opuscula Entom., Suppl., **5**: 1-236.

Beadle, L. C. 1932. Scientific results of the Cambridge Expedition to the East African lakes, 1930-1.—4. The waters of some East African lakes in relation to their fauna and flora. Linn. Soc. London Jour., Zool., **38**: 157-211.

———. 1943. An ecological survey of some inland saline waters in Algeria. Linn. Soc. London Jour., Zool., **41**: 218-242.

Boone, Eleanor and L. G. M. Baas-Becking. 1931. Salt effects on eggs and nauplii of *Artemia salina* L. Jour. Gen. Physiol., **14**: 753-763.

Braun-Blanquet, J. 1932. Plant sociology, the study of plant communities. Transl. of "Pflanzensoziologie" by G. D. Fuller & H. S. Conard. New York: McGraw-Hill. 439 pp.

———. 1951. Pflanzensoziologie. Grundzüge der Vegetationskunde. 2. Aufl. Wien: Springer. 631 pp.

Bray, J. R. 1956. A study of mutual occurrence of plant species. Ecology, **37**: 21-28.

Bretz, J H. 1923. The channeled scablands of the Columbia Plateau. Jour. Geol., **31**: 617-649.

———. 1928. The channeled scabland of eastern Washington. Geog. Rev., **18**: 446-477.

Brink, P. and K. G. Wingstrand. 1949. The mountain fauna of the Virihaure area in Swedish Lapland. K. Fysiogr. Sällsk i Lund, Handl., N. F., **60**(2): 1-69.

Brown, R. T. and J. T. Curtis. 1952. The upland conifer-hardwood forests of northern Wisconsin. Ecol. Monog., **22**: 217-234.

Brundin, L. 1934. Die Coleopteren des Torneträskgebietes. Ein Beitrag zur Ökologie und Geschichte der

Käferwelt in Schwedisch-Lappland. Lund: Bloms. 436 pp.

Cain, S. A. 1947. Characteristics of natural areas and factors in their development. Ecol. Monog., **17:** 185-200.

Clarke, G. L. and D. F. Bumpus. 1950. The plankton sampler—an instrument for quantitative plankton investigations. Amer. Soc. Limnol. & Oceanog., Spec. Pub., No. 5: 1-8.

Cole, L. C. 1949. The measurement of interspecific association. Ecology, **30:** 411-424.

———. 1957. The measurement of partial interspecific association. Ecology, **38:** 226-233.

Culberson, W. L. 1955. The corticolous communities of lichens and bryophytes in the upland forests of northern Wisconsin. Ecol. Monog., **25:** 215-231.

Curtis, J. T. and R. P. McIntosh. 1951. An upland forest continuum in the prairie-forest border region of Wisconsin. Ecology, **32:** 476-496.

Damman, A. W. H. and D. M. de Vries. 1954. Testing of grassland associations by combinations of species. Biol. Jaarb. [Antwerpen], **21:** 35-46.

Daubenmire, R. F. 1942. An ecological study of the vegetation of southeastern Washington and adjacent Idaho. Ecol. Monog., **12:** 53-79.

Decksbach, N. K. 1924. Seen und Flüsse des Turgai-Gebietes (Kirgisen-Steppen). Internatl. Ver. Theoret. Angew. Limnol., Verhandl., **2:** 252-288.

———. 1929. Zur Klassifikation der Gewässer vom astatischen Typus. Arch. Hydrobiol., **20:** 399-406.

Dexter, R. W. 1956. A new fairy shrimp from western United States, with notes on other North American species. Wash. Acad. Sci., Jour., **46:** 159-165.

Dice, L. R. 1945. Measures of the amount of ecologic association between species. Ecology, **26:** 297-302.

———. 1952. Natural communities. Ann Arbor: Univ. Mich. Press. 547 pp.

Fairbanks, C. W. 1950. A study of microcrustacea of some of the alkali lakes and potholes of the Columbia Basin area. Master's thesis, Dept. of Zool., Washington State College, Pullman.

Fenneman, N. M. 1931. Physiography of western United States. New York: McGraw-Hill. 534 pp.

Fisher, L. C. 1941. Climate of Washington. *In* Climate and man. Yearbook of Agriculture. U. S. Dept. Agr., Washington: Government Printing Office. pp. 1170-1181.

Forbes, S. A. 1907. On the local distribution of certain Illinois fishes: an essay in statistical ecology. Ill. State Lab. Nat. Hist. (Nat. Hist. Surv.), Bull. 7: 273-303.

———. 1925. Method of determining and measuring the associative relations of species. Science, N. S., **61:** 524.

Forsslund, K.-H. 1945. Studier över de lägre djurlivet i nordsvensk skogsmark. (Germ. summ.) Statens Skogsförsöksanst. [Sweden], Meddel., **34:** 1-283.

Franz, H. 1943. Die Landtierwelt der mittleren Hohen Tauern. Ein Beitrag zur tiergeographischen und -soziologischen Erforschung der Alpen. Akad. Wiss. Wien, Math.-Nat. Kl., Denkschr., **107:** 1-522.

———. 1950. Qualitative und quantitative Untersuchungsmethoden in Biozönotik und Ökologie. (French summ.) Acta Biotheoret., **9:** 101-114.

Gajl, K. 1925. Über zwei faunistische Typen aus der Umgebung von Warschau auf Grund von Untersuchungen an Phyllopoda und Copepoda (excl. Harpacticidae). Acad. Polon. Sci. Lettres, Cl. Sci. Math. Nat., Bull. Internatl., Sér. B, **1924:** 13-55.

Gardner, J. L. 1951. Vegetation of the creosotebush area of the Rio Grande valley in New Mexico. Ecol. Monog., **21:** 379-403.

Gause, G. F. 1930. Studies on the ecology of the Orthoptera. Ecology, **11:** 307-325.

Gauthier, H. 1928. Recherches sur la faune des eaux continentales de l'Algérie et de la Tunisie. Alger: Minerva. 419 pp.

Gilbert, Margaret L. and J. T. Curtis. 1953. Relation of the understory to the upland forest in the prairie-forest border region of Wisconsin. Wisc. Acad. Sci. Arts & Letters, Trans., **42:** 183-195.

Gisin, H. 1947. Analyses et synthèses biocénotiques. Arch. Sci. Phys. Nat., Pér. 5, **29:** 42-75.

———. 1951. La biocénotique. Année Biol., 3e Sér., **27:** 81-88.

Gleason, H. A. 1920. Some applications of the quadrat method. Torrey Bot. Club, Bull., **47:** 21-33.

———. 1926. The individualistic concept of the plant association. Torrey Bot. Club, Bull., **53:** 7-26.

———. 1939. The individualistic concept of the plant association. Amer. Midland Nat., **21:** 92-110.

Goodall, D. W. 1952. Quantitative aspects of plant distribution. Cambridge Phil. Soc., Biol. Rev., **27:** 194-245.

———. 1953. Objective methods for the classification of vegetation. I. The use of positive interspecific correlation. Austral. Jour. Bot., **1:** 39-63.

———. 1954a. Objective methods for the classification of vegetation. III. An essay in the use of factor analysis. Austral. Jour. Bot., **2:** 304-324.

———. 1954b. Vegetational classification and vegetational continua. (Germ. summ.) Angew. Pflanzensoz. [Wien], Festschr. Aichinger, **1:** 168-182.

Greig-Smith, P. 1952. Ecological observations on degraded and secondary forest in Trinidad, British West Indies. II. Structure of the communities. Jour. Ecol., **40:** 316-330.

Griggs, R. F. 1934. The problem of arctic vegetation. Wash. Acad. Sci., Jour., **24:** 153-175.

———. 1936. The vegetation of the Katmai district. Ecology, **17:** 380-417.

Hale, M. E., Jr. 1955. Phytosociology of corticolous cryptogams in the upland forests of southern Wisconsin. Ecology, **36:** 45-63.

Harris, S. W. 1954. An ecological study of the waterfowl of the potholes area, Grant County, Washington. Amer. Midland Nat., **52:** 403-432.

Hesse, R., W. C. Allee, and K. P. Schmidt. 1937. Ecological animal geography. New York: Wiley. 597 pp. 2nd ed. 1951, 715 pp.

Hughes, R. E. and D. V. Lindley. 1955. Application of biometric methods to problems of classification in ecology. Nature [London], **175:** 806-807.

Hutchinson, G. E. 1937a. A contribution to the limnology of arid regions, primarily founded on observations made in the Lahontan Basin. Conn. Acad. Arts Sci., Trans., **33:** 47-132.

———. 1937b. Limnological studies in Indian Tibet. Internatl. Rev. Ges. Hydrobiol. Hydrogr., **35**: 134-176.

Hutchinson, G. E., Grace E. Pickford, and Johanna F. M. Schuurman. 1932. A contribution to the hydrobiology of pans and other inland waters of South Africa. (Germ. summ.) Arch. Hydrobiol., **24**: 1-154.

Iljinski, A. P. and M. A. Poselskaja. 1929. A contribution to the question of the associability of plants. (Russ. with Engl. summ.) Trudy Prikl. Bot., Genet., i Selek. (Bull. Appl. Bot., Genet., & Plant-Breeding), **20**: 459-474.

Iversen, J. 1936. Biologische Pflanzentypen als Hilfsmittel in der Vegetationsforschung.—Ein Beitrag zur ökologischen Charakterisierung und Anordnung der Pflanzengesellschaften. Skalling-Lab. [København], Meddel., **4**: 1-224.

———. 1954. Über die Korrelation zwischen den Pflanzenarten in einem grönländischen Talgebiet. Vegetatio, 5/6: 238-246.

Jaccard, P. 1902. Lois de distribution florale dans la zone alpine. Soc. Vaud. Sci. Nat., Bull., **38**: 69-130.

———. 1908. Nouvelles recherches sur la distribution florale. Soc. Vaud. Sci. Nat., Bull., **44**: 223-270.

———. 1912. The distribution of the flora in the alpine zone. New Phytol., **11**: 35-50.

———. 1932. Die statistisch-floristische Methode als Grundlage der Pflanzensoziologie. Handb. Biol. Arbeitsmeth., ed Abderhalden, 11, **5**(1): 165-202.

Jenkin, Penelope M. 1932. Reports on the Percy Sladen Expedition to some Rift Valley lakes in Kenya in 1929. I. Introductory account of the biological survey of five freshwater and alkaline lakes. Ann. Mag. Nat. Hist., Ser. 10, **9**: 533-552.

———. 1936. Reports on the Percy Sladen Expedition to some Rift Valley lakes in Kenya in 1929. VII. Summary of the ecological results, with special reference to the alkaline lakes. Ann. Mag. Nat. Hist., Ser. 10, **18**: 133-181.

Johnsgard, P. A. 1956. Effects of water fluctuation and vegetation change on bird populations, particularly waterfowl. Ecology, **37**: 689-701.

Katz, N. J. 1930. Die grundlegenden Gesetzmässigkeiten der Vegetation und der Begriff der Assoziation. Beitr. Biol. der Pflanz., **18**: 305-333.

Kiser, R. W. 1939. The Cladocera and Copepoda of the alkaline lakes of the Grand Coulee and adjacent region. Master's thesis, Zool. Dept., Univ. of Washington, Seattle.

Koch, L. F. 1957. Index of biotal dispersity. Ecology, **38**: 145-148.

Kontkanen, P. 1949. On the determination of affinity between different species in synecological analyses. (Finnish summ.) Ann. Entom. Fenn., **14**(Suppl.): 118-125.

———. 1950a. Quantitative and seasonal studies on the leafhopper fauna of the field stratum on open areas in North Karelia. (Finnish summ.) Soc. Zool.-Bot. Fenn. Vanamo, Ann. Zool., **13**(8): 1-91.

———. 1950b. Sur les diverses méthodes de groupement des récoltes dans la biocénotique animale. Vie et Milieu, **1**: 121-130; Actual. Sci. et Indust., 1115.

Kühnelt, W. 1943a. Die Leitformenmethode in der Ökologie der Landtiere. Biologia Gen., **17**: 106-146.

———. 1943b. Über die Beziehungen zwischen Tier- und Pflanzengesellschaften. Biologia Gen., **17**: 566-593.

———. 1951a. Sur la structure des associations biotiques terrestres. Année Biol., 3e Sér., **27**: 117-127.

———. 1951b. Über die Struktur des Lebensgemeinschaften des Festlandes. Zool.-Bot. Gesell. Wien, Verhandl., **92**: 56-66.

Kulczyński, S. 1928. Die Pflanzenassoziationen der Pieninen. Acad. Polon. Sci. Lettres, Cl. Sci. Math. Nat., Bull. Internatl., Sér. B, **1927**(Suppl. 2): 57-203.

Lenoble, F. 1927. À propos des associations végétales. Soc. Bot. France, Bull., **73**: 873-893.

———. 1928. Associations végétales. et espèces. Arch. Bot. [Caen] **2**(Bul. Mens. **1**): 1-14.

McIntosh, R. P. 1957. The York Woods, a case history of forest succession in southern Wisconsin. Ecology, **38**: 29-37.

Mason, H. L. [illegible] Evolution of certain floristic associations in [illegible] North America. Ecol. Monog., **17**: 201-210.

Matuszkiewicz, W. 1948. Roślinność lasów okolic Lwowa. (Engl. summ.) Univ. Mariae Curie-Skłodowska, Lublin, Ann., Sect. C, **3**: 119-193.

———. 1950. Badania fitosocjologiczne nad lasami bukowymi w Sudetach. (Russ. & Engl. summs.) Univ. Mariae Curie-Skłodowska, Lublin, Ann., Sect. C, Suppl., **5**: 1-196.

———. 1952. Zespoły leśne Białowieskiego Parku Narodowego. (Russ. & Germ. summs.) Univ. Mariae Curie-Skłodowska, Lublin, Ann., Sect. C, Suppl., **6**: 1-218.

Moore, J. E. 1952. The Entomostraca of southern Saskatchewan. Canad. Jour. Zool., **30**: 410-450.

Motyka, J. 1947. O zadaniach i metodach badań geobotanicznych. (French summ.) Univ. Mariae Curie-Skłodowska, Lublin, Ann., Sect. C, Suppl., **1**: 1-168.

Motyka, J., B. Dobrzański, and S. Zawadzki. 1950. Wstępne badania nad łąkami południowo-wschodniej Lubelszczyzny. (Russ. & Engl. summs.) Univ. Mariae Curie-Skłodowska, Lublin, Ann., Sect. E, **5**: 367-447.

Nash, C. B. 1950. Associations between fish species in tributaries and shore waters of western Lake Erie. Ecology, **31**: 561-566.

Naumann, E. 1932. Grundzüge der regionalen Limnologie. Binnengewässer, **11**: 1-176. Stuttgart: Schweizerbart'sche Verlagsbuchhandlung.

Nichols, G. E. 1929. Plant associations and their classification. Internatl. Congr. Plant Sci., Ithaca 1926, Proc., **1**: 629-641.

Odum, E. P. 1950. Bird populations of the Highlands (North Carolina) Plateau in relation to plant succession and avian invasion. Ecology, **31**: 587-605.

Pennak, R. W. 1942. Ecology of some copepods inhabiting intertidal beaches near Woods Hole, Massachusetts. Ecology, **23**: 446-456.

———. 1951. Comparative ecology of the interstitial fauna of fresh-water and marine beaches. Année Biol., 3e Sér., **27**: 449-480.

———. 1953. Fresh-water invertebrates of the United States. New York: Ronald. 769 pp.

Poore, M. E. D. 1955. The use of phytosociological methods in ecological investigations. III. Practical application. Jour. Ecol., **43**: 606-651.

———. 1956. The use of phytosociological [illegible] in ecological investigations. IV. General discussion of phytosociological problems. Jour. Ecol., **44**: 28-50.

Quézel, P. and P. Verdier. 1953. Les méthodes de la phytosociologie sont-elles applicables à l'étude des groupements animaux? Quelques associations ripicoles de Carabiques dans le Midi de la France et leurs rapports avec les groupements végétaux correspondants. Vegetatio, **4**: 165-181.

Raabe, E.-W. 1952. Über den "Affinitätswert" in der Pflanzensoziologie. Vegetatio, **4**: 53-68.

Rabeler, W. 1947. Die Tiergesellschaften der trockenen Callunaheiden in Nordwest-Deutschland. Naturhist. Gesell. Hannover, Jahresber., **94-98**: 357-375.

Ramensky, L. G. 1924. Die Grundgesetzmässigkeiten im Aufbau der Vegetationsdecke. (Russian) Wjestn. opytn. djela Woronesch., 37 pp. (Bot. Centbl., N. F., **7**: 453-455, 1926).

———. 1930. Zur Methodik der [illegible]leichenden Bearbeitung und Ordnung von Pflanzen[illegible]sten und anderen Objekten, die durch mehrere, verschiedenartig wirkende Faktoren bestimmt werden. Beitr. Biol. der Pflanz., **18**: 269-304.

Raup, H. M. 1941. Botanical problems in boreal America. Bot. Rev., **7**: 147-248.

———. 1942. Trends in the development of geographic botany. Assoc. Amer. Geog., Ann., **32**: 319-354.

———. 1956. Vegetational adjustment to the instability of the site. Paper given at meetings of Amer. Inst. Biol. Sci., Storrs, Conn., Aug. 28, 1956.

Rawson, D. S. and J. E. Moore. 1944. The saline lakes of Saskatchewan. Canad. Jour. Res., Sect. D, Zool. Sci., **22**: 141-201.

Renkonen, O. 1938. Statistisch-ökologische Untersuchungen über die terrestrische Käferwelt der finnischen Bruchmoore. (Finnish summ.) Soc. Zool.-Bot. Fenn. Vanamo, Ann. Zool., **6**(1): 1-231.

———. 1944. Die Carabiden- und Staphylinidenbestände eines Seeufers in SW-Finnland. Ein Beitrag zur Theorie der statistischen Insektensynökologie. Ann. Entom. Fenn., **10**: 33-104.

———. 1949. Discussion on the ways of insect synecology. Oikos, **1**: 122-126.

Rodhe, W. 1948. Environmental requirements of freshwater plankton algae. Experimental studies in the ecology of phytoplankton. Symbol. Bot. Upsal., **10**(1): 1-149.

Scheygrond, A. 1932. Het plantendek van de Krimpenerwaard IV. Sociographie van het hoofd-associatie-complex Arundinetum-Sphagnetum. Nederland. Kruidk. Arch., **1932**: 1-184.

Schwenke, W. 1953. Biozönotik und angewandte Entomologie. (Ein Beitrag zur Klärung der Situation der Biozönotik und zur Schaffung einer biozönotischen Entomologie). Beitr. Entom., **3**(Sonderheft): 86-162.

Shelford, V. E. 1915. Principles and problems of ecology as illustrated by animals. Jour. Ecol., **3**: 1-23.

Sørensen, T. 1948. A method of establishing groups of equal amplitude in plant sociology based on similarity of species content and its application to analysis of the vegetation on Danish commons. K. Danske Vidensk. Selsk., Biol. Skr., **5**(4): 1-34.

Stanković, S. 1931. Sur les particularités limnologiques des lacs égéens. Internatl. Ver. Theoret. Angew. Limnol., Verhandl., **5**: 158-196.

Stewart, G. and W. Keller. 1936. A correlation method for ecology as exemplified by studies of native desert vegetation. Ecology, **17**: 500-514.

Strenzke, K. 1952. Untersuchungen über die Tiergemeinschaften des Bodens: Die Oribatiden und ihre Synusien in den Böden Norddeutschlands. Zoologica [Stuttgart], **37**(104): 1-173.

Thornthwaite, C. W. 1931. The climates of North America according to a new classification. Geog. Rev., **21**: 633-655.

———. 1948. An approach toward a rational classification of climate. Geog. Rev., **38**: 55-94.

Tischler, W. 1951. Zur Synthese biozönotischer Forschung. Acta Biotheoret., **9**: 135-162.

Tuomikoski, R. 1942. Untersuchungen über die Vegetation der Bruchmoore in Ostfinnland. I. Zur Methodik der pflanzensoziologischen Systematik. (Finnish summ.) Soc. Zool.-Bot. Fenn. Vanamo, Ann. Bot., **17**(1): 1-203.

———. 1948. Entomologian synekologisista tilastoista ja hyönteisyhteisöjen typologiasta. (Germ. summ.) Ann. Entom. Fenn., **14**: 101-115.

Tüxen, R. and H. Ellenberg. 1937. Der systematische und der ökologische Gruppenwert. Ein Beitrag zur Begriffsbildung und Methodik der Pflanzensoziologie. Naturhist. Gesell. Hannover, Jahresber., **81-87**: 171-184 (Florist.-Soziol. Arbeitsgem. in Niedersachsen, Mitt. 3).

de Vries, D. M. 1953. Objective combinations of species. Acta Bot. Neerland., **1**: 497-499.

de Vries, D. M., J. P. Baretta, and G. Hamming. 1954. Constellation of frequent herbage plants, based on their correlation in occurrence. Vegetatio, **5/6**: 105-111.

Ward, H. B. and G. C. Whipple. 1918. Fresh-water biology. New York: Wiley. 1111 pp.

Webb, W. L. 1950. Biogeographic regions of Texas and Oklahoma. Ecology, **31**: 426-433.

Whittaker, R. H. 1951. A criticism of the plant association and climatic climax concepts. Northwest Sci., **25**: 17-31.

———. 1952. A study of summer foliage insect communities in the Great Smoky Mountains. Ecol. Monog., **22**: 1-44.

———. 1954. Plant populations and the basis of plant indication. (Germ. summ.) Angew. Pflanzensoz. [Wien], Festschr. Aichinger, **1**: 183-206.

———. 1956. Vegetation of the Great Smoky Mountains. Ecol. Monog., **26**: 1-80.

Williams, C. B. 1944. Some applications of the logarithmic series and the index of diversity to ecological problems. Jour. Ecol., **32**: 1-44.

———. 1949. Jaccard's generic coefficient and coefficient of floral community, in relation to the logarithmic series and the index of diversity. Ann. Bot., N. S., **13**: 53-58.

Wilson, Mildred S. 1953. New and inadequately known North American species of the copepod genus *Diaptomus*. Smithson. Misc. Coll., **122**(2): 1-30.

Young, R. T. 1924. The life of Devil's Lake, North Dakota. North Dakota Biol. Sta., Publ., 116 pp.